D1108378

ALLOYS OF IRON RESEARCH, MONOGRAPH SERIES

FRANK T. SISCO, EDITOR

THE ALLOYS OF IRON AND MOLYBDENUM

ALLOYS OF IRON RESEARCH, MONOGRAPH SERIES

These monographs are a concise but comprehensive critical summary of research on ferrous alloys as reported in the technical literature of the world. They contain a discussion of all available data on binary and higher ferrous alloy systems, and on the effect of the alloying elements on carbon steel and on simple and complex alloy steels and special alloy cast irons. They provide a reliable foundation for further research and in one volume supply to the practical metallurgist, steel worker, foundryman, and engineer the essential information now scattered through more than two thousand journals and textbooks in many languages.

The authors are responsible for selection and evaluation of the data, for arrangement of subject matter, and for style of presentation. Each book, however, has been reviewed in manuscript by men especially qualified to criticize all statements. Indebtedness for this cooperation is recognized in the Acknowledgments. Finally, each manuscript has been reviewed and approved for publication by the Iron Alloys Committee.

The Committee expresses its appreciation to *The Engineering Foundation*, the *iron and steel industry of the United States and the American Iron and Steel Institute*, *Battelle Memorial Institute*, *The American Foundrymen's Association*, and *National Bureau of Standards*, for financial support, which made the laborious review of the world's literature possible; and to the libraries, engineering societies, and the technical press in the United States, Canada, England, Germany, France, Italy, Sweden, Japan, and Czechoslovakia, for cooperation in making available inaccessible reports and in permitting the use of published data.

THE ALLOYS OF IRON AND MOLYBDENUM

BY

J. L. GREGG

Metallurgist, Battelle Memorial Institute

This monograph has been prepared at Battelle Memorial Institute as a part of the Institute's contribution to Alloys of Iron Research

First Edition

Published for
The Engineering Foundation
by
McGRAW-HILL BOOK COMPANY, Inc.
NEW YORK AND LONDON
1932

PRINTED IN THE UNITED STATES OF AMERICA

THE MAPLE PRESS COMPANY, YORK, PA.

PREFACE

One purpose of this monograph is to collect in readily usable form the important facts on molybdenum steels and the other alloys of molybdenum and iron, with or without additional alloying elements. Another important purpose is to point out the gaps in the information, so that the need for research to fill those gaps will be evident.

The information available is scattered through volumes of journals and textbooks in many languages. Even if a reader has all the literature at his disposal, it is a time-consuming task to find all pertinent information on any given point, and even more difficult to be certain that nothing of importance has been missed. Bibliographies are a help, but unless copiously annotated, they may hinder the reader by their very completeness, leading him to articles of little interest or value as well as to those that do serve his purpose. While abstracts of current literature are indispensable in keeping up with a given metallurgical field, the assembly of really complete information takes much time, even with their aid.

Since many firms and individuals are interested in molybdenum as an alloying element, the review of the literature by each interested group entails wasteful duplication. This monograph is intended to accomplish what many individuals would otherwise have to do for themselves, to achieve greater completeness than could result from individual effort, and to put the facts into a connected statement.

Although published abstracts have been used in locating the original literature, they have been relied upon only for the elimination of duplicate and secondary articles, the original sources of the important data having been studied, specially abstracted, and the articles themselves consulted repeatedly in the preparation of the monograph.

More than a thousand articles were located, and eight hundred were studied in detail and specially abstracted for the information included herein. The articles to which definite reference has been made are listed in the Bibliography, where they are arranged chronologically by year of publication, and alphabetically by author for each year.

Although a few references to patents are given, no search of the patent literature has been made.

The data have not been weighed to the extent of actually repeating tests that appear unreliable, but discrepancies or early misapprehensions that have been corrected by more careful and extensive work have been eliminated. Where discrepancies still exist and no reasonable decision can be made as to the correctness of one or the other of two conflicting sets of data or views, both have been stated. The conclusions given in the literature are presented first, and the comments of the author of this monograph put at the end of each chapter or section.

Attention is called especially to the method of recording mechanical properties. In the ordinary tensile test, four values are usually determined: tensile strength, elongation, reduction of area, and a property variously reported as elastic limit, proportional limit, or yield point. There is little confusion in the meaning of the first three properties, but the last property may be determined by several different methods; in many of the data found in the literature the method for determining "elastic limit," "proportional limit," or "yield point" is not obvious.

Some proposed definitions of terms given in Appendix III to Report of Committee E-1 of Methods of Testing of the American Society for Testing Materials in *Proceedings*, v. 31, part 1, 1931, pp. 602–604, are:

Elastic Limit.—The greatest stress which a material is capable of developing without a permanent deformation remaining on complete release of the stress.

Proportional Limit.—The greatest stress which a material is capable of developing without a deviation from the law of proportionality of stress to strain (Hooke's law).

Yield Strength.—The stress at which a material exhibits a specified limiting permanent set.

The "yield strength" in materials that have a "sharp-kneed" stress-strain diagram, such as most steels at ordinary temperatures, may be determined by observing the load at which appreciable strain occurs without increase in stress, i.e., by the "drop of the beam method" or by visible stretching when gage lengths are compared with dividers. The yield strength of other materials may be determined from a curve in which stress is plotted against strain or, more roughly, by setting dividers to indicate a given total deformation and observing the stress required to produce this strain. In reporting values of yield strength based on a specified "set" it is desirable to state the value of set in parenthesis as: yield strength (set = 0.1 per cent) = 52,000 lb. per sq. in.

Although the methods by which many of the data reported in the monograph as yield strength were not given, it is believed that the great majority represent the property defined above as "yield strength," and this term is generally used herein. In tables of tensile values "yield strength" is given in the headings, and for data published in English the manner in which the values were reported in the original article is indicated. The German term "Streckgrenze" is translated as "yield strength." In a few tables values are reported as "elastic limit," and these were determined by removal of the load and observing the first load that produced a permanent set.

The review of the literature revealed the fact that investigators were interested chiefly in the effect of molybdenum on steel and cast iron. The amount of scientific research on the constitution of the pure alloys is very small when compared with the numerous investigations of molybdenum in commercial ferrous products. As a large part of this book contains data of interest to the practical man as well as to the researcher, and as the book is likely to be used mostly in America, it has been considered advisable to report many of the temperatures in both Fahrenheit and centigrade degrees. In converting from one scale to the other only round numbers have been given. This, it is believed, is sufficiently accurate. Because the data, in text, tables, and charts, were drawn from both foreign and domestic journals, it is obviously impossible to indicate which scale was used by the original investigator, but since all foreign journals, and an increasing number of domestic publications, use only centigrade, most of the conversions are from degrees centigrade to degrees Fahrenheit.

In accord with tentative standards proposed by the American Society for Testing Materials (1932 Preprint 4), and with the minutes of meetings of International Electrotechnical Commission, Advisory Committee 1, held at Stockholm, June 30 to July 5, 1930, the unit of magnetizing force H, is termed "oersted" and the unit of induction, B, is termed "gauss." The magnetic induction which remains in a ferromagnetic material when the effective magnetizing force has been reduced to zero from a point on the normal induction curve is termed "residual induction," which is also in accordance with the American Society for Testing Materials' tentative standard.

J. L. Gregg.

Columbus, Ohio,
November, 1932.

ACKNOWLEDGMENTS

Although the author is responsible for most of the selection and arrangement of data herein, so many others have cooperated in the work that a list of those who might properly be classed as joint authors would be long.

The preparation of the monograph was undertaken by Battelle Memorial Institute as a part of its contribution to Alloys of Iron Research, and the Institute staff has been freely called upon all through its preparation. The laborious searching of the literature and its preliminary abstracting in order to select the articles of most importance for detailed study have been done chiefly by Miss Lois F. McCombs, Bibliographer, with the aid, during the first part of the work, of G. T. Motok, Assistant Metallurgist. Miss Thelma R. Reinberg, Librarian, has been helpful throughout. Useful data that might otherwise have been missed have been unearthed by Dr. H. W. Gillett, Director, who has also helped in the general revision of the first draft.

The sections on equilibrium diagrams and on nitriding steels are due chiefly to Dr. O. E. Harder, Assistant Director, and his criticisms have been utilized in the whole monograph. Likewise the section on tool steels is due chiefly to F. Sillers, Jr., Metallurgist, who has helped with other parts. The experience of various others of the staff has been solicited in appraisal of data in many of the sections. Through the acquaintance of the staff with many metallurgists, it has been possible to obtain many unpublished data, and to obtain from specialists detailed opinions and advice in the evaluation of conflicting data. The sources of the heretofore unpublished data should be evident from the text, and the author wishes to make grateful acknowledgment of the cooperation of those who made the inclusion of this information possible. The following list, while not complete, will indicate the extent of this valuable cooperation:

R. J. Allen	Worthington Pump and Machinery Corp.
E. G. Brick	Cadillac Motor Car Co.
Paul Carpenter	Arrow Head Steel Products Co.
H. S. Clarke	Delaware and Hudson Railroad Corp.
W. W. Crawford	Edward Valve and Manufacturing Co.

Col. T. C. Dickson	Watertown Arsenal
J. V. Emmons	Cleveland Twist Drill Co.
R. H. Frank	Bonney-Floyd Co.
Arthur J. Herschmann	Agent for Vitkovice Works
N. B. Hoffman	Colonial Steel Co.
Lt. Col. G. F. Jenks	Watertown Arsenal
J. B. Johnson	War Department, Air Corps
Floyd C. Kelley	General Electric Co.
Karl H. Langguth	Western Crucible Steel Castings Co.
J. P. Larkin	Nitralloy Corp.
H. H. Lester	Watertown Arsenal
Lt. Gerald D. Linke	U. S. Navy
Frank B. Lounsberry	Ludlum Steel Co.
E. A. Lucas	Molybdenum Corporation of America
James T. MacKenzie	American Cast Iron Pipe Co.
John A. Mathews	Crucible Steel Company of America
N. L. Mochel	Westinghouse Electric and Manufacturing Co.
W. H. Phillips	Molybdenum Corporation of America
J. T. Norton	Ludlum Steel Co.
Edwin Pugsley	Winchester Repeating Arms Co.
R. G. Roshong	Hoover Co.
L. W. Spring	Crane Co.
Jerome Strauss	Vanadium Corporation of America
W. P. Sykes	General Electric Co.
J. B. Thorpe	Climax Molybdenum Co.
D. Z. Zuege	Sivyer Steel Casting Co.

Finally, the first draft or a selected portion has been read by those listed below, and the revision made in line with their useful comments:

E. G. Brick	Cadillac Motor Car Co.
G. M. Eaton	Spang, Chalfont and Co.
J. V. Emmons	Cleveland Twist Drill Co.
J. P. Gill	Vanadium-Alloys Steel Co.
M. A. Grossmann	Illinois Steel Co.
V. O. Homerberg	Nitralloy Corp.
Karl H. Langguth	Western Crucible Steel Castings Co.
A. W. Lorenz	Bucyrus-Erie Co.
James T. MacKenzie	American Cast Iron Pipe Co.
M. J. R. Morris	Republic Steel Corp.
W. H. Phillips	Molybdenum Corporation of America
R. S. Sergeson	Republic Steel Corp.
Howard J. Stagg	Halcomb Steel Co.
W. P. Sykes	General Electric Co.
J. B. Thorpe	Climax Molybdenum Co.

J. L. GREGG.

COLUMBUS, OHIO,
November, 1932.

CONTENTS

PAGE

PREFACE v

ACKNOWLEDGMENTS ix

CHAPTER I

INTRODUCTION 1
General Survey of Work—Properties of Molybdenum and Iron—Molybdenum Minerals—Occurrence of Molybdenum Ores—Extraction of Molybdenum.

CHAPTER II

IRON-MOLYBDENUM ALLOYS 18
Constitution—Methods Used in Determining the Iron-molybdenum Diagram—Properties—Uses—Author's Summary.

CHAPTER III

CONSTITUTION AND MANUFACTURE 56
Iron-carbon and Molybdenum-carbon Alloys—Iron-molybdenum-carbon Alloys—Melting Molybdenum Steel—Casting and Working Molybdenum Steel—Author's Summary.

CHAPTER IV

METALLOGRAPHY AND PHYSICAL PROPERTIES OF MOLYBDENUM STEEL. 83
Effect of Molybdenum on Critical-point Phenomena—Effect on Heat-treating Ranges—Microstructure—Miscellaneous Physical Properties—Magnetic Properties—Author's Summary.

CHAPTER V

PROPERTIES AND USES OF MOLYBDENUM STEEL 107
Mechanical Properties of Molybdenum Steels—Mechanical Properties at Low and High Temperatures—Special Properties—Chemical Properties—Uses—Cast Molybdenum Steel—Author's Summary.

CHAPTER VI

MOLYBDENUM CAST IRON 156
Manufacture—Influence of Molybdenum on Structure—Mechanical Properties—Special Properties—Effect of Temperature—Uses—Author's Summary.

CHAPTER VII

CHROMIUM-MOLYBDENUM STEEL 206
Mechanical Properties of Chromium-molybdenum Structural

PAGE

Steels—Other Properties—Properties of Miscellaneous Chromium-molybdenum Steels—Uses—Author's Summary.

CHAPTER VIII

NICKEL-MOLYBDENUM AND NICKEL-CHROMIUM-MOLYBDENUM STEELS . 259

Nickel-molybdenum Steels—Nickel-chromium-molybdenum Structural Steels—Miscellaneous Nickel-chromium-molybdenum Steels—Author's Summary.

CHAPTER IX

MOLYBDENUM IN HIGH-SPEED STEELS 315

Compositions of Molybdenum High-speed Steels—Mechanical Properties—Cutting Performance—Possible Limitations and Advantages in the Use of Molybdenum—Development Work at Watertown Arsenal—Author's Summary.

CHAPTER X

MOLYBDENUM IN NITRIDING STEELS 358

Nitriding Steels—Effects of Molybdenum in Nitriding Steels—Properties before and after Nitriding—Uses—Author's Summary.

CHAPTER XI

OTHER IRON-MOLYBDENUM ALLOYS 390

Manganese-molybdenum Steels—Miscellaneous Structural Steels Containing Molybdenum—Corrosion- and Heat-resistant Alloys—Miscellaneous Alloys—Author's Summary.

APPENDIX I

THE IRON-CARBON-MOLYBDENUM SYSTEM 439

BIBLIOGRAPHY 445

NAME INDEX 479

SUBJECT INDEX 487

THE ALLOYS OF IRON AND MOLYBDENUM

CHAPTER I

INTRODUCTION

General Survey of Work—Properties of Molybdenum and Iron—Molybdenum Minerals—Occurrence of Molybdenum Ores—Extraction of Molybdenum

The word molybdenum is derived from the Greek word *molybdos*, meaning lead, which according to Fleck[69] resulted from the use of the word for lead as well as for all dark metallic sulphides. The minerals graphite and molybdenite (MoS_2) were considered as identical for many centuries and, as Fleck stated, were not recognized as separate entities until late in the Phlogiston period.

The element molybdenum was discovered in 1778 by Scheele,[69, 205] who obtained an oxide of molybdenum by heating molybdenite with nitric acid. Metallic molybdenum, according to Pokorny,[205] was first produced by Hjelm in 1782. At the beginning of the nineteenth century Berzelius succeeded in producing molybdenum by reduction with hydrogen.

In his work with the electric arc furnace in the latter part of the nineteenth century Moissan studied molybdenum and succeeded in producing fused molybdenum, molybdenum-carbon alloys, and iron-molybdenum alloys.

At the present time commercially pure molybdenum in the form of sheet and wire is produced by hydrogen reduction of the oxide, followed by pressing and sintering the metallic powder and then working the sintered bars into the desired shapes. A surprisingly large amount of molybdenum, according to Tyler and Petar,[298] is used in electric industry.

Molybdenum is added to steel or cast iron in the form of either the ferroalloy, calcium molybdate, or a fused salt of molybdenum.

Ferromolybdenum is commonly made by reduction of the sulphide (MoS_2) with carbon or silicon, while calcium molybdate is usually made by adding lime to the oxide formed by roasting the sulphide ore.

A. GENERAL SURVEY OF WORK

The outstanding works that have led to the present knowledge and utilization of molybdenum in iron are discussed below. Emphasis has been placed on the earlier investigations, and many recent contributions have been omitted in this brief résumé.

1. Iron-molybdenum Alloys.—As previously mentioned, Moissan, late in the nineteenth century, studied iron-molybdenum alloys which were rich in iron. In 1907, Lautsch and Tammann[34] attempted to determine the equilibrium diagram for this alloy system, but in the light of recent work their results are far from satisfactory, due to the impurity of their alloys.

In 1926, Sykes[183] determined the iron-molybdenum equilibrium diagram, and subsequent work has resulted in only minor modifications of this diagram. He also determined the properties of the commercially pure alloys and found precipitation hardening phenomena in both iron-rich and molybdenum-rich alloys.

2. Early Reports on Molybdenum Steel.—Molybdenum was probably first detected in iron alloys by Kote, who, according to articles by Stromeyer, in 1831 and 1833[1, 2] analyzed several iron-rich meteorites, which he found to contain from 1 to 10 per cent molybdenum.

An early, but unintentional, use of molybdenum in steel is cited by Sargent,[92, 102] who quotes the following note from "Helmet and Body Armor in Modern Warfare" by Major D. Bashford, Dean of the Metropolitan Museum of Art, New York City:

> As this is written I learn from my friend, Dr. M. Mayajima of Tokyo, this interesting point, which he in turn had from the metallurgist, Dr. D. Kochi of the Faculty of Technology of the Imperial University of Tokyo. It appears that years ago a German steel expert analyzed a part of a sword blade made by the famous Japanese artist Masamune (1330) and he discovered the rare element molybdenum, doubtless as an impurity, in a certain proportion. This led the discoverer to determine the local source of Masamune's alloy iron; thereupon he purchased

this iron in large lots, much to the surprise of the Japanese who later, when they analyzed captured German cannon, decided where a part at least of the molybdenum was obtained.

An unsigned letter in *Stahl und Eisen* in 1896[10] asserted that a steel containing 2 per cent molybdenum has a silver-white color, a velvety fracture, and exceptional hardness. In 1894, Blair[52] mentioned in his book that the addition of 1 per cent molybdenum to an otherwise good steel rendered it red-short and worthless.

In 1896, according to Lipin,[13, 15] a steel containing 0.54 per cent carbon and 3.72 per cent molybdenum was made at the Putilow works in St. Petersburg, and its properties were compared with those of a steel containing 0.55 per cent carbon and 3.80 per cent tungsten. In general the properties of the two steels were similar. The molybdenum steel forged well, and its surface was free from cracks. In the annealed condition it was weaker than the tungsten steel, but after hardening it had approximately the same strength; it showed less tendency to crack on hardening.

The effects of molybdenum in steel were studied in the laboratory of the Creusot works of Schneider et Cie. in 1894, according to a recent report.[314] At that time a 400-kg. ingot was cast and rolled into armor plate, and subsequently this company produced a large quantity of molybdenum-containing steels.

During the last decade of the nineteenth century Moissan developed the electric arc furnace and methods for making molybdenum and other alloys in such a furnace. He[9] recommended molybdenum as a deoxidation agent for steels, stating that its oxide was volatile and would therefore be removed, while any residual molybdenum would not decrease the ductility of the steel. Apparently he did not learn that molybdenum would not reduce iron oxide at steel-making temperatures. In the German Patent 82,624, Nov. 9, 1894,[7] he described a method for introducing molybdenum and other refractory elements into steels or other material, in which an aluminum-molybdenum alloy was used as an addition agent, and stated that if desirable the aluminum can be removed from the final alloy by blowing air into the melt.

The magnetic properties of several molybdenum steels were given by Mme. Curie[14] in 1898, who found that such steels made excellent permanent magnets.

Mathews,[19] in 1902, described work in which he made three molybdenum steels and found that two of the heats were red-short and unforgeable. He attributed the poor quality of these steels to incorrect melting and forging practice rather than to their molybdenum content. These steels were almost free from silicon and manganese and are, therefore, not comparable with normally deoxidized materials.

In 1904, Guillet[24] reported the results of an investigation of two series of molybdenum steels. One contained approximately 0.20 per cent molybdenum, the other 0.80 per cent. These alloys were made by the Société Commentry-Fourchambault at the Imphy plant and used by several later workers. Guillet's work indicated that, in general, the effects of molybdenum were similar to those of tungsten, but that one part of molybdenum was equivalent to four parts of tungsten. His work has been quoted extensively in the literature since 1904. Other investigators have found, however, that one part of molybdenum is equivalent to only about two parts of tungsten.

3. Modern Reports on Molybdenum Steel.—Contemporary studies on molybdenum steel may be considered to have been initiated by Swinden,[52, 61] whose work was published in 1911 and 1913. He made a thorough study of the effects of molybdenum on steel, and his reports give an accurate picture of the effects of molybdenum. Many of his data are included in subsequent sections of this monograph. In his later work Swinden[61] investigated several steels containing approximately 0.50 per cent molybdenum and a small amount of either nickel, chromium, or vanadium. He found that such steels compared favorably with the alloy structural steels then used but that they had no outstanding characteristics.

The advantages of molybdenum in steels of the structural type were recognized by Wills, whose U. S. Patents 1,278,082, Sept. 3, 1918, and 1,288,344, Dec. 17, 1918, describe the advantages of using molybdenum in such steels. The former patent covers steels ranging from a substantial fraction of 1 per cent molybdenum to not materially more than 1 per cent. The latter patent covers the use of the same quantity of molybdenum in steels containing other alloying elements.

The next outstanding study of molybdenum steels was made by Gillett and Mack, whose results were incorporated in a book,[151] published in 1925. These authors reviewed the literature to that date and carried out experimental work on molybdenum structural steels. It was thoroughly established by that time that a few tenths per cent of molybdenum in combination with another alloying element such as chromium produced very desirable effects in steels, and this work showed that the same was true when molybdenum was added to steels containing manganese as an alloying element.

Commercial use of steels containing molybdenum, especially chromium-molybdenum steels, grew rapidly; one of the important uses in which they became firmly established was in aircraft tubing, on account of their suitability for welding combined with their mechanical properties. In 1926, the position of molybdenum as an alloying element was recognized by the listing of the "4100" series in the Society of Automotive Engineers' standard steels.

Recent work, notably that of Pohl and his coworkers[(235)] and Rys,[(398)] has shown that a small quantity of molybdenum tends to decrease the loss in strength resulting from heating to temperatures up to 500 to 600°C. (930 to 1110°F.), and that low-carbon, low-molybdenum steels can be successfully used in boiler construction and other types of service where it is desirable to use a steel that maintains its resistance to creep at moderate temperatures. The resistance to deformation at moderately high temperatures is conferred by molybdenum and by the similar element tungsten upon a wide variety of ferrous alloys, both pearlitic and austenitic. The effect is one of the outstanding properties of molybdenum and may perhaps be related to the specific effect molybdenum has in raising the tempering temperature required to soften a quench-hardened steel.

In addition to the outstanding work just mentioned, during the last ten or fifteen years many articles have been published on the properties and characteristics of steels containing molybdenum. Most of these articles deal with steels containing some other alloying element or elements in addition to molybdenum. Such articles include descriptions of molybdenum-containing steels of the high-speed type, steels used for nitriding, and steels of the structural type.

The elaborate investigation of the effects of molybdenum on nickel-chromium steels reported by Jones[(176)] showed definitely that a small quantity of molybdenum decreases the susceptibility of these steels to temper-brittleness. Practically all of the steels now used for nitriding contain some molybdenum, chiefly because the element prevents the steels from becoming brittle at nitriding temperature.

Immediately after the World War quite a furore was caused by the announcement that Arnold had developed a molybdenum high-speed steel superior to the available tungsten high-speed steels. This work was reported by Arnold and Ibbotson(76) in 1919. Several commenters in America and Germany pointed out that the use of molybdenum in place of tungsten in high-speed steel was not novel,[1] and to date there has been little commercial replacement of the tungsten high-speed steels by those containing molybdenum, though work at Watertown Arsenal(395) has indicated that some replacement is probably technically feasible, whether or not it is economically desirable.

4. Cast Iron.—The effect of molybdenum in cast iron was studied by Campion(73) in 1918. The first comprehensive work, however, was reported by Piwowarsky(161) in 1925. Within the last few years several important reports appeared on this subject, that of the Italian investigators Musatti and Calbiani(385) being the most comprehensive. Trade booklets issued by the Climax Molybdenum Co. and the High Speed Steel Alloys, Ltd.,(458) have pointed out the advantages of molybdenum cast iron. It is also apparent that an appreciable quantity of molybdenum cast iron is now being produced, even though the information regarding the properties conferred by molybdenum is still quite meager.

The important commercial use of molybdenum cast iron in automobile brake drums designed for severe service together with indications that the beneficial effects it confers on steel for high-temperature service may also be found in cast iron suggests that molybdenum may achieve an importance as an alloying element in cast iron comparable to that in steel.

B. PROPERTIES OF MOLYBDENUM AND IRON

Although a consideration of the properties of the elements iron and molybdenum does not come within the field of this work, some of these are given below as a means of convenient reference. No attempt has been made to discuss the chemical compounds

[1] U. S. Patent 722,504 issued Mar. 10, 1903, to Halcomb covered a chromium-molybdenum high-speed steel, and Patent 779,171 issued Jan. 3, 1905, to Mathews covered a chromium-molybdenum-vanadium high-speed steel.

formed by molybdenum, but the properties of the trioxide (MoO_3) are mentioned because clouds of this oxide are the "smoke" which is the outward and visible sign of loss of molybdenum. It is understood, however, that a very small quantity of molybdenum makes a large cloud of "smoke."

5. Molybdenum.—In the periodic arrangement of the elements molybdenum occurs in the subgroup containing chromium and tungsten, and as it lies between these two elements its properties

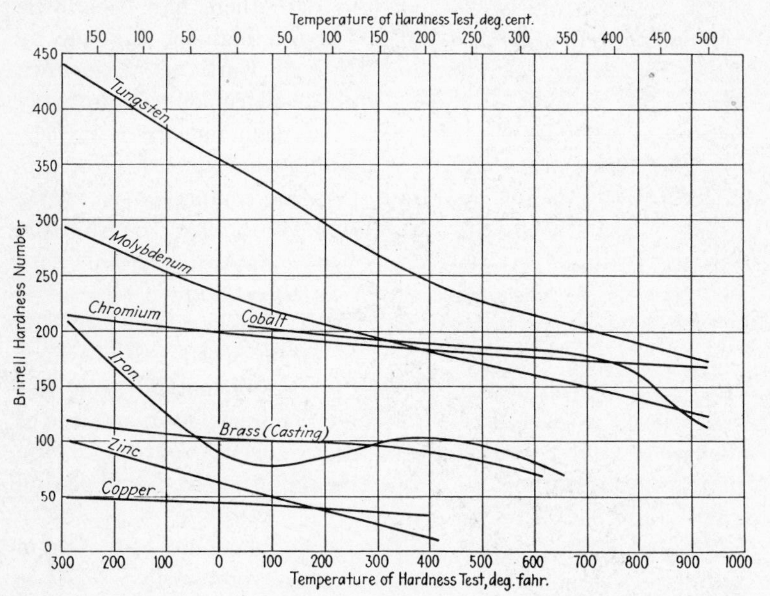

FIG. 1.—Hardness of some common metals at various temperatures. (*Grossmann and Bain.*[450])

would in general be expected to be intermediate between these two members of the group. The properties of molybdenum as listed by the Fansteel Products Co. in the booklet "Rare Metals"[440] are given in Table 1.

The physical and chemical properties of molybdenum were reviewed by Pokorny,[205] who stated that molybdenum is malleable both when hot and cold. Molybdenum powder prepared by reduction of the oxide is superficially oxidized in air at ordinary temperatures. In oxygen it is completely burned at a temperature of 500 to 600°C. (930 to 1110°F.).

As evidenced by the tensile strengths of wires reported by Fink[44] and listed in Table 2, molybdenum has a high strength and can be drawn into fine wire.

The hardness-temperature curves given by Grossmann and Bain,[450] and presented in Fig. 1, show that molybdenum possesses considerable hardness at temperatures up to 500°C. (930°F.).

TABLE 1.—PROPERTIES OF MOLYBDENUM*

Atomic number	42
Atomic weight	96
Density, at 20°C	10.2
Atomic volume	8.8
Tensile strength, lb./sq. in	260,000†
Tensile strength, lb./sq. in., wire	256,000 to 313,000†
Tensile strength, lb./sq. in., sheet	99,600†
Compressibility per unit volume per kg./sq. cm	0.46×10^{-6}
Brinell hardness	147
Scleroscope hardness, rod	12†
Scleroscope hardness, sheet	35†
Melting point, °C	2620
Melting point, °F	4750
Boiling point, °C	3700
Boiling point, °F	6690
Vapor pressure at 1517°C	6430×10^{-12} mm.
Specific heat, cal./gram/°C. at 0°C	0.0647
Linear coefficient of expansion per °C	5.45×10^{-6}
Thermal conductivity, cal./cu. cm	0.346
Heat of combustion, cal./gram	1,812
Heat of combustion, cal./gram atom to oxide	173,950
Temperature coefficient of resistance at 20°C	0.0033
Resistivity, microhm/cu. cm. at 20°C., annealed	5.7
Magnetic susceptibility, $\times 10^{6}$	0.910‡
Electrochemical equivalent, mg./coulomb	0.1658

* Fansteel Products Co.[440] unless otherwise noted.
† "International Critical Tables."
‡ Honda and Shimizu.[459]

TABLE 2.—TENSILE STRENGTH OF MOLYBDENUM WIRE*

Diameter of wire, in.	Lb./sq. in.
0.005	200,000 to 260,000
0.0028	230,000 to 270,000
0.0015	270,000 to 310,000

* Fink.[44]

The trioxide of molybdenum (MoO_3) is formed by roasting the sulphide and by oxidation of lower oxides.[205] It is white powder, which turns deep yellow when hot. Its melting point is about 795°C. (1455°F.), but it begins to sublime at a temperature 50°C. (90°F.) below its melting point according to Pokorny.[205] In recent work by Feiser[441] volatilization of MoO_3 was evident at a temperature of 610°C. (1130°F.), and the boiling point was found to be 1115°C. (2040°F.).

TABLE 3.—PROPERTIES OF PURE IRON*

Atomic number	26
Atomic weight	55.84
Density (solid, at 20°C.)	7.84
(liquid, at 1530°C.)	6.9
Thermal expansion at 20°C.	11.7×10^{-6}
Specific heat, cal./gram/°C. at 20°C.	0.1065†
Latent heat of fusion at freezing temperature, cal./gram	64.5
Melting point, °C	1535
Melting point, °F	2795
Normal boiling point, °C	3000
Normal boiling point, °F	5430
Resistivity ohm-cm. $\times 10^{-6}$ at 20°C	10

* Properties furnished by National Bureau of Standards.
† "International Critical Tables."

6. Iron.—Some of the properties of iron given by the National Bureau of Standards are listed in Table 3. As may be observed, the melting point of molybdenum is approximately 1090°C. (1960°F.) higher than that of iron and is only 380°C. (685°F.) below the boiling point of iron.

C. MOLYBDENUM MINERALS

Molybdenum occurs in nature only in combination with other elements. Its trioxide (MoO_3) occurs in combinations with the oxides of iron, cobalt, lead, tungsten, and several other rarer oxidation products. The most common and commercially important occurrence is, however, as the sulphide molybdenite, which is widely distributed throughout the world. The data on the minerals are taken chiefly from Dana[105] and Eardley-Wilmot.[148]

7. Molybdenite.—The mineral molybdenite, molybdenum sulphide (MoS_2), contains 60 per cent molybdenum and 40 per cent sulphur. It usually occurs in flakes or scales quite similar in appearance to graphite but for the bluish-gray color. It crystallizes in the hexagonal system and has a pronounced basal cleavage. The specific gravity is between 4.7 and 4.8, and the hardness on Mohs' scale is between 1 and 1.5. The mineral is usually found in acid igneous rock and, less frequently, in metamorphic rock.

8. Wulfenite.—The mineral wulfenite, lead molybdate ($PbMoO_4$), contains 26.15 per cent molybdenum and often chromium, calcium, copper, iron, vanadium, and aluminum as impurities. It may occur in a variety of colors but is usually some shade of yellow. It crystallizes in the tetragonal system and often forms tabular crystals. It has a specific gravity between 6.7 and 7.0 and a hardness on Mohs' scale between 2.7 and 3. Deposits of wulfenite are confined almost exclusively to veins containing other lead minerals. It has been commercially mined in Austria, Spain, Yugoslavia, and in several parts of the United States.

9. Molybdite.—The mineral molybdite is a hydrous ferric molybdate which approximates the composition $Fe_2O_3 \cdot 3MoO_3 \cdot 7H_2O$. It is an alteration product of molybdenite and is often associated with this mineral. Its color may be either lemon or straw yellow, and it usually occurs in the form of an earthy powder or as capillary crystals. Its specific gravity is about 4.5, and its hardness on Mohs' scale is between 1 and 2.

10. Rare Minerals of Molybdenum.—Some of the rarer minerals containing molybdenum are:

Powellite ($Ca[Mo, W]O_4$), containing about 48 per cent molybdenum.
Ilsemannite, ($MoO_2 \cdot 4MoO_3$), containing about 68 per cent molybdenum.
Belonesite ($MgMoO_4$), containing about 52 per cent molybdenum.
Pateraite ($CoMoO_4$), containing about 44 per cent molybdenum.

In addition to these, Eardley-Wilmot[148] lists several other minerals known to contain small amounts of molybdenum, and several doubtful minerals.

D. OCCURRENCE OF MOLYBDENUM ORES

Although molybdenum minerals are widely disseminated through the world, there are comparatively few deposits from which molybdenum ores can be obtained.[137] About three-quarters of the world's occurrences of molybdenum are in acid igneous rocks, and the remainder is in metamorphic rocks. It is frequently found associated with cassiterite, wolframite, and bismuth minerals. Wulfenite is in certain localities an oxidation product of lead veins and is likely to be associated with vanadinite and pyromorphite.

The distribution of molybdenum ores, their concentration, and the use and prices of molybdenum products are discussed in a recent *Bureau of Mines Economic Paper* prepared by Petar.[487]

11. Deposits in North America.—Developments to date have indicated that the United States possesses the largest known molybdenite deposits. Figure 2 by Hess[137] shows the principal

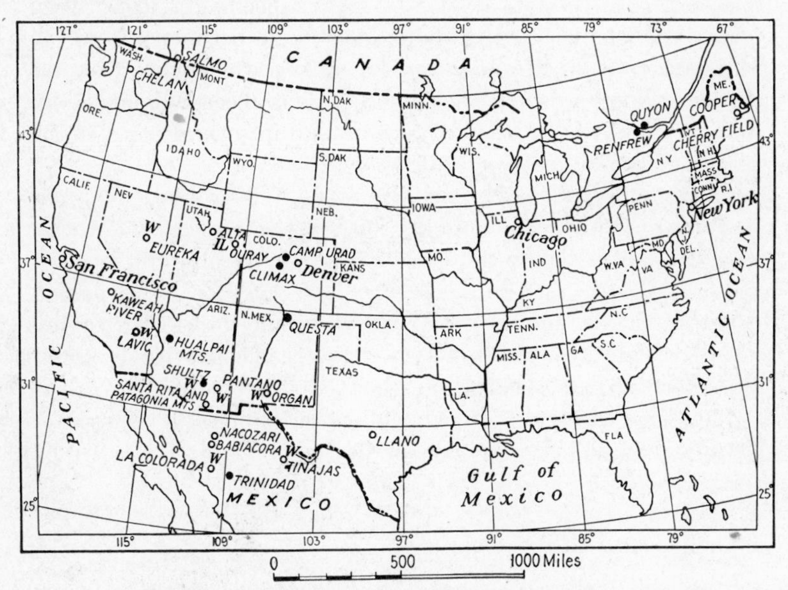

Fig. 2.—Principal molybdenum deposits in United States, Canada, and Mexico. *W*, wulfenite; *IL*, ilsemannite; others are molybdenite. ● Productive mine; ○ mine producing little or no ore. (*Hess.*[137])

molybdenum deposits in the United States, Canada, and Mexico. Attempts to mine molybdenite ore have been made in about twelve states, but in 1928 molybdenum ores were mined only in Arizona, New Mexico, and Colorado.

Deposits of wulfenite have been found in Arizona and Nevada.[71] Molybdenum ores have been obtained from several mines in Arizona, but in 1928 a mine at Helvetia was the only one in operation.[220] There, molybdenite is found in contact-metamorphic deposits and in quartz veins cutting pre-Cambrian granite and associated with aplite.[137]

Molybdenite is widely distributed in California, but there has been but little commercial production.[71] Wulfenite occurs in a few localities in the southern part of the state.

In New Mexico there is an important deposit of molybdenite at Sulphur Gulch between Questa and Red River just south of the Colorado state line. It is not so large as the deposit at Climax, Colo., but is richer in molybdenum.[137, 220] During 1929, geophysical prospecting by the Molybdenum Corporation of America substantially increased the known reserves at Questa.

Molybdenite is widely distributed in Colorado, nearly every mountain county containing deposits. The largest known deposit of molybdenite is at Climax,[148, 220, 429] which, according to Thorpe of the Climax Molybdenum Co., has so far yielded 80 per cent of the world's production. It yields a low-grade ore containing only 1 per cent or less of molybdenite. The mill at Climax is capable of handling 2,000 tons of ore daily. Another large deposit of molybdenite which is now depleted occurred at Camp Urad.

In Alaska, the only large deposit of molybdenite is on Shakan Island, where this mineral is associated with pyrrhotite and chalcopyrite.

The largest deposit of molybdenite in Canada was near Quyon, Quebec,[148] and is reported to be worked out. Since 1916, this deposit has yielded 80 per cent of the Canadian output of molybdenite. Workable deposits of molybdenite have also been found in Ontario and British Columbia.

Little information seems to be available on the molybdenite deposits in Mexico, but molybdenite has been mined in several localities. Near Tinajas, Chihuahua, there is a mine in which considerable quantities of wulfenite are associated with vanadinite.[148]

12. South America.—Molybdenum deposits occur in several localities in South America. In Bolivia, molybdenite occurs in the Illampu range in the province of Larecajia and in Tasna, Chicahs Paria. Molybdenite is found, in Chile, near Cupane and in the province of Tacna. In 1927, Chile produced 1.5 tons of molybdenite concentrate.[220] Wulfenite occurs at Antiaquia, Columbia; and at Paramorico, near Pamplona, there is a deposit which contains 10 per cent molybdenum trioxide.[148] Large deposits of molybdenite occur in Peru. Those in the

Ricran district in the province of Jauja, Junin, are claimed to be among the largest in the world.[137]

13. Europe.—In Europe, Norway is the greatest producer of molybdenite. In 1927, Norway produced 155 metric tons of molybdenite concentrate.[220] The average grade of milling ore does not seem to contain over 1 per cent molybdenite. Molybdenum deposits occur in several locations in Germany and Austria. Molybdenite and wulfenite occur in Italy. Ores of molybdenum occur in several localities in Russia. In Yugoslavia, at Mezica, wulfenite is found associated with oxidized lead and zinc minerals.[137] In Spain, an important deposit of wulfenite is situated near Granada.[148] Deposits of molybdenite are found along the Baltic coast in Sweden. A deposit on the island of Ekholmen was worked as early as 1880. There are several deposits of molybdenite on the British Isles, but there is no known deposit of commercial importance.

14. Asia.—Molybdenite occurs in southern China, and concentrates have been shipped from this district. Occurrences of molybdenite have been reported in twelve different localities in India, but the only shipments have been from the Tavoy tungsten mines in Burma. Molybdenite has been mined in a number of provinces in Japan, where wulfenite also occurs. In Korea, molybdenite has been produced in the Chosen District.[148]

15. Other Occurrences.—Molybdenite deposits are found in South Africa and in the Transvaal. All the states of Australia have produced some molybdenum, but the largest amounts have come from Queensland, New South Wales, and Victoria. Queensland has been producing molybdenite since 1905.[220] Some molybdenite has been mined in the West Indies on the Island of Virgin Gorda owned by Great Britain.[137]

E. EXTRACTION OF MOLYBDENUM

Molybdenite ore is usually treated by flotation[84] to yield a concentrate containing from 75 to 80 per cent molybdenum sulphide.[224] In the preparation of metallic molybdenum or its alloys, the concentrate may be directly reduced, but it is commonly roasted to the oxide before reduction. Unalloyed molybdenum is most generally used in the wrought condition and, in order that it may be sufficiently malleable, it is prepared by reduction of the purified oxide. Iron-molybdenum alloys may be prepared from metallic molybdenum or ferromolybdenum, but the alloys containing small quantities of molybdenum, such as the usual steels containing molybdenum, are often most cheaply prepared by the addition of calcium molybdate or even the roasted concentrates to the molten steel in the furnace.

Molybdenum oxide or salts of molybdenum can be readily reduced to metallic molybdenum at temperatures considerably below the melting point of the metal, as is evidenced by the reduction of calcium molybdate in steel-making furnaces. The high melting point of molybdenum introduces difficulties in the preparation of solid ingots of metallic molybdenum. For this reason, the only commercially successful method used in the production of wire and sheet molybdenum has been reduction of the oxide by hydrogen, followed by a sintering of the metallic powder and working the resulting product. Various other methods have been suggested for the reduction of molybdenum, but none of them yields a metal of high purity.

16. Suggested Methods for the Reduction of Molybdenum Oxides.—Debray,[3] in 1858, mentioned the production of metallic molybdenum by reduction of the oxide with hydrogen and later[4] he used this method in determining the atomic weight of molybdenum. Other writers[214] have reported the conditions necessary for complete reduction by this method.

Soft malleable molybdenum was produced by Moissan[8] by reduction of the oxide with carbon in an arc furnace. The metal had a density of 9.01. Escard[74] produced metallic molybdenum by heating molybdenite, lime, and fluorspar in an arc furnace. The metal produced contained 98.95 per cent molybdenum and 0.67 per cent iron. Molybdenum powder was obtained by Wedekind and Jochem[208] by reducing the oxide with calcium or zinc. Several other methods by which metallic molybdenum can be extracted were given by Pokorny[205] and Eardley-Wilmot.[148]

17. Manufacture of Pure Molybdenum.—The process used[1] in producing commercially pure molybdenum consists in the reduction by hydrogen of the purified oxide.[85] The crude molybdenum oxide is dissolved in ammonia, and molybdic acid precipitated by the addition of nitric acid. This acid is converted to the yellow-brown molybdic oxide by roasting below 1000°C. (1830°F.). The oxide is then reduced by hydrogen at a temperature of about 1000°C. (1830°F.). In this reduction,

[1] Fansteel Products Co.

the oxide is placed in a nickel or nichrome tray in a tube through which dry hydrogen is passed. About forty hours are required to reduce the oxide to a workable metal. The metallic powder is pressed into rods, which are sintered at 2400°C. (4350°F.) by the direct passage of an electric current. The sintered rods are either rolled into sheets or swaged preparatory to wire drawing.

A commercial grade of molybdenum powder is produced by carbon reduction of the oxide, but there is little or no information in the literature on this process.

18. Manufacture of Ferromolybdenum.—The manufacture of ferromolybdenum was discussed by Keeney,[90] who stated that it was first made in crucibles, from roasted molybdenite, but that it is now made in the electric furnace, either directly from the raw molybdenite or from the molybdate slag obtained from wulfenite ($PbMoO_4$).

Ferromolybdenum can be obtained directly from the raw molybdenite by reduction with either carbon or silicon. In the process using carbon as the reducing agent, lime is used to slag the sulphur according to the following reaction:

$$2MoS_2 + 2CaO + 3C = 2Mo + 2CaS + 2CO + CS_2$$

Iron, in the form of turnings, is added to produce a ferroalloy of the desired composition. Keeney asserted that there is no difficulty in producing an alloy containing only 0.1 per cent sulphur and that the carbon content will be between 1.3 and 3 per cent. If a lower-carbon alloy is desired, the product is refined with an oxidizing slag containing iron ore.

The reduction of molybdenite with silicon proceeds as follows:

$$MoS_2 + Si = Mo + SiS_2$$

In making a 50 per cent ferromolybdenum, ferrosilicon can be substituted for the silicon.

Wulfenite ($PbMoO_4$) ores are smelted in a lead blast furnace with coke and soda ash to produce lead bullion and a slag containing approximately 33 per cent of MoO_3. This slag is fused with iron and carbon to produce a 60 to 65 per cent ferromolybdenum in accordance with the following reaction:

$$Na_2MoO_4 + 3C = Mo + 3CO + Na_2O$$

Ferromolybdenum containing 80 per cent molybdenum and less than 1 per cent carbon cannot be tapped from the electric furnace because of its high melting point. In producing such an

s tapped off, and after the furnace is cold the
ved. A 50 to 60 per cent low-carbon alloy can
according to Keeney, a considerable quantity
oduced. The composition of ferromolybdenum
tion on steel manufacture.

1,833,125, Nov. 24, 1931, Read described a
method for obtaining a low-phosphorus, high-silicon ferromolybdenum from ores containing an appreciable amount of phosphorus. The molybdenum ore or oxide salt is reduced with silicon in the presence of a highly basic slag.

19. Manufacture of Calcium Molybdate.—High-purity calcium molybdate, according to Bonardi,[77] can be obtained by fusion of wulfenite ($PbMoO_4$) and subsequent wet treatment; but salt of the quality used in steel making is now obtained from molybdenite (MoS_2). The following description of the manufacture of calcium molybdate from molybdenite was given by Hardy,[344] who claimed that it was the method used by the largest producer in the United States.

Molybdenite concentrates analyzing approximately 50 per cent molybdenum are roasted in a multiple-hearth furnace. As they descend through the furnace, the sulphur is oxidized and the trioxide of molybdenum formed. As the material falls on the next to the last hearth, its sulphur content does not exceed 0.25 per cent and its temperature has been kept below 590°C. (1095°F.) in order to minimize loss of molybdenum by volatilization of the trioxide. On the next to the last hearth, hydrated lime is added by means of a screw conveyor and mixed with the roasted concentrates. When the mixture falls on the last hearth, which is kept at a temperature between 650 and 760°C. (1200 and 1400°F.), the molybdenum trioxide unites vigorously with the lime to form calcium molybdate ($CaMoO_4$). From the last hearth the molybdate passes through crushers and samplers to storage bins.

Theoretically, one part by weight of molybdenum requires 0.583 part of lime, CaO, but a slight excess is added. The small quantities of iron, alumina, etc., together with about 10 per cent of silica originally in the concentrate, are found in the calcium molybdate. The salt is ground to pass a twenty-mesh screen and packed in paper bags with sufficient calcium molybdate in each bag to represent exactly 5 lb. of metallic molybdenum.

The following analysis of a composite sample of calcium molybdate was given by Hardy[344] as typical of the commercial salt:

Substance	Per cent	Per cent
Metallic molybdenum equivalent to	40.50	
Molybdenum trioxide (MoO_3)	.....	60.75
Lime (CaO)	.....	23.30
Iron equivalent to	2.60	
Iron oxide (Fe_2O_3)	.....	3.72
Alumina (Al_2O_3)	.....	0.79
Silica (SiO_2)	.....	9.70
Sulphur	.....	0.22
Phosphorus	.....	0.014
Ignition loss (including combined water and carbon dioxide)	.....	1.37
Total	.....	99.864

"Molyte," marketed by the Molybdenum Corporation of America, is a fused product consisting principally of calcium and molybdenum oxides and is used as an addition agent in steel manufacture. This product is described in U. S. Patent 1,681,123, Aug. 14, 1928, and the process of manufacture in U. S. Patent 1,681,124, Aug. 14, 1928. In addition to lime and molybdenum oxide or oxides of molybdenum, Molyte contains fluxes such as silica. According to the patent specification, the material comprises "a mass fused from a mixture of molybdenum oxide and a flux-forming oxide, the mass containing molybdenum oxides lower in oxygen content than molybdenum trioxide." The process for making this material consists in roasting molybdenite (MoS_2) to remove sulphur and then fusing the roasted concentrate and a fluxing agent, including lime, in the presence of a reducing agent.

According to a private communication from E. A. Lucas, Molyte has a greater density than the commercial calcium molybdate and will, therefore, sink more rapidly through the bath of slag. Molyte also requires less reduction in the furnace, as the molybdenum trioxide is partly reduced in the manufacturing process. Molyte, like calcium molybdate, is sold in bags of 5 lb. of contained molybdenum each.

CHAPTER II

IRON-MOLYBDENUM ALLOYS

Constitution of Iron-molybdenum Alloys—Methods Used in Determining the Iron-molybdenum Diagram—Properties of Iron-molybdenum Alloys—Uses of Iron-molybdenum Alloys—Author's Summary

This chapter deals exclusively with alloys substantially free from carbon and other alloying elements; the more extensively used and more complex alloys, *i.e.*, steels and cast irons containing molybdenum, are discussed in subsequent chapters. The relatively pure iron-molybdenum alloys have not been exhaustively studied and, although they have been carefully investigated by several competent workers, knowledge regarding the properties and behavior of the alloys is far from complete.

A. CONSTITUTION OF IRON-MOLYBDENUM ALLOYS

The earliest investigations of the iron-molybdenum constitution were limited to chemical analyses of residues obtained by dissolving the alloys in acids. Somewhat later, Lautsch and Tammann made use of thermal analyses and proposed a diagram. Only within the last few years has the system been thoroughly studied with alloys of high purity and various modern methods of research. A brief résumé of earlier investigations is given; this is followed by results of recent investigations and, finally, by a discussion giving information now available on this system.

20. Earlier Investigations.—An early investigation of the constitution of iron-molybdenum alloys was reported by Carnot and Goutal[12] in 1897. By dissolving two samples of molybdenum steel in hydrochloric acid and analyzing the residues, they found indications of the compound Fe_3Mo_2. These residues showed the following compositions, which are close to the theoretical values for Fe_3Mo_2:

Element	Sample 1	Sample 2	Fe_3Mo_2
Iron, per cent	46.52	46.66	46.58
Molybdenum, per cent	53.48	53.34	53.42

In 1906, Vigouroux[33] reported studies of iron-molybdenum alloys, which he prepared by reducing the oxides with aluminum. Analyses of his alloys indicated the compounds Fe_2Mo, Fe_3Mo_2, FeMo, and $FeMo_2$.

The following year, Lautsch and Tammann[34] reported a rather extensive investigation of the iron-molybdenum system. The molybdenum used in preparing the alloys was made by the aluminothermic reaction and contained 3.5 per cent iron and 0.4 per cent aluminum. The iron contained 0.07 per cent carbon, 0.09 per cent silicon, 0.08 per cent manganese, 0.01 per cent phosphorus, 0.015 per cent sulphur, and 0.023 per cent copper, or a total of 0.288 per cent impurities. Their alloys may have been further contaminated with carbon from the carbon resistor furnace in which they were melted, as suggested by Arnfelt.[211] The entire range of compositions was investigated, and the alloys up to 60 per cent molybdenum were examined microscopically and by thermal analysis.

They determined the liquidus lines up to 60 per cent molybdenum, located the eutectic at about 42.5 per cent molybdenum, and recognized the solubility of molybdenum in iron. Impurities probably lowered the liquidus and solidus lines of their alloys and may have changed other values. Their diagram indicated an arrest at 1310°C. (2390°F.) for the alloys containing 30 to 60 per cent molybdenum, which probably corresponded to the eutectic temperature. While a compound was reported in alloys containing 50 to 60 per cent molybdenum, its composition was not determined. They constructed a ternary diagram, using Fe—*X*—Mo, in which *X* represented the compound.

Apparently, Lautsch and Tammann[34] made no attempt to study the physical properties of the alloys which they prepared nor did they discuss any possible commercial uses. Their diagram for the iron-molybdenum system remained the best information available for nearly twenty years and was made the basis of discussion in later publications, such as Portevin's[51] "Les alliages pseudo-binaires."

21. Recent Investigations.—Subsequent to the initial work on the constitution of iron-molybdenum alloys, considerable progress was made along other lines. One of the more important achievements was the production and study of the physical properties of ductile molybdenum of high purity. With the advances in the science and technique of physical metallurgy, coupled with the demands of industry for new materials to meet special requirements, came the reports of several important investigations on the iron-molybdenum system. A number of the outstanding investigations were carried out in the recent brief period 1926–1930.

W. P. Sykes [183] made a thorough study of high-purity iron-molybdenum alloys. He used iron and molybdenum in powder form for alloys up to 80 per cent molybdenum, and the oxides of iron and molybdenum, mixed and reduced, for alloys richer in molybdenum than 80 per cent. The iron powder contained 0.1 to 0.2 per cent iron oxide, less than 0.005 per cent carbon, and was obtained by hydrogen reduction of ignited oxalate previously precipitated from a solution of ferrous sulphate. The molybdenum metal powder, hydrogen-reduced, contained no carbon and was about 99.8 per cent pure. From the mixed powders, rods ½ × ½ × 10 in. were formed under a pressure of 20 tons per sq. in. Alloys containing up to 60 per cent molybdenum were melted in a tungsten resistor furnace in alundum tubes. Alloys richer in molybdenum than 60 per cent were fused by passing an electric current through them, all the melts being made in a hydrogen atmosphere. An optical pyrometer was used for most of the temperature measurements above 1400°C. (2550°F.); the melting point of iron was checked to within ±3°C. (±5°F.) by the optical instrument.

From the results of thermal analysis, microscopic examination, and other tests, Sykes[183] constructed an equilibrium diagram for the iron-molybdenum system. His diagram will not be reproduced here or discussed at this time, because certain modifications have been made as the result of later researches, and it seems advisable to present a diagram which represents the latest information from all sources.

Thermal analyses of alloys containing up to 4.9 per cent molybdenum, prepared from electrolytic iron and molybdenum powder, were reported by Müller.[201] The thermal analyses located the liquidus and solidus lines and the A_4, A_3, and A_2 critical points.

Laissus[199] studied the cementation of electrolytic iron, steels of different carbon contents, and gray iron by heating the samples in ferromolybdenum powder (carbon 1.86 per cent, molybdenum 71.85 per cent, balance mostly iron) from 2½ to 10 hr. at temperatures from 800 to 1200°C. (1470 to 2190°F.). In addition to determining depth of case, he determined the hardness of the cemented case as well as its resistance to oxidation and to corrosion in water.

Arnfelt[211] prepared alloys of iron and molybdenum by melting together electrolytic iron and molybdenum powder in a carbon-tube vacuum furnace, using magnesia crucibles. His work included a limited amount of microscopic examination and X-ray analysis, the latter chiefly by the powder method, of residues obtained by dissolving "tempered" specimens in hydrochloric acid. Arnfelt's tempered specimens were heated 30 hr. at 1000°C. (1830°F.).

A further study of the iron-molybdenum system was made by Takei and Murakami.[297] Their alloys with less than 50 per cent molybdenum were prepared from electrolytic iron and a molybdenum powder containing about 0.1 per cent carbon, while alloys with higher molybdenum contents were prepared from reduced iron and molybdenum powder. When the molybdenum content exceeded 90 per cent, the specimens could not be melted completely, but they were considered sufficiently homogeneous for microscopic examination. The alloys in the lower molybdenum range were melted, cast in an iron mold, and the molybdenum content was determined by analysis. The study of these alloys was mainly microscopic, but magnetic analysis, electric-resistance measurements, and dilatometric methods were applied to some of the specimens. Further, the intermetallic compound was separated from one of the specimens by electrolysis, and its composition determined by chemical analysis.

The diffusion of molybdenum into iron at 1250°C. (2280°F.) was studied by Grube and Lieberwirth,[343] who heated electrolytic iron and molybdenum powder in a hydrogen atmosphere for 72 hr. They reported the microstructures, compositions, certain physical properties, and some corrosion tests of the alloyed zones.

Chartkoff and Sykes[323] recently determined the crystal structures of the iron-rich and the molybdenum-rich alloys by means of the powder method of X-ray analysis.

22. The Iron-molybdenum Equilibrium Diagram.—The equilibrium diagram shown in Fig. 3, based largely on work of Sykes[183] and Takei and Murakami,[297] represents the best information available at the present time. There are some points which are not in complete agreement, but these will be discussed in detail later.

The liquidus line for the iron-rich alloys descends with the addition of molybdenum to a minimum at the eutectic point *C*, which is placed at 1440°C. (2625°F.). To the right of the eutectic temperature the liquidus line apparently rises continuously with

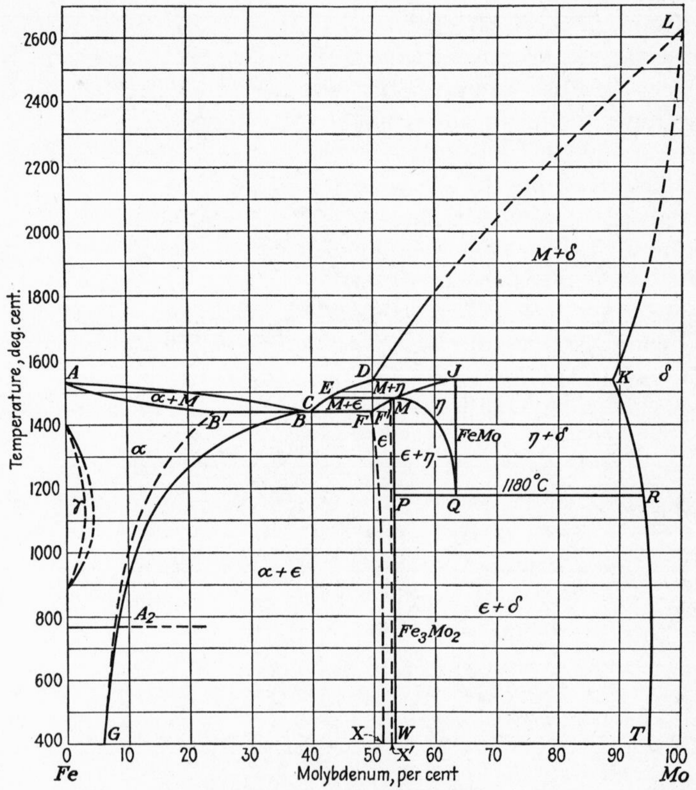

FIG. 3.—The iron-molybdenum equilibrium diagram. (*Based on data by Sykes*[183] *and Takei and Murakami.*[297])

the increase of molybdenum along the line *CD* to the temperature of the peritectic reaction at 1540°C. (2805°F.). Above this temperature, the liquidus line rises with increase of molybdenum content, presumably along line *DL*, although it was determined only to a temperature of about 1800°C. (3270°F.). The solidus line for the iron-rich alloys is represented by *AB* according to Takei and Murakami,[297] or *AB'B* according to Sykes.[183]

The solidus line for the eutectic temperature is represented by line *BF* according to Takei and Murakami, and by *B'F* according to Sykes, while for the alloys of higher molybdenum content the solidus lines would be *FM*, *MJ*, *JK*, and *KL*.

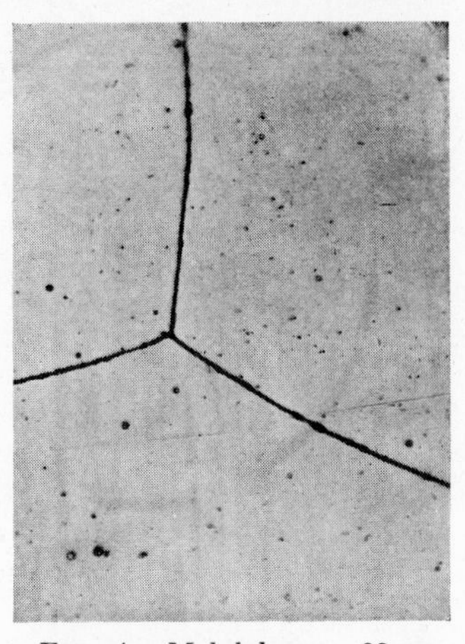

FIG. 4.—Molybdenum 22 per cent, iron 78 per cent. Water-quenched from 1425°C. (2590°F.). 500 ×. (*Sykes.*[183])

There is a disagreement with reference to the range of line *CF* which, in this figure, is drawn according to the Japanese investigators, while the work by Sykes[183] would extend line *CF* to approximately the composition of the intermetallic compound Fe_3Mo_2 at 53.42 per cent molybdenum.

Figure 4 shows the microstructure of a 22 per cent alloy, water-quenched from 1425°C. (2590°F.). The structure seems to be

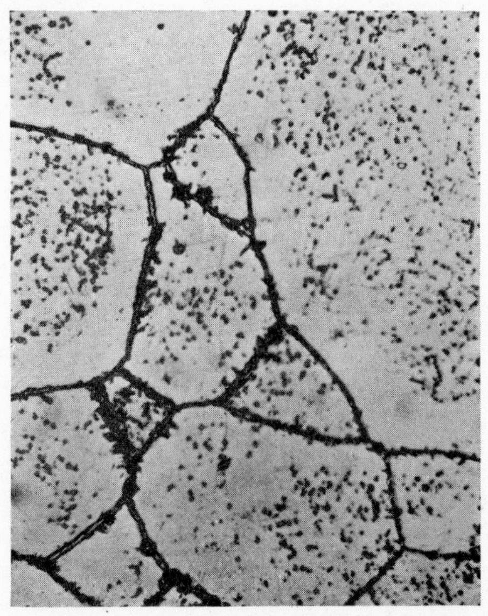

FIG. 5.—Molybdenum 22 per cent, iron 78 per cent. Cooled from 1425°C. (2590°F.) to room temperature in 30 sec. 500 ×. (*Sykes.*[183])

that of a homogeneous solid solution. On the other hand,

an alloy of the same composition, when cooled from 1425°C. (2590°F.) in 30 sec., showed a duplex structure as in Fig. 5. Still slower cooling increases the amount of precipitated phase as shown in Fig. 6, which represents the structure of the same alloy after cooling from 1425°C. (2590°F.) to room temperature in 1 hr.

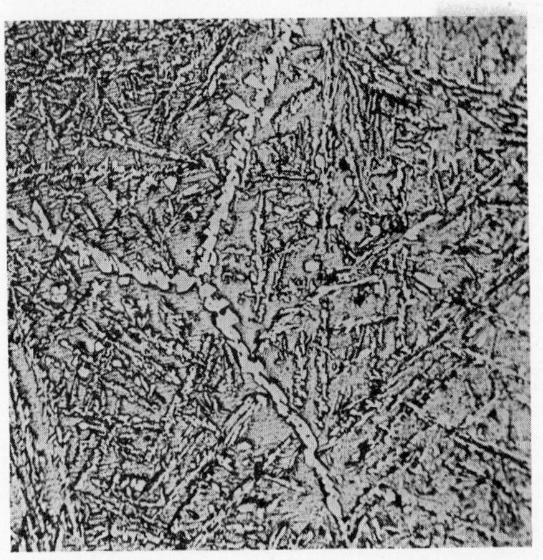

Fig. 6.—Molybdenum 22 per cent, iron 78 per cent. Cooled from 1425°C. (2590°F.) to room temperature in 1 hr. 250 ×. (*Sykes.*[183])

The solid phases which have been identified in the iron-molybdenum system are as follows:

Alpha phase: A solution of molybdenum in alpha iron.
Gamma phase: A solution of molybdenum in gamma iron.
Delta phase: A solution of iron in molybdenum.
Epsilon phase: The compound Fe_3Mo_2, or a solution of iron in the compound.
Eta phase: The compound FeMo, or a solution of iron in FeMo.

23. The Alpha Phase.—The alpha phase exists from the solidus temperature to room temperature, with the exception of a small area occupied by the gamma phase, and is found as the single constituent in alloys containing up to 38 per cent molybdenum at the eutectic temperature and 6 per cent molybdenum at room temperature, according to Takei and Murakami.[297] Sykes[183] placed the solid solubility of molybdenum in the alpha phase at the eutectic temperature at 22 to 24 per cent molybdenum, and the solubility at different temperatures, according to Sykes, would be represented by the line $B'G$.

Both investigators determined the range of solid solubility of molybdenum in iron by microscopic examination of a series of specimens of different molybdenum content and cooled from different temperatures, usually by quenching. The lack of agreement is due to different interpretations of certain microstructures. Sykes fused an alloy containing 30 per cent molybdenum and water-quenched it from 1435°C. (2615°F.). He

FIG. 7.—Molybdenum 30 per cent, iron 70 per cent. Fused and water-quenched from 1435°C. (2615°F.). 200×. (*Sykes.*[183])

considers that the darkened structure obtained is a eutectic, while Takei and Murakami contend that the resulting acicular structure is due to separation of the epsilon phase along the cleavage planes of the alpha solid solution. The structure obtained by Sykes is shown in Fig. 7. Takei and Murakami support their contention by showing that an alloy containing 29.5 per cent molybdenum quenched in ice water from 1400°C. (2550°F.) shows no eutectic. The evidence appears to favor them, because, according to Sykes's diagram, the alloy should contain nearly equal amounts of alpha solid solution and eutectic. Both investigations are in agreement concerning the solubility of molybdenum in iron at ordinary temperatures and place it at 6 per cent molybdenum.

Under equilibrium conditions, alloys containing more than 6 per cent molybdenum at ordinary temperatures show the alpha phase plus the epsilon phase; the latter increases in amount as the molybdenum content increases up to a point slightly above 50 per cent molybdenum, at which concentration the epsilon phase alone is found.

Under conditions other than equilibrium, the microstructures found in this range depend also upon previous thermal history of the specimen. The important factors regarding thermal history are the temperature to which the alloy was heated, the

Fig. 8.—Molybdenum 35 per cent, iron 65 per cent. Fused, cooled from 1475°C. (2685°F.) to 1430°C. (2605°F.) in 5 min., and water-quenched. 800×. (*Sykes.*[183])

rate of cooling, and the temperature and time of reheating after cooling.

Alloys containing molybdenum up to the maximum solubility in iron, which has been placed at about 22 to 38 per cent by the different investigators, can be rendered homogeneous by heating above the line *GB* or *GB'* for the particular composition and quenching drastically.

Slower rates of cooling cause the epsilon phase to precipitate, particularly in the high molybdenum-content alloys. The effect of the rate of cooling on the microstructure of a 35 per cent molybdenum alloy is illustrated by Figs. 8 to 10 from Sykes's paper. Figure 8 shows the microstructure of an alloy which had been fused, cooled from 1475°C. (2685°F.) to 1430°C. (2605°F.)

in 5 min., and then water-quenched. Figure 9 represents the microstructure of this alloy as cooled from the melt to room

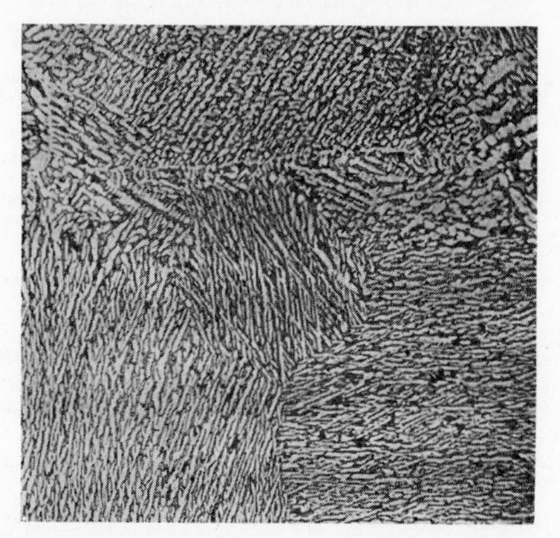

FIG. 9.—Molybdenum 35 per cent, iron 65 per cent. Fused and cooled to room temperature in 30 min. 100 ×. (*Sykes.*[183])

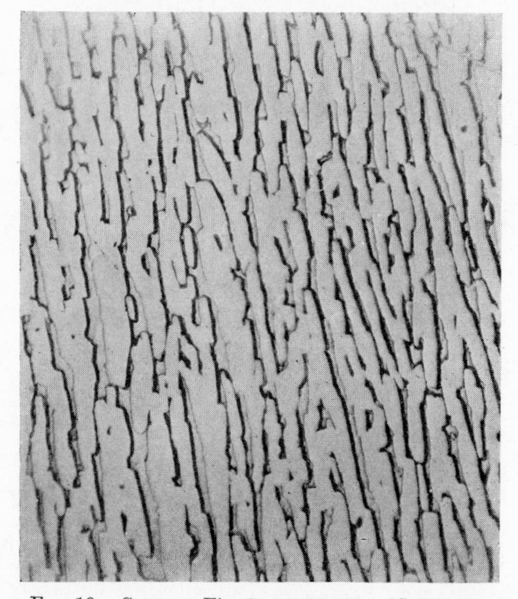

FIG. 10.—Same as Fig. 9 at 2,000 ×. (*Sykes.*[183])

temperature in 30 min. Figure 10 shows this same structure at a higher magnification. Sykes considered these structures to be the eutectic composed of the alpha solid solution and the epsilon phase, while Takei and Murakami again attributed the acicular structure to the precipitation of epsilon along the cleavage planes of the alpha solid solution.

Reheating the quenched alloys to temperatures above about 550°C. (1020°F.) starts the precipitation of the epsilon phase in the supersaturated alloys. The rate of the precipitation of the phase and the rate of agglomeration increase with increase in temperature.

24. The Gamma Phase.—The addition of molybdenum to iron lowers the A_4 point and raises the A_3 point. Sykes found the A_4

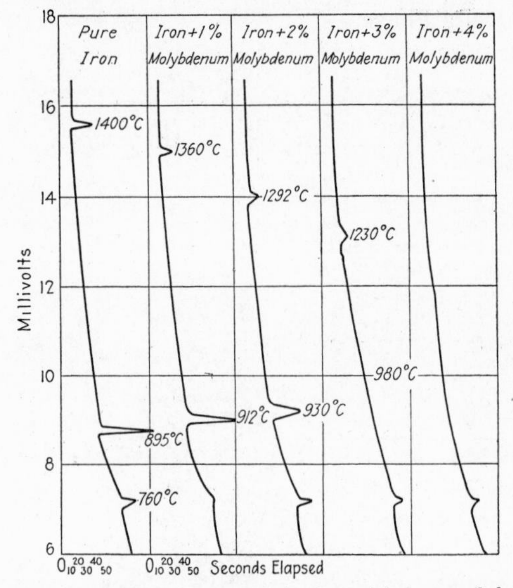

FIG. 11.—Inverse rate cooling curves of the iron-rich iron-molybdenum alloys. (*Sykes.*[183])

point in an alloy containing 3 per cent molybdenum at 1230°C. (2245°F.) and the A_3 point for the same alloy at 980°C. (1795°F.). His values were obtained by inverse-rate cooling curves which are reproduced in Fig. 11. He did not observe these critical points in an alloy containing 4 per cent molybdenum. In constructing his diagram, however, he estimated that the limit of the gamma field is from 4 to 4.5 per cent molybdenum. In the iron-molybdenum diagram (Fig. 3) the values have been placed according to Sykes's[183] work with the broken line for the values beyond 3 per cent molybdenum. Alloys falling within the gamma field recrystallize on cooling, first from alpha to gamma and then from gamma to alpha, which is a means of producing grain refinement. This influence of molybdenum on the gamma field is not unusual, because a similar phenomenon has been found in the iron-silicon, iron-chromium, iron-vanadium, and iron-tungsten systems.

Müller[201] studied these same critical points by means of heating and cooling curves, using the differential method. He found the same general relation but was unable to detect these critical points in an alloy containing 2.38 per cent molybdenum, although he found them in a 2 per cent alloy.

25. The Delta Phase.—The delta phase is the solution of iron in molybdenum, the maximum solubility being given at the

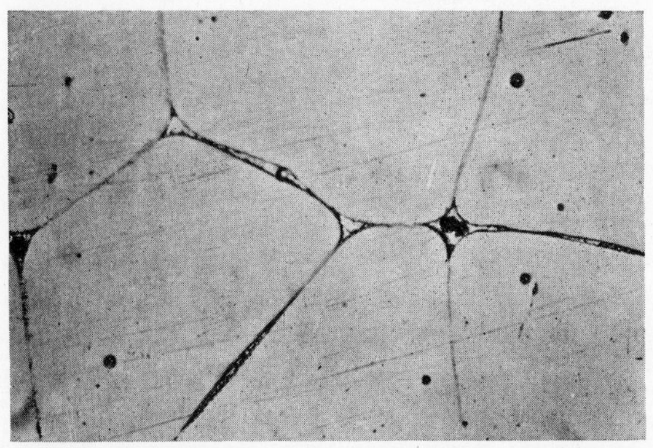

FIG. 12.—Molybdenum 88 per cent, iron 12 per cent. Cooled from 1700°C. (3090°F.) to 1530°C. (2785°F.) in 30 min., held at 1530°C. for 30 min., and water-quenched. 500×. (*Sykes.*[183])

peritectic temperature *DJK* as 11 per cent iron. The solubility decreases with decreasing temperature and is placed at 5 per cent iron at ordinary temperatures. Takei and Murakami[297] reported a delta prime phase formed by a eutectoid transformation at the temperature *DJK*, but the evidence for the existence of this phase is quite meager.

Figure 12 shows the structure of an alloy containing 88 per cent molybdenum which had been heated to 1700°C. (3090°F.), cooled to 1530°C. (2785°F.) in 30 min., held at that temperature for 30 min., and then water-quenched. Holding this alloy at a temperature just below the peritectic temperature evidently resulted in the formation of nearly all delta. The effect of reheating a quenched alloy containing 87.5 per cent molybdenum is shown in Fig. 13, in which it will be noted that the epsilon phase has precipitated and agglomerated.

Alloys within the delta field precipitate the eta or epsilon phase on slow cooling, depending upon the temperature at which saturation is reached, or, after being quenched and reheated, precipitate the epsilon phase.

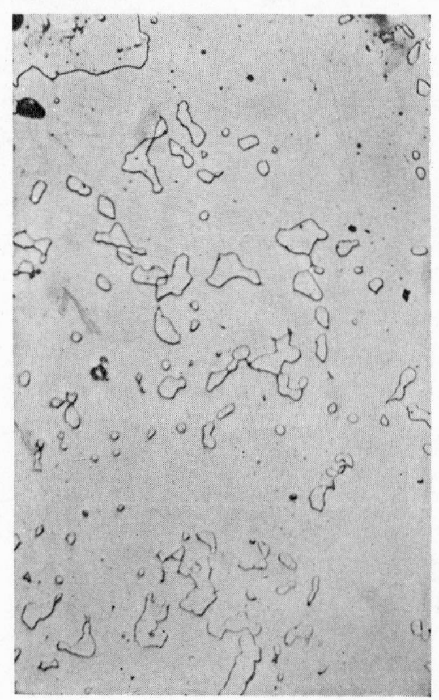

FIG. 13.—Molybdenum 87.5 per cent, iron 12.5 per cent. Water-quenched from 1530°C. (2785°F.), and aged 15 hr. at 775°C. (1425°F.) 500 ×. (*Sykes.*[183])

26. The Epsilon Phase.—The epsilon phase has been identified as the intermetallic compound Fe_3Mo_2, which has a theoretical composition of 53.42 per cent molybdenum, or a solution of iron in this compound. Takei and Murakami[297] concluded that iron dissolves in the epsilon phase at the eutectic temperature, so that homogeneous structures exist in all alloys between 50 per cent molybdenum and the theoretical value for the compound.

On the other hand, Sykes[183] concluded that the compound has a very limited range over which it is a homogeneous solid solution and reported the presence of the eutectic structure in an alloy containing 53 per cent molybdenum, which had been heated 12 hr. at 1400 to 1450°C. (2550 to 2640°F.) and held at 1425 to 1435°C. (2595 to 2615°F.) for 1 hr. The range of the epsilon field is, therefore, not completely established.

The structure of an alloy containing 45 per cent molybdenum is shown in Fig. 14. This sample was cooled from 1600°C. (2910°F.) to room temperature in 1 hr. The eutectic and the compound are shown. Figure 15 shows the structure of an alloy containing 51 per cent molybdenum.

27. The Eta Phase.—The eta phase was first detected by Takei and Murakami,[297] and its existence was later confirmed by Sykes.[183] This phase is the result of a peritectic reaction between the melt, containing about 50 per cent molybdenum, and delta solid solution, containing about 89 per cent molybdenum, along line *DJK*. At the temperature indicated, the eta phase corresponds to the compound FeMo which has a theoretical molybdenum content of 63.2 per cent.

It may be of interest to illustrate the nature of the peritectic reaction in this case by following the solidification of two alloys of selected composition through the transformation.

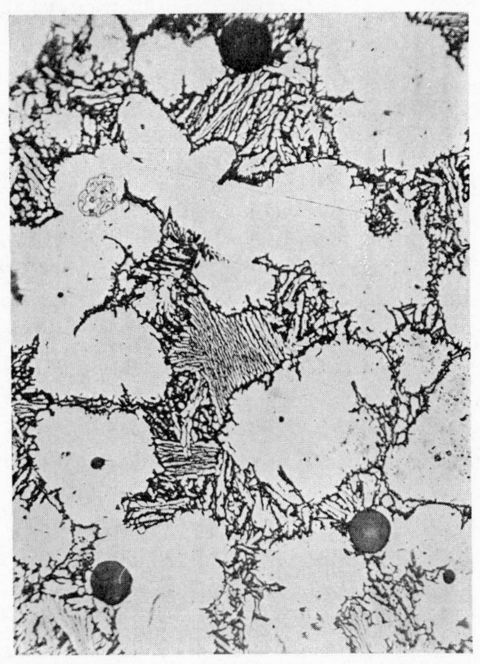

FIG. 14.—Molybdenum 45 per cent, iron 55 per cent. Cooled from 1600°C. (2910°F.) to room temperature in 1 hr. 200 ×. (*Sykes*.[183])

First, let us consider an alloy consisting of 70 per cent molybdenum and 30 per cent iron. Just above line *DJK* (Fig. 3) the system is composed of nearly equal parts of the melt, of a composition denoted by point *D*, and of solid delta of composition *K*. When the peritectic reaction occurs, the melt reacts with part of the solid delta to form the solid compound FeMo, or eta phase. At the completion of the reaction there will be 19.5 per cent of the delta phase and the remainder eta.

Considering an alloy containing 55 per cent molybdenum at a temperature just above *DJK*, the system consists of a little over 10 per cent of the delta phase and the remainder melt. Again at *DJK*, the peritectic reaction takes place, in which the melt and the delta react to form the eta phase. When the reaction is complete, the system consists of about 38.5 per cent eta phase and the remainder melt. The region of eta is represented by the area *MJQ*.

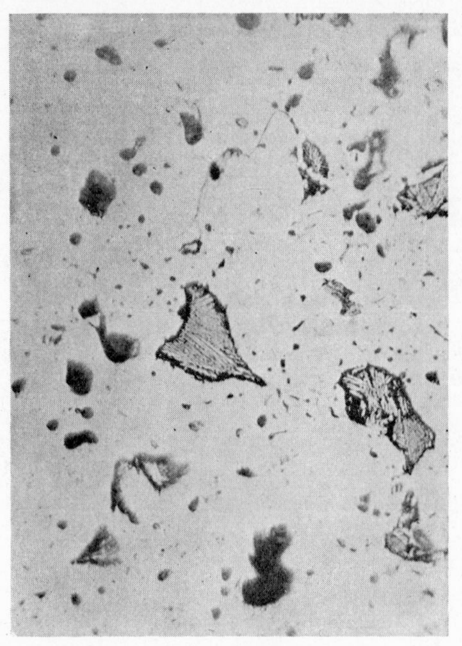

FIG. 15.—Molybdenum 51 per cent, iron 49 per cent. (Data on cooling not given). 200×. (*Sykes.*[183])

Alloys of composition *D* to *J*, below *DJK*, are composed of melt of the composition represented by the line *DE* in equilibrium with the eta phase represented by the line *MJ*.

Upon cooling to temperatures below about 1530°C. (2785°F.), the eta phase may show a separation of the epsilon phase along the line *MQ* and finally, at the temperature *PQR*, pass through a eutectoidal transformation, the eta changing to a mixture of epsilon and delta. The temperature of this change has been established as 1180°C. (2155°F.).

The microstructure of an alloy containing 70 per cent molybdenum and 30 per cent iron is shown in Fig. 16. This alloy had been heated to 1600°C. (2910°F.) for 5 min. and then cooled to a black heat in about 30 sec.

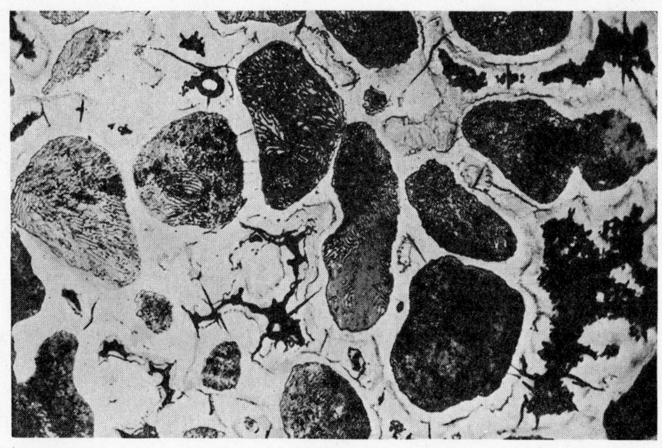

FIG. 16.—Molybdenum 70 per cent, iron 30 per cent. Heated at 1600°C. (2910°F.) for 5 min. and cooled to a black heat in about 30 sec. 500×. (*Sykes.*[183])

B. METHODS USED IN DETERMINING THE IRON-MOLYBDENUM DIAGRAM

The methods which have been used in determining the iron-molybdenum equilibrium diagram are thermal analysis, magnetic analysis, dilatometric analysis, microscopic examination, X-ray analysis, and electric-resistance measurements. The methods used in these various tests and the results obtained are discussed in the following pages.

28. Thermal Analysis.—Sykes[183] used the optical pyrometer to determine liquidus and solidus lines. The high temperature of these lines practically limits their determination to the use of the optical pyrometer.

Sykes also used thermal analysis as a means of locating the A_3 and A_4 lines in the alloys containing 3.5 per cent or less molybdenum. By this means he also detected the A_2 point in alloys containing up to 20 per cent molybdenum, although its intensity decreased with an increase in molybdenum. He found that this point is slightly lowered by the addition of molybdenum. Takei and Murakami[297] reported similar observations and indicated that the A_2 transformation is present in all alloys containing the alpha phase.

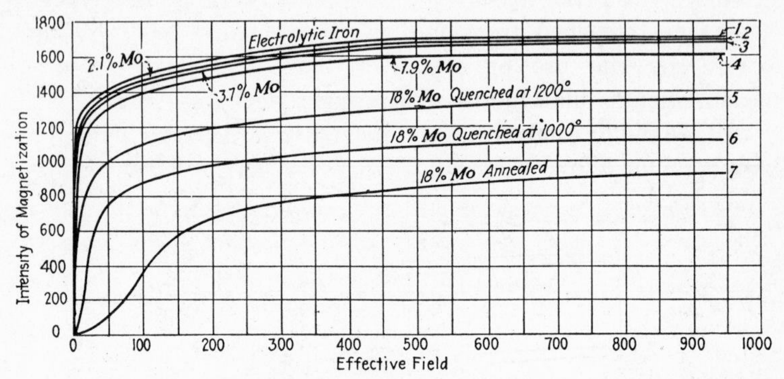

Fig. 17.—Results of magnetic analyses of iron-molybdenum alloys. (*Takei and Murakami.*[297])

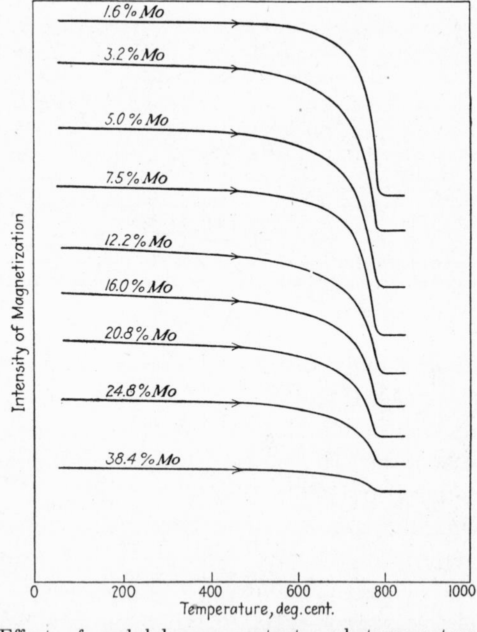

Fig. 18.—Effect of molybdenum content and temperature on intensity of magnetization of annealed iron-molybdenum alloys. (*Takei and Murakami.*[297])

Takei and Murakami reported that they were not able to detect by means of thermal analysis the eutectoid transformation in alloys containing 90 per cent molybdenum, although the existence of such a reaction was indicated by certain microstructures. The equilibrium diagram has been worked out more extensively on the basis of the microstructures observed in specimens quenched from various temperatures and, to some extent, by the use of magnetic analysis, electric-resistance measurements, dilatometric analysis, etc.

29. Magnetic Analysis.—The magnetic properties of the iron-molybdenum alloys were studied by Takei and Murakami.[297]

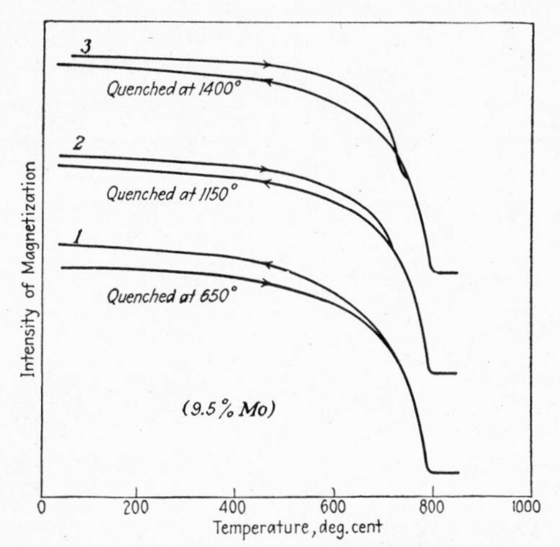

FIG. 19.—Effect of temperature on the intensity of magnetization of a quenched iron-molybdenum alloy containing 9.5 per cent molybdenum. (*Takei and Murakami.*[297])

By the addition of molybdenum, the intensity of magnetization is gradually decreased; the amount of decrease is small in the range of alloys consisting of the alpha phase alone, whereas in those consisting of the two phases, alpha plus epsilon, the decrease is more pronounced (see Figs. 17 to 21).

The intermetallic compound Fe_3Mo_2 (the epsilon phase) was found to be non-magnetic. In alloys containing both alpha and epsilon phases, magnetic intensity decreases, owing to the disappearance of the magnetic phase as the amount of epsilon phase increases. Annealed specimens have lower magnetic intensities than quenched specimens, if annealing increases the amount of the epsilon phase present. Magnetic intensities decrease with increase in temperature, showing a break in the curve at the magnetic transformation point for iron, which is slightly lowered with increase in the amount of molybdenum. The effect of molybdenum content and temperature on the intensity of magnetization of annealed alloys is shown in Fig. 18.

For quenched specimens, the higher the quenching temperature within the alpha plus epsilon field, the higher is the magnetic intensity due to solution of the epsilon phase. This relation is illustrated by Fig. 19 which shows the effect of increased quenching temperature on the intensity of magnetization of a 9.5 per cent molybdenum alloy. This effect is more pronounced

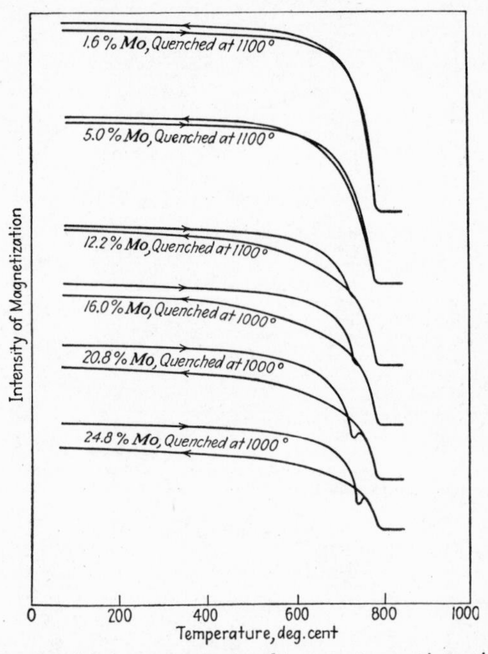

FIG. 20.—Effect of molybdenum content and temperature on intensity of magnetization of quenched iron-molybdenum alloys. (*Takei and Murakami.*[297])

as the molybdenum content increases up to the maximum solubility of molybdenum in alpha phase, as may be observed by comparing Fig. 21, which shows the results of tests with an alloy containing 16 per cent molybdenum, with Fig. 19. On heating quenched specimens, there may appear a break in the curve before the magnetic-change temperature is reached; this is attributed to precipitation of the epsilon phase on heating.

30. Dilatometric Analysis.—Takei and Murakami[297] found that the alloys containing up to 2 per cent molybdenum showed an abrupt break in the temperature-dilatation curve at a temperature corresponding to the alpha → gamma transformation, while in those containing more than 4 per cent molybdenum this change was not noticed. This fact is in general agreement with other observations regarding the extent of the gamma field. The results obtained by Takei and Murakami[297] are shown in Fig. 22.

In iron-rich alloys containing more than 7.5 per cent molybdenum, quenched from a high temperature, an abrupt shrinkage

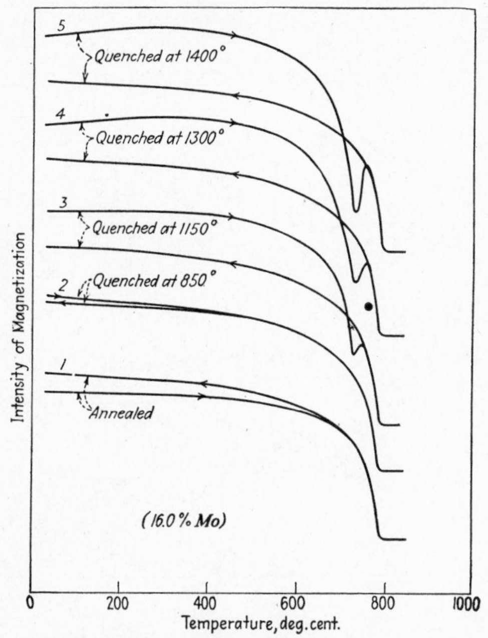

FIG. 21.—Effect of temperature and heat treatment on the intensity of magnetization of a 16 per cent molybdenum alloy. (*Takei and Murakami.*[297])

at 700 to 720°C. (1290 to 1330°F.) was observed, which the authors attributed to a precipitation of the epsilon phase from the supersaturated alpha solid solution.

Sykes[183] observed that the formation of the compound Fe_3Mo_2 resulted in a decrease in volume, which caused the alloys containing 40 to 85 per cent molybdenum to be porous. Sykes also observed a shrinkage on aging a 22 per cent molybdenum alloy that had been quenched from 1425°C. (2600°F.), which seems to confirm the idea that precipitation of epsilon from the supersaturated alpha solid solution is accompanied by shrinkage. The maximum shrinkage, 0.455 per cent, of this alloy seemed to correspond with the maximum hardness developed on aging 5 hr. at 650°C. (1200°F.).

Dimensional changes during the eutectoid transformation, at 1180°C. (2155°F.), of the alloys containing about 63 per cent

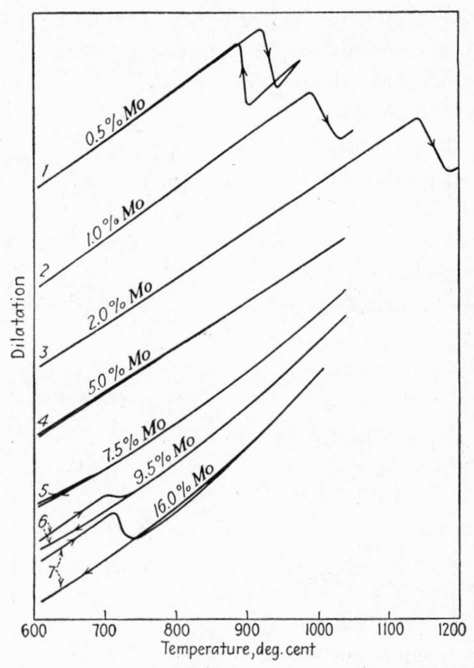

FIG. 22.—Effect of molybdenum content on dimensional changes in iron-molybdenum alloys during heating and cooling. (*Takei and Murakami.*[297])

molybdenum were reported by Takei and Murakami. In this case there is a shrinkage at the formation of the eta phase and an expansion in its change to the epsilon plus delta complex.

31. Microscopic Analysis.—The metallurgical microscope has been the most extensively used tool in working out the iron-molybdenum equilibrium diagram. The general procedure has been to hold the sample at a given temperature to establish equilibrium conditions and then cool rapidly in order to preserve the structure. Of course, samples cooled at different rates have also been studied. The etching reagents used to bring out the structures are discussed below.

Sykes[183] used a 10 per cent solution of nitric acid in alcohol, known as "nital," for most of his specimens. The compound Fe_3Mo_2 (the epsilon phase) is not attacked by this reagent and thus may be identified in specimens containing the alpha plus epsilon phases. However, when the compound Fe_3Mo_2 is freshly precipitated, it is darkened by this reagent probably similar to the cementite in troostite. Sykes[183] recommended a solution of 30 per cent sulphuric acid, to which has been added 5 per cent concentrated nitric acid, for developing the structure of the compound Fe_3Mo_2.

Takei and Murakami[297] likewise used the 30 per cent sulphuric acid plus 5 per cent nitric acid. They also used 10 per cent potassium hydroxide plus 10 per cent potassium ferricyanide. For the molybdenum-rich alloys, a 1 per cent hydrogen peroxide solution was used.

Arnfelt[211] heat-tinted polished specimens to a blue or red color and then examined the resulting structures. He found that each phase was attacked at a characteristic relative reaction velocity by the oxygen of the air. The ferrite phase is identified by its bright-blue temper color. He also used alkaline hydrogen peroxide for etching.

32. X-ray Analysis.—Chartkoff and Sykes[323] prepared the iron-rich solid solutions by sintering the mixed powder in an atmosphere of hydrogen for a period of 20 to 30 hr. at a temperature 25 to 50°C. (45 to 90°F.) below the melting point of the eutectic. The molybdenum-rich solid solutions of iron were prepared by adding the iron as a solution of iron ammonium oxalate to the oxide of molybdenum, followed by hydrogen reduction. The pressed metal powder was rendered homogeneous by sintering 20 to 30 hr. slightly below the peritectic temperature.

The specimens for X-ray examination of iron-rich alloys were prepared by filing and passing the chips through bolting cloth. The molybdenum-rich alloys were cut into strips so that an edge approximately ½ mm. wide and 5 mm. broad could be exposed to the X-ray beam.

The addition of molybdenum to iron was found to expand the lattice about 1.3 per cent at saturation, while tungsten expanded the lattice only about 0.50 per cent. The molybdenum lattice was found to shrink approximately 0.90 per cent with 12 per cent by weight of iron in solid solution. On the other hand, it was found that the tungsten lattice was expanded by the addition of iron, thus showing that there is not complete similarity between the iron-molybdenum and iron-tungsten systems.

The authors concluded that iron replaces the molybdenum atomically in the molybdenum lattice but, in the case of the tungsten lattice, the iron, up to the saturation value, goes into the interstices of the tungsten lattice, thus accounting for the expansion.

Regarding the intermetallic compounds of iron-molybdenum, the authors studied specimens of sintered blocks and metal filings and reported that the diffraction patterns of alloys in the range of the compounds are typified by several groups of many lines each, indicating a crystal system of low order of symmetry and large dimensions.

X-ray diffraction studies were also made by Arnfelt,[211] who found that X-ray photograms of the iron-molybdenum alloys had diffuse and indistinct lines. In order to obtain sharper interferences, an alloy containing 25 per cent molybdenum was tempered at 1000°C. (1830°F.) for 30 hr. The alloy was treated with hydrochloric acid, and the resulting residue investigated by means of powder photograms. He considered that this product was analogous to the trigonal iron-tungsten phase and had the following lattice parameter: $a = 4.743$ Å; $c = 25.63$ Å; $c/a = 5.40$.

The crystals of this phase were found to have a composition corresponding to the formula Fe_3Mo_2. Arnfelt calculated the volume of the unit cell as 499.6 Å^3.

No phase in the iron-molybdenum system was found which would correspond to the hexagonal phase in the iron-tungsten alloys.

33. Electric Resistance.—Takei and Murakami[297] studied the electric resistance of some iron-molybdenum alloys, principally as a means of establishing the equilibrium diagram. The electric resistance of the iron-rich alloys was measured during heating and cooling, a specimen cast in the form of a rod being used. Annealed specimens containing the alpha and the epsilon phases showed a break corresponding to the solution of the epsilon phase on heating. Otherwise, there were no marked changes in the curves which are reproduced in Fig. 23. Quenched specimens in the alpha plus epsilon region showed an abrupt change in resistance on heating. This seems to correspond to the precipitation of the epsilon phase, resulting in a decrease in resistance. Thus the duplex structure, which more nearly represents the equilibrium condition, has a lower resistance than the supersaturated solid solution. Takei and Murakami also studied the electric resistance of an alloy containing 60 per cent molyb-

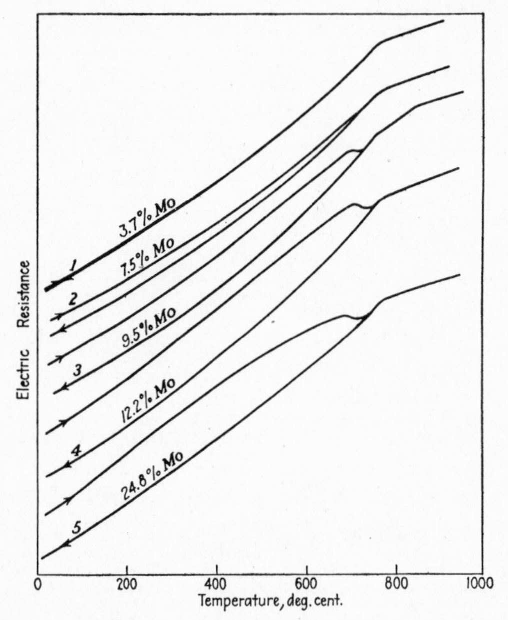

FIG. 23.—Effect of molybdenum content and temperature on electric resistance of iron-molybdenum alloys. (*Takei and Murakami.*[297])

denum, as a means of locating the eutectoid temperature. They found an abrupt change between 1180 and 1190°C. (2155 and 2175°F.). On heating, as shown in Fig. 24, there was a marked increase in resistance corresponding to the reaction of the epsilon and delta phases to form the eta phase. This change was reversed on cooling, although the resistance is not strictly reversible, owing to the cracks caused by a volume change.

34. Other Methods of Determining the Equilibrium Diagram. Hardness tests have been rather extensively used in confirming the diagram, but it seems better to place that discussion under the mechanical properties.

There is a close correlation between the hardness of different alloys and that which would be predicted from the equilibrium diagram. Although the tensile tests reported to date have been limited to an alloy containing 12 per cent molybdenum, the effect of various heat treatments on the tensile properties is consistent with the diagram, as reported earlier in this discussion.

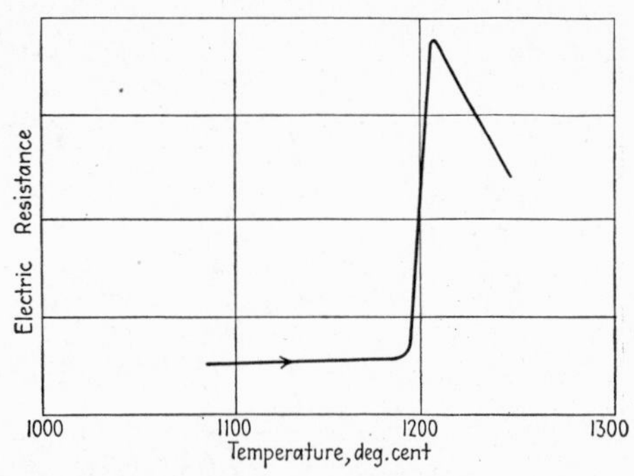

FIG. 24.—Change in electric resistance of a 60 per cent molybdenum, 40 per cent iron alloy on heating through the eutectoid temperature. (*Takei and Murakami.*[297])

C. PROPERTIES OF IRON-MOLYBDENUM ALLOYS

The available information on the mechanical properties of the iron-molybdenum alloys is not very extensive. The hardness values have been reported on a number of alloys, but information on other properties such as endurance, machinability, resistance to wear, effect of heat treatment, effect of temperature, resistance to impact, fabricating properties, and physical properties is limited or entirely lacking.

35. Tensile Properties.—Sykes[183] investigated the tensile properties of a 12 per cent molybdenum alloy, which was tested in the form of 0.030-in. wires. The results of this test, together with the effect of various heat treatments on the tensile strength and elongation, are shown in Table 4.

According to the equilibrium diagram (Fig. 3, page 22), a 12 per cent molybdenum alloy is a homogeneous solid solution at 1300°C. (2375°F.). The tensile-strength values suggest that this solid solution is retained at room temperature by quenching. By cooling to room temperature in 30 min., however, there is some precipitation, which causes an increase in strength of about

50 per cent; but it is of interest to note that the elongation has also increased.

TABLE 4.—TENSILE PROPERTIES OF 12 PER CENT MOLYBDENUM, 88 PER CENT IRON ALLOY*

Quenched from 1300°C. (2375°F.) and aged at 625°C. (1155°F.)	Tensile strength, lb./sq. in.	Elongation in 2 in., per cent	Remarks (all wires 0.030-in. diameter)
30 min.:			
A	66,000	6.3	Semi-wedge reduction
B	60,000	4.7	Full-wedge reduction
Average	63,000	5.5	
1 hr.:			
A	61,500	4.7	Smooth fracture at slight angle to axis of wire—no measurable reduction
B	66,500	6.3	Semi-wedge reduction
Average	64,000	5.5	
5 hr.:			
A	85,000	3.1	Semi-wedge reduction
B	76,500	6.2	Semi-wedge reduction
Average	80,700	4.7	
10 hr.:			
A	150,000	1.5	No measurable reduction—both fractures smooth, at angle to axis of wire
B	127,000	1.5	
Average	138,500	1.5	
20 hr.:			
A	153,000	0.7	Fracture rough. } No measurable reduction
B	142,000	0.7	Fracture smooth. }
Average	147,000	0.7	
50 hr.:			
A	123,000	0.7	Fracture smooth. } No measurable reduction
B	150,000	0.7	Fracture rough. }
Average	136,500	0.7	
As quenched from 1300°C. (2375°F.):			
A	56,500	6.2	Full-wedge reduction
B	60,000	4.7	Full-wedge reduction
Average	58,200	5.5	
As cooled from 1300°C. (2375°F.) to room temperature in 30 min.:			
A	91,800	5.5	Reduction about 5 per cent—rough fractures
B	93,300	7.7	
Average	92,500	6.6	
Pure iron, furnace-cooled from 1400°C. (2550°F.)	24,000	19.5	Fracture occurs within single grain—full-wedge reduction

* Sykes.[183]

The precipitation strengthening on aging at 625°C. (1155°F.) was slow, as maximum hardness was developed only after 10 to 20 hr., which was accompanied by a decrease in the elongation. Other aging tests show that precipitation takes place more rapidly at higher temperatures.

36. Hardness.—Sykes[183] found that the hardness of the alloys containing up to 3.5 per cent molybdenum depended upon the rate of cooling.

The quenched alloys show an increased hardness attributed to grain refinement in the alpha to gamma and gamma to alpha

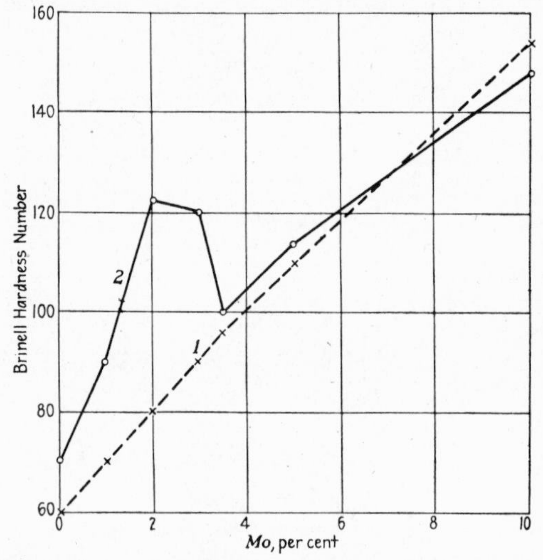

FIG. 25.—Effect of rate of cooling through gamma region on the hardness of iron-molybdenum alloys. 1. Cooled from 1475°C. (2685°F.) to 500°C. (930°F.) in 1 hr.; 2, water-quenched from 1475°C. (*Sykes.*[183])

transformations. This effect reaches a maximum in the 2 per cent molybdenum alloy, a specimen of which when quenched in water from 1475°C. (2685°F.) had a Brinell hardness of over 120, as compared with 80 for the same specimen cooled from the same temperature to 500°C. (930°F.) in 1 hr. (Fig. 25).

In general, the iron-molybdenum alloys containing more than 4 per cent molybdenum display a continuous rise in hardness as the molybdenum content increases up to about 40 per cent. Alloys in the range of 40 to 85 per cent molybdenum, while sufficiently hard to scratch glass, are porous and brittle and, hence, are unsuited for Brinell or Rockwell hardness determinations.

Of the iron-rich alloys containing more than about 4 per cent molybdenum, the slowly cooled alloys were harder than the quenched specimens, which phenomenon is attributed to precipitation of the epsilon phase (Fe_3Mo_2) on slow cooling.

Sykes found iron very effective in raising the hardness of molybdenum. As little as 3 per cent iron by weight increased the Brinell hardness of molybdenum from 125 to 281 and the Rock-

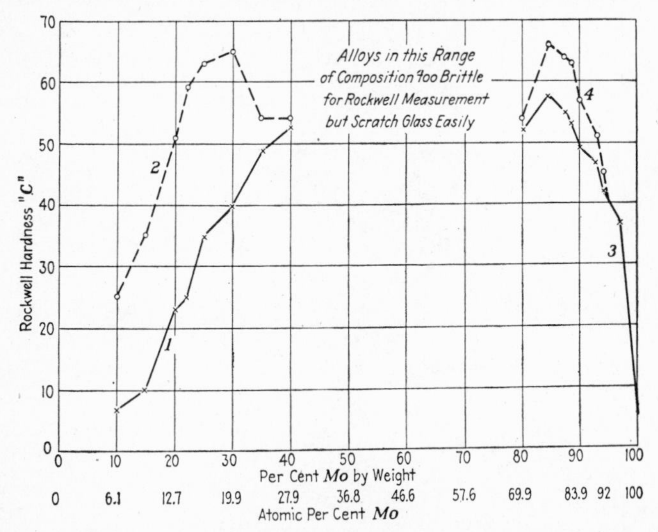

FIG. 26.—Primary and secondary hardness of iron-molybdenum alloys. 1, Quenched from 1425°C. (2600°F.); 2, quenched from 1425°C. and aged 20 hr. at 625°C. (1155°F.); 3, quenched from 1525°C. (2775°F.); 4, quenched from 1525°C. and aged 20 hr. at 775°C. (1425°F.) (*Sykes.*[183])

well hardness from *C*-5 to *C*-37, while an alloy containing 5.5 per cent iron, after quenching from 1525°C. (2775°F.) had a Brinell of 490 and a Rockwell of *C*-58.

The iron-rich alloys, containing more than 6 per cent molybdenum, after quenching showed an age-hardening phenomenon, which is apparently comparable to the aging of duralumin, but the aging temperature is considerably higher, beginning at about 500°C. (930°F.).

These alloys, in common with the duralumin-type alloys, require 100 hr. or longer to reach their maximum hardness at the low aging temperature, reaching maximum hardness in a shorter time as the temperature is increased; but as the temperature increases, the alloys show a softening effect. The effect of various heat treatments on the hardness of these alloys is illustrated in Table 5 and in Fig. 26.

TABLE 5.—BRINELL AND ROCKWELL HARDNESS OF IRON-MOLYBDENUM ALLOYS*

Composition	As quenched from 1425°C. (2600°F.)		After aging 20 hr. at 625°C. (1155°F.)	
	Brinell	Rockwell C	Brinell	Rockwell C
Pure iron	60			
Iron with 3 % molybdenum	100			
5 % molybdenum	110			
10 % molybdenum	146	7	218	25
15 % molybdenum	173	10	240	35
20 % molybdenum	200	23	437	51
22 % molybdenum	225	26	530	59
25 % molybdenum	233	35	545	63
30 % molybdenum	272	40	620	65
35 % molybdenum	Too brittle	49	Too brittle	54
40 % molybdenum	Too brittle	53	Too brittle	54
	As quenched from 1525°C. (2775°F.)		After aging 20 hr. at 775°C. (1425°F.)	
Pure molybdenum	125	5		
Molybdenum with 1½ % iron	235	23		
3 % iron	281	37		
7 % iron	349	47	440	51
10 % iron	375	49	520	57
11½ % iron	412	53	550	63
12½ % iron	464	55	585	64
15½ % iron	490	58	640	66
20 % iron	Cracks	52	Cracks	54

* Sykes.(183)

Hardness tests on two iron-molybdenum alloys containing 23.36 per cent molybdenum were made by the Western Electric Co., Inc.[1] The alloys were prepared by mixing powdered electro-

[1] These results, together with data on other alloy systems, have been recently published. See Seljesater and Rogers, *Trans. A.S.S.T.*, v. 19, 1932, pp. 553–576.

lytic iron and Fansteel high-purity molybdenum powder in the desired proportions and then melting in a magnesia clay crucible in an Arsem furnace. The billets were heated to 1095°C. (2000°F.) and forged to bars of the sizes indicated. The bars were then reheated to 1270°C. (2320°F.), held at this temperature 25 and 40 min. for bars *A* and *B* respectively, and quenched in water. The hardness values after aging at different temperatures were then determined. The results are shown in Table 6.

TABLE 6.—EFFECT OF AGING ON THE HARDNESS OF IRON-MOLYBDENUM ALLOYS CONTAINING 23.36 PER CENT MOLYBDENUM*

Bar *A* area = 0.782 cm.²				Bar *B* area = 0.602 cm.²			
Aging temperature		Aging time, hr.	Rockwell *C* hardness	Aging temperature		Aging time, hr.	Rockwell *C* hardness
°C.	°F.			°C.	°F.		
27	80	...	25	27	80	...	24
315	600	1	25				
425	800	1	25				
540	1000	1	30				
590	1100	1	35	590	1100	1	32
590	1100	2	40	590	1100	2	52
				590	1100	4	59
650	1200	1	57	650	1200	1/5	58
650	1200	2	59	650	1200	2/3	59
650	1200	3	60	650	1200	2 1/2	59
650	1200	5	60				
705	1300	3/4	58				
760	1400	3/4	57				
760	1400	2 3/4	57				
790	1450	1	57				
815	1500	1 1/6	54				

* Western Electric Company, Inc.

It is of interest to note that the foregoing alloys were quenched from only 1270°C. (2320°F.), which according to the diagram is below the solubility line, while Sykes quenched his alloys from 1425°C. (2600°F.), and yet the hardness is essentially the same, both in the quenched and in the aged conditions, for alloys of the same compositions.

The effects of different aging temperatures on the hardness of a quenched 25 per cent molybdenum alloy are shown in Fig. 27.

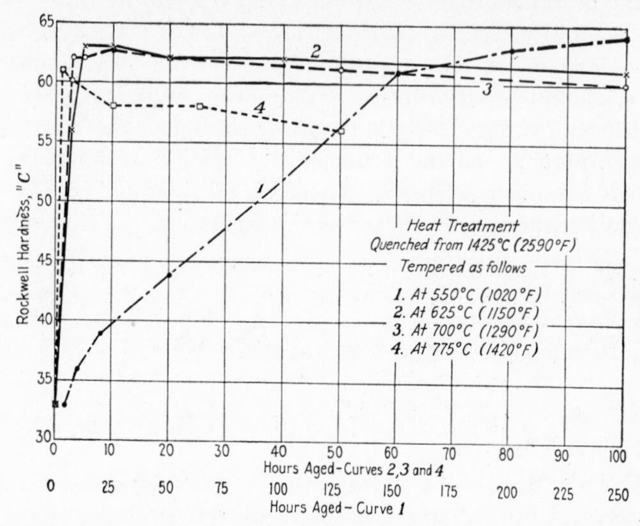

FIG. 27.—Effect of aging on the hardness of an alloy containing 25 per cent molybdenum and 75 per cent iron. (*Sykes.*(183))

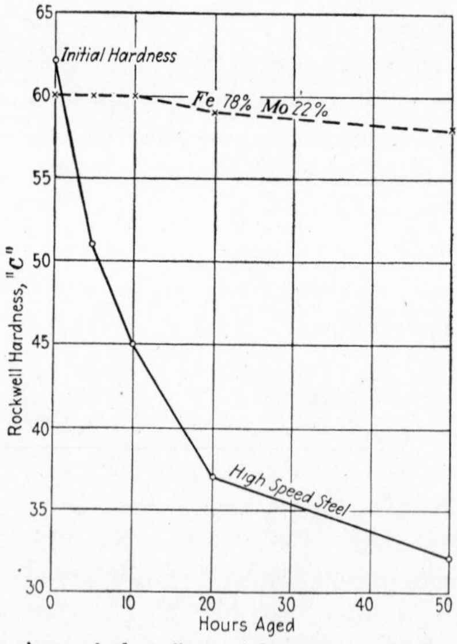

FIG. 28.—Comparison of the effect of heating at 600°C. (1110°F.) on the hardness of high-speed steel and an alloy containing 22 per cent molybdenum and 78 per cent iron. (*Sykes.*(183))

It will be noted that at 550°C. (1020°F.) the hardness is still increasing after 250 hr., while at 775°C. (1420°F.) the maximum hardness is obtained in 1 or 2 hr., after which it decreases slowly. The stability of the hardness of iron-molybdenum alloys is further illustrated by Fig. 28, which shows the effects of heating at 600°C. (1110°F.) on the hardness of a 22 per cent molybdenum alloy as compared with a high-speed steel.

37. Endurance.—Published information available at this time does not show any results of endurance or fatigue tests on iron-molybdenum alloys.

38. Machinability.—Sykes reported that a 22 per cent molybdenum alloy, after heating 1 hr. at 1400°C. (2550°F.) and cooling to room temperature in about 1 hr., machined about as readily as annealed high-speed steel. Presumably all alloys of lower molybdenum content are machinable.

According to the same author, the molybdenum-rich alloys containing 10 to 16 per cent iron, even in their softest state, can be machined with steel tools only with difficulty.

39. Resistance to Wear.—Sykes reported good resistance to wear in an alloy containing 22 per cent and in another with 84 to 87 per cent molybdenum. The uses are discussed later.

40. Effect of Heat Treatment.—The effect of heat treatment on the properties of iron-molybdenum alloys has been touched upon in the discussion of the equilibrium diagram (page 21) and under the sections on tensile strength and hardness (page 42). Results show that the solubility of molybdenum in iron and of iron in molybdenum increases with increasing temperature. The alloys of both the iron-rich and molybdenum-rich sides of the diagram, which show an increase in solubility of the minor phase on heating, show a decrease in hardness when quenched from the region of the homogeneous solid solution. Slower rates of cooling give higher strength and higher hardness values.

Alloys which are retained in the form of a supersaturated solid solution on quenching show the precipitation-hardening phenomenon on reheating. Precipitation hardening begins in the iron-rich alloys at a temperature of 500°C. (930°F.) and at a somewhat higher temperature for the molybdenum-rich alloys. It is possible to produce some precipitation hardening, accompanied by increase in tensile strength, with little or no decrease in elongation. However, at high hardness and tensile-strength values, the toughness is decreased. Heating to higher temperatures increases the rate of the precipitation hardening but also tends to decrease the hardening effect, owing to an agglomeration or coalescence of the precipitated phase.

Other changes can be effected by heat treating, as, for example, in the alloys containing 60 to 63 per cent molybdenum, which undergo a eutectoidal change at 1180°C. (2155°F.). These alloys undergo simultaneously some volume changes, which tend to make them porous and brittle. A similar type of phenomenon is found in the alloys containing large amounts of the epsilon phase. Apparently the alloys in the range of from about 40 to 80 per cent molybdenum are not likely to be of commercial importance.

41. Effect of Temperature.—The effect of temperature on the iron-molybdenum alloys is indicated in the above discussion of the effect of heat treatment. No direct data are available with respect to the effect of either short-time or long-time tests at elevated temperatures.

Under "Practical Applications," to be discussed later, Sykes's results will be reviewed to show that some of these alloys retain good hardness and wear-resisting properties at elevated temperatures.

42. Resistance to Impact.—No data are available with reference to the resistance of iron-molybdenum alloys to impact.

43. Fabricating.—Most research work on iron-molybdenum alloys has been on cast samples or on samples made by pressing and sintering into the desired form.

In studying the effects of various elements on the hardening of iron by nitrogen, Eilender and Meyer[438] made some iron-molybdenum alloys in a Tammann furnace which were stated to contain between 0.05 and 0.08 per cent carbon. The alloys contained 0.25, 0.54, 1.55, 2.15, 3.50, and 8.6 per cent molybdenum. It was difficult to forge these alloys, for they could be forged only at temperatures above 1000°C. (1830°F.) or below 800°C. (1470°F.). The alloy containing 3.50 per cent molybdenum could not be forged at any temperature. Although no explanation of the poor forgeability of these alloys was given, it appears to the author that the difficulties may have resulted from attempting to forge them at temperatures in which the gamma-alpha transformation occurs.

The Western Electric Co., Inc.,[1] prepared two samples of an alloy containing 23.36 per cent molybdenum which were prepared first in a billet by melting together the desired proportions of the two metals; the billet was then forged to a bar. This alloy was reported to forge satisfactorily at 1095°C. (2000°F.). This would seem to indicate that, with the exception noted above, the iron-rich alloys containing up to 23.0 per cent of molybdenum could be forged.

44. Physical Properties and Physical Constants.—While the physical properties of the component metals iron and molybdenum are well-known, corresponding information on their alloys is less plentiful. The available data have been largely discussed in connection with the equilibrium diagram and so will not be repeated here.

To what has already been said concerning magnetic properties might be added a word with respect to the behavior of the alloys at elevated temperatures. With increase in temperature the intensity of magnetization of the annealed alloys decreases as shown in Fig. 18 (page 34). The rate of decrease up to the A_2 point is small for all the alloys studied. With specimens quenched from 1000 or 1100°C. (1830 or 2010°F.) the intensity of magnetization is slightly higher on heating than cooling, as shown in Fig. 20. This is attributed to the fact that the epsilon phase supersaturates the alpha phase. On heating, however, a temperature is reached at which the epsilon phase is precipitated, and this is accompanied by a falling off in intensity of magnetization. It should also be pointed out that this difference of intensity of magnetization on heating and cooling of quenched alloys increases with increase in molybdenum, owing to greater supersaturation.

The electric properties were also discussed in connection with the equilibrium diagram (page 40). The same is true of the physical constants. No data were found on densities, specific heat, heat of fusion, specific volume, and the like.

Data on the resistivity based on the work of Burgess and Aston are given in Table 7.

D. USES OF IRON-MOLYBDENUM ALLOYS

Since the work on iron-molybdenum alloys has been rather recent, it is not surprising to find that the published information

[1] See footnote, p. 46.

on the use of these alloys is very limited. The following discussion covers the uses of these alloys as far as data are available in the literature at the present time. It is, however, doubtless true that a number of other uses have been found, although they have not been reported in the technical press.

TABLE 7.—RESISTIVITY OF IRON-MOLYBDENUM ALLOYS*

Molybdenum, per cent	Specific resistance, microhm-cm.	Tempering temperature	
		°C.	°F.
5.12	27.8	900	1650
9.84	29.9	1000	1830
12.0	32.6	1000	1830
13.69	35.1	1000	1830

* "International Critical Tables."

45. Practical Applications.—Sykes[183] reported on the practical application of two types of iron-molybdenum alloys, one containing 22 per cent molybdenum and the other, a high-molybdenum alloy, containing 13 to 16 per cent of iron.

The 22 per cent molybdenum alloy was used for swaging die hammers used on tungsten bars, which were at a temperature as high as 1400 to 1510°C. (2550° to 2750°F.). This alloy was used to replace high-speed steel and had a life which averaged from thirty to fifty times that obtained with the most satisfactory high-speed steel.

The dies were prepared by heating pressed powders in a reducing atmosphere at 1400°C. (2550°F.) for 1 hr. to form the solid solution, after which they were cooled to room temperature in about 1 hr. In this condition the alloy machined almost as readily as annealed high-speed steel.

The machined alloy was then heated for 10 min. at 1400°C. (2550°F.), in order to dissolve the compound Fe_3Mo_2, cooled in water until almost dark, and then cooled in air. Further heat treatment consisted in heating 12 hr. at 625°C. (1155°F.), which is the most effective method for age-hardening this alloy. In this alloy, of 78 per cent iron and 22 per cent molybdenum, the initial hardness was only 60 on the Rockwell *C* scale, as compared with about 62 for high-speed steel. This alloy after heating for 50 hr. at 600°C. (1110°F.) showed Rockwell hardness of *C*-58, as compared with *C*-32 for the high-speed steel, showing that this iron-molybdenum alloy is much more stable at this temperature than the high-speed steel.

The other molybdenum alloy which Sykes[(183)] mentioned, containing 13 to 16 per cent of iron, is reported to have given excellent results as dies for drawing tungsten and molybdenum wire at temperatures between 600 to 800°C. (1110 to 1470°F.).

The Western Electric Co., Inc., has considered iron-molybdenum alloys for permanent magnets. The coercive force of an alloy containing 23.36 per cent molybdenum with the balance iron increased on heating the quenched alloy, a maximum value of 200 oersteds being observed after reheating at 650°C. (1200°F.). The residual induction in gausses ranged from 6,000 to 7,000. What practical application they are making of this alloy is not known.

According to Floyd C. Kelley,[1] an alloy consisting of the iron-molybdenum eutectic as determined by Sykes[(183)] has been used with good results as a bonding material for cemented tantalum carbide tools. Iron and molybdenum metal powders are mixed in eutectic proportions and added in the desired amounts to tantalum carbide, after which the product is thoroughly mixed, pressed, and fired in the manner generally used in the production of cemented carbide tools. According to Kelley, the iron-molybdenum eutectic alloy is one of the best bonding materials which has been found for tantalum carbide, one of its chief advantages being the extreme hardness which can be obtained in the sintered material.

E. AUTHOR'S SUMMARY

1. The general outline of the iron-molybdenum equilibrium diagram has been worked out and many of the details have been established. There is, however, need for additional information as is indicated below:

a. The solubility of molybdenum in iron at the eutectic temperature is a subject of disagreement between Sykes and the Japanese investigators and requires further study.

b. The exact composition of the eutectic has not been established.

c. There is a lack of agreement regarding the homogeneity range of the epsilon phase at various temperatures.

[1] Lecture, Columbus Chapter, American Society for Steel Treating, Dec. 1, 1931.

d. The liquidus and solidus lines for the molybdenum-rich alloys have not been determined above 1800°C. (3270°F.).

e. The possibility of a eutectoidal transformation in the molybdenum-rich alloys needs further study.

f. The crystal structures of phases other than the alpha and delta solid solutions have not been determined.

g. As indicated in the text, there is a lack of agreement regarding the identification and interpretation of some of the microstructures found in the iron-molybdenum alloys.

h. Finally, in further studies of this system additional attention should be given to obtaining equilibrium conditions at various temperatures and concentrations.

2. The magnetic properties of iron-molybdenum alloys have been studied almost entirely as a means of establishing the equilibrium diagram, and with the exception of the work by the Western Electric Co., Inc., no consideration seems to have been given to the commercial utilization of these alloys on account of their magnetic properties.

3. The electric properties of the alloys have received only very limited study.

4. The hardness of these alloys has been determined for the compositions 0 to 40 and 80 to 100 per cent molybdenum. In the range of 40 to 80 per cent molybdenum the alloys are too brittle to permit accurate hardness determinations.

The alloys containing 10 to 35 and 80 to 95 per cent molybdenum show secondary hardness and retain full hardness after prolonged heating at relatively high temperatures, about 500°C. (930°F.) for the iron-rich and about 600°C. (1110°F.) for the molybdenum-rich alloys. Further study should be given to the hardness of these alloys at elevated temperatures such as 500 to 600°C. (930 to 1110°F.).

5. The data on the tensile properties of these alloys are limited to an alloy containing 88 per cent iron and 12 per cent molybdenum.

The properties found in the alloy and the known hardness of alloys of other compositions suggest the desirability of further information regarding the tensile properties of iron-molybdenum alloys, particularly at elevated temperatures.

6. Sykes has shown that an alloy containing 88 per cent iron and 12 per cent molybdenum can be drawn to 0.030-in. diameter wire, and the Western Electric Co., Inc., found that a 23.36 per cent molybdenum alloy could be forged. Further work is needed

on forging and drawing of alloys of these and other compositions. The limits of the temperature ranges in which the iron-molybdenum alloys can be worked should be determined.

7. The only uses of iron-molybdenum alloys which have been reported are those by Sykes[183] as follows:

a. A 22 per cent molybdenum alloy for swaging die hammers used on tungsten bars.

b. An 84 to 87 per cent molybdenum alloy which was used for dies in drawing tungsten and molybdenum wire.

c. The eutectic alloy as a bonding material for tantalum carbide tools.

The known properties of the various iron-molybdenum alloys suggest that further research should find additional commercial applications for these alloys.

CHAPTER III

CONSTITUTION AND MANUFACTURE OF MOLYBDENUM STEEL

Iron-carbon and Molybdenum-carbon Alloys—Iron-molybdenum-carbon Alloys—Melting Molybdenum Steel—Casting and Working Molybdenum Steel—Author's Summary

Before attempting to determine a ternary equilibrium diagram, it is necessary to obtain the three binary diagrams formed by pairs of the component elements. The iron-molybdenum diagram has been discussed in the preceding chapter, and the iron-carbon and molybdenum-carbon diagrams will be discussed before considering the ternary alloys. Although portions of the pertinent binary diagrams have been determined, very little is known about the ternary diagram iron-molybdenum-carbon.

The useful iron-molybdenum-carbon alloys may be considered as steels or cast iron containing molybdenum and are here designated as such. Methods for adding molybdenum to steel, and the effects of molybdenum on the casting and subsequent working of steel, will be considered.

A. IRON-CARBON AND MOLYBDENUM-CARBON ALLOYS

Before studying the ternary alloys containing iron, molybdenum, and carbon, the iron-carbon and molybdenum-carbon systems will be examined briefly.

46. Iron-carbon Alloys.—The iron-carbon equilibrium diagram is to be considered in detail in another monograph of this series, and the purpose of this brief discussion is only for convenient reference in connection with the discussion of iron-molybdenum-carbon alloys.

The so-called metastable, or iron-cementite, diagram taken from the September, 1930, issue of *Metal Progress* is shown in Fig. 29. In this diagram, the *PSK* line, or the temperature of pearlite transformation (usually designated as A_1), is shown at 720°C. (1330°F.). The eutectoid composition is shown as 0.90 per cent carbon and the maximum solubility of carbon in gamma iron or austenite at 1.70 per cent carbon. In accordance with recent work, a few tenths of 1 per cent carbon are shown as soluble in alpha iron or ferrite, the solubility decreasing with decreasing temperature.

47. Molybdenum-carbon Alloys.—In 1893 and 1894, Moissan reported[5, 6] the preparation of molybdenum-carbon alloys

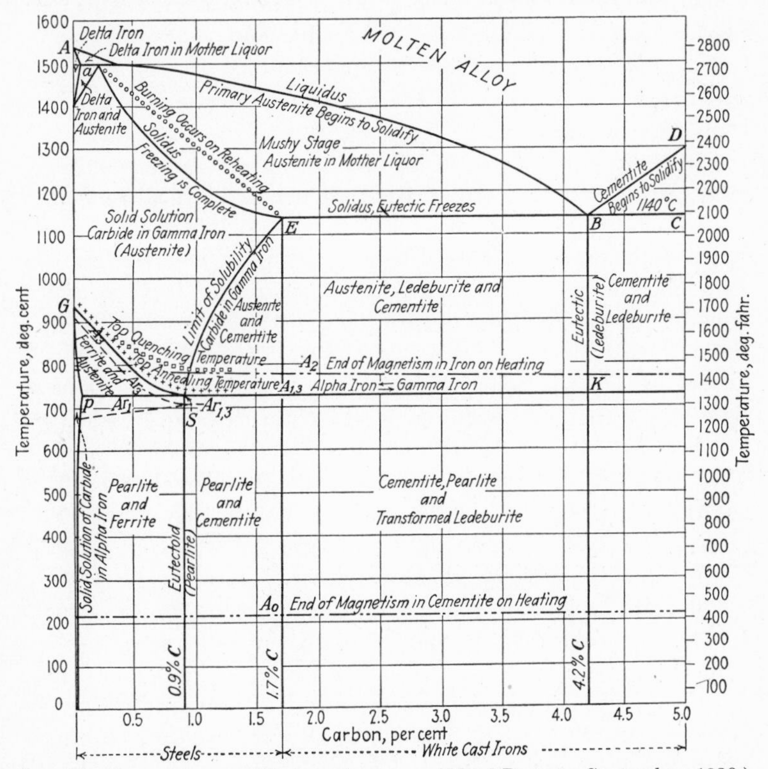

Fig. 29.—Iron-carbon equilibrium diagram. (*Metal Progress*, September, 1930.)

containing 9.77, 9.88, and 9.90 per cent carbon by heating molybdenum oxide, prepared by roasting ammonium molybdate, and carbon together in the electric arc. He later produced, by the same method,[8, 9] mixtures consisting of small prismatic crystals and graphite. The combined carbon contents of 5.62, 5.53, and 5.48 per cent obtained would indicate the formation of the compound Mo_2C, containing 5.88 per cent carbon. The crystals of this assumed compound had a density of 8.9. In 1904, Moissan and Hoffmann[27] heated mixtures consisting of 25 grams of molybdenum, 25 grams of aluminum, and 0.2 gram of carbon in the electric arc to the boiling point of aluminum and obtained gray powders. The analyses of the powders indicated the formation of the compound MoC (88.89 per cent molybdenum and 11.11 per cent carbon), as the molybdenum content of the samples ranged from 87.96 to 89.68 per cent. Under the microscope this powder appeared as glistening prismatic crystals. Its density was 8.40, and it would scratch quartz but not ruby. The authors ascribed the formation of MoC rather than Mo_2C to the higher temperatures attained in these experiments.

Friederich and Sittig[(150)] formed alloys, which they believed to be Mo_2C and MoC, by melting the components in the correct (stoichiometric) proportions. The melting points of the assumed compounds were determined by passing a current directly through the rod samples and calculating the melting points from the power required to fuse them. They found the melting point of Mo_2C to be between 2225 and 2325°C. (4040 and 4220°F.) and of MoC to be 2565°C. (4650°F.). Agte and Alterthum[(301)] determined the melting points of refractory carbides by means of a micro-optical pyrometer and reported the melting point of Mo_2C as 2685°C. (4870°F.) and what was assumed to be MoC as 2695°C. (4880°F.). These melting points were reported to have a possible error of ±50°C. (90°F.). The actual presence of the definite compound MoC was not proved. Nischk[(124)] made a microscopic examination of alloys containing from 0.22 to 6.07 pre cent carbon and found that those containing 5.22 per cent or less carbon contained metallic molybdenum, while the alloy containing 6.07 per cent carbon consisted of the homogeneous carbide Mo_2C. The alloys were etched with potassium ferricyanide in sodium hydroxide; this colored the carbide but not the molybdenum.

The crystal structures of the molybdenum-carbon alloys were studied by X-ray methods by Westgren and Phragmén.[(185)] They reported that in the alloys in the neighborhood of the assumed compound Mo_2C the molybdenum atoms formed a close-packed hexagonal structure. The dimensions of the lattice varied slightly with the carbon content, from which it was concluded that this phase was a solid solution rather than the compound Mo_2C. The lattice dimensions in Ångström units for this phase in alloys of the carbon content shown below were:

Atomic per cent carbon	*a*	*c*	*c/a*
30	2.993	4.725	1.579
39	3.004	4.725	1.573

These authors reported that tungsten-carbon alloys had an analogous phase which was considered to be a solid solution rather than the definite compound W_2C, but later investigators[188, 212] have concluded that this phase is a compound rather than a solid solution. They detected a compound WC with a simple hexagonal lattice, but a similar molybdenum compound could not be found by X-ray methods.

H. H. Lester, of Watertown Arsenal, confirmed the existence of the hexagonal close-packed lattice of Mo_2C and found that the lattice of the alloy corresponding to the formula Mo_2C had the following parameters: $a = 3.023$ Å, $c = 4.746$ Å, $c/a = 1.570$. The calculated density was 8.909, and the measured density 8.88. The difference between the calculated and measured values was at least partly due to graphite inclusions in the sample.

Molybdenum-carbon alloys containing up to 10 per cent carbon were prepared by Takei[246] by heating the pressed powders in a Tammann furnace and subsequently fusing in an arc furnace. Microscopic examination gave evidence of a solid solubility of carbon in molybdenum of 0.3 per cent, which did not vary with temperature. The alloys containing from 5.5 to 6.0 per cent carbon consisted of a single phase, thereby indicating the presence of a phase corresponding to the compound Mo_2C in which small amounts of both components are soluble. Alloys containing more than 6 per cent carbon contained flakes of graphite, and no evidence of a carbide having the formula MoC was found. A eutectic between Mo and Mo_2C was located at about 4 per cent carbon. Analysis of a residue produced by electrolysis corre-

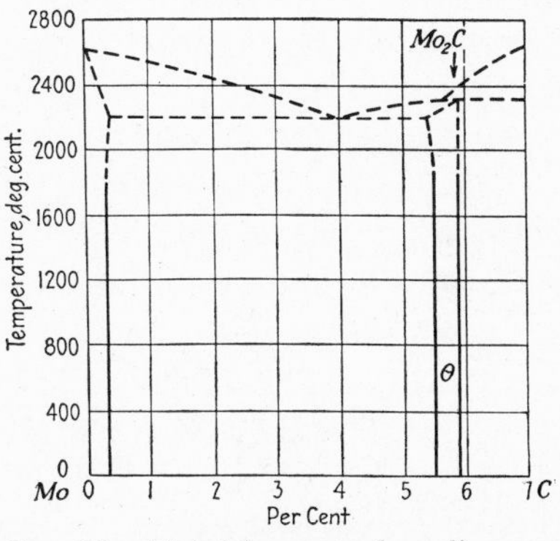

FIG. 30.—Molybdenum-carbon diagram. (*Takei.*[246])

sponded to the compound Mo_2C. X-ray diffraction patterns were in agreement with those of Westgren and Phragmén. The probable equilibrium diagram for the molybdenum-rich alloys, as drawn by Takei, is shown in Fig. 30. This diagram should be considered as highly speculative but consistent with the best data so far obtained. The theta phase is probably the compound Mo_2C capable of dissolving small amounts of either of its components.

B. IRON-MOLYBDENUM-CARBON ALLOYS

The data so far reported are insufficient to give even a general idea of the equilibrium conditions in the ternary system iron-molybdenum-carbon.[1] Several investigators have analyzed residues separated electrolytically from molybdenum steels with the object of determining the state of combination of the molybdenum. Their investigations, however, have not yielded conclusive information concerning the exact compounds of molybdenum formed, or their solubility in the iron-rich matrix. Microscopic examination has yielded a little information on constituents in the iron-molybdenum-carbon system, and the effect of molybdenum on such properties as electric resistance has given some indication with respect to the solid solubility of molybdenum in the iron-rich matrix.

48. Residue Analysis.—In 1897, Carnot and Goutal[(12)] dissolved two molybdenum steels in dilute hydrochloric acid and analyzed the residues. The residues contained 46.5 per cent iron and 53.5 per cent molybdenum, which corresponds to the compound Fe_3Mo_2. From this they assumed the existence of this compound in the steels.

In one of his studies on molybdenum steels, Swinden[(52)] made some very careful analyses of residues obtained from annealed samples of steels containing varying amounts of carbon and molybdenum. The residues were obtained by electrolytic dissolution in dilute hydrochloric acid. The mass of steel dissolved and the weights of the residues were determined. From 85 to 98 per cent of the carbon and from 74 to 98 per cent of the molybdenum remained in the residues. There appeared to be no relation between the molybdenum content and the ratio of carbon to molybdenum found in the residues. The results of these analyses are shown in Table 8. In only two cases, steels 11 and 16, did the residues contain more carbon

[1] See Appendix I.

than is required to form Fe_3C with all of the iron, and these contained less carbon than some of the other steels. Swinden was rather reluctant to draw definite conclusions from these results; but he put forth the hypothesis that the molybdenum is combined not with the carbon but with the iron, and that the iron-molybdenum compound is partially decomposed by galvanic action in the preparation of the residues.

TABLE 8.—RESIDUE ANALYSES OF MOLYBDENUM STEELS*

Mark	Steel analysis, per cent		Carbide analysis, per cent			Ratio		
	C	Mo	Fe	Mo	C	Fe	Mo	C
3	0.869	1.018	88.41	6.31	5.28	3930	161	1081
4	1.215	1.096	88.88	4.89	6.23	3762	120	1229
7	0.883	2.186	83.53	11.38	5.09	3370	282	963
8	1.210	2.109	85.59	10.56	5.85	5260	386	1673
11	0.865	4.002	69.00	25.53	5.47	1217	263	430
12	1.060	4.019	73.80	20.92	5.28	4229	697	1408
13	0.135	8.012	39.68	58.64	1.68	7666	6513	1500
16	0.775	7.847	56.62	39.78	3.60	2479	1012	767
17	1.125	7.920	59.24	35.60	5.16	3340	1169	1342
Special test on current strength								
11	0.865	4.002	70.28	24.29	5.43	1222	248	442
11	0.865	4.002	70.39	24.39	5.22	1300	262	449

Mark	Empirical formula	Possible compounds
3	$Fe_{24.10}MoC_{6.71}$	$6.7Fe_3C \cdot Fe_{4.26}Mo$
4	$Fe_{31.22}MoC_{10.20}$	$32.8Fe_3C \cdot Mo_{3.2}Fe$
7	$Fe_{11.91}MoC_{3.45}$	$6.8Fe_3C \cdot Fe_{3.4}Mo_2$
8	$Fe_{13.63}MoC_{4.33}$	$16.7Fe_3C \cdot 1.2Fe_2Mo_3$
11	$Fe_{4.63}MoC_{1.64}$	$15.4Fe_3C \cdot Mo_{10}C$
12	$Fe_{6.06}MoC_{2.02}$	$14.1Fe_3C \cdot 7Mo$
13	$Fe_{5.03}Mo_{4.34}C$	$Fe_3C \cdot 2Mo_{2.17}Fe$
16	$Fe_{3.23}Mo_{1.32}C$	$4.3Fe_3C \cdot Mo_{5.6}Fe$
17	$Fe_{2.87}MoC_{1.14}$	$4.7Fe_3C \cdot Mo_5C$
Special test on current strength		
11	$Fe_{4.97}MoC_{1.78}$	$11.6Fe_3C \cdot Mo_7C$
11	$Fe_{4.95}MoC_{1.71}$	$27.6Fe_3C \cdot Mo_{16}C$

* Swinden.[52]

Arnold and Read[65] made similar residue analyses of five annealed steels containing from 2.43 to 20.70 per cent molybdenum and from 0.71 to 0.82 per cent carbon. They also tested one of these steels in the quenched condition. The results of their work are shown in Table 9, in which each residue composition is the result of at least two analyses. These results were interpreted as indicating the formation of a non-magnetic, "remarkable" double carbide having the composition Fe_3Mo_3C or, more probably, $Fe_6Mo_6C_2$. As shown in the table, the composition of the residue from the steel containing 0.82 per cent carbon and 20.70 per cent molybdenum corresponded almost exactly to this formula. The residue obtained from this steel in the quenched condition also corresponded to the formula Fe_3Mo_3C, but the relative amounts of the constituents remaining in the residues were smaller. Arnold and Read considered that in Swinden's work the correct compositions of the residues were obtained, but that his results should be interpreted as indicating the formation of the compounds Fe_3Mo_3C and Fe_3C.

TABLE 9.—RESIDUE ANALYSES OF MOLYBDENUM STEELS*

Composition, per cent		Weight removed, grams	Weight of residue, grams	Remaining in residue, per cent		Analysis of residue, per cent			Formulas
C	Mo			Mo	C	C	Fe	Mo	
0.78	2.43	7.081	0.9376	95.27	93.45	5.51	75.34	17.50	$6Fe_3C + Fe_3Mo_3C$
0.75	4.95	7.3690	0.8653	78.16	84.85	5.42	61.54	32.96	$7Fe_3C + 3Fe_3Mo_3C + 2C$
0.71	10.15	8.5405	1.5568	96.46	94.31	3.67	42.08	53.71	$Fe_3C + 3Fe_3Mo_3C + C$
0.79	15.46	8.8480	2.2646	97.20	92.85	2.865	35.94	58.70	$Fe_3C + 8Fe_3Mo_3C$
0.82	20.70	10.0883	3.0389	87.60	94.51	2.56	37.30	59.90	Fe_3Mo_3C
0.82†	20.70	8.2677	1.6102	55.12	57.00	2.38	39.27	57.91	Fe_3Mo_3C
0.82‡	20.70	8.5354	1.9418	66.23	64.28	2.57	36.64	60.30	Fe_3Mo_3C

* Arnold and Read.[65]
† Water-quenched, 1200°C. (2190°F.).
‡ Oil-quenched, 1200°C. (2190°F.).

Later, Arnold and Ibbotson[76] made residue analyses on steels of the high-speed type in which part or all of the tungsten was replaced by molybdenum. The molybdenum-bearing steels contained about 3 per cent chromium, one of them containing tungsten, one vanadium, and another both tungsten and vanadium. The compositions of the residues were compatible with the formation of Fe_3C, Cr_4C, and Fe_3Mo_3C. The steels containing vanadium were assumed to contain the compound V_4C_3, and those containing tungsten the compounds WC and Fe_2W.

Recently, several investigators have determined the crystal structures of residues obtained from tungsten and molybdenum steels; their results are given in the section dealing with X-ray analysis.

49. Microscopic Examination.—Guillet[24,25,30] studied two series of molybdenum steels, one containing 0.2 per cent carbon with from 0.45 to 9.30 per cent molybdenum and the other 0.8 per cent carbon with from 0.50 to 14.64 per cent molybdenum. His work indicated that the effect of molybdenum in iron-carbon

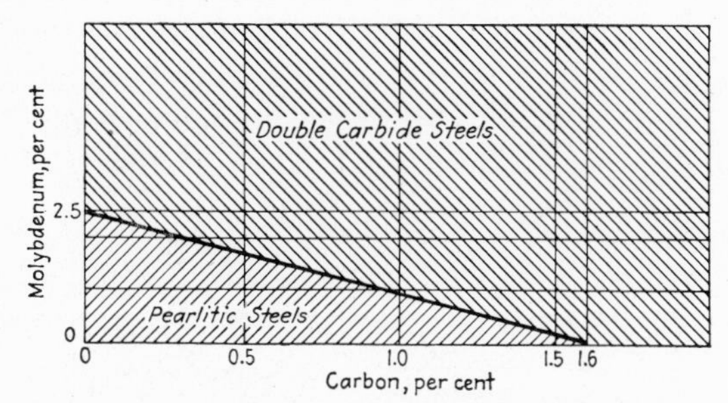

Fig. 31.—Molybdenum steel diagram. (*Guillet.*[30])

alloys was similar to that of tungsten, but that one part of molybdenum was equivalent to four parts of tungsten. He also observed that molybdenum had a refining action on the pearlite. The presence of a special constituent, thought to be a double carbide, was observed in some steels. Based upon the presence of this constituent in steel in the hot-worked condition, he constructed one of his well-known diagrams showing two fields as indicated in Fig. 31. According to Oberhoffer,[160] the "double carbide" found by Guillet represents the remains of the ledeburite structure, and the line separating the two fields in the diagram, therefore, represents the maximum solubility of carbon in iron containing various amounts of molybdenum.

The changes in carbon content of the eutectoid resulting from the addition of molybdenum as determined by Swinden[52] and Reed[492] by microscopic examination are shown in Fig. 32. Reed observed that an alloy containing 0.33 per cent carbon and

7.80 per cent molybdenum contained "free delta ferrite," and his curve was drawn to indicate the existence of this phase in the low-carbon, high-molybdenum alloys.

Hultgren[89] in his microscopic study of tungsten steels examined one iron-molybdenum-carbon alloy and found one "supposedly molybdenum carbide" and two "supposedly double carbides." One "double carbide" formed a rib-shaped eutectic with austenite. The molybdenum carbide occurred in rounded grains and was believed to be harder than cementite but not so hard as the tungsten carbide WC.

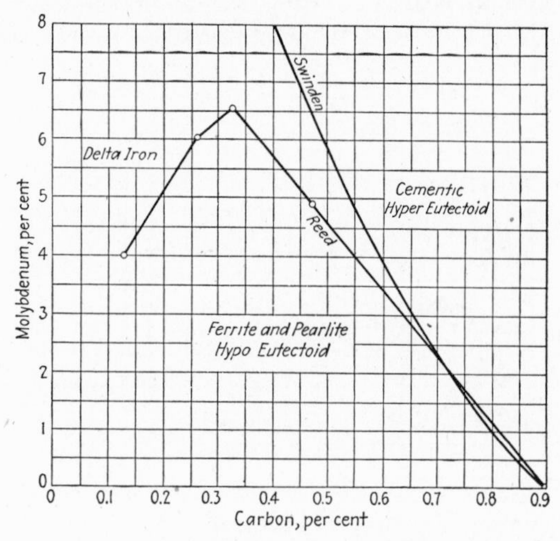

FIG. 32.—Eutectoid concentration curve of molybdenum steel. (*Swinden*[52] and *Reed*.[492])

H. H. Lester,[1] of Watertown Arsenal, studied some iron-molybdenum-carbon alloys by microscopic and X-ray methods and drew the following conclusions from his work:

1. Only one carbide, Mo_2C, was found when pure molybdenum was heated with carbon. A double carbide of iron, molybdenum, and carbon was found in steel containing molybdenum. There is some question whether Mo_2C as such exists in steel.

2. These carbides are soluble in steel at melting temperatures but tend to segregate at an early stage in cooling and probably do not respond to normal heat treatments.

3. No evidence was found showing a definite relation between these carbides and abnormality.

[1] Unpublished report.

4. Molybdenum added in quantities of less than 2 per cent of the total weight tends to go into solid solution with the iron.

5. With carbon content as low as 0.21 per cent and molybdenum 3 per cent, Mo_2C or at least a double carbide is formed and tends to exist in the ingot as a segregated constituent.

6. The double carbide forms preferentially to the iron carbide.

7. Intermetallic compounds of iron and molybdenum do not form so readily as the carbides and for this reason probably have no important bearing on the properties of molybdenum steels.

8. Solid Mo_2C tends to absorb carbon and to hold it in solid solution. The solubility of carbon in the carbide seems to be very high. The addition of carbon to the carbide reduces its melting point, fusion being obtained in some cases as low as 1700°C. (3090°F.). Upon cooling the solid carbide containing carbon in solution, graphite flakes are formed between the plates of Mo_2C. Even when care was used to carburize the molybdenum at temperatures below 1500°C. (2730°F.) there still remained about 0.12 per cent of graphite in the final product.

9. The double carbide may be detected by etching with $H_2O_2 + NaOH$, although Mo_2C in the pure state does not respond to the reagent.

10. The double carbide etches with sodium picrate.

11. X-ray diffraction patterns showed that the iron lines were blurred by molybdenum. The Mo_2C lattice was expanded—owing probably to solution of carbon in Mo_2C.

50. X-ray Examination.—The compounds formed in high-speed steels were studied by Westgren and Phragmén[247] by X-ray diffraction methods. The patterns obtained showed faint lines connotative of a phase separate from iron and cementite. Diffraction studies of residues obtained by electrolytic dissolution proved that this phase was distinct from all iron-carbon, tungsten-carbon, and iron-tungsten phases and must, therefore, be a carbide containing both iron and tungsten. It had a face-centered cubic lattice, the edge of the elementary cube being 11.04 Å. Investigation of especially prepared alloys indicated that this phase probably corresponded to the formula Fe_4W_2C, and contained 112 atoms in the elementary cube. An analogous iron-molybdenum-carbon phase was reported, but no details were given regarding its occurrence or crystallographic parameters.

Wood[415] made an X-ray study of tungsten magnet steels and the residues obtained from such steels. He detected a space lattice corresponding to that found by Westgren and Phragmén, and also a lattice representative of the carbide WC. Chemical analyses of the residues indicated a variable composition, which was considered proof of the impossibility of determining the compounds present in steel by analysis of their residues.

51. Effects of Molybdenum.—As has been pointed out, from 6 to 30 per cent molybdenum can exist in solid solution in iron. When molybdenum is added to iron-carbon alloys, however, the molybdenum may occur in the iron-rich matrix, or it may unite with portions of the iron and/or carbon to form a definite compound. The fact that molybdenum forms a solid solution with iron indicates that at least some of the molybdenum must occur in solid solution in the iron-rich phase. Consideration of the effect of molybdenum on the electric conductivity of steels should give some clue regarding its state of existence; for if a metal is in solid solution it should decrease the conductivity, while if it occurs as a precipitate, it should have a negligible effect on the conductivity.

In 1898, Le Chatelier(16) determined the electric resistance of steels of doubtful antecedents and found that molybdenum had little or no effect on this property. Portevin(40) determined the resistance of several steels, in both the annealed and the hardened condition. He found an increased resistance with increased molybdenum content and concluded that up to 5 per cent molybdenum existed in solid solution, but, as Swinden(52) observed, the carbon and other components varied so greatly that the effect of molybdenum was masked. In the steels containing 0.2 per cent carbon, quenching increased the resistance only about 5 per cent; but in steels containing 0.8 per cent carbon, the resistance was almost doubled by quenching. Swinden,(52) from his measurements of the resistance of a series of steels as normalized, as rolled, and after quenching and tempering, concluded that the molybdenum did not exist in solid solution. Variations in the condition of the steel had little effect on its resistance. In considering these data together with data subsequently obtained, Swinden(61) concluded that an increasing molybdenum content had the following effects on annealed steels:

1. In the mildest steels it increases resistance.
2. In steels containing about 0.45 per cent carbon the resistance is not affected.
3. In steels containing about 0.90 per cent carbon the resistance is generally decreased.
4. In 1.2 per cent carbon steels the resistance is decreased.

These results are interpreted as signifying that in low-carbon steels an appreciable quantity of molybdenum remains in solid solution, but that, as the carbon is increased, increasing amounts of molybdenum unite to form one or more compounds. Resistance measurements were made on steels quenched from 800 and 1200°C. (1470 and 2190°F.), but it is dangerous to use those results in interpreting the behavior of molybdenum because of the unknown amounts of retained austenite.

Dupuy and Portevin[(66)] determined the electromotive force against copper for two series of molybdenum steels containing, respectively, 0.2 and 0.8 per cent carbon. For each series, when the electromotive force was plotted against molybdenum content, an S-shaped curve resulted, which was interpreted as indicating that molybdenum was not soluble in amounts greater than 1 per cent.

The influence of molybdenum on the transformation points of steel has been carefully studied by several investigators, but this subject will be treated in a later chapter.

52. Author's Remarks on Constitution.—The non-magnetic residues obtained by Arnold and Read and the X-ray diffraction study of Westgren and Phragmén are good evidence of the formation of an iron-molybdenum carbide, the composition of which probably corresponds to the formula Fe_4Mo_2C. The residue analysis of molybdenum steels, it is believed, cannot be taken as evidence for the formation of definite chemical compounds unless supported by other methods. Molybdenum must certainly have some solid solubility in both ferrite and austenite containing carbon, for 6 per cent of molybdenum is soluble in pure iron at room temperature. The results so far reported, however, are insufficient to indicate the amount of molybdenum soluble at any temperature.

The iron-molybdenum-carbon system probably contains an iron-rich solid solution of molybdenum in iron and at least one complex carbide, the composition of which is in the neighborhood of Fe_4Mo_2C. The data obtained do not prove, or even indicate, that this carbide is the only phase not found in the binary alloys. With such meager data on the phases present in the ternary system iron-molybdenum-carbon, it is impossible to construct even a probable diagram covering the iron-rich corner of the system.[1]

[1] See Appendix I.

C. MELTING MOLYBDENUM STEEL

Molybdenum can be easily introduced, either alone or together with other alloying elements, into steel made by any of the usual processes. In molten iron containing small amounts of molybdenum, the iron is oxidized in preference to the molybdenum and, consequently, after the molybdenum is in the molten alloy, there is practically no loss of this element. The molybdenum can, therefore, be introduced at any time during the refining process, and the recovery from scrap is almost complete.[103, 111, 121]

Any difficulties encountered in adding molybdenum to steel result either from the high melting point of the element or from the easy volatilization of molybdic oxide (MoO_3), which melts at about 800°C. (1470°F.) and has an appreciable vapor pressure[1] at as low a temperature as 550°C. (1020°F.). The disadvantage of the high melting point is usually overcome by adding the element either in the form of a ferroalloy, with its consequent lower melting point, or in the form of a salt of molybdenum, usually calcium molybdate, in which instance the molybdenum is reduced directly into the steel bath. When ferromolybdenum is used, there is not sufficient oxidation of molybdenum to cause an appreciable loss by volatilization. When a salt, such as calcium molybdate, is used, it does not decompose at steel-making temperatures to such a degree that there will be any appreciable loss of molybdic acid by volatilization.[344]

53. Molybdenum Addition Agents.—Molybdenum metal can be obtained as a powder and, as such, can be added to the bath of molten iron or steel or, as in the crucible process, with the charge. The use of the metallic powder, however, is unsatisfactory because of its high melting point (about 2600°C., 4710°F.) and the possibility that it will not be completely dissolved or uniformly diffused through the alloy.[92]

Molybdenum can be conveniently added to steel in the form of a ferroalloy. The 1930 "National Metals Handbook," issued by the American Society for Steel Treating, gives the composition of ferromolybdenum as:

	Per Cent
Molybdenum	55 to 65
Sulphur, maximum	0.25
Silicon, maximum	1.50
Carbon, maximum	0.50 to 2.00

[1] Private communication.

The approximate melting point of ferromolybdenum is given as 1630°C. (2965°F.).

A tentative specification, A 132-31T, of the American Society for Testing Materials gives the following requirements for the chemical composition of ferromolybdenum:

	Per Cent
Carbon, maximum	2.50
Molybdenum	50.00 to 60.00
Sulphur, maximum	0.25
Phosphorus, maximum	0.10
Copper, maximum	0.25

The Molybdenum Corporation of America, according to a private communication from W. H. Phillips, produces the following four grades of ferromolybdenum:

No. 1. Special

	Per Cent
Carbon	0.50, maximum
Silicon	0.50, maximum
Sulphur	0.10, maximum
Phosphorus	0.10, maximum
Molybdenum	60.0 to 70.0

No. 2. Special, High Silicon

	Per Cent
Carbon	0.25, maximum
Silicon	5.00, approximately
Sulphur	0.15, maximum
Phosphorus	0.10, maximum
Molybdenum	60.0 to 70.0

No. 3. Medium Carbon Grade

	Per Cent
Carbon	1.00, maximum
Silicon	0.50, maximum
Sulphur	0.25, maximum
Phosphorus	0.10, maximum
Molybdenum	60.0 to 65.0

No. 4. Standard

	Per Cent
Carbon	2.00, maximum
Silicon	1.00, maximum
Sulphur	0.25, maximum
Phosphorus	0.10, maximum
Molybdenum	55.0 to 65.0

Grade 1 is a special carbon-reduced alloy in which the carbon is held to a maximum of 0.50 per cent, with a low silicon content. Grade 2 is a silicon-reduced alloy in which the carbon content is below 0.25 per cent. Grade 3 is a medium carbon grade produced by carbon reduction in which the carbon is held below 1.00 per cent, with low silicon. It is claimed that Grade 4 has the highest "solubility," and that its melting point is about 100°C. (180°F.) lower than any other grade on the market.

A special molybdenum-iron alloy[431] is marketed by the Climax Molybdenum Co. for the addition of molybdenum to cast iron. It contains from 60 to 65 per cent molybdenum and is claimed to have a lower melting point than the standard ferromolybdenum.

The use of calcium molybdate ($CaMoO_4$ or $CaO \cdot MoO_3$) for introducing molybdenum into the steel bath was patented by Alan Kissock as U. S. Patent 1,300,279, Apr. 15, 1919, which was modified and appeared as Reissue 16,396, July 27, 1926. This reissued patent has, however, been declared invalid by the U. S. Circuit Court of Appeals. The development and advantages of this addition agent were described by Kissock in 1920.[91] The first commercial tests were made at the U. S. Naval Gun Factory in Washington in September, 1918, where calcium molybdate made from wulfenite ores was added to a 6-ton electric-furnace heat with substantially complete recovery of molybdenum. After calcium molybdate had been added successfully to other electric-furnace heats, its addition to open-hearth heats was attempted, which also resulted in high recoveries of molybdenum. Calcium molybdate is a desirable addition agent, because a comparatively pure salt can be cheaply produced. It is particularly advantageous for use in low-carbon steels, because it contains no carbon.

Practically all of the molybdenum-containing steels now used contain less than 1 per cent of this element, and the molybdenum in such steels can be conveniently and economically introduced by means of calcium molybdate. The pure salt contains 48 per cent molybdenum, but the commercial material ordinarily used contains excess lime and has a molybdenum content of about 40 per cent. According to Hardy,[344] pure precipitated calcium molybdate melts at 1345°C. (2450°F.) and becomes very liquid at 1400°C. (2550°F.).

The calcium molybdate is reduced, even during the refining period in the open hearth, yielding in addition to the metallic molybdenum, which enters the bath, calcium oxide (CaO), which goes into the slag. While calcium molybdate additions are satisfactory for adding small amounts of molybdenum, when more than 1 or 1.5 per cent molybdenum is introduced by calcium molybdate, the large quantity of lime added may be undesirable; consequently, in making steels containing several per cent of molybdenum, part of the molybdenum is usually added in the form of ferromolybdenum.

Although molybdic oxide (MoO_3) is generally considered as an unsatisfactory addition agent because of its easy volatilization, it has been recently recommended[(325)] that in some cases molybdic oxide can be "buried" in the cold scrap, such as in an induction furnace.

As mentioned in Chap. I (page 17), the Molybdenum Corporation of America manufactures a product sold under the trade name of "Molyte" which is used in a manner similar to calcium molybdate. While this material is claimed to contain lower oxides of molybdenum than those entering into calcium molybdate, its behavior in the steel-making furnace is similar to calcium molybdate in that the molybdenum oxides are reduced and other elements slagged. According to the information available, statements regarding the behavior of calcium molybdate in steel making are in general also true for Molyte.

According to a private communication, roasted molybdenite concentrates have been used by one manufacturer for introducing molybdenum into steel. The practice was discontinued about a year ago on account of commercial rather than technical reasons. As far as could be learned, the concentrates were used in quite the same manner as calcium molybdate and with similar results to those obtained with the calcium salt in respect to both the properties of the steel and the recovery of molybdenum.

In U. S. Patent 1,797,728, Mar. 24, 1931, McIntosh claims that to produce a molybdenum steel characterized by a high sulphur content the mineral molybdenite (MoS_2, containing 40 per cent sulphur and 60 per cent molybdenum) can be added directly to the ladle as the steel is tapped. The molybdenum sulphide is claimed to alloy readily with practically no loss of either component.

According to *The Iron Age*,[(419)] the price of calcium molybdate was reduced from $0.95 to $0.85 per pound of contained molybdenum in October, 1930; the price of ferromolybdenum remained at $1.00 per pound of contained molybdenum.

The prices of ferromolybdenum and calcium molybdate as reported in the *Daily Metal Trade* for the past few years are as follows:

DOLLARS PER POUND OF CONTAINED MOLYBDENUM

Date	Ferro-molybdenum	Calcium molybdate
July 3, 1925	1.50 to 2.00	
July 3, 1926	1.50 to 2.00	
July 2, 1927	1.45	1.20
July 3, 1928	1.20	0.95
July 3, 1929	1.20	0.95
July 3, 1930	1.20	0.95
July 3, 1931	1.00	0.85

54. Open-hearth Process.—Quite recently, Hardy[344] discussed the various methods for producing molybdenum-containing steel, and particularly the use of calcium molybdate.

In the acid and in the basic open-hearth processes the usual methods of utilizing calcium molybdate, according to Hardy, are:

1. It is charged with the scrap.
2. It is added after the lime begins to "come up" and before slag is formed.
3. It is added after the slag is formed but at least 2 hr. before tapping.

The last two methods are most generally followed, because it is usually necessary to obtain a preliminary analysis in order to determine the quantity of molybdenum which must be added. Bags of the salt are either thrown in by hand or dumped from a charging box. Calcium molybdate cannot be successfully added to the ladle because of the time required for reduction and diffusion of the molybdenum, and for the same reasons it should not be added immediately before tapping.

According to Schmid,[103] care should be taken to prevent the draft from carrying off part of the powdered molybdate. Hardy cites data for a 169,000-lb. heat of steel, analyzing 0.19 per cent molybdenum on the ladle test, that indicate a complete recovery of molybdenum from the calcium molybdate added. Other data by the same author for an 80,000-lb. acid open-hearth heat indicate a recovery of 94 per cent, the ladle analysis being 0.50 per cent molybdenum.

Ferromolybdenum, according to Schmid,[103] may be added to the furnace as the charge is melting, or 10 or 15 min. before tapping, or it also may be added to the ladle. The best practice, however, is to add the ferromolybdenum as the charge is melting down because of the better diffusion and the resulting greater uniformity of the steel. The loss of molybdenum when using the ferroalloy should not exceed 5 or 10 per cent. Schmid found it rather difficult to account for the loss of molybdenum but was inclined to attribute most of it to oxidation and volatilization of the molybdic oxide.

55. Bessemer Process.—Calcium molybdate, according to Hardy,[344] may be thrown into the converter, the iron poured on top of the salt, and the heat blown with almost complete recovery of molybdenum.

56. Crucible Process.—Ferromolybdenum, rather than calcium molybdate, is usually recommended for the crucible process owing to the action of the lime, liberated from the salt, on the crucible; but the Climax Molybdenum Co.[325] concludes that, in making steels containing not more than 0.50 per cent molybdenum, the amount of lime liberated is insufficient to introduce any difficulties. The calcium molybdate should be placed in the middle of the charge in the crucible. Ferromolybdenum is included in the crucible charge with the last two-thirds of the charge.[102]

57. Electric-furnace Processes.—Hardy[344] stated that in the basic electric-furnace process calcium molybdate may be added with the charge, provided no "slagging off" is required, but that the common practice is to add the molybdate on the bare metal after skimming off the first slag. The final carbide slag assures rapid reduction of the molybdate, and small additions of the salt may be made at any time prior to 30 min. before tapping.

For the acid electric process he gives as the best practice the addition of calcium molybdate with the charge, and as an earlier practice the addition of the molybdate after the charge has melted. Data given by Hardy indicate a 95 per cent recovery of molybdenum in producing an 0.26 per cent molybdenum steel by the earlier method. The lime from the calcium molybdate, of course, thins the slag, but it can be readily thickened by the addition of sand.

Ferromolybdenum can be added with the charge in either process or added at any time during the refining period.

According to Gill and Trembour,[446] in producing steel in the basic electric furnace, non-oxidizable alloys such as tungsten, molybdenum, nickel, and copper should be charged directly with the scrap. Furthermore, "molybdenum oxides may be charged without admixture of a deoxidizer, and in a heat that is to be melted under oxidizing conditions."

Tests on the recovery of molybdenum when added as Molyte, made by the Molybdenum Corporation of America in cooperation with a steel manufacturer, showed that the average recovery of molybdenum from 12 electric-furnace heats containing between 0.20 and 0.30 per cent molybdenum was approximately 95 per cent.

58. Other Processes.—In the production of steel in the induction furnace, the Climax Molybdenum Co.[325] recommends the use of molybdic oxide (MoO_3) buried in the charge. The oxide is advantageous because of its low-sulphur, high-molybdenum content and its negligible quantity of slag-forming elements. The oxide is presumably reduced by the metal before it becomes hot enough to volatilize.

Molybdenum steels have been produced in laboratory arc furnaces at the Colorado School of Mines[48] by the direct reduction of molybdenite (MoS_2) and iron oxide (Fe_2O_3). Although steel was actually made by this method, the working of the process, in the reviewer's opinion, was not such as to encourage further development.

D. CASTING AND WORKING MOLYBDENUM STEEL

The effect of molybdenum on the casting of ingots and their subsequent reduction may be masked by unconsidered variables, and its real effects can be obtained only by consideration of the observations reported by various workers.

59. Casting Molybdenum Steel.—The lack of definite mention of difficulties in casting steel containing molybdenum, together with the knowledge that many tons of steel containing up to 6 or 8 per cent molybdenum have been successfully produced in the form of forged or rolled bars, is good evidence that the addition of molybdenum to steel does not increase the difficulty of producing sound ingots.

Even though sound ingots are produced, an alloying element may segregate to a very undesirable extent, and data will be given to show the degree to which molybdenum segregates. Sargent[92, 102] has given analyses of drillings taken from various portions of two molybdenum-containing ingots to prove that molybdenum does not segregate or cause segregation (size of ingot or heat not given). The analyses of the two ingots are given in Table 10, and Fig. 33 shows the locations from which the drillings were taken. These data are credited to R. M. Bird of the Bethlehem Steel Co.

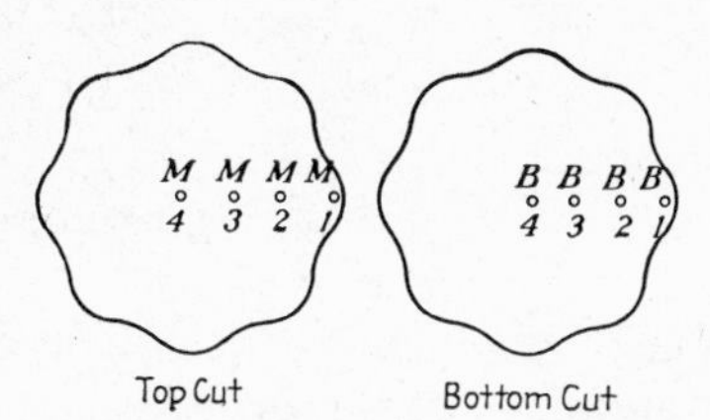

FIG. 33.—Location of drillings for analyses given in Table 10. (*Sargent.*[92, 102])

In his study of the mechanical properties of molybdenum steels, Jones[176] found that one of the steels, containing 1.28 per cent molybdenum, exhibited indications of serious segregation, and that the results obtained with this steel were erratic. A steel containing 0.60 per cent molybdenum did not display any apparent segregation.

A committee of The Iron and Steel Institute in the *Second Report on the Heterogeneity of Steel Ingots*[209] concluded from a study of a nickel-chromium-molybdenum steel ingot that "molybdenum indicates a definite tendency to segregate in conformity with the tendencies of the other segregating elements." The weight of the ingot investigated was 119 tons and its size 75 in. across the flats at the top, 67 in. at the bottom, and 180 in. in height, exclusive of the hot top. Twenty-three samples for analysis were taken from a vertical plane through the center of the ingot. The ladle analysis was 0.345 per cent carbon, 0.54 per cent manganese, 0.157 per cent silicon, 0.035 per cent sulphur, 0.028 per cent phosphorus, 2.48 per cent nickel, 0.68 per cent chromium, and 0.632 per cent molybdenum. The molybdenum analyses varied from 0.550 to 0.990 per cent, as shown in Fig. 34, while the carbon analyses varied from 0.275 per cent to 0.610 per cent, as shown in the same figure, and exhibited only a slight tendency to increase as the molybdenum increased. The variation of nickel content in this ingot amounted to only 5 per cent, while chromium showed a variation of 30 per cent; on the same basis the molybdenum content varied by 70 per cent. The authors of the report considered that, in so far as the few analyses could reveal, the segregation of carbon, sulphur, and phosphorus was not materially affected by the alloying elements in the ingot of the size studied.

TABLE 10.—ANALYSES OF DRILLINGS FROM A MOLYBDENUM STEEL INGOT*
(Location of drillings shown in Fig. 33)

Drillings	Composition, per cent							
	C	Mn	P	S	Si	Ni	Cr	Mo
No. 192724 B1								
Heat	0.390	0.53	0.031	0.026	0.218	0.18	1.02	0.35
M1	0.380	0.51	0.031	0.023	0.235	....	1.00	0.37
M2	0.398	0.48	0.031	0.026	0.210	....	1.04	0.34
M3	0.426	0.47	0.035	0.028	0.204	....	1.06	0.38
M4	0.420	0.53	0.032	0.027	0.215	....	1.05	0.37
B1	0.368	0.50	0.030	0.021	0.206	....	1.02	0.39
B2	0.390	0.43	0.031	0.020	0.240	....	1.04	0.34
B3	0.380	0.51	0.030	0.023	0.240	....	1.02	0.37
B4	0.350	0.47	0.026	0.023	0.235	....	1.00	0.34
No. 192734 B1								
Heat	0.400	0.45	0.044	0.033	0.204	1.61	0.08	0.43
M1	0.398	0.46	0.035	0.032	0.195	1.68	....	0.44
M2	0.394	0.46	0.035	0.037	0.197	1.70	....	0.47
M3	0.402	0.46	0.038	0.042	0.198	1.70	....	0.48
M4	0.442	0.47	0.042	0.046	0.184	1.70	....	0.48
B1	0.374	0.46	0.033	0.023	0.179	1.68	....	0.45
B2	0.364	0.46	0.033	0.031	0.190	1.64	....	0.44
B3	0.312	0.44	0.031	0.029	0.174	1.68	....	0.40
B4	0.308	0.43	0.026	0.025	0.174	1.65	....	0.40

* Sargent.[92,102]

Maita[377] explained the formation of "corner ghosts" in steel ingots as resulting from ruptures in the ingot during cooling and concluded that they may occur in steels of any composition, but that chromium favors while molybdenum tends to prevent their formation.

The heterogeneity of an ingot of nickel-chromium-molybdenum steel made by the Harmet process, which consists in deformation of the solidifying ingot by pressing into a mold, was studied by Křížž.[366] The ingot was sectioned longitudinally, and drillings were obtained from various portions adjacent to the cut section.

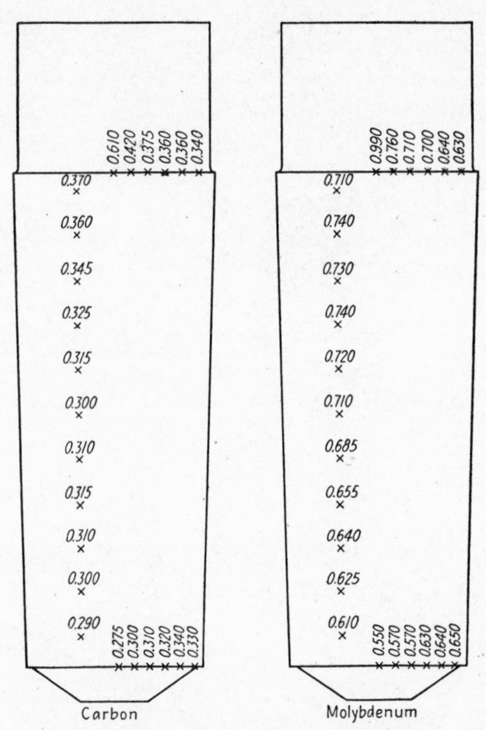

Fig. 34.—Carbon and molybdenum analyses of large ingot. (*Committee of the Iron and Steel Institute.*[209])

As the following analysis indicates, there was little segregation of molybdenum:

Element	Average per cent	Lowest per cent	Highest per cent
Carbon	0.30	0.27	0.43
Manganese	0.55	0.53	0.58
Nickel	2.07	2.03	2.09
Chromium	0.40	0.39	0.43
Molybdenum	0.25	0.23	0.27

The manufacture of a 3000-lb. nitrided crankshaft from a 10,000-lb. ingot was described by Merten.[480] The steel contained 0.34 per cent carbon, 1.06 per cent molybdenum, and 0.82 per cent aluminum. The molybdenum was added as calcium molybdate with the charge. After polishing and prior to nitriding, a small flaw or inhomogeneity about a quarter of an inch in length was observed on one of the journals, which upon nitriding broadened and appeared to be harder than the surrounding area. It was considered to be a segregation of molybdenum, although no evidence for this belief was presented.

In the preparation of small quantities (75 grams) of molybdenum steels in an Arsem furnace, using ingot iron and metallic molybdenum, Reed[492] observed a marked segregation of molybdenum in the bottom of the ingots. Melting an ingot in which molybdenum had segregated did not produce a better distribution as may be observed from the following data:

Section of ingot	Ingot 542 melted once, composition, per cent		Ingot 543 melted twice, composition, per cent	
	C	Mo	C	Mo
Top section annealed......	0.49	2.09	0.42	2.04
Middle section............	0.52	4.56	0.49	4.52
Lower section.............	0.52	6.12	0.50	6.07

In connection with these data it may be well to mention that appreciable segregation of some alloying elements, including manganese and tungsten, was observed in melts treated in a similar manner.

60. Working Molybdenum Steel.—Although several early investigators have reported difficulty in forging steels containing molybdenum, the more recent workers have almost unanimously found that molybdenum-containing steels are at least as easy to forge as steels containing no molybdenum.

According to Swinden,[52] Thomas Blair, in a pamphlet, "Tungsten and Chromium Alloys," published in 1894, reported a case in which "1 per cent molybdenum rendered good iron red-short and utterly worthless." In 1896, however, Lipin,[13, 15] in studying the properties of a steel containing 0.54 per cent carbon and 3.72 per cent molybdenum, found that the steel forged well and was free from cracks.

Mathews,[19] in work reported in 1902, made three steels containing molybdenum, two of which were red-short and were spoiled in forging; however, he attributed the red-shortness to incorrect melting and forging practice rather than to the molybdenum content.

Guillet[24, 25, 30] and others determined the properties of two series of molybdenum steels, one series containing approximately 0.2 per cent carbon with molybdenum from 0.45 to 9.30 per cent and the other containing approximately 0.80 per cent carbon with molybdenum from 0.50 to 14.64 per cent. Steels containing 0.2 per cent carbon could not be forged when they contained as much as 10 per cent molybdenum, and those containing 0.80 per cent carbon could not be forged when they contained as much as 5 per cent molybdenum.

Burgess and Aston[38] investigated the forging characteristics of 1-lb. ingots of iron-rich alloys, some of which contained molybdenum. The alloys were prepared by melting in magnesia-lined crucibles in a resistance furnace. Practically carbon-free alloys containing as much as 15 per cent molybdenum forged well at all temperatures. Alloys containing from 0.6 to 1.2 per cent carbon and as much as 10 per cent molybdenum could be forged with care, but an alloy containing 1 per cent carbon and 15 per cent molybdenum could not be forged at any temperature. The alloys were not analyzed; and the compositions given are, therefore, only approximate.

In his comprehensive study of molybdenum steels, Swinden[52] made steels containing as much as 8 per cent molybdenum and as much as 1.36 per cent carbon. The ingots were cog-hammered to 1¼-in. square bars and rolled to ⅝-in. rounds without difficulty, but he observed that the high-carbon steels were "extremely stiff." His recovery of 90 per cent of the raw materials in the form of round bars is proof of the good forgeability of molybdenum steel. He attributed the difficulties encountered by early workers in forging steels containing molybdenum to the use of powdered molybdenum very high in sulphur and oxides.

Arnold and Read[65] forged crucible-melted steels to ¾-in. rounds without difficulty but found that, as the molybdenum increased, the hardness was raised, and the white oxide of molybdenum formed on the bars as the forging temperature increased. They attributed the red-shortness observed by Blair, Mathews, and Guillet to oxygen introduced with incompletely deoxidized metallic molybdenum.

According to Gillett and Mack,[151] it is fairly well agreed that molybdenum steel forges well, and that it readily frees itself from scale. These authors maintain it is at least as free from flaws and other defects as other steels of comparable grade. In a discussion of molybdenum steels Rowe[242] also called attention to the advantageous flaking off of the scale from molybdenum-containing steels during forging or rolling. He also concluded that the addition of molybdenum to nickel-chromium steel increases the yield of sound billets. According to J. A. Mathews, however, it was reported that during the war a thousand tons of nickel-chromium-molybdenum steel ingots were made to deliver only a hundred tons of billets, the low yield being due mainly to the air-hardening properties of this steel, which caused cracks to form on cooling after rolling.

In a private communication Mathews stated that no difficulty has been experienced in forging molybdenum steels containing about 0.70 per cent carbon and from 2 to 15 per cent molybdenum.

> While they are somewhat hard at heat and require more power to reduce them in rolling, yet they are not so hard as the same steels plus chromium and, in general, the yields with straight molybdenum steel of about 9 per cent molybdenum and 0.70 per cent carbon were much better than is customary with tungsten-chromium or molybdenum-chromium high-speed steels.

Brinell hardness and compression tests at temperatures of 1040°C. (1900°F.) and 1205°C. (2200°F.) reported by Camp and Francis[146] indicated that chromium-molybdenum steels were harder at these temperatures than other alloy steels. The authors stated that such results show that more power will be required for forging chromium-molybdenum steels, but that these results give no indication of the relative flowing properties of the steels, such as their ability to fill dies in drop-forging.

Jones[176] mentioned the success achieved by a British firm in producing large forgings of molybdenum-containing steels of high elastic limit and excellent mechanical properties. Both Schmid[103] and Sargent[102] found that molybdenum-containing steels can be worked satisfactorily as compared with molybdenum-free steels, and that the yield from the former is greater.

In a study of the effect of oxygen on the properties of various structural steels, Oberhoffer, Hochstein, and Hessenbruch[286] made two molybdenum steels, one of which had a normal oxygen content of 0.027 or 0.028 per cent, while air was blown through the other before the addition of ferromolybdenum to increase its oxygen content, two analyses indicating 0.046 and 0.168 per cent oxygen. The normal steel contained 0.34 per cent carbon and 1.20 per cent molybdenum, while the high-oxygen steel contained 0.25 per cent carbon and 1.22 per cent molybdenum. The normal steel solidified quietly and forged well, but the high-oxygen steel was very wild during casting and extremely brittle at forging temperatures.

Recent work by Pohl, Krieger, and Sauerwald[491] indicated that in a hot bending test an overheated steel containing 0.155 per cent carbon and 0.30 per cent molybdenum did not crack so badly as overheated carbon steels. The authors found, however, that there was little difference between the grain-size increase of the molybdenum and carbon steels on overheating.

E. AUTHOR'S SUMMARY

1. The molybdenum-rich end of the molybdenum-carbon system is most probably approximated by Takei's diagram shown in Fig. 30 (page 59). It is not believed that acceptable evidence has been presented for the existence of a carbide MoC.

2. There are not sufficient data on equilibrium conditions in the iron-molybdenum-carbon system to warrant the presentation of even a probable diagram.[1] There is at least one ternary compound formed in the system, which probably corresponds to the formula Fe_4Mo_2C.

3. Small quantities of molybdenum can be economically introduced into steel by calcium molybdate ($CaMoO_4$).

4. Molybdenum is not a deoxidizing agent and, like nickel and copper, is not lost on remelting.

5. The studies of segregation in steels containing molybdenum may be considered as having proved that molybdenum segregates like other carbide-forming elements, such as tungsten and chromium. It seems probable that in ingots of normal size, containing less than 1 per cent molybdenum, the segregation is not serious. In 100-ton ingots of even low molybdenum content, or in steels containing several per cent molybdenum, segregation

[1] See Appendix I.

may be serious; the data available are insufficient to give definite evidence with respect to the amount of segregation in such cases.

6. There is little doubt that steels properly made containing as much as 8 per cent molybdenum can be readily forged or rolled, although, as Swinden has pointed out, the high-carbon steels containing molybdenum are "stiff." The difficulty in forging high-carbon steels containing molybdenum is consistent with the improved high-temperature strength that seems to be conferred by molybdenum. The fact that appreciable quantities of chromium-molybdenum steels are formed into seamless tubing for use in the aircraft industry certainly indicates that a small quantity of molybdenum has no deleterious effect on the workability of steels. The production of a large tonnage of molybdenum steels containing chromium, S.A.E. 4100 series, those containing nickel, S.A.E. 4600 series, and those containing both nickel and chromium gives further evidence of the workability of molybdenum-bearing steels.

CHAPTER IV

METALLOGRAPHY AND PHYSICAL PROPERTIES OF MOLYBDENUM STEEL

Effect of Molybdenum on Critical-point Phenomena—Effect of Molybdenum on Heat-treating Ranges—Effect of Molybdenum on Microstructure—Effect of Molybdenum on Miscellaneous Physical Properties—Effect of Molybdenum on Magnetic Properties—Author's Summary

Molybdenum steels can probably be best discussed by considering the effect of molybdenum on the various characteristics of steel. This treatment is regarded as particularly advantageous for molybdenum because the element usually exerts its influence by modifying and stabilizing the structure rather than by markedly changing the properties of any phases present in carbon steels.

A. EFFECT OF MOLYBDENUM ON CRITICAL-POINT PHENOMENA

The effects of molybdenum on critical-point phenomena cannot be exactly formulated, at least from the available data, and caution should be observed in comparing results of different investigators. The findings given below are, therefore, arranged with reference to authors rather than to phases of the subject.

In iron-carbon alloys the changes in equilibria represented by the lines *GS* and *PSK* in Fig. 29 (page 57) are evidenced by an abnormal liberation of heat on cooling and by an abnormal absorption of heat on heating. In any steel the temperature at which alpha iron begins to separate along the line *GS* on cooling is commonly designated as the upper critical point and referred to as the Ar_3 point. Similarly the temperature at which pearlite is formed, represented in the diagram by *PSK*, is known as the lower critical temperature, or Ar_1. The critical points observed on heating are described by using the subscript *c* in place of *r*. These critical points can be conveniently determined from heating or cooling curves in which either temperature is plotted against time or rate of change of temperature is plotted against temperature. Since the thermal change at the upper critical point is very slight, it is frequently necessary to resort to quenching specimens from different temperatures near the critical point and then making a microscopic examination in order to fix the exact position of Ac_3. Such a procedure is also being used to advantage in locating the exact position of the lower critical point Ac_1. In general, the critical points can also be determined from change in magnetic properties or change in length or volume as the samples are heated or cooled.

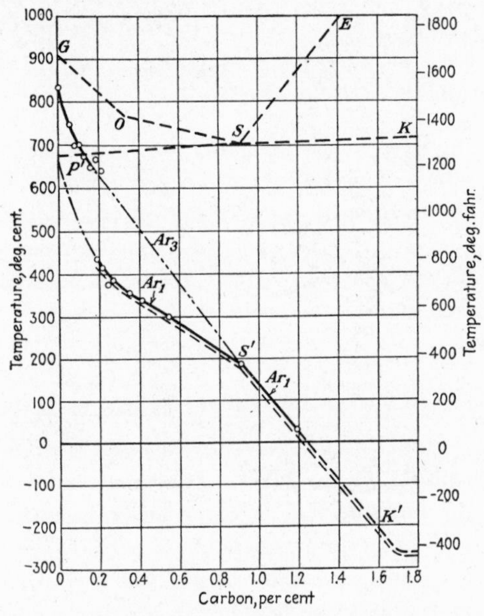

Fig. 35.—Transformation temperatures of carbon steels on slow cooling and on cooling 1000°C. per second. (*Esser.*[333])

The critical points are usually determined with very slow heating or cooling rates in order to approach equilibrium conditions. If, however, the Ar point is obtained with rapid cooling, it is considerably lowered even in carbon steels. With certain cooling rates Ar_1 is slightly lowered (often designated by Ar'), but with an increased cooling rate the transformation is split, part occurs at a temperature slightly below the temperature found by slow cooling and part at a temperature several hundred degrees centigrade lower. The transformation occurring at the lower temperature is frequently designated by Ar''. If the cooling rate is further increased, the higher, or Ar', transformation either vanishes or merges with the Ar'' transformation; *i.e.*, no transformation occurs above a temperature of 200 to 300°C. (390 to 570°F.). The transformation temperatures as determined by Esser[333] for the entire range of carbon steels cooled at a rate of 1000°C. (1800°F.) per sec. are shown in Fig. 35; the temperatures at which the transformations take place on slow cooling are also plotted in this figure. When a transformation occurs only at the low temperature, roughly 200 to 300°C. (390 to 570°F.), the austenite transforms wholly or in part not to pearlite but to martensite, which is the structure of steel in its hardest condition.

The addition of molybdenum to steels tends to decrease the rate of cooling at which the splitting or lowering appears, and in cooling from sufficiently high temperatures some steels containing molybdenum exhibit split or lowered transformation points even on very slow cooling, such as result from cooling in the furnace. This is of practical importance, for it indicates that molybdenum steels can be hardened by less drastic quenching rates than carbon steels.

61. Early Investigations.—Mathews[19] was the first investigator to report that molybdenum lowered the critical points of steel. Saladin[28] obtained heating and cooling curves for several steels containing molybdenum with a new instrument especially designed for obtaining such curves. He found that the transformation points observed on cooling were at considerably lower temperatures than those observed on heating. Pains were taken to prove that these lowered points on cooling were characteristic of the steels and not of his instrument.

Carpenter[29] studied the transformations in two molybdenum steels and several steels containing both molybdenum and chromium. He found that the effects of molybdenum were similar to tungsten in that the Ar points were lowered by molybdenum, but that a given quantity of molybdenum was equivalent to a larger quantity of tungsten. The phenomena observed by Carpenter and other earlier workers have been subsequently confirmed by more elaborate investigations; hence, none of their data will be given here.

62. Swinden's Investigations.—Swinden's[61] report in 1913 describes a remarkably complete study of the effects of molybdenum on the critical points of steel. He studied eighteen steels containing from 0.20 to 1.36 per cent carbon, which may be considered as four series containing respectively 1, 2, 4, and 8 per cent molybdenum. Heating and cooling curves were obtained by the inverse-rate method, in which the time required for the temperature to change a given number of degrees is plotted against the temperature of the sample.

One of the most interesting of Swinden's findings was that, in general, when the steels were heated only slightly above the Ac_3

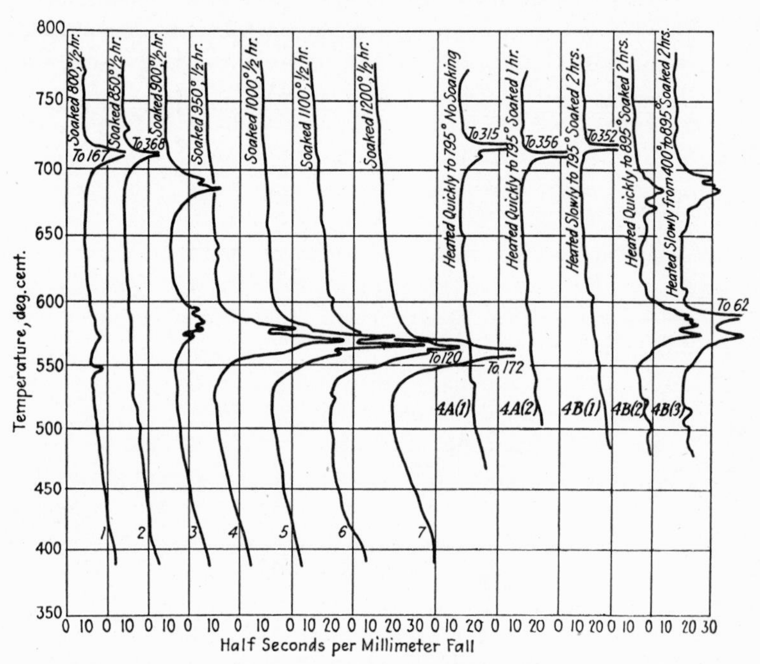

FIG. 36.—Cooling curves for steel containing 1.21 per cent carbon and 1.10 per cent molybdenum (*Swinden.*[61])

point, the eutectoid transformation on cooling occurred at a temperature normal for carbon steels, but that, if they were cooled from temperatures several hundred degrees above the Ac_3 point, this transformation was either split or lowered. This behavior is illustrated in Fig. 36, which shows curves for a steel containing 1.21 per cent carbon and 1.10 per cent molybdenum. Curves 1 and 2, representing the steel cooled from 850°C. (1560°F.), and curves 4*A* (1), 4*A* (2) and 4*B* (1), of the steel cooled from 795°C. (1460°F.), show that the Ar_1 transformation occurred at a temperature normal for carbon steels, namely, about 715°C. (1320°F.). When this steel was cooled from 900°C. (1650°F.), however, as illustrated in curve 3, the split transformation appeared, and critical points were found at about 685°C. (1265°F.) and 585°C. (1085°F.). When this same steel was cooled from even higher temperatures, as shown in curves 5, 6, and 7, there was only one critical point, at about 570°C. (1060°F.). Curves 4*B* (2) and 4*B* (3) were given to refute the contention that the split transformation found on cooling from 900°C. (1650°F.) resulted from a too rapid heating and insufficient soaking. Since this is a hypereutectoid steel, the Ar_3 transformation is not indicated by the cooling curves.

All of the steels studied by Swinden yielded cooling curves similar to those just described, with the exception that, as the

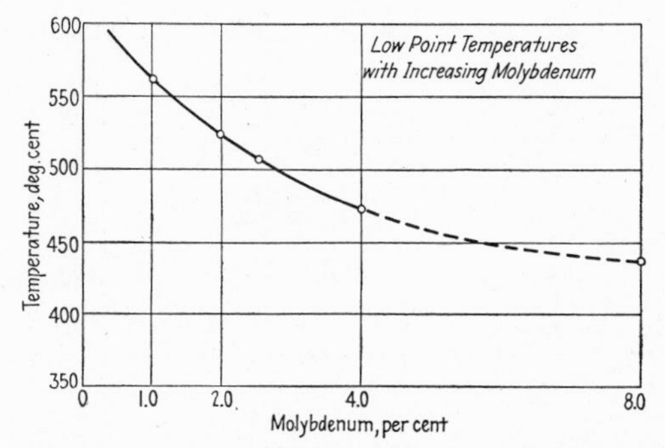

Fig. 37.—Transformation temperatures of slowly cooled molybdenum steels. (*Swinden.*[61])

percentage of molybdenum increased, it became more difficult to produce the transformation at a temperature normal for carbon steels.

The temperature from above which a steel must be cooled in order to exhibit a lowered transformation temperature Swinden called the "lowering temperature." He found that the time of soaking below this temperature had but slight effect on the position or magnitude of the transformations, but that increased soaking time had some tendency to decrease the lowering temperature. In other words, it seems that both time and temperature are involved in the securing of a practically homogeneous austenite, which is apparently needed to produce splitting or lowering. The effect of the rate of cooling on the *Ar* points was not studied sufficiently to warrant definite conclusions.

The lowering temperature increased as the carbon and as the molybdenum increased. In the series containing 1 per cent molybdenum, the temperature from which a steel must be cooled in order to obtain the maximum lowering of the transformation increased from about 850°C. (1560°F.) for the alloy containing 0.20 per cent carbon to about 900°C. (1650°F.) for the alloy containing 1.2 per cent carbon. In the steels containing 4 or 8 per cent molybdenum and more than 0.7 per cent carbon, this temperature was between 1150 and 1200°C. (2100 and 2190°F.).

The normal Ar_1 point, produced by cooling from only slightly above the Ac points, was independent of the molybdenum content as it remained practically constant at a temperature of between 700 and 710°C. (1290 and 1310°F.). The positions of the lowered points were independent of the carbon content. Although the position of the normal Ar_1 point was independent of the molybdenum content, the temperatures of the lower point (Ar'') decreased with increasing molybdenum content, as shown in Fig. 37.

If a steel is cooled from above the lowering temperature and subsequently reheated to a temperature above the Ac_3 point, but below the lowering temperature it will exhibit the lowered transformation. The normal transformation can, however, be recovered by reheating several times to a temperature between Ac_3 and the lowering temperature and cooling through the Ar points.

A point corresponding to Ar_2 in the 0.20 per cent carbon series, and to $Ar_{3.2}$ in the 0.45 per cent carbon series, was observed at the practically constant temperature of 760°C. (1400°F.). The recalescence data did not give any information in reference to the variation of the eutectoid composition with increasing molybdenum content.

In the heating curves, there was no marked shift in the transformation temperatures, but, as the molybdenum increased, the magnitude of the transformations appeared to decrease. This may be explained by a decrease in the quantity of pearlite due to an increasing amount of carbon being in the complex carbide.

63. Other Investigators.—Cooling curves on a steel containing 0.20 per cent carbon and 0.94 per cent molybdenum were obtained by French,[107] and his results are essentially in agreement with Swinden's, except that a transformation point was found at about 860°C. (1580°F.) when the steel was cooled from 960°C. (1760°F.). He also studied the influence of the rate of cooling on the critical points and found that with an increased cooling rate the temperature from which the steel must be cooled in order to produce the split or lowered transformation was decreased. The temperature of the lowered transformation was not appreciably decreased by increased cooling rates, but the transformation was gradually suppressed.

Gillett and Mack[151] gave cooling curves for steels containing from 0.37 to 3.00 per cent molybdenum and from 0.36 to 0.65 per cent carbon. On cooling from 800°C. (1470°F.), which is above the Ac_3 point, the curves were indistinguishable from curves for similar carbon steels, but when the steels were cooled from 860°C. (1580°F.) splitting or lowering of the transformation resulted. In the steel containing 0.38 per cent carbon and 0.37 per cent molybdenum, the Ar_1 point was lowered as the maximum temperature increased, but not split. In the steels containing 0.67 per cent or more molybdenum, Ar'' appeared on cooling from high temperatures. The authors concluded that, in the molybdenum steels studied, Ar'' occurs at a temperature above which martensite is stable, and that such steels can only be fully hardened by quenching to prevent "self-tempering" during cooling from Ar''.

The effects of small quantities of molybdenum on steels of the structural type, as determined by Jones,[176] are shown in Table 11. As this table indicates, the addition of 0.60 per cent molybdenum to a steel containing approximately 0.30 per cent carbon lowers the Ar_1 point about 20°C. (36°F.), while the addition of 1.23 per cent molybdenum causes Ar_1 to split. The steels were cooled from 900°C. (1650°F.) at a rate of 0.75°C. (1.35°F.) per minute.

Murakami and Takei[483] determined the critical points in molybdenum steels from the change in magnetic properties with change in temperature and by the use of the dilatometer. The steels used contained from 1 to 70 per cent molybdenum and as much as 6 per cent carbon. Curves were obtained for both furnace and air cooling. Their results are in general agreement with Swinden's conclusions. They found that lowering of the transformation temperature could be produced by air cooling from slightly below the lowering temperature as determined by furnace cooling. The influence of the composition on the lowering of the critical points on furnace cooling is shown in Fig. 38 and on air cooling in Fig. 39.

Heating and cooling curves recently obtained by Reed[492] on alloys used in determining the influence of molybdenum on

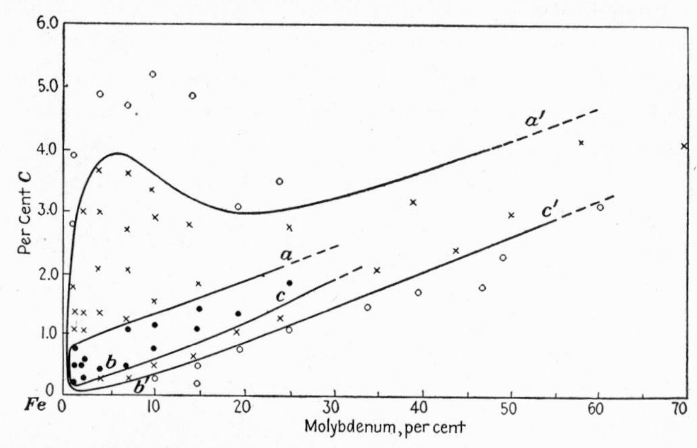

FIG. 38.—Transformation in furnace-cooled molybdenum steels. × Alloys in which the lowering takes place when cooled from 1000°C. in furnace; • alloys in which the lowering takes place when cooled from 800°C. in furnace; ○ alloys in which no lowering takes place. (*Murakami and Takei.*[483])

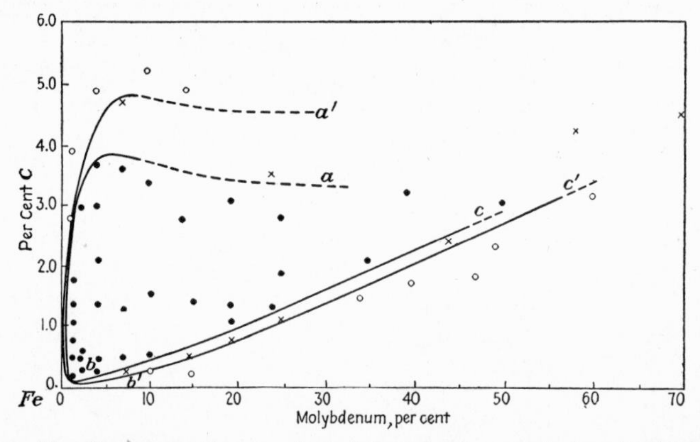

FIG. 39.—Transformation in air-cooled molybdenum steels. × Alloys in which the lowering takes place when cooled from 1000°C. in air; • alloys in which the lowering takes place when cooled from 800°C. in air; ○ alloys in which no lowering takes place. (*Murakami and Takei.*[483])

the carbon content of the eutectoid indicated that molybdenum raises the *Ac* and *Ar* points, and that "molybdenum reduces hysteresis to a minimum." No explanation was given for this finding, which apparently contradicts the results of Swinden and others. It appears to the author that the failure of molybdenum to lower the Ar_1 transformation may have resulted from failure to cool the steels from a sufficiently high temperature. The temperature from which the steels were cooled was not reported.

64. Importance of Critical-point Lowering.—The tendency of molybdenum to lower the critical points proves that molybdenum increases the ease of hardening in the sense that molybdenum-containing steels can be hardened by less drastic quenching than similar steels lacking this element. This ease of hardening is probably of chief importance in that it decreases the difference

TABLE 11.—EFFECT OF SMALL AMOUNTS OF MOLYBDENUM ON CRITICAL POINTS*

Steel	Composition, per cent		Heating			Cooling		
	C	Mo	Ac_1 (maximum), °C.	Ac_2 (maximum), °C.	Ac_3 (end), °C.	Ar_3 (maximum), °C.	Ar_2 (maximum), °C.	Ar_1 (maximum), °C.
1	0.29	....	739	769	834	797	765	706
2	0.30	0.60	739	768	842	787	764	684
3	0.26	1.23	742	767	871	816	761	678; 552

*Jones.[176]

in hardness between the core and surface of the quenched steel or, expressed in another way, its chief importance is in the decrease in the mass effect. The fact that in some molybdenum steels the lowering of the critical points occurs only when the steels have been cooled from certain temperatures appreciably above the Ac_3 point indicates that the proper temperature for heating molybdenum steels for hardening may be above that for carbon steels.

In all molybdenum steels, with the exception of a few cooled very rapidly, transformations occurred above room temperature. Molybdenum, therefore, differs from manganese and nickel in that no quantity of molybdenum renders austenite stable at room temperatures. This is not at all surprising, for molybdenum not only forms a stable carbide, and probably double carbides, but, as mentioned in the discussion of the iron-molybdenum diagram, it tends to decrease the gamma field or to render alpha iron stable over a greater temperature range.

In general, the critical-point phenomena in molybdenum steels are consistent with the idea that at least a portion of the molybdenum separates in the form of a carbide at low temperatures, and that this carbide is stable up to temperatures appreciably above the *Ac* transformation. At the lowering temperature considerable quantities of the carbide are apparently dissolved in the austenite matrix.

B. EFFECT OF MOLYBDENUM ON HEAT-TREATING RANGES

In carbon steels the optimum physical properties, by which is meant the maximum hardness coexistent with the maximum ductility, can be secured only by quenching within rather narrow temperature limits. If the proper hardening temperature is exceeded, the resulting hardness remains almost unchanged, but the ductility is appreciably lowered, owing to the excessive grain growth produced at the higher quenching temperatures. It has been stated by Gillett and Mack(151) and others that molybdenum steels not only can be but should be heated to higher temperatures than carbon steels before quenching. The data given below uphold this statement. Quenched molybdenum steels also require a higher tempering temperature to effect a softening comparable with carbon steels.

The heat treatment of steels containing several per cent molybdenum is discussed in the section dealing with high-speed steels.

65. Quenching Range.—The effect of quenching temperature on the mechanical properties of three steels containing molybdenum, as determined by three different investigations, is shown in Table 12. Mathews,(111) as well as others, in discussing the virtues of molybdenum steel, spoke of the wide safe heat-treating range, which is indicated by the data in this table. Data on the effects of smaller amounts of molybdenum on the quenching range are not available, and it is not known whether or not the small amounts of molybdenum now used in commercial steels really widen the quenching range.

The "National Metals Handbook" for 1930 gave as recommended practice in the heat treatment of an S.A.E. 1025 steel (carbon steel with 0.20 to 0.30 per cent carbon) a quenching temperature from 855 to 885°C. (1575 to 1625°F.). The data just cited indicate that this range is the low limit of temperature for quenching molybdenum steel of the same carbon content, and that this range can be exceeded by 100°C. (180°F.) without injury to the steel.

TABLE 12.—EFFECT OF QUENCHING TEMPERATURE ON MECHANICAL PROPERTIES OF MOLYBDENUM STEELS

Reference	Quenched from		Tensile strength, lb./sq. in.	Yield strength, lb./sq. in.	Elongation, per cent	Reduction of area, per cent	Brinell hardness	Izod impact, ft-lb.
	°C.	°F.						
1	870	1600	101,600	90,400	22.0*	64.2		
1	925	1700	102,000	88,440	22.5*	62.9		
1	980	1800	103,500	89,040	24.0*	65.4		
1	1035	1900	100,600	88,630	23.0*	64.2		
1	1095	2000	103,700	88,800	22.0*	62.3		
2	815	1500	163,500	140,000	18.5*	62.7	319	58
2	870	1600	161,700	139,500	17.0*	63.1	321	62
2	925	1700	160,400	138,400	17.5*	61.7	321	60
2	980	1800	158,500	138,300	18.0*	61.5	319	61
2	1035	1900	159,600	139,600	16.8*	57.9	317	56
2	1095	2000	157,000	140,000	17.0*	59.0	317	55
3	785	1445	88,700	57,500	24.2†	52.3	179	
3	830	1525	104,075	69,500	18.8†	51.4	207	48
3	875	1610	105,375	75,000	21.0†	63.0	232	68
3	910	1670	109,250	77,000	22.8†	65.5	245	69
3	980	1800	106,000	76,000	23.2†	64.8	235	67

Reference 1. Data by McKnight[101] on a 0.20 per cent carbon, 0.70 per cent molybdenum steel quenched in oil from indicated temperatures and tempered at 540°C. (1000°F.).

Reference 2. Data by Schmid[103] on a 0.27 per cent carbon, 0.66 per cent manganese, 0.83 per cent chromium, 0.42 per cent molybdenum steel quenched in water from indicated temperatures and tempered at 565°C. (1050°F.).

Reference 3. Data by French[107] on a 0.20 per cent carbon, 0.94 per cent molybdenum steel quenched from indicated temperatures in oil and tempered at 540°C. (1000°F.).

* Gage length not given.

† Gage length, 2 in.

Okochi, Majima, and Satô[75] suggested that, in quenching molybdenum steels, they first be heated to approximately 900°C. (1650°F.), cooled slowly to 750°C. (1380°F.), and then quenched in water. They found that Brinell hardness values equivalent to those obtained on quenching from the higher temperature could be produced by this method, and that the tendency to crack was not nearly so great. It was also suggested by Angell[306] that low-alloy steels might be advantageously treated by this method, and his values obtained for a chromium-molybdenum steel quenched from a comparatively low temperature after having first been heated to the normal quenching temperature are given in the chapter on chromium-molybdenum steels.

66. Tempering Range.—The fact that molybdenum, like tungsten, can confer the property of "red hardness" on steel, as discussed in the section dealing with molybdenum in high-speed steel, indicates that this element makes the steel more resistant to tempering. The curves shown in Fig. 40, of which 1 to 3 inclusive show the loss in strength of quenched molybdenum

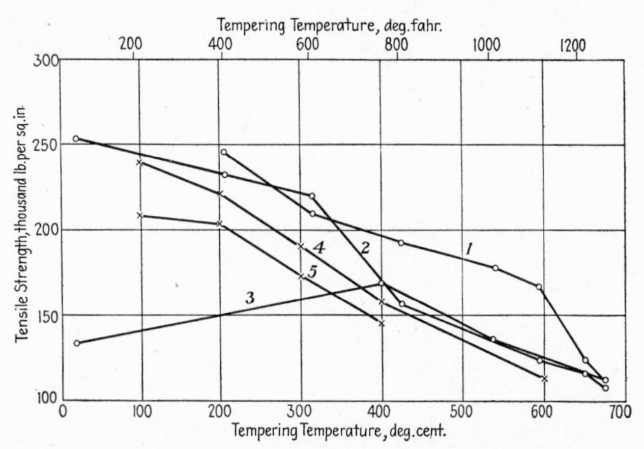

FIG. 40.—Effect of tempering on tensile strength of molybdenum and carbon steels. 1, 0.32 per cent C, 0.83 per cent Mo, water-quenched from 845°C. (1550°F.) (*McKnight* from *Gillett and Mack*.[151]) 2, Same as No. 1 but oil quenched. 3, 0.20 per cent C, 0.94 per cent Mo, water-quenched from 910°C. (1670°F) (*French*.[170]) 4, 0.34 per cent C, water-quenched from 950°C. (1740°F.) (*Hanemann and Kühnel*.[60]) 5, Same as No. 4 but 0.20 per cent C.

steels on tempering and 4 and 5 show the loss in strength of comparable carbon steels on tempering, indicate that even the low-carbon steels containing less than 1 per cent molybdenum are somewhat less readily softened by tempering than molybdenum-free steels. The effect of small amounts of molybdenum on the softening during tempering is not known.

Figure 41, taken from the book by Gillett and Mack,[151] proves quite definitely that the presence of 1 per cent or more of molybdenum in medium-carbon steels decreases the tendency to soften on tempering. These authors concluded that molybdenum steels require decidedly higher tempering temperatures to be softened to the same degree as other comparable alloy steels, and that this resistance to tempering makes them attractive for use where strength at high temperatures is desired.

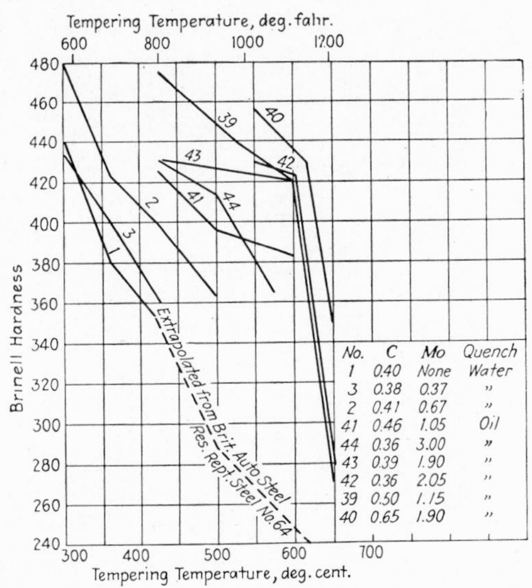

FIG. 41.—Effect of tempering on hardness of molybdenum steels. (*Gillett and Mack.*[151])

C. EFFECT OF MOLYBDENUM ON MICROSTRUCTURE

Guillet[24, 25] made the first comprehensive study of the effects of molybdenum on the microstructure of steels, and on the basis of this study he constructed the diagram shown in Fig. 31 (page 63). He reported the structures of the various steels in the forged, hardened, and annealed condition. Swinden[52] also studied the microstructures of four series of steels in various conditions. These two investigations give a very good picture of the effect of molybdenum on the microstructure of steel. In general, it is shown that molybdenum tends to refine the structure. This refinement is due to the retarding effect of molybdenum on the transformations and to its tendency to decrease grain growth at elevated temperatures.

In studying a low-carbon, low-molybdenum steel, French[107] found that the precipitated ferrite was distributed throughout the matrix in more irregular grains than are generally found in carbon steels, and that the finely divided state of the matrix suggested a strong and tough alloy.

The fineness of the sorbitic structure in molybdenum steels has been commented on by Andrew,[248] who concluded that it results from a strained condition produced by the molybdenum hindering the free movement of the carbide particles, thus preventing them from coalescing into larger masses. Inasmuch as the quantity of molybdenum usually used in steel is insufficient to form a carbide with all of the carbon, Andrew believed that molybdenum probably does not exist as a carbide in the steel, for if it did it would not influence the fineness of the structure. He suggested that elements such as molybdenum, tungsten, and manganese can exist as carbides in steel when present in certain amounts, and that when present in smaller amounts they probably form solid solutions with the ferrite. An interesting study of the microstructures of chromium-molybdenum steels by Pulsifer and Greene[125] is mentioned in Chap. VII (page 244).

67. Rolled or Forged Condition.—Guillet[24, 25] found that in forged steels containing molybdenum the pearlite was extremely fine. In the series containing approximately 0.2 per cent carbon, when the molybdenum content exceeded 5 per cent, a second undarkened constituent appeared. In the series containing 0.8 per cent carbon, the white constituent appeared when the molybdenum content exceeded 1.2 per cent. From these studies, Guillet divided the molybdenum steels into two classes: (1) those containing only the constituents found in carbon steels, designated as pearlitic steels, and (2) those containing the special constituent believed to be a double carbide. In the steels containing 0.2 per cent carbon, illustrated in Fig. 31 (page 63), those containing less than 2 per cent molybdenum were in class 1, while those containing more than 2 per cent molybdenum were in class 2. In steels containing about 0.8 per cent carbon the division occurred at about 1 per cent molybdenum.

In agreement with Guillet, Swinden[52] found that in the rolled steels pearlite was very fine or, as he expressed it, the pearlite was "very sorbitic." He found excess ferrite in some steels and excess cementite in others but found no evidence of the special constituent described by Guillet. In the low-molybdenum steels excess cementite appeared at the grain boundaries, but in steels containing 4 per cent or more molybdenum it occurred in the form of small globules. Oberhoffer[160] attributed the divergent results to the fact that Guillet's "double carbide" was ledeburite and maintained that his diagram represented the saturation of austenite by carbon as affected by the molybdenum content.

68. Annealed Condition.—Swinden found that annealing "concentrated" the pearlite, and that excess cementite (complex carbide?), when present, occurred in massive, vermicular forms standing out in relief throughout the mass. The structures were coarsened considerably by annealing, but the pearlite was not massive in any of the steels.

69. Quenched Condition.—Both Guillet and Swinden found that in the quenched condition all of the steels had a ground mass of martensite. The high-carbon steels investigated by Swinden contained what he called specks of free "cementite," while some of Guillet's contained undissolved "double carbide." Guillet found that, as the cooling velocity decreased, or as the carbon content increased, the quantity of excess carbide was increased.

70. Quenched and Tempered.—Tempering, according to Swinden,[52] converts the martensite to a dense troostite and shows up the free cementite clearly as white specks. In some cases, pearlite was formed.

D. EFFECT OF MOLYBDENUM ON MISCELLANEOUS PHYSICAL PROPERTIES

The effect of molybdenum on the electric and magnetic properties of steel has been studied by several investigators. The electric properties were usually obtained with the object of explaining structural changes, while magnetic properties were investigated with the object of developing useful alloys for permanent magnets. The thermal expansion of molybdenum steels has been utilized in studying transformations with the dilatometer, but the resulting curves have not furnished precise data regarding the effect of molybdenum on the coefficient of expansion. Few data are available on other physical properties, except, of course, the mechanical properties.

71. Electric Conductivity.—Le Chatelier[16] studied the effects of various alloying elements on the electric resistance of steels and reported that molybdenum, as well as chromium and tungsten, did not increase the electric resistance. From this he concluded that molybdenum occurred in steel in the form of a definite compound and was not in solution in the matrix. Mathews[19] and Portevin[40, 72] determined the electric resistances of steels containing molybdenum, but its effect has been comprehensively studied only by Swinden.[52, 61] Maurer and Schilling[158] investigated the change in electric resistance of two molybdenum steels on tempering.

Swinden's[61] values for the electric resistance of molybdenum steels after various heat treatments are given in Table 13. These values were determined in the temperature range 16 to 20°C. (60 to 70°F.). From these data, Swinden concluded that the effect of molybdenum on the electric resistance depended on the carbon content of the steel. In the annealed condition the 0.20 per cent carbon series showed a slight increase in resistance with increasing molybdenum content, in the 0.45 per cent carbon series the molybdenum had little effect on resistance, while in the 0.9 and 1.20 per cent carbon series molybdenum caused a distinct decrease in resistance. These phenomena are explicable on the basis of an increasing quantity of molybdenum being extracted from solution in the iron to form the complex carbide. The much greater resistance produced by quenching above the lowering temperature, 1200°C. (2190°F.), than that produced by quenching below the lowering temperature, 800°C. (1470°F.), is significant in furnishing additional evidence that the degree of dissociation or solution of the complex carbide increases with increased quenching temperature.

Maurer and Schilling,[158] in an investigation conducted to study the behavior of high-speed steel, determined the change in electric resistance of two quenched molybdenum steels on tempering. One steel contained 0.74 per cent carbon and 4.25 per cent molybdenum, while the other contained 0.66 per cent carbon and 7.50 per cent molybdenum. Resistance decreased rapidly as the steels were tempered, and breaks in the resistance-tempering temperature curve were used to explain reactions on tempering.

72. Thermal Conductivity.—Data on electric and thermal conductivity of molybdenum steels, with Wiedemann-Franz ratios, from Okochi, Majima, and Satô[75] are given in Table 14. The values are apparently for the forged steels, not heat-treated, and are for a mean temperature of 50°C. (120°F.).

The Wiedemann-Franz ratio is the ratio of thermal to electric conductivity and, within certain limits, has been found to be a constant. If electric and thermal conductivity have been correctly determined, their ratio as given in the table should be substantially constant.

TABLE 13.—ELECTRIC RESISTANCE OF MOLYBDENUM STEELS*

Composition, per cent						Resistivity, microhms/cm. cube					
C	Mo	Mn	Si	S	P	Annealed	Normalized	Rolled	Hardened and tempered†	Quenched 800°C. (1470°F.)	Quenched 1200°C. (2190°F.)
0.195	1.030	0.218	0.047	0.025	0.016	13.48	14.51	14.18	14.22	16.0	
0.445	1.054	0.230	0.087	0.026	0.014	14.77	16.55	17.40	16.86	21.0	
0.869	1.018	0.270	0.122	0.039	0.018	18.55	20.47	21.00	20.25	36.3	
1.215	1.096	0.250	0.124	0.032	0.017	19.54	20.32	23.10	21.15	39.53	45.31
0.246	2.176	0.216	0.064	0.026	0.015	13.55	16.73	18.66	17.93	16.5	18.96
0.442	2.181	0.270	0.075	0.025	0.015	14.97	16.42	20.66	19.47	20.1	24.82
0.883	2.186	0.263	0.078	0.025	0.014	16.13	18.80	22.90	20.10	33.44	
1.210	2.109	0.238	0.071	0.023	0.015	18.47	21.72	24.80	20.80	38.52	48.66
0.190	4.110	0.242	0.036	0.020	0.017	14.95	16.40	20.22	19.12	16.82	23.66
0.487	4.009	0.292	0.038	0.024	0.016	14.89	16.39	24.60	19.52	19.54	34.04
0.865	4.002	0.230	0.051	0.022	0.016	15.53	18.42	25.70	19.88	26.95	36.42
1.060	4.019	0.230	0.039	0.020	0.016	16.92	19.37	27.10	19.78	36.03	
0.135	8.012	0.216	0.049	0.022	0.017	23.70	25.76	25.83	25.25	25.23	32.72
0.361	8.167	0.274	0.056	0.025	0.016	15.32	17.20	19.00	18.79	17.2	34.03
0.445	8.109	0.252	0.080	0.022	0.019	14.38	16.79	28.00	19.06	17.5	37.38
0.775	7.857	0.230	0.041	0.024	0.017	15.38	17.87	27.40	19.92	22.07	46.07
1.125	7.920	0.234	0.075	0.027	0.017	16.13	18.86	22.60	19.50	36.2	55.57
1.360	2.540	0.205	0.122	0.024	0.022	20.13	21.79	31.30	22.40	41.5	

* Swinden.(61)

†Quenched in oil from 950°C. (1740°F.) for 0.2 per cent carbon, 900°C. (1650°F.) for 0.45 per cent carbon, 850°C. (1560°F.) for 0.9 per cent carbon, 800°C. (1470°F.) for 1.2 per cent carbon, and tempered 15 min. at 550°C. (1020°F.).

TABLE 14.—PHYSICAL PROPERTIES OF MOLYBDENUM STEELS*

Number	Composition, per cent		Electric resistance microhms/cm. cube at 15°C.	Thermal conductivity, cal./sq.cm./cm./sec./°C., at 50°C.	Ratio of thermal to electric conductivity	Thermal coefficient of expansion/°C. × 10^{-5} at 50°C.
	C	Mo				
1	0.35	1.05	16.02	0.129	2.067	1.16
2	0.63	0.69	19.37	0.093	1.794	1.23
3	0.70	0.70	15.05	0.127	1.911	1.17
4	0.64	0.32	19.24	1.104‡	2.001	1.28
5	0.55	1.58	20.31	0.102	2.072	1.28
6	0.61	1.60	20.89	0.102	2.131	1.29
7	0.64	1.24	21.59	0.081	1.749	1.29
8†	0.54	3.65	31.44	0.087	2.735	1.29

* Okochi, Majima, and Satô.[75]
† Contains 1.02 per cent nickel.
‡ Probably a misprint in original article.

73. Coefficient of Expansion.—Values of the linear thermal coefficient of expansion for several molybdenum steels, as determined by Okochi, Majima, and Satô,[75] are listed in Table 14.

74. Thermo-electric Properties.—Dupuy and Portevin [59,66] determined the thermo-electric properties of the two series of molybdenum steels studied by Guillet and other French workers. Both the annealed and hardened steels were used, and the electromotive force was developed with copper as the second element. Values were determined with the fixed junction at 0°C. (32°F.) and the other junction at either −80°C. (−112°F.) or 100°C. (212°F.). The values determined for a sample of electrolytic iron and the molybdenum steels are given in Table 15, in which the values of electromotive force must be in microvolts per degree centigrade, instead of millivolts per degree, as given in the text of the article.

The decrease in e.m.f. of the higher-carbon steels followed by an increase as the molybdenum content increases was considered to indicate a limited solubility of molybdenum in iron, which still appears to be an acceptable conclusion.

E. EFFECT OF MOLYBDENUM ON MAGNETIC PROPERTIES

Inasmuch as both tungsten and chromium steels are good permanent-magnet steels, it is to be expected that molybdenum steels will also have the properties desired in permanent magnets.

75. Outline of Investigations.—Mme. Curie,[14] in 1898, showed that molybdenum steels had about the same magnetic properties as the tungsten steel used for permanent magnets. Mathews[111] reported that, in 1902, he and E. L. French tested steels containing from 2.0 to 4.0 per cent molybdenum, which gave satisfactory tests for permanence but were low in residual induction and much more sensitive to hardening than the corresponding tungsten magnet steels. Values on magnetic properties of several steels containing molybdenum and vanadium were reported by Burgess and Aston,[43] but the compositions were not such as to give the best magnetic values. Several reviews[37, 47, 56, 71, 98] contained statements that molybdenum steels were used in permanent magnets without giving data about magnetic properties or mentioning definite applications. No authoritative report of the actual use of molybdenum steels in magnets has been found, and it is probable they have found little or no application in magnets. Stogoff and Messkin[296] recently studied the magnetic properties of molybdenum steels and confirmed Mme. Curie's conclusions regarding their desirable magnetic properties.

TABLE 15.—THERMAL ELECTROMOTIVE FORCE OF MOLYBDENUM STEELS IN MICROVOLTS PER DEGREE CENTIGRADE. FIXED JUNCTION AT 0°C. (32°F.)*

(Sample in contact with copper)

Composition, per cent		Annealed		Hardened	
C	Mo	−80°C. (−112°F.)	+100°C. (+212°F.)	−80°C. (−112°F.)	+100°C. (+212°F.)
Electrolytic iron		+12.20	+8.70		
0.19	0.45	+10.00	+8.35	Cracked	
0.16	1.00	10.80	7.70	+10.00	+8.00
0.14	2.20	10.70	7.80	10.10	7.92
0.29	4.50	8.60	6.30	−12.00?	3.98
0.77	0.50	+ 4.50	+3.00	− 4.40	−6.50
0.81	1.21	4.70	3.20	Cracked	
0.81	1.98	5.20	4.30	+ 1.10	+0.10
0.82?	5.75?	0.30	−2.10	Cracked	

* Dupuy and Portevin.[59,66]

Messkin[283] studied the effect of tempering temperature on a steel containing 0.96 per cent carbon and 2.18 per cent molybdenum quenched in oil from 825°C. (1515°F.). This study is, however, of more interest in relation to tempering phenomena than in illustrating the effect of molybdenum on the magnetic properties of steel.

76. Magnetic Properties.—The value of a steel for permanent magnets is usually estimated from the residual induction (*Br*) and coercive force (*Hc*) of correctly hardened samples. These values are points on the demagnetization curve and should be obtained after magnetizing the steel to saturation. Residual induction is the flux density, frequently expressed in gausses, that would remain in an infinitely long bar after the bar had been magnetized to saturation and the extraneous magnetizing force reduced to zero. Coercive force is the magnetizing force, expressed in oersteds, that is required to reduce the flux density to zero in an infinitely long rod that had been magnetized to saturation. In practice, the effect of the infinitely long rod is provided by suitable compensation or correction for demagnetization by the ends. For permanent magnets, a high coercive force is necessary and a high residual induction is desirable. Some investigators attempt to evaluate permanent-magnet steels by multiplying the residual induction by the coercive force ($Br \times Hc$) and considering that the value of the steel is proportional to this product.

77. Mme. Curie's Investigation.—The analyses and magnetic values of steels tested by Mme. Curie[14] after quenching in water from indicated temperatures are shown in Table 16.

TABLE 16.—MAGNETIC PROPERTIES OF MOLYBDENUM STEELS QUENCHED IN WATER*

Number	Composition, per cent		Quenching temperature		*Br*, gausses	*Hc*, oersteds	$Br \times Hc \times 10^{-3}$
	Mo	C	°C.	°F.			
A.......	3.48	0.51	850	1560	6700	60	402
B.......	4.05	1.24	800	1470	6000	82	492
B.......	4.05	1.24	800	1470	6700	85	570
C.......	3.91	1.72	770	1420	6400	73	467
C.......	3.91	1.72	830	1525	5200	79	411
C.......	3.91	1.72	800	1470	7000	78	546

* Curie.[14]

Empirical aging tests indicated that the permanence of the magnetism in magnets made from these steels was on a par with the permanence of tungsten steel magnets.

78. Investigation by Stogoff and Messkin.—The magnetic properties of eight molybdenum steels and, for comparison, one carbon steel were determined by Stogoff and Messkin.[296] Their samples were made in crucibles, forged to 16-mm. (0.63-in.) square bars, annealed at 1000°C. (1830°F.), and machined to test samples 10 mm. (0.39 in.) square by 200 mm. (7.87 in.) long. These samples were hardened from a lead bath at different temperatures in both water and oil. Hardening cracks occurred only in the samples quenched in water from above 900°C. (1650°F.).

The steels studied by Stogoff and Messkin may be divided into two principal groups. Steels 1 to 5 inclusive, in Table 17, contain about 1.4 per cent carbon with molybdenum increasing from 0.16 to 4.48 per cent, while steels 2, 6, and 7 have a molybdenum content of about 2.5 per cent with carbon varying from 0.65 to 1.31 per cent. A comparison of the properties of steel 8 with carbon steel 9 will show the effect of 4.4 per cent molybdenum on a steel containing 0.8 per cent carbon.

Magnetic values of the steels under discussion are given in Table 17. These values were determined by the ballistic method, using a maximum magnetizing force of 600 gausses. Stogoff and Messkin considered steel 7, containing 0.96 per cent carbon and 2.18 per cent molybdenum, as having the best properties. Additional tests on this steel as quenched from different temperatures were made, and the results are listed in Table 18. These values indicate that the steel is not exceptionally sensitive to heat treatment. A tungsten magnet steel tested by these authors after quenching in water from 850°C. (1560°F.) had a residual induction of 10,890, a coercive force of 65.0, and a product of 707.8×10^3. Artificial aging tests of magnetized magnets indicated that the permanence of the molybdenum steel was at least equal to that of a tungsten steel. Additional tests were made on steel 8, containing 0.81 per cent carbon and 4.33 per cent molybdenum, but its magnetic values for equivalent heat treatments were not so satisfactory as those of the steel containing less molybdenum.

79. Other Work.—The effects of various alloying elements, including molybdenum, on the magnetic induction in commercial

TABLE 17.—MAGNETIC PROPERTIES OF MOLYBDENUM STEELS*

Material	Composition, per cent		Hardening medium	Br, gausses			Hc, oersteds			Product $Br \times Hc \times 10^{-3}$		
				Hardening temperature			Hardening temperature			Hardening temperature		
	C	Mo		800°C. (1475°F.)	850°C. (1560°F.)	900°C. (1650°F.)	800°C. (1475°F.)	850°C. (1560°F.)	900°C. (1650°F.)	800°C. (1475°F.)	850°C. (1560°F.)	900°C. (1650°F.)
1	1.33	0.16	Water at 15°C. (60°F.)	9,680	8,861	8,609	65.0	67.5	69.5	629.2	598.1	598.3
2	1.31	2.54	Water at 15°C. (60°F.)	10,466	9,461	9,067	60.5	67.6	64.2	633.2	639.6	582.1
3	1.24	3.11	Water at 15°C. (60°F.)	9,207	7,178	5,126	69.4	75.0	74.0	639.0	538.3	379.3
4	1.46	4.36	Water at 15°C. (60°F.)	8,445	......	......	67.5	....	....	570.0		
5	1.51	4.48	Water at 15°C. (60°F.)	8,550	......	......	68.5	....	....	585.6		
1	1.33	0.16	Oil	9,960	10,248	9,513	29.3	30.0	30.5	291.8	307.4	337.7
2	1.31	2.54	Oil	10,180	9,271	8,700	67.3	70.0	66.0	685.1	649.0	574.2
3	1.24	3.11	Oil	9,000	8,160	5,272	71.4	77.0	74.0	642.6	628.3	390.1
4	1.46	4.36	Oil	8,064	7,055	......	66.2	71.0	....	533.8	500.9	
5	1.51	4.48	Oil	8,695	7,387	......	66.0	70.0	....	573.9	517.1	
6	0.65	2.49	Water at 15°C. (60°F.)	11,393	11,276	10,975	57.0	58.0	56.7	649.4	654.0	622.8
7	0.96	2.18	Water at 15°C. (60°F.)	10,680	9,540	9,780	76.0	80.5	75.5	811.7	768.0	738.4
2	1.31	2.54	Water at 15°C. (60°F.)	10,466	9,461	9,067	60.5	67.6	64.2	633.2	639.6	582.1
6	0.65	2.49	Oil	11,150	11,138	10,666	60.0	58.3	59.5	669.0	649.3	532.6
7	0.96	2.18	Oil	10,080	8,340	8,160	75.3	82.0	80.0	759.0	683.9	652.9
2	1.31	2.54	Oil	10,180	9,271	8,700	67.3	70.0	66.0	685.1	649.0	574.2
8	0.81	4.33	Water at 15°C. (60°F.)	9,900	9,866	10,140	71.6	72.2	73.2	708.8	712.8	742.2
9	0.80	....	Water at 15°C. (60°F.)	9,610	8,144	9,815	61.0	47.4	64.7	586.2	382.0	635.0
8	0.81	4.33	Oil	9,870	9,428	9,395	76.5	77.2	76.0	716.8	728.3	714.4
9	0.80	....	Oil	10,388	10,143	9,028	26.8	27.7	67.0	278.4	281.0	604.9

* Stogoff and Messkin.(296)

steels were recently studied by Gerold.[445] His results indicated that the decrease in magnetic induction for a given magnetizing force was directly proportional to the amount of molybdenum, provided the molybdenum content was under 2 per cent. The decrease in induction due to 1 per cent of molybdenum, as taken from Gerold's curves, was for several magnetizing forces:

Magnetizing Force, amp. turns/cm.	Decrease in Induction, gausses
25	1500
50	950
100	750
300	600

TABLE 18.—MAGNETIC PROPERTIES OF A STEEL CONTAINING 0.96 PER CENT CARBON AND 2.18 PER CENT MOLYBDENUM AFTER VARIOUS HARDENING TREATMENTS*

Quenching temperature		Br, gausses	Hc, oersteds	Product, $Br \times Hc \times 10^{-3}$
°C.	°F.			
Quenched in water				
775	1425	10,836	52.5	568.9
800	1475	10,680	76.0	811.7
825	1515	10,317	75.0	773.8
850	1560	9,540	80.5	768.0
900	1650	9,780	75.5	738.4
Quenched in oil				
775	1425	10,466	50.6	529.6
800	1475	10,080	75.3	759.0
825	1515	9,047	77.3	699.3
850	1560	8,340	82.0	683.9
900	1650	8,160	80.0	652.8

* Stogoff and Messkin.[296]

F. AUTHOR'S SUMMARY

1. Molybdenum tends to lower the critical points observed in cooling, which indicates that such steels can be hardened by less drastic quenching than molybdenum-free steels. The maximum lowering of the critical points only results on cooling from temperatures appreciably above the critical range for carbon steel.

2. Molybdenum raises both the optimum quenching temperature and the tempering temperature required to produce a given softening.

3. Small quantities of molybdenum refine the structures normal for carbon steels. With larger quantities a separate constituent appears, which is probably a double carbide, possibly Fe_4Mo_2C.

4. Molybdenum apparently increases the electric resistance of low-carbon steels, thereby indicating that it is in solution in the iron-rich phase. It decreases the resistance of high-carbon steel, indicating the formation of a complex compound. Thermal conductivity, of course, varies with electric conductivity.

5. The magnetic properties of molybdenum steels show that permanent magnets made from such steels can be at least equal to magnets made from the best tungsten magnet steels, and molybdenum steels could be substituted for the widely used tungsten magnet steels. Of course, as Mathews[111] pointed out, the molybdenum steels may be more sensitive to heat treatment, and additional *comparative* studies of tungsten and molybdenum magnet steels are needed to determine the value of the latter type of steel.

CHAPTER V

PROPERTIES AND USES OF MOLYBDENUM STEEL

Mechanical Properties of Molybdenum Steels—Mechanical Properties at Low and High Temperatures—Special Properties of Molybdenum Steels—Chemical Properties of Molybdenum Steels—Uses of Molybdenum Steels—Cast Molybdenum Steel—Author's Summary

Because molybdenum is most frequently used in conjunction with some other alloying element, the properties of steels containing only molybdenum in addition to elements always present are not at all well-known. Many early investigators studied steels containing several per cent molybdenum and overlooked the fact that a few tenths of 1 per cent molybdenum have a pronounced effect on some of the properties of steel.

It has recently been found that a small quantity of molybdenum decreases the loss of strength at medium-high temperatures, 400 to 600°C. (750 to 1110°F.), and considerable space will be devoted to the high-temperature properties of molybdenum steel.

The chemical properties of molybdenum steel do not appear to be of much practical importance, for molybdenum apparently has little effect on the rate of chemical attack.

A. MECHANICAL PROPERTIES OF MOLYBDENUM STEELS

Although the mechanical properties have been reported for practically all molybdenum steels investigated, there are too few data to enable an exact evaluation of the effects of molybdenum, particularly in small amounts, on these properties.

The mechanical properties are, of course, dependent on heat treatment and size as well as on the chemical composition of the heat-treated sample. All data on heat-treated steels given in this section are for material treated in sections equivalent to or slightly larger than the usual tensile specimen. While the effect of molybdenum, when present with other alloying elements, in influencing depth of hardening or decreasing "mass effect" has been studied, no results are available regarding its effectiveness in the absence of other alloying elements, such as nickel and chromium.

TABLE 19.—MECHANICAL PROPERTIES OF ROLLED OR FORGED MOLYBDENUM STEELS
(No heat treatment)

Composition, per cent		Tensile strength, lb./sq. in.	Yield strength, lb./sq. in.	Elongation in 2 in., per cent	Reduction of area, per cent	Brinell hardness	Charpy impact, m-kg.	Investigator
C	Mo							
0.19	1.03	75,100	50,200	33.3	64.3	...	...	Swinden(52)
0.25	2.18	117,800	....	21.0	57.0	...	...	Swinden(52)
0.19	4.11	119,200	75,200	21.7	52.7	...	...	Swinden(52)
0.13	8.01	92,300	....	25.7	52.2	...	...	Swinden(52)
0.44	1.05	121,800	77,000	19.5	49.2	...	...	Swinden(52)
0.44	2.18	151,000	....	16.7	46.4	...	...	Swinden(52)
0.49	4.01	188,100	120,000	13.5	33.8	...	...	Swinden(52)
0.36	8.17	148,300	....	19.4	45.9	...	...	Swinden(52)
0.44	8.11	215,000	154,100	19.7	34.0	...	...	Swinden(52)
0.84	1.02	179,100	116,400	14.5	34.4	...	...	Swinden(52)
0.88	2.19	198,900	129,000	12.1	32.1	...	...	Swinden(52)
0.86	4.0	230,400	....	8.0	17.3	...	...	Swinden(52)
0.77	7.85	193,800	149,000	9.8	18.4	...	...	Swinden(52)
1.27	1.09	131,400	....	1.0	2.0	...	...	Swinden(52)
1.21	2.11	216,900	169,300	7.0	9.6	...	...	Swinden(52)
1.36	2.54	184,200	172,000	2.1	2.4	...	...	Swinden(52)
1.06	4.02	239,200	179,800	10.6	18.4	...	...	Swinden(52)
1.12	7.92	245,700	190,000	8.4	16.4	...	...	Swinden(52)
0.33	0.96	105,800	91,500	16.5*	49.6	222	...	Swinden(61)
0.19	0.45	69,500	53,500	18.5*	69.3	131	24†	Guillet(24)
0.16	1.00	91,000	56,200	17.0*	66.5	118	27†	Guillet(24)
0.14	2.29	117,600	96,300	7.5*	12.1	212	15†	Guillet(24)
0.29	4.50	185,700	146,700	6.0*	7.5	387	3†	Guillet(24)
0.73	0.50	163,800	117,700	7*	7.5	286	1†	Guillet(24)
0.81	1.21	171,350	111,400	6.5*	5.6	293	1†	Guillet(24)
0.81	1.98	203,500	144,600	4	5.2	332	2†	Guillet(24)
0.10	0.24	58,240	56,000	37	75	92	...	Hadfield(67)
0.10	0.45	60,480	58,240	31	57	90	...	Hadfield(67)
0.06	0.52	47,040	44,800	.....	....	126	...	Hadfield(67)
0.11	0.94	89,600	76,200	.....	....	...	...	Hadfield(67)
0.12	1.55	69,440	42,560	32	55	131	...	Hadfield(67)
0.13	1.78	67,200	60,500	24	59	179	...	Hadfield(67)
0.11	3.00	76,160	38,080	34	67	133	...	Hadfield(67)
0.07	7.14	82,880	51,520	30	57	160	...	Hadfield(67)
0.09	12.50	109,760	62,720	14	38	174	...	Hadfield(67)
0.08	18.70	129,920	85,120	2	2	275	...	Hadfield(67)
0.32	7.55	112,000	78,400	19	44	188	...	Hadfield(67)
0.44	11.74	121,000	82,900	15	21	212	...	Hadfield(67)
0.28	0.95	110,850	62,250	9.4	44.6	...	...	Mathews(19)
0.44	0.30	124,000	91,000	19	33	228	...	Cutter‡
0.32	0.83	116,000	98,200	14	30.5	255	...	McKnight‡

* Gage length not given.
† Size of impact specimen not given.
‡ Unpublished work quoted by Gillett and Mack.(151)

The values of "yield strength" given above may have been obtained in different manners by the various investigators, so caution should be used in comparing values obtained by one investigator with those of another. The "elastic limits" reported by Swinden represent the loads giving the first permanent elongation of the bar as measured by calipers, while those determined by Gillett and Mack were determined with an extensometer and were reported as "yield points."

80. Forged or Rolled.—Available data on the mechanical properties of forged or rolled molybdenum steels are listed in Table 19. The results reported by Swinden were obtained from rolled sections, while the results reported by the other investigators were obtained from forged sections.

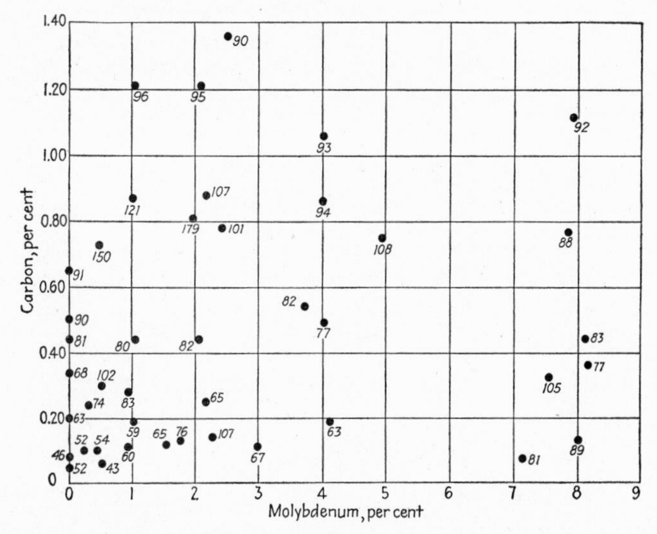

FIG. 42.—Tensile strength in thousand pounds per square inch of annealed molybdenum steels. Collected from various sources.

Owing to the few data and the dependence of mechanical properties on methods and temperature of working, it is difficult to obtain exact expressions of the effect of molybdenum on the mechanical properties of these steels. However, it is apparent that, for a given carbon content, the tensile strength, yield strength, and hardness increase with increasing molybdenum, while the elongation, reduction of area, and impact resistance decrease.

81. Annealed.—The tensile properties and Brinell hardness values of annealed molybdenum steels are listed in Table 20, and the tensile strengths plotted in Fig. 42. In this figure values from Hanemann and Kühnel[60] and Meyer and Wesseling[159] for carbon steels are given for comparison. The values plotted indicate that in annealed steels the addition of a small quantity of molybdenum to a low-carbon steel slightly increases the tensile strength, but its addition to steels containing 0.80 or 0.90 per cent carbon decreases the tensile strength.

TABLE 20.—MECHANICAL PROPERTIES OF ANNEALED MOLYBDENUM STEELS

Composition, per cent		Annealed		Tensile strength, lb./sq. in.	Yield strength, lb./sq. in.	Elongation in 2 in., per cent	Reduction of area, per cent	Brinell hardness	Investigator
C	Mo	°C.	°F.						
0.19	1.03	950	1750	58,580	31,140	35.5	65.75	99	Swinden(52)
0.25	2.18	950	1750	65,070	31,580	33.3	62.5	116	Swinden(52)
0.19	4.11	950	1750	63,390	31,470	42.7	72.5	116	Swinden(52)
0.13	8.01	950	1750	79,070	41,660	31.1	58.75	143	Swinden(52)
0.44	1.05	950	1750	79,990	41,130	25.0	39.2	131	Swinden(52)
0.44	2.18	950	1750	82,280	43,410	27.7	44.3	143	Swinden(52)
0.49	4.01	950	1750	77,060	42,220	28.3	52.0	143	Swinden(52)
0.36	8.17	950	1750	77,060	34,720	36.6	68.23	143	Swinden(52)
0.44	8.11	950	1750	83,220	38,640	32.22	57.5	156	Swinden(52)
0.87	1.02	950	1750	121,070	58,240	17.22	22.25	228	Swinden(52)
0.88	2.19	950	1750	107,070	54,770	18.8	27.5	207	Swinden(52)
0.86	4.0	950	1750	94,300	45,920	20.5	34.0	179	Swinden(52)
0.77	7.85	950	1750	87,580	45,140	22.2	35.5	170	Swinden(52)
1.21	1.09	950	1750	95,540	58,350	5.55	7.5	207	Swinden(52)
1.21	2.11	950	1750	95,200	61,710	9.4	13.5	196	Swinden(52)
1.06	4.02	950	1750	92,960	42,560	15.5	20.5	196	Swinden(52)
1.12	7.92	950	1750	92,290	48,830	16.1	24.0	187	Swinden(52)
1.36	2.54	950	1750	89,600	47,040	7.22	7.5	196	Swinden(52)
0.10	0.24	800	1475	51,520	40,320	45	75	95	Hadfield(67)
0.10	0.45	800	1475	53,520	42,560	41	72	90	Hadfield(67)
0.06	0.52	800	1475	42,560	29,120	.....	.....	90	Hadfield(67)
0.11	0.94	800	1475	60,480	47,040	.....	.....	127	Hadfield(67)
0.12	1.55	800	1475	64,960	44,800	35	79	121	Hadfield(67)
0.13	1.78	800	1475	76,160	67,200	30	62	121	Hadfield(67)
0.11	3.00	800	1475	67,200	29,120	36	72	99	Hadfield(67)
0.07	7.14	800	1475	80,640	44,800	28	59	142	Hadfield(67)
0.09	12.50	800	1475	127,680	71,680	11	21	269	Hadfield(67)
0.08	18.70	800	1475	120,960	73,920	1	1	364	Hadfield(67)
0.32	7.55	800	1475	105,300	64,960	21	42	192	Hadfield(67)
0.44	11.74	800	1475	118,720	80,640	15	29	223	Hadfield(67)
0.14	2.29	900	1650	107,250	83,210	3.5*	7.5	...	Guillet(24)
0.73	0.50	900	1650	150,490	107,110	3*	4.5	...	Guillet(24)
0.81	1.98	900	1650	178,800	132,710	2*	5.2	...	Guillet(24)
0.30	0.53	900	1650	101,850	81,500	16.3*	.....	...	Cohade(79)
0.54	3.72	Full?	....	82,290	33,569	19	.....	...	Lipin(13)
0.28	0.95	700	1300	83,800	52,633	10.9	43.5	...	Mathews(19)
0.78	2.43	800	1475	102,600	56,500	15.6	29.1	...	Arnold and Read(65)
0.75	4.95	800	1475	111,500	88,700	11.6	19.9	...	Arnold and Read(65)
0.71	10.15	800	1475	110,100	87,000	11.6	23.5	...	Arnold and Read(65)
0.79	15.46	800	1475	123,800	91,800	14.5	24.9	...	Arnold and Read(65)
0.82	20.70	800	1475	120,300	88,800	13.6	19.3	...	Arnold and Read(65)
0.24	0.32	870	1600	73,700	49,050	31.7	61.0	†	Camp and Francis(148)

* Gage length not given.
† Izod impact 17.7 ft-lb. Size of specimen not given.

Arnold alternating-impact tests were made by Swinden[52] on his series of steels. In the annealed condition, molybdenum apparently had little effect on the number of alternations required to produce fracture. He also made crushing tests in which cylinders with a diameter of 0.564 in. and a length of 1.128 in. were subjected to a load of 56,000 lb. or 224,000 lb. per sq. in. and determined the decrease in height. Again molybdenum had no appreciable effect on the properties of the annealed alloys.

Prömper and Pohl[235] found that the addition of 0.35 per cent molybdenum to steel plates used for boiler construction did not affect the mechanical properties of the steels at ordinary temperatures, and that they could be fabricated as easily as molybdenum-free steels. The work of these investigators is described later in the section dealing with mechanical properties of steel at elevated temperatures.

From consideration of all the data available it appears that, except for a slight hardening of the low-carbon steels, molybdenum has only a slight effect on the mechanical properties of steels in the annealed condition.

82. Normalized.—Normalizing, according to the definition given in the "National Metals Handbook," 1930 edition, consists in heating iron-base alloys above the critical-temperature range, followed by cooling in still air. The properties of any steel given such a treatment will depend, to some extent, on the size of the piece treated and the temperature from which the sample is cooled. The data available, however, are practically all for sections slightly larger than a convenient test piece, and the temperatures from which the specimens were cooled are given in most cases.

The tensile properties and Brinell-hardness data for normalized molybdenum steels are listed in Table 21, and the tensile-strength data are shown graphically in Fig. 43. The values for carbon steels are from *The British Engineering Standards Association Report*[88] and Meyer and Wesseling.[159] According to these data, molybdenum increases the strength of steel in the normalized condition. Comparison of these data with those on annealed steels given in Table 20 indicates that the normalizing treatment has a relatively greater effect on yield strength than on tensile strength, and that the ratio of yield strength to tensile strength is, therefore, greater for the normalized steels than for the annealed steels.

Swinden's[52] crushing tests on normalized steels established the fact that molybdenum stiffened such steels, but that the effect

TABLE 21.—MECHANICAL PROPERTIES OF NORMALIZED (AIR-COOLED) MOLYBDENUM STEEL

Composition, per cent		Normalized		Tensile strength lb./sq. in.	Yield strength, lb./sq.in.	Elongation in 2 in., per cent	Reduction of area, per cent	Brinell hardness	Izod impact, ft-lb.	Investigator
C	Mo	°C.	°F.							
0.33	0.96	900	1650	90,500	65,760	22.0*	52.4	159	.....	Swinden[61]
0.19	1.03	900	1650	67,690	49,930	35.5*	73.0	116	.....	Swinden[52]
0.25	2.18	900	1650	91,010	65,500	30.0	64.2	170	.....	Swinden[52]
0.19	4.11	900	1650	85,460	63,590	29.0	63.6	170	.....	Swinden[52]
0.13	8.01	900	1650	81,670	58,490	29.8	59.5	163	.....	Swinden[52]
0.44	1.05	900	1650	117,470	84,690	20.1	49.4	228	.....	Swinden[52]
0.44	2.18	900	1650	110,430	79,900	23.4	55.5	217	.....	Swinden[52]
0.49	4.01	900	1650	119,860	81,020	22.0	52.9	228	.....	Swinden[52]
0.36	8.17	900	1650	102,590	70,470	28.4	57.5	196	.....	Swinden[52]
0.44	8.11	900	1650	117,110	85,480	21.7	39.6	235	.....	Swinden[52]
0.87	1.02	900	1650	151,560	102,520	13.2	27.9	302	.....	Swinden[52]
0.88	2.19	900	1650	160,230	114,780	13.8	32.6	302	.....	Swinden[52]
0.86	4.0	900	1650	167,150	130,370	14.5	38.5	321	.....	Swinden[52]
0.77	7.85	900	1650	146,570	92,590	15.7	38.9	286	.....	Swinden[52]
1.21	2.11	900	1650	191,990	142,000	3.92	2.84	340	.....	Swinden[52]
1.21	1.09	900	1650	158,730	116,880	10.9	17.8	321	.....	Swinden[52]
1.06	4.02	900	1650	178,860	135,950	10.7	22.0	340	.....	Swinden[52]
1.12	7.92	900	1650	202,270	148,670	12.77	16.1	340	.....	Swinden[52]
1.36	2.54	900	1650	118,850	....	0.4	1.5	332	.....	Swinden[52]
0.20	0.94	785	1450	76,700	38,500	35.5	65.4	159	71§	French[107]
0.20	0.94	830	1525	76,700	21,750	35.8	67.3	161	65§	French[107]
0.20	0.94	875	1610	76,450	23,000	35.8	66.2	163	57§	French[107]
0.20	0.94	910	1670	76,325	29,650	33.2	64	163	61§	French[107]
0.20	0.94	980	1800	77,300	32,000	32.2	62.6	166	57§	French[107]
0.15	0.34	?	?	61,500	41,450	25.5†	64.4	...	.....	Prömper and Pohl[235]
0.38	0.37	900	1650	107,500	65,500‡	24.0	54.0	200	22‖	Gillett and Mack[151]
0.41	0.67	900	1650	121,500	62,500‡	16.0	46.5	230	11.5‖	Gillett and Mack[151]
0.41	0.67	840	1550	119,000	71,000‡	21.0	51.5	230	14‖	Gillett and Mack[151]
0.46	1.05	900	1650	140,000	75,000‡	17.5	43.3	280	7‖	Gillett and Mack[151]
0.39	1.90	900	1650	141,500	75,000‡	16.5	35.2	275	7‖	Gillett and Mack[151]
0.36	2.05	900	1650	143,250	75,000‡	20.0	49.1	275	11‖	Gillett and Mack[151]
0.50	1.15	900	1650	149,000	75,000‡	19.5	41.4	295	9‖	Gillett and Mack[151]
0.44	0.30	815	1500	117,000	86,000	21	40	217	.....	Cutter¶
0.44	0.30	870	1600	119,000	81,000	21	37	228	.....	Cutter¶

* Gage length not given.
† Gage length 8 in.
‡ Yield point by extensometer.
§ Size of impact specimen 2.2 × 0.394 × 0.394 in.
‖ Size of impact specimen 0.450-in. diameter.
¶ Quoted by Gillett and Mack.[151]

was not great. From his alternating-impact tests it was impossible to determine any definite influence of molybdenum.

Gillett and Mack[151] compared the mechanical properties obtained by French[107] for normalized molybdenum steels, containing 0.20 per cent carbon and 0.94 per cent molybdenum, with the properties obtained by The British Engineering Standards Association[88] for a normalized steel, containing 0.20 per cent carbon and 0.90 per cent manganese, and pointed out that the molybdenum steel in the normalized condition is no better

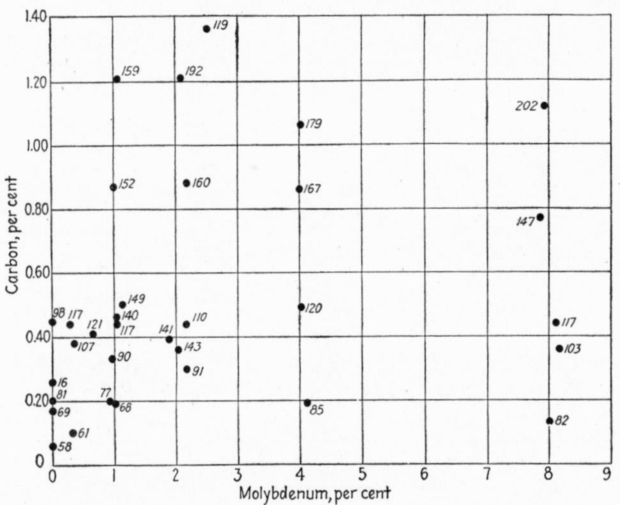

FIG. 43.—Tensile strength in thousand pounds per square inch of normalized molybdenum steels. Collected from various sources.

than normalized manganese steel, and that the yield strength is decidedly lower.

83. Tensile Properties of Heat-treated Steels.—The available data on heat treatment and tensile properties of molybdenum steels are listed in Table 22. The tensile strength of steels quenched in oil and tempered between 500 and 550°C. (930 and 1020°F.) is shown graphically in Fig. 44. From this figure it appears that 1 per cent or less molybdenum markedly increases the strength in steels containing above 0.30 per cent carbon and has little effect on steels containing less carbon. Apparently no gain in strength is produced by increasing molybdenum above 1 per cent and, for the medium-carbon steels, an increased molybdenum concentration appears to decrease the strength.

The effect of molybdenum on the tensile properties of steels containing from 0.19 to 0.30 per cent carbon, after quenching in oil and tempering between 500 and 550°C. (930 and 1020°F.), is shown in Fig. 45. In this figure, the values for the carbon steel were taken from The British Engineering Standards Association.[88] Similarly, the effect of molybdenum on the tensile properties of steels containing from 0.44 to 0.50 per cent carbon and treated in the same manner is shown in Fig. 46. Because

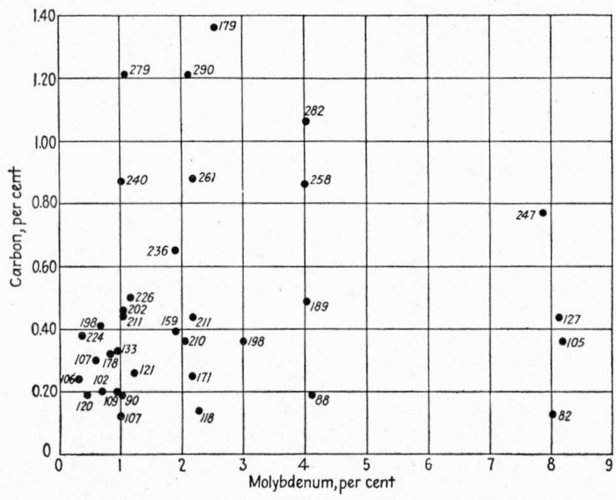

Fig. 44.—Tensile strength in thousand pounds per square inch of molybdenum steels quenched in oil and tempered between 500 and 550°C. (930 and 1020°F.). Collected from various sources.

of the scarcity of points in these figures, the curves as drawn should be considered as tentative. According to Fig. 45, in steels containing about 0.25 per cent carbon, molybdenum in concentrations up to at least 2 per cent gradually increases tensile and yield strength and slightly lowers elongation and reduction of area. According to Fig. 46, in steels containing about 0.45 per cent carbon, the addition of 1 per cent molybdenum more than doubles tensile and yield strength and slightly decreases elongation and reduction of area. As the molybdenum is increased above 1 per cent, all of the tensile properties are slightly decreased. As the curves of tensile strength and yield strength are drawn, maxima occur at about 1 per cent molybdenum; however, it is possible that tests on steels containing less molybdenum could change the location of the maxima. The strength-

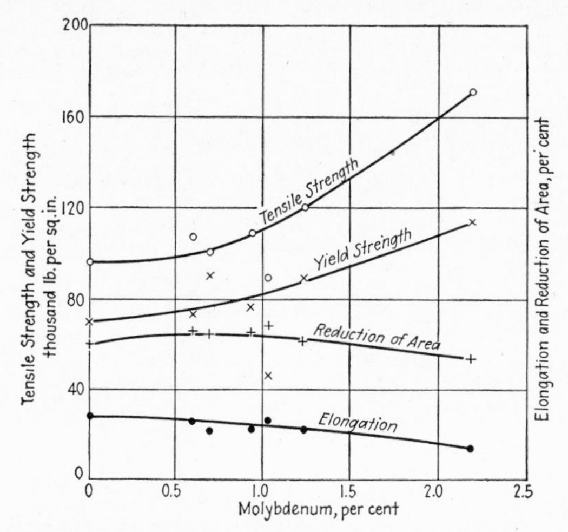

FIG. 45.—Tensile properties of molybdenum steels containing 0.19 to 0.30 per cent carbon. Quenched in oil and tempered between 500 and 550°C. (930 and 1020°F.). Data from various sources.

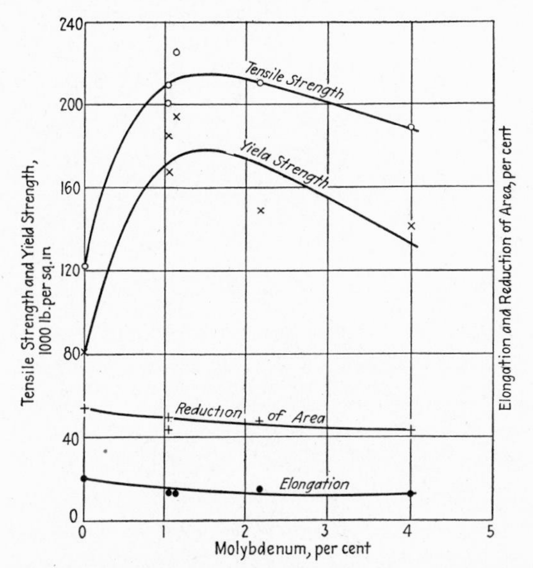

FIG. 46.—Tensile properties of molybdenum steels containing 0.44 to 0.50 per cent carbon. Quenched in oil and tempered between 500 and 550°C. (930 and 1020°F.). Data from various sources.

TABLE 22.—MECHANICAL PROPERTIES OF HEAT-TREATED MOLYBDENUM STEELS

Steel number	Composition, per cent		Quenched		Quenching medium	Tempered		Tensile strength, lb./sq. in.	Yield strength, lb./sq. in.	Elongation in 2 in., per cent	Reduction of area, per cent	Brinell hardness	Izod impact, ft-lb.	Investigator
	C	Mo	°C.	°F.		°C.	°F.							
1	0.13	8.01	900	1650	Oil	550	1020	82,100	53,500	30.9	65.6	163	......	Swinden[52]
2	0.14	2.29	850	1560	Water	...	....	117,700	117,700	6.0*	11.5	228	......	Guillet[25]
3	0.16	1.00	850	1560	Water	...	....	107,000	66,400	3.0*	12.4	196	......	Guillet[25]
4	0.19	0.45	850	1560	Water	...	....	119,800	68,700	2.0*	12.7	207	......	Guillet[25]
5	0.19	1.03	950	1750	Oil	550	1020	90,100	47,100	27.4	68.4	241	......	Swinden[52]
6	0.19	4.11	950	1750	Oil	550	1020	88,200	66,500	30.2	64.0	286	......	Swinden[52]
7	0.20	0.70	870	1600	Oil	540	1000	101,600	90,400	22.0*	64.2	...	......	McKnight[101]
8	0.20	0.94	785	1450	Oil	540	1000	88,700	57,500	24.2	52.3	179	......	French[107]
8	0.20	0.94	830	1525	Oil	540	1000	104,075	69,500	18.8	51.4	207	48†	French[107]
8	0.20	0.94	875	1610	Oil	540	1000	105,375	75,000	21.0	63.0	232	68†	French[107]
8	0.20	0.94	910	1670	Oil	540	1000	109,250	77,000	22.8	65.5	245	69†	French[107]
8	0.20	0.94	980	1800	Oil	540	1000	106,000	76,000	23.2	64.8	235	67†	French[107]
8	0.20	0.94	830	1525	Water	...	....	168,450	50,000	6.8	18.3	316	16†	French[107]
8	0.20	0.94	830	1525	Water	400	750	143,800	81,500	13.0	46.1	268	23†	French[107]
8	0.20	0.94	830	1525	Water	540	1000	130,675	99,500	17.2	50.2	252	37†	French[107]
8	0.20	0.94	830	1525	Water	675	1250	102,025	90,000	22.0	63.8	207	78†	French[107]
8	0.20	0.94	910	1670	Water	...	....	133,100	38,000	9.8	31.2	294	38†	French[107]
8	0.20	0.94	910	1670	Water	400	750	169,200	123,750	11.2	49.5	285	44†	French[107]
8	0.20	0.94	910	1670	Water	540	1000	135,700	106,000	15.2	56.4	273	45†	French[107]
8	0.20	0.94	910	1670	Water	675	1250	112,200	103,000	20.2	62.2	235	72†	French[107]
9	0.24	0.32	850	1560	Water	550	1020	106,000	84,900	24.0	66.1	...	102.5†	Camp and Francis[146]
10	0.25	2.18	950	1750	Oil	550	1020	171,100	115,400	15.5	54.4	387	......	Swinden[52]
11	0.26	1.23	900	1650	Oil	550	1020	120,900	89,600	23.0	62.0	264	27‡	Jones[176]
11	0.26	1.23	820	1510	Oil	550	1020	110,600	67,200	22.0	57.0	236	24‡	Jones[176]
11	0.26	1.23	900	1650	Oil	650	1200	120,500	96,300	20.0	59.0	258	15‡	Jones[176]
11	0.26	1.23	900	1650	Oil	670	1240	110,000	85,100	22.0	64.0	239	26‡	Jones[176]
11	0.26	1.23	820	1510	Oil	670	1240	93,200	65,000	26.0	68.0	195	77‡	Jones[176]
12	0.29	4.50	850	1560	Water	...	....	173,500	119,800	2.0*	12.7	444	......	Guillet[24]

13	0.30	0.60	900	1650	Oil	550	1020	107,000	73,900	26.0	66.0	228	51‡	Jones(176)
13	0.30	0.60	820	1510	Oil	550	1020	106,100	76,100	24.0	63.0	222	52‡	Jones(176)
13	0.30	0.60	900	1650	Oil	600	1110	106,100	73,900	25.0	64.0	223	53‡	Jones(176)
13	0.30	0.60	900	1650	Oil	650	1200	98,400	71,700	27.0	67.0	209	54‡	Jones(176)
13	0.30	0.60	900	1650	Oil	670	1240	93,600	62,700	27.0	66.0	200	82‡	Jones(176)
13	0.30	0.60	820	1510	Oil	670	1240	92,500	62,700	26.0	68.0	196	86‡	Jones(176)
14	0.32	0.83	845	1550	Water	205	400	246,500	231,000	11.0	41.0	475	.....	McKnight‖
14	0.32	0.83	845	1550	Water	315	600	210,000	165,500	11.0	42.5	445	.....	McKnight‖
14	0.32	0.83	845	1550	Water	425	800	193,000	182,500	13.5	51.0	430	.....	McKnight‖
14	0.32	0.83	845	1550	Water	540	1000	178,500	169,500	16.0	53.0	385	.....	McKnight‖
14	0.32	0.83	845	1550	Water	595	1100	167,500	163,500	15.5	52.5	340	.....	McKnight‖
14	0.32	0.83	845	1550	Water	650	1200	124,500	118,000	20.0	56.5	270	.....	McKnight‖
14	0.32	0.83	845	1550	Water	675	1250	112,500	103,500	23.0	66.5	240	.....	McKnight‖
15	0.33	0.96	900	1650	Oil	500	930	126,300	98,100	17.5*	57.2	279	.....	Swinden(61)
15	0.33	0.96	900	1650	Oil	550	1020	133,200	111,300	18.0*	54.8	281	.....	Swinden(61)
15	0.33	0.96	900	1650	Oil	600	1110	131,000	112,400	20.0*	54.8	281	.....	Swinden(61)
15	0.33	0.96	850	1560	Water	500	930	182,900	159,700	15.5*	47.2	402	.....	Swinden(61)
15	0.33	0.96	850	1560	Water	550	1020	183,700	159,600	14.0*	49.6	387	.....	Swinden(61)
15	0.33	0.96	850	1560	Water	600	1110	184,600	164,000	15.0*	47.2	364	.....	Swinden(61)
15	0.33	0.96	850	1560	Water	650	1200	154,600	132,600	19.5*	61.1	321	.....	Swinden(61)
16	0.36	2.05	875	1610	Oil	550	1020	210,500	187,500	14.0	45.0	430	27§	Gillett and Mack(151)
16	0.36	2.05	875	1610	Oil	650	1200	139,000	130,000	19.0	56.0	275	51§	Gillett and Mack(151)
16	0.36	2.05	925	1700	Water	545	1015	....	....	....	....	420	.....	Gillett and Mack(151)
17	0.36	3.00	900	1650	Oil	425	800	217,500	200,000	10.5	36.0	430	12.5§	Gillett and Mack(151)
17	0.36	3.00	900	1650	Oil	500	930	198,250	190,000	13.5	40.4	415	20§	Gillett and Mack(151)
17	0.36	3.00	900	1650	Oil	575	1065	176,500	166,000	14.5	45.6	355	.....	Gillett and Mack(151)
18	0.36	8.17	950	1750	Oil	550	1020	105,400	75,400	25.3	54.8	351	.....	Swinden(52)
19	0.38	0.37	870	1600	Water	300	575	224,000	190,000	11.0	41.3	450	15.5§	Gillett and Mack(151)
19	0.38	0.37	870	1600	Water	360	680	207,750	185,000	12.0	44.4	420	15.5§	Gillett and Mack(151)
19	0.38	0.37	870	1600	Water	420	790	187,500	170,000	13.5	50.6	375	26§	Gillett and Mack(151)
20	0.39	1.90	775	1425	Oil	550	1020	159,750	130,000	13.0	41.0	330	26§	Gillett and Mack(151)
20	0.39	1.90	775	1425	Oil	650	1200	112,250	98,000	22.0	56.8	240	53§	Gillett and Mack(151)
20	0.39	1.90	925	1700	Water	650	1200	139,000	125,000	17.0	52.0	275	.....	Gillett and Mack(151)
20	0.39	1.90	900	1650	Oil	425	800	....	....	....	....	430	.....	Gillett and Mack(151)
20	0.39	1.90	900	1650	Oil	600	1110	....	....	....	....	425	.....	Gillett and Mack(151)

TABLE 22.—(*Continued*)

Steel number	Composition, per cent		Quenched		Quenching medium	Tempered		Tensile strength, lb./sq. in.	Yield strength, lb./sq. in.	Elongation in 2 in., per cent	Reduction of area, per cent	Brinell hardness	Izod impact, ft-lb.	Investigator
	C	Mo	°C.	°F.		°C.	°F.							
21	0.41	0.67	870	1600	Water	360	680	223,250	190,000	12.5	45.9	425	17.5§	Gillett and Mack[151]
21	0.41	0.67	870	1600	Water	420	790	198,500	185,000	13.5	49.4	390	22.5§	Gillett and Mack[151]
21	0.41	0.67	870	1600	Water	500	930	178,250	160,000	14.5	47.9	370	28§	Gillett and Mack[151]
22	0.44	1.05	900	1650	Oil	550	1025	210,600	168,600	14.1	49.2	387	.....	Swinden[52]
23	0.44	2.18	900	1650	Oil	550	1025	211,500	149,000	14.1	47.2	444	.....	Swinden[52]
24	0.44	8.11	900	1650	Oil	550	1025	127,400	77,800	21.1	49.2	444	.....	Swinden[52]
25	0.46	1.05	900	1650	Oil	425	800	219,000	190,000	11.7	40.0	420	29.5§	Gillett and Mack[151]
25	0.46	1.05	900	1650	Oil	500	930	201,750	185,000	13.7	43.8	405	36§	Gillett and Mack[151]
25	0.46	1.05	900	1650	Oil	600	1110	194,500	180,000	16.0	46.9	400	36§	Gillett and Mack[151]
26	0.49	4.01	900	1650	Oil	550	1025	188,900	139,800	11.2	41.6	444	.....	Swinden[52]
27	0.50	1.15	850	1560	Oil	425	800	249,250	215,000	9.5	30.2	475	12.5§	Gillett and Mack[151]
27	0.50	1.15	850	1560	Oil	525	975	225,750	195,000	13.0	34.8	435	19§	Gillett and Mack[151]
27	0.50	1.15	850	1560	Oil	625	1150	217,000	195,000	13.0	40.4	420	29.5§	Gillett and Mack[151]
28	0.65	1.90	825	1515	Oil	550	1025	236,000	210,000	8.5	27.5	455	13§	Gillett and Mack[151]
28	0.65	1.90	825	1515	Oil	650	1200	164,700	147,000	10.0	40.8	365	25§	Gillett and Mack[151]
29	0.77	7.85	850	1560	Oil	550	1025	247,300	216,800	7.7	23.2	512	.....	Swinden[52]
30	0.86	4.0	850	1560	Oil	550	1025	258,000	203,900	4.2	4.8	512	.....	Swinden[52]
31	0.87	1.02	850	1560	Oil	550	1025	240,500	193,700	9.1	25.2	418	.....	Swinden[52]
32	0.88	2.19	850	1560	Oil	550	1025	260,900	178,800	5.6	12.0	512	.....	Swinden[52]
33	1.06	4.02	800	1475	Oil	550	1025	282,200	267,000	7.0	23.2	532	.....	Swinden[52]
34	1.12	7.92	800	1475	Oil	550	1025	....	....	....	....	512	.....	Swinden[52]
35	1.21	1.09	800	1475	Oil	550	1025	279,000	203,900	4.9	12.0	512	.....	Swinden[52]
36	1.21	2.11	800	1475	Oil	550	1025	270,950	....	....	....	512	.....	Swinden[52]
37	1.36	2.54	800	1475	Oil	550	1025	179,200	....	0	0	532	.....	Swinden[52]

* Gage length not given.

† Size of impact specimen 2.2 × 0.394 × 0.394 in.

‡ Size of impact specimen 5 × 1.5 × 0.75 in.

§ Size of impact specimen 0.450-in. diameter.

‖ Quoted by Gillett and Mack.[151]

ening by molybdenum of hypoeutectoid steels, hardened and tempered at 500°C. (930°F.) or above, seems to be considerable.

Figure 47, taken from the book by Gillett and Mack,[151] shows that 1 per cent or less molybdenum in steels containing approximately 0.40 per cent carbon gives increased strength at all tempering temperatures.

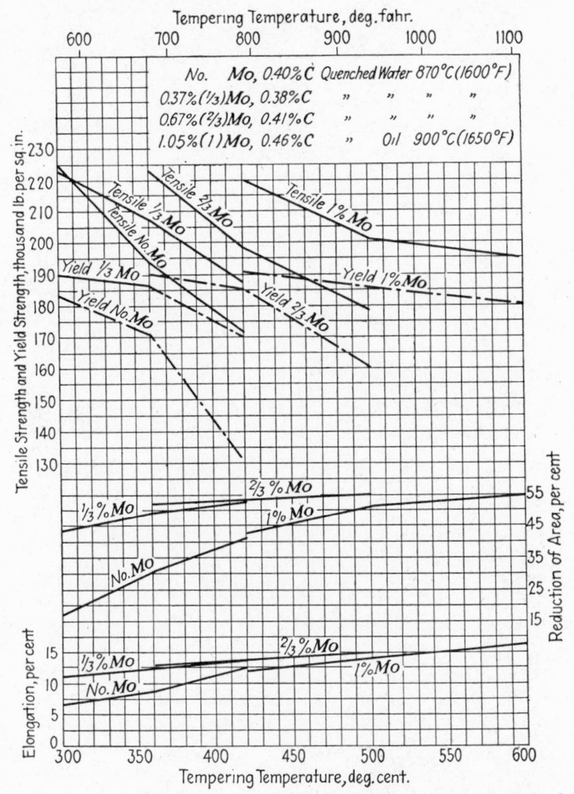

FIG. 47.—Effect of molybdenum on tensile properties of hardened and tempered steels. (*Gillett and Mack.*[151])

In order to show the effect of a small quantity of molybdenum on the properties of a steel of the structural type, Camp and Francis[146] gave the data listed in Table 23. Their steel was cast into 18 × 21-in. ingots, rolled to ⅞-in. diameter rods, and heat-treated at that size. From these results the authors concluded that the addition of 0.32 per cent molybdenum is equivalent to about a 0.10 per cent increase in carbon, and that the ratio of yield strength to tensile strength is slightly raised by the molybdenum, while reduction in area is materially increased.

Table 23.—Tensile Properties of 0.24 Per Cent Carbon, 0.32 Per Cent Molybdenum Steel*
(Quenched in water from 850°C. (1560°F.). Heat-treated as ⅞-in. rounds)

Tempered		Tensile strength, lb./sq. in.	Yield† strength, lb./sq. in.	Elongation in 2 in., per cent	Reduction of area, per cent	Izod impact,‡ ft-lb.
°C.	°F.					
...	....	126,800	109,300	18.5	54.5	23.5
450	840	113,400	92,800	20	65.9	92.5
500	930	108,300	88,000	20	65.0	93.5
550	1020	106,000	84,900	24	66.1	102.5
575	1065	102,600	82,900	22.5	67.0	97.0
600	1110	99,600	78,900	24	69.2	108.5

* Camp and Francis.[146]
† Reported as yield point, by drop of beam.
‡ Size of impact specimen not given.

84. Hardness of Heat-treated Steels.—Inasmuch as the Brinell hardness is approximately proportional to the tensile strength, little discussion concerning the effect of molybdenum on the hardness is warranted. The Brinell-hardness values for heat-treated molybdenum steels are listed in Table 22. Figure 41 (page 95), used to illustrate the effect of molybdenum on tempering, shows the variation in Brinell hardness with tempering temperature for several molybdenum steels.

The hardness values for steels, containing approximately 0.30 per cent carbon and 0, 0.60, and 1.23 per cent molybdenum, after cooling at various rates, as determined by Jones,[176] are given in Table 24. These values indicate that as little as 0.60 per cent molybdenum greatly increases the hardness of the heat-treated steel.

The effect of molybdenum on the hardness of high-carbon steels is discussed in the section dealing with molybdenum in high-speed steels.

Brinell-hardness values on some molybdenum steels made in a laboratory furnace were reported by Reed[492] but are not included here, because details of treatment were not given.

Secondary hardness was found in a steel containing 0.14 per cent carbon and 3.08 per cent molybdenum by Matsushita and Nagasawa.[479] When the quenched steel was heated to 600 to

650°C. (1110 to 1200°F.), an increase in hardness was noted. With increasing tempering temperatures the hardness fell rapidly. A similar phenomenon was observed in other low-carbon alloy steels and was attributed to the transformation of metastable solid solution into a stable one.

TABLE 24.—BRINELL HARDNESS VALUES OF STEELS COOLED AT DIFFERENT RATES BETWEEN 800 AND 500°C. (1470 AND 930°F.)*

Composition, per cent		Cooling rates and Brinell hardness values		
C	Mo	100°C./sec. (180°F./sec.)	16°C./sec. (29°F./sec.)	4°C./sec. (7°F./sec.)
0.29	0	277	170	132
0.30	0.60	463	422	204
0.26	1.23	439	428	237

* Jones.[176]

85. Impact Resistance of Heat-treated Steels.—The available values of single-blow impact resistance are listed in Table 22 (page 116). Gillett and Mack[151] found that for a given hardness there is little difference in impact values between steels containing molybdenum and steels free from this element. Camp and Francis,[146] however, in a discussion of their values for a steel containing 0.24 per cent carbon and 0.32 per cent molybdenum, claimed that the impact values produced in this steel were superior to those of carbon or chromium steels.

Swinden[52] made Arnold alternating-stress tests on a series of molybdenum steels and from his results it appears that molybdenum has little or no effect on the number of blows required to fracture. Stanton repeated-impact tests by Gillett and Mack[151] also failed to show any effect of molybdenum on the blows required to fracture.

86. Compressive Properties of Heat-treated Steels.—As in the case of the normalized and annealed steels, Swinden[52] made compressive tests on molybdenum steels quenched in oil and tempered at 550°C. (1020°F.). All tests were made by subjecting cylinders 0.564 in. in diameter (0.25 sq. in. area) and 1.128 in. long to a load of 56,000 lb. and determining the decrease in height. Their decrease in height in percentage is listed as compression in Table 25 and 100 minus this value as rigidity Owing to the absence of similar values for carbon steels, it is difficult to determine the effect of molybdenum from these data.

Table 25.—Compressive Tests on Molybdenum Steels Quenched in Oil and Tempered at 550°C. (1020°F.)*
(Load = 224,000 lb./sq. in.)

Composition, per cent		Length, in.		Rigidity, per cent	Compression, per cent
C	Mo	Before crushing	After crushing		
0.19	1.03	1.123	0.600	53.4	46.6
0.44	1.05	1.123	1.098	97.8	2.2
0.87	1.02	1.125	1.120	99.6	0.4
1.21	1.09	1.125	1.125	100.0	Nil
0.25	2.18	1.125	1.012	89.9	10.1
0.44	2.18	1.125	1.125	100.0	Nil
0.88	2.19	1.127	1.095	97.2	2.8
1.21	2.11	1.125	1.125	100.0	Nil
0.19	4.11	1.123	0.654	58.3	41.7
0.49	4.01	1.125	1.120	99.6	0.4
0.86	4.0	1.125	1.120	99.6	0.4
1.06	4.02	1.124	1.124	100.0	Nil
0.13	8.01	1.125	0.605	53.7	46.3
0.36	8.17	1.123	0.778	69.3	30.7
0.44	8.11	1.120	0.855	76.3	23.7
0.77	7.85	1.126	1.125	100.0	Nil
1.12	7.92	1.124	1.124	100.0	Nil
1.36	2.54	1.127	1.115	98.9	1.1

* Swinden.[52]

87. Endurance Properties of Heat-treated Steels.—The endurance or fatigue properties of molybdenum steels have been investigated by Gillett and Mack.[151] Their endurance curves, made on an Upton-Lewis machine, are given in Fig. 48. From a comparison of endurance limits of molybdenum steels with those of other alloy steels, these authors concluded that in practically all steels investigated the endurance limit is directly proportional to the tensile strength and independent of composition. They discovered, however, that in drastically quenched steels, tempered at a low temperature, the endurance limit was apt to be low or the stress-cycle values erratic, owing to internal strains in the heat-treated pieces. They pointed out that molybdenum may be of advantage in securing high endurance values as it may enable the steel to stand high or prolonged tempering without much softening.

In further discussion of the endurance properties of molybdenum steels, Gillett and Mack stated that, for the grades of steel used most frequently by the engineer, it appears that claims made for their superior endurance properties are unwarranted, if their endurance properties are compared with other steels on the basis of strength or hardness. However, for the same heat treatment, molybdenum steels are frequently superior in endurance, because of the higher tempering temperatures required to produce equivalent softening.

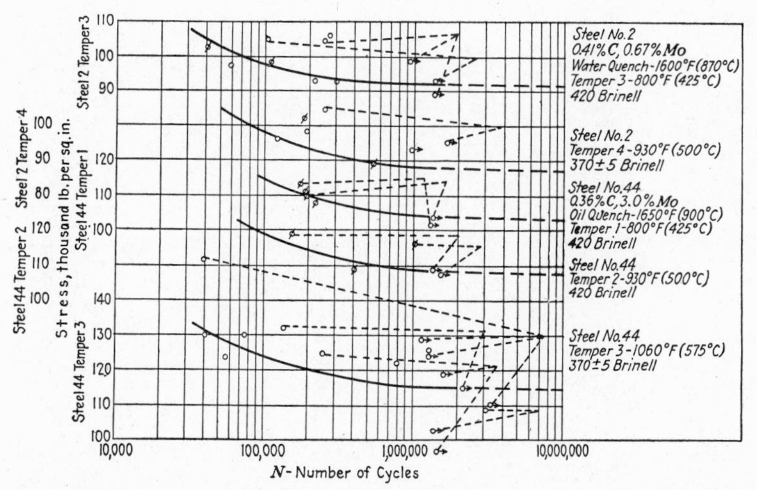

FIG. 48.—Endurance properties of molybdenum steels. (*Gillett and Mack.*[151])

In a discussion, Mathews[478] stated that a recently developed free-cutting steel made by the addition of molybdenum sulphide was found to have a fatigue value, as determined in a rotary machine, of 76,000 lb. per sq. in., which is approximately 50 per cent of its tensile strength. Izod values for this steel were reported to have been equal to or superior to those obtained on steel of equal hardness to which molybdenum sulphide had not been added. The amount of molybdenum sulphide added to the steel under discussion was equivalent to 0.10 to 0.30 per cent sulphur.

B. MECHANICAL PROPERTIES AT LOW AND HIGH TEMPERATURES

The properties of molybdenum steels at temperatures below atmospheric are only of slight interest, but, because of the ability of molybdenum to increase the strength at elevated temperatures, the properties at those temperatures are of great interest. Considerable space is, therefore, devoted to the discussion of the strength of molybdenum steels at high temperatures.

88. Properties at Low Temperatures.—The only results of tests on molybdenum steels at temperatures below atmospheric

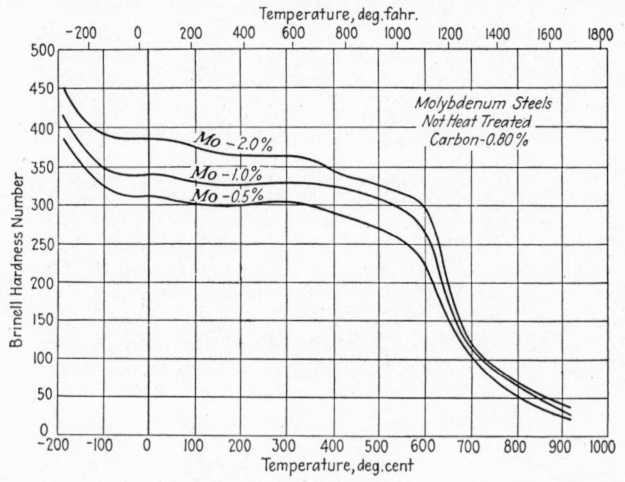

FIG. 49.—Brinell hardness of molybdenum steels at various temperatures. Not heat-treated. (*Robin.*[42])

appear to be those reported by Robin,[41] who determined Brinell-hardness values for temperatures as low as −190°C. (−310°F.) on a forged steel containing 0.8 per cent carbon and 2 per cent molybdenum. In this steel, and in most of the steels tested including carbon steels, he found that hardness increased with decreasing temperature, and that the rate of hardening also increased with decreasing temperature in such a manner as to form a section of a parabola or hyperbola. From his curve, the hardness of the molybdenum steel appeared to be about 390 at 0°C. (32°F.) and about 460 at −190°C. (−310°F.).

89. Properties at High Temperatures.—Brinell-hardness values of several molybdenum steels at temperatures up to

900°C. (1650°F.) were determined by Robin.[42] His hardness-temperature curves for three steels containing 0.8 per cent carbon and from 0.5 to 2.0 per cent molybdenum are shown in Fig. 49. He did not give the exact analysis of the steels, but they were evidently those described by Guillet as being of the following compositions:

Mark	Composition, per cent	
	C	Mo
Mo 0.5..	0.73	0.50
Mo 1.0..	0.81	1.21
Mo 2.0..	0.81	1.98

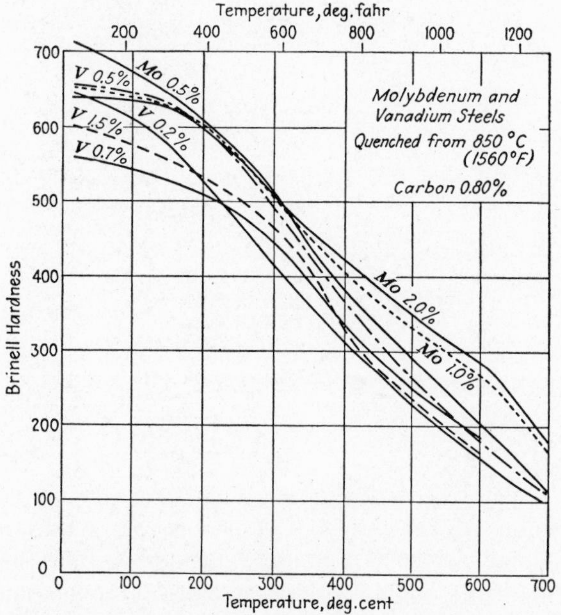

FIG. 50.—Brinell hardness of quenched molybdenum steels at elevated temperatures. (*Robin.*[42])

Hardness-temperature curves, also by Robin, on the same steels quenched from 850°C. (1560°F.) are shown in Fig. 50. Robin concluded that, for temperatures below 600°C. (1110°F.), molybdenum is the most effective element for decreasing the drop in hardness resulting from increasing temperature, the addition agents next in potency being tungsten and vanadium.

Recently, several German authors published data indicating that steels containing several tenths of 1 per cent of molybdenum are much stronger than carbon steels at temperatures of 400 to 500°C. (750 to 930°F.). Prömper and Pohl[235] compared the properties of a molybdenum steel and a vanadium steel with carbon boiler steels and found that the two former were much

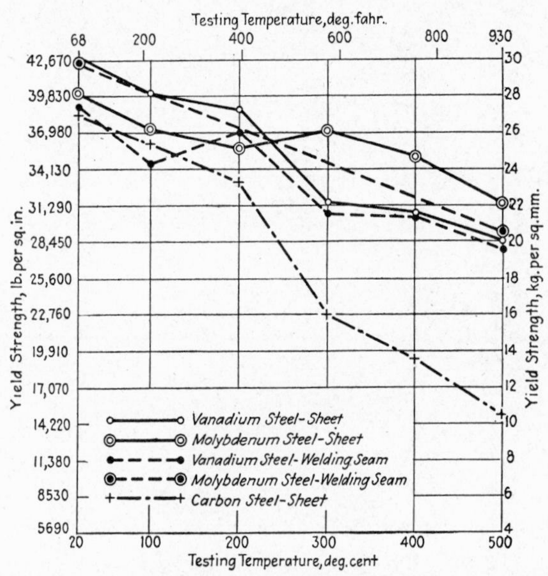

FIG. 51.—Yield strength of structural (boiler) steels at elevated temperature. (*Prömper and Pohl.*[235])

stronger at elevated temperatures than the carbon steels. The molybdenum steel contained 0.34 per cent molybdenum, and the vanadium steel 0.19 per cent vanadium. The properties of these steels at room temperature differ little from carbon steel, and they can be fabricated as economically as the unalloyed steels.

The tensile values at various temperatures reported by Prömper and Pohl[235] for a normalized steel containing 0.15 per cent carbon and 0.34 per cent molybdenum are listed in Table 26. Figure 51, from the same article, compares the yield strength of this steel with vanadium and carbon steels having similar properties at room temperature and clearly indicates the superiority of both alloy steels at elevated temperature. This illustration also shows that satisfactory welds can be made in both alloy steels.

TABLE 26.—PROPERTIES OF MOLYBDENUM STEEL AT VARIOUS TEMPERATURES*

(Steel containing 0.15 per cent carbon, 0.34 per cent molybdenum, normalized. Load applied at 70 lb./sq. in./sec.)

Testing temperature		Tensile strength, lb./sq. in.	Yield strength, lb./sq. in.	Elongation in 8 in., per cent	Reduction of area, per cent	Impact resistance, m-kg./sq. cm.
°C.	°F.					
20	68	61,500	41,500	25.5	64.4	21.9
100	210	58,400	37,000	19.5	62.5	19.3
200	390	63,000	35,700	17.8	55.1	19.7
300	575	63,200	37,000	19.8	58.8	15.3
400	750	56,500	35,000	21.2	65.0	11.8
500	930	46,500	31,400	25.5	70.7	18.1

* Prömper and Pohl.[235]

Creep or flow tests, also by Prömper and Pohl, indicated the superiority of molybdenum steels at temperatures up to 500°C. (930°F.). Table 27 lists the analyses of the steels, while the tensile properties at temperatures of 20 and 500°C. (70 and 930°F.) are shown in Table 28. Creep or flow test results on these types of steel are given in Table 29, the numbered steels being those described in Table 27. From Table 29 it appears that the steel containing 0.15 per cent carbon with 0.39 per cent molybdenum will permanently withstand a decidedly greater load at 500 or 510°C. (930 or 950°F.) than a carbon steel containing twice as much carbon.

A rapid method for the alleged determination of the flow or creep limit of structural steels, which has been described by Pohl, Scholz, and Juretzek,[393] consists in heating a tensile specimen to the desired temperature and applying increased tensile stresses, each stress being applied until no further elongation occurs. The maximum stress at which the sample ceases to stretch after the load has been applied for several hours is considered to be the

TABLE 27.—COMPOSITION OF STEELS TESTED*

Steel	Number	Thickness, in.	Composition, per cent							
			C	Si	Mn	P	S	Cr	V	Mo
Vanadium....	1	1.26	0.20	0	0.53	0.017	0.027	0.180	0.18	0
Molybdenum.	2	0.91	0.15	0	0.49	0.019	0.021	0.190	0	0.39
Carbon......	3	1.26	0.105	0	0.37	0.011	0.034	0.050	0	0
Carbon......	4	1.26	0.09	0.094	0.36	0.037	0.034	0.050	0	0
Carbon......	5	0.99	0.14	0	0.50	0.021	0.038	.....	0	0
Carbon......	6	0.87	0.19	0	0.50	0.039	0.042	0.200	0	0
Carbon......	7	0.87	0.31	0	0.42	0.022	0.036	0.170	0	0

* Prömper and Pohl.(235)

TABLE 28.—TENSILE PROPERTIES OF MOLYBDENUM AND OTHER STEELS AT 20 AND 500°C. (68 AND 930°F.)*

(Analyses in Table 27. Load applied at 70 lb./sq. in./sec.)

Steel	Number	Testing temperature		Tensile strength, lb./sq. in.	Yield strength, lb./sq. in.	Elongation in 8 in., per cent	Reduction of area, per cent
		°C.	°F.				
Vanadium....	1	20	68	64,000	46,900	24.0	60.2
Molybdenum..	2	20	68	58,000	42,700	27.0	52.8
Carbon.......	3	20	68	49,800	27,900	26.0	60.0
Carbon.......	4	20	68	48,600	27,700	31.0	65.0
Carbon.......	5	20	68	58,600	38,300	27.0	59.1
Carbon.......	6	20	68	61,400	40,500	24.5	56.0
Carbon.......	7	20	68	66,400	38,700	22.5	51.0
Vanadium....	1	500	930	42,700	31,900	29.0	58.1
Molybdenum..	2	500	930	46,700	31,900	27.5	70.0
Carbon.......	3	500	930	20,500	15,200	46.0	82.0
Carbon.......	4	500	930	21,500	16,900	54.5	79.0
Carbon.......	5	500	930	27,300	19,600	53.0	85.2
Carbon.......	6	500	930	31,300	20,800	59.0	78.3
Carbon.......	7	500	930	33,100	25,000	34.5	75.0

* Prömper and Pohl.(235)

TABLE 29.—CREEP TESTS OF MOLYBDENUM AND OTHER STEELS*
(The compositions of the numbered steels are given in Table 27. Gage length 200 mm. [8 in.])

Steel	Testing temperature		Number	Load, lb./sq. in.	Loading time, hr.	Increase in length, in.	Permanent elongation, per cent
	°C.	°F.					
Vanadium....	500	930	..	14,200	1,000	0	0
Vanadium....	510	950	..	14,200	15	0	0
Vanadium....	510	950	..	14,200	240	0	0
Vanadium....	510	950	..	17,100	372	0.0630	0.8†
Vanadium....	510	950	..	18,800	240	0.0394	0.5
Molybdenum..	510	950	2	14,200	14	0	0
Molybdenum..	510	950	2	14,200	240	0	0
Molybdenum..	510	950	..	17,100	372	0.0157	0.2
Molybdenum..	510	950	..	18,800	240	0.0394	0.5
Carbon.......	510	950	3	14,200	7	0.6594	8.38
Carbon.......	510	950	3	14,200	7	0.5079	6.45
Carbon.......	510	950	3	14,200	9	0.4803	6.1
Carbon.......	510	950	3	10,700	101	1.8110	23.0
Carbon.......	510	950	4	9,500	382	1.5354	19.5
Carbon.......	510	950	4	8,900	35	0.1575	2.0
Carbon.......	510	950	4	8,000	480	0.1575	2.0
Carbon.......	510	950	4	7,100	240	0	0
Carbon.......	500	930	5	14,200	263	1.5748	20.0
Carbon.......	500	930	5	10,000	711	0.1575	2.0
Carbon.......	500	930	5	8,250	309	0.0591	0.75
Carbon.......	500	930	6	14,200	584	1.3780	17.5
Carbon.......	500	930	6	11,400	379	0.3150	4.0
Carbon.......	500	930	7	14,200	651	1.3780	17.5
Carbon.......	500	930	4	14,200	111	1.5748	20.0
Carbon.......	500	930	7	10,000	333	0.0591	0.75

* Prömper and Pohl.[235]
† Temperature at 542.5°C. for 10 min. during loading.

flow or creep limit. In developing this test, three steels were used:

Steel	Composition, per cent							
	C	Si	Mn	P	S	Mo	Ni	Cr
Carbon........	0.10	0	0.49	0.030	0.042			
Molybdenum...	0.155	0	0.50	0.014	0.020	0.34		
Nickel.........	0.28	0.30	0.64	0.034	0.043	....	2	0.14

The tensile properties of these steels at temperatures up to 500°C. (930°F.) are listed in Table 30. The alleged flow or creep limits are plotted in Fig. 52. The authors pointed out that a comparison of the properties of the three steels does not give a direct indication of the effect of the alloying elements, because the carbon steel has a decidedly lower carbon content than the molybdenum steel, and the nickel steel contained even more carbon than the molybdenum steel. It is possible that, if the molybdenum steel had contained 0.28 per cent carbon and 0.64

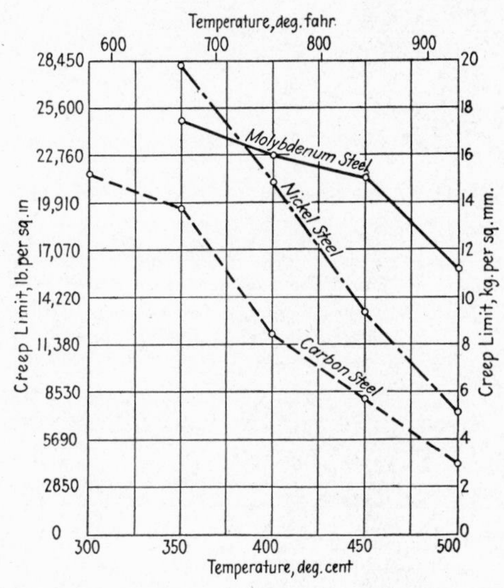

Fig. 52.—Flow or creep limits of structural steels. (*Pohl, Scholz and Juretzek.*[393])

per cent manganese, as did the nickel steel, its flow limit might have been higher than that of the nickel steel even below 400°C. (750°F.). While the flow limit of all three steels decreased with increasing temperature, the decrease for the molybdenum steel was notably less than for the two others.

Christmann,[324] in an article discussing steels suitable for boiler construction, also stated that molybdenum steels lose strength less rapidly at elevated temperatures and listed the properties of the steels used commercially. His statements with respect to the properties of molybdenum steels at elevated temperature are in general agreement with the conclusions reached by the authors of the two papers just discussed.

TABLE 30.—TENSILE PROPERTIES OF MOLYBDENUM AND OTHER STEELS AT TEMPERATURES AS HIGH AS 500°C. (930°F.)*
(Plates 1 in. [25 mm.] thick. Load applied at 70 lb./sq. in./sec.)

Steel	Testing temperature		Tensile strength, lb./sq. in.	Yield strength, lb./sq. in.	Elongation in 8 in., per cent	Reduction of area, per cent
	°C.	°F.				
Carbon	20	68	48,800	32,100	28.2	68.0
Carbon	300	575	57,600	22,300	23.7	56.9
Carbon	350	660	52,100	19,200	26.3	62.6
Carbon	400	750	43,800	16,900	31.7	67.5
Carbon	450	840	36,600	15,600	32.8	71.4
Carbon	500	930	28,200	15,400	38.2	75.0
Molybdenum	20	68	65,000	42,800	24.7	66.0
Molybdenum	300	575	61,900	31,000	16.9	55.2
Molybdenum	350	660	60,500	29,200	25.1	59.6
Molybdenum	400	750	56,900	28,700	23.1	64.2
Molybdenum	450	840	53,500	27,600	21.3	65.2
Molybdenum	500	930	47,800	27,500	23.0	67.0
Nickel	20	68	85,400	56,000	27.0	51.0
Nickel	300	575	87,900	42,400	22.8	33.8
Nickel	350	660	84,500	37,600	27.0	53.0
Nickel	400	750	76,800	34,000	29.7	57.3
Nickel	450	840	61,400	33,900	31.5	64.0
Nickel	500	930	50,200	32,100	46.3	65.3

* Pohl, Scholz, and Juretzek.[393]

A comparative method used at the Krupp laboratories, according to Jungbluth,[357] for determining the permanence of dimension of steel at elevated temperatures consists in loading rods supported at both ends and determining the degree to which the rods are permanently bent when maintained at the desired temperature for a given time. The rods tested are 7.5 m. (24.6 ft.) long and from 5 to 10 mm. (0.2 to 0.4 in.) thick. The compositions of eleven steels tested at 500°C. (930°F.) in this manner are given in Table 31, where the steels are numbered in such a manner that the permanent bend produced decreases with increasing specimen number. The amount of permanent bend (time not given) occurring in these steels at 500°C. (930°F.) is shown diagrammatically in Fig. 53. The yield strength at atmospheric temperature is also shown in this figure. Jungbluth

TABLE 31.—ANALYSES OF STEELS USED IN COMPARATIVE CREEP TESTS*
(Listed in order of permanence of dimension or resistance to creep at 500°C. [930°F.])

Number	Composition, per cent						
	C	Si	Mn	Ni	Cr	Mo	V
1	0.13	0.24	0.40				
2	0.15	0.23	0.26	4.96			
3	0.30	0.30	0.49	4.32	1.52		
4	0.43	0.24	0.58				
5	0.40	0.14	0.48	....	0.99		
6	0.12	0.15	0.52	3.00			
7	0.39	0.33	0.39	0.49	13.90		
8	0.47	0.37	0.74	....	1.59	0.43	0.33
9	0.32	0.19	0.54	....	1.12	0.35	
10	0.19	0.12	0.50	....	....	0.48	
11	0.17	0.18	0.38	....	0.83	0.55	

* Jungbluth.[357]

maintained that with reference to creep at 500°C. (930°F.) the steels may be divided into two groups—those containing molybdenum and those without molybdenum. The steels containing molybdenum are all characterized by their high resistance to creep.

Jungbluth considered either one of the two steels (11), 1.0 per cent chromium, 0.5 per cent molybdenum, or (10), 0.5 per cent molybdenum, suitable for use at a temperature as high as 500°C. (930°F.). Figure 54 gives the limits within which the tensile and yield strength of these two types of steels should fall at temperatures up to 600°C. (1110°F.), as well as the expected properties for steels similar to 1 to 4 of Table 31. For higher temperatures, he recommended a chromium-molybdenum steel containing at least 6 per cent chromium or a nickel-chromium alloy such as "Nichrotherm." He also suggested that a molybdenum steel with a higher carbon content than listed might have desirable properties at temperatures above 600°C. (1110°F.).

In a discussion of steels suitable for use at high temperatures, Bailey, Dickenson, Inglis, and Pearson[422] stated that the addition of molybdenum to a low-carbon steel very greatly improves the strength at elevated temperatures, particularly in the range 400 to 500°C. (750 to 930°F.). They also indicated that considerable work has recently been done on steels containing from 0.10 to 0.20 per cent carbon and from 0.30 to 0.40 per cent molybdenum but did not give any data. According to these investigators this steel has a remarkably high creep resistance at a temperature of 550°C. (1020°F.).

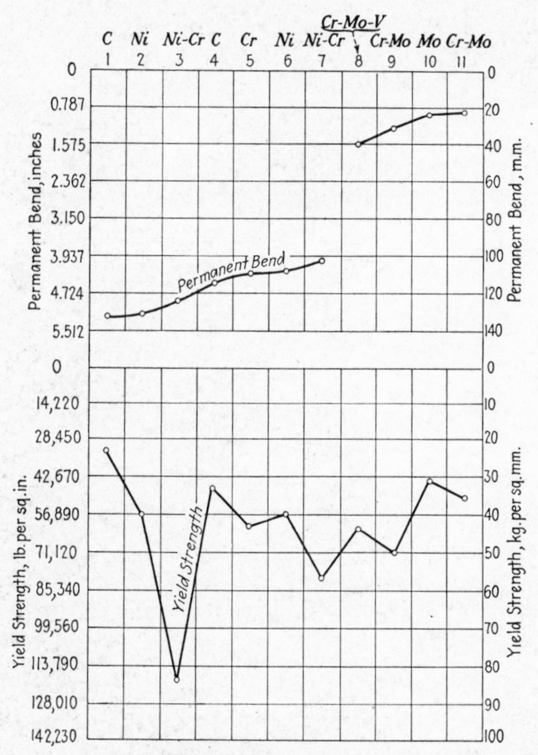

FIG. 53.—Creep in steels at 500°C. (930°F.) and yield strength at atmospheric temperature. (*Jungbluth.*[357])

A private communication from Arthur J. Herschmann, American agent for the Vitkovice Mines Steel and Iron Works Corporation in Czechoslovakia, stated that a molybdenum steel is used in the radiation superheater as well as in the superheater of the Löffler boilers. The molybdenum content of the steel averages 0.6 per cent. The following data were given for a steel containing 0.29 per cent carbon, 0.59 per cent manganese, 0.22 per cent silicon, and 0.6 per cent molybdenum.

Tensile strength at 20°C. (70°F.), lb./sq. in.	106,300
Tensile strength at 550°C. (1020°F.), lb./sq. in.	63,100
Yield strength at 20°C. (70°F.), lb./sq. in.	72,100
Yield strength at 550°C. (1020°F.), lb./sq. in.	58,300
Elongation in 100 mm. (3.94 in.) at 20°C. (70°F.), per cent	14
Elongation in 100 mm. (3.94 in.) at 550°C. (1020°F.), per cent	18
Permanent strength at 550°C. (1020°F.), lb./sq. in.	9,200

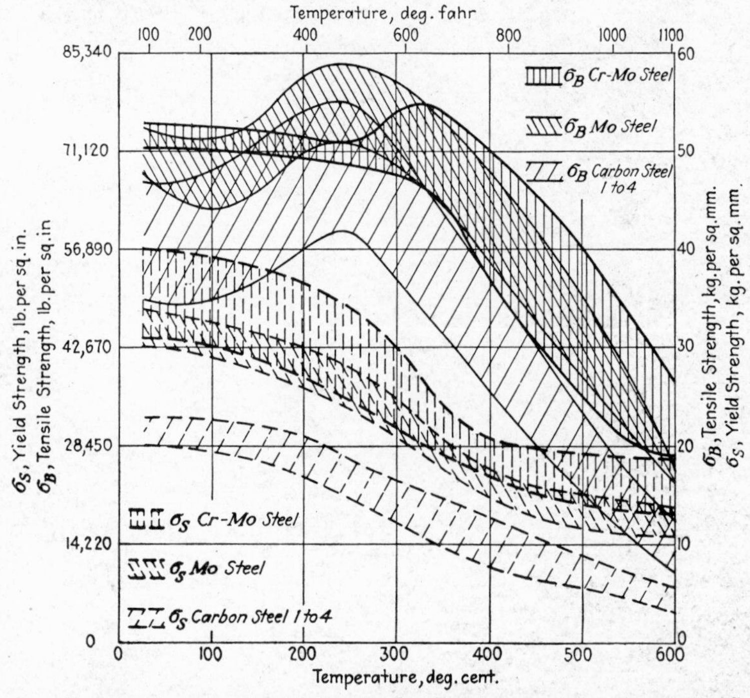

Fig. 54.—Tensile properties of structural steels at temperatures up to 600°C. (1110°F.) (*Jungbluth.*[357])

The permanent strength represents the stress that will produce an elongation of 0.0005 (per cent?) per hour between the twenty-fifth and thirty-fifth hour of test. It was stated that

. . . the data given above show that the permanent strength of this steel is much higher than that of a carbon steel having a tensile strength of 85,100 lb. per sq. in. Tubes made of such material have given good results in extended use. They can be welded without difficulty, and welds between such tubes and tubes made of carbon steel are also readily obtained.

Pomp and Höger,[511A] in a recent comparison of "accelerated" creep and actual creep tests (which showed that for some steels at least the accelerated method was wholly unreliable and gave unsafe values), presented some short-time tensile and some actual creep data on normalized molybdenum steels at elevated temperature as follows:

Mark	Composition, per cent								
	C	Si	Mn	P	S	Cr	Ni	Mo	Cu
G	0.14	0.32	0.43	0.024	0.027	0.03	0.20	0.30	
H	0.13	0.15	0.86	0.017	0.019	....	tr.	0.25	0.24
J	0.12	0.28	0.29	0.012	0.014	0.71	0.30	0.30	

Mark	Tensile strength, lb./sq. in.	Yield strength (0.05 % set), lb./sq. in.	Elongation, per cent	Reduction of area, per cent
Room-temperature tensile properties				
G	67,000	41,000	25.5	70
H	66,000	41,000	25.5	69
J	62,000	36,000	29.5	76
Short-time tensile properties at 400°C. (750°F.)				
G	66,500	21,000	27.5	70
H	66,500	20,500	25	68.5
J	59,000	30,500	23	72
Short-time tensile properties at 500°C. (930°F.)				
G	53,500	22,200	20	74
H	51,000	19,500	23	74
J	48,500	23,500	24	73.5

During the last 100 hr. of actual creep tests, a rate of flow of about 1 per cent in 10,000 hr. was obtained at the following loads and temperatures:

Mark	400°C. (750°F.), lb./sq. in.	500°C. (930°F.), lb./sq. in.
G	37,800	Less than 24,000
H	36,500	20,000
J	44,800	25,500

These steels at 500°C. (930°F.) are considered by Pomp and Höger to show about the same behavior as carbon steel at 400°C. (750°F.).

C. SPECIAL PROPERTIES OF MOLYBDENUM STEELS

The effect of molybdenum on those properties of steel not readily classifiable is given below.

The effect of molybdenum on forgeability probably belongs in this division, but the available data on this property have been presented in the discussion of the manufacture of molybdenum steels.

90. Machinability.—According to Schmid,[(103)] Mathews,[(111)] and others, molybdenum steels are easier to machine than other steels of equivalent hardness.[1] Gillett and Mack[(151)] call attention to the reported easy machinability of molybdenum steels but do not give any values for steels containing only molybdenum as an alloying element.

Some production data which show that a chromium-molybdenum steel can be machined more cheaply than a chromium-nickel steel of the same hardness were reported by Pierce.[(141)] The former steel contained 0.30 per cent carbon, 0.51 per cent chromium, and 0.24 per cent molybdenum, while the latter conformed to S.A.E. 3135. Both steels were treated to give a Brinell hardness from 217 to 241. The total time required for machining the parts was decreased 22 per cent by use of the chromium-molybdenum steel, and the tool costs were likewise decreased.

Gillett and Mack[(151)] reported tests made by an automobile producer in which two lots of steering knuckles, totaling twenty thousand, were made respectively from a 0.30 per cent carbon, 1.25 per cent nickel, 0.60 per cent chromium, and from a 0.30 per cent carbon, 0.60 per cent chromium, 0.20 per cent molyb-

[1] Mathews, in a private communication, stated that this applied to chromium-molybdenum steels rather than to molybdenum steels.

denum steel. Both steels were heat-treated to give a Brinell hardness between 270 and 320. For all machining operations, which included drilling, reaming, tapping, and turning, the average life per tool grind for the chromium-molybdenum steel was over twice that for the nickel-chromium steel. A similar comparison for axle shafts showed an advantage of 36 per cent in favor of the chromium-molybdenum steel. Another example is given which shows that the time required for machining a chromium-molybdenum steel is about half that required for a 3.5 per cent nickel steel of the same strength and hardness.

In a discussion of steels for automobile drive shafts, Rolf[(240)] maintained that chromium-molybdenum steels could be machined on a production basis when they were harder than allowable for other steels.

According to French,[(190)] however, tests made by French and Digges[(170)] have shown that, when machinability is measured by tool life in rough turning, superior machining properties in one hardness range do not necessarily mean superior machinability in a different hardness range, and the superior machinability of chromium-molybdenum steels occurs only at high tensile strengths. They found that at low tensile strengths the carbon steels had the best machinability and the 3.5 per cent nickel steels the next best, but that there was little difference between the 1 per cent chromium, chromium-molybdenum, or chromium-vanadium steels of similar carbon content. In a discussion of the paper by French and Digges, Wickenden reported that in cutting tests a 3.5 per cent nickel steel (S.A.E. 2340) consumed less power than a chromium-molybdenum steel (S.A.E. 4140), but that the carbon content of the latter steel was at the upper limit.

Jones[(176)] studied the machinability of several molybdenum steels, including those containing nickel, chromium, and both nickel and chromium. One group was heat-treated to a Brinell hardness of 340 and the other to 280. The machinability was estimated from the difficulty to machine and by the appearance of the machined steels. All of the steels containing less than 3 per cent nickel machined well.

The addition of molybdenum had little effect on the machining qualities of the steels. Nickel-molybdenum steels with high nickel content showed little improvement over nickel steel in their machining qualities. The nickel-chromium-molybdenum steels containing less than 3 per cent of nickel were distinctly superior to nickel-chromium steels with or without molybdenum in which the percentage of nickel was over 3.5 per cent.

Bullens,[189] however, definitely stated that nickel-chromium-molybdenum steels with an yield strength of 165,000 lb. per sq. in. can be machined more easily than chromium-vanadium steels with the same yield strength.

The machinability with shallow cuts of various alloy steels was recently studied by Digges.[436] Six different steels, including a chromium-molybdenum steel (S.A.E. 4140), were investigated, and each steel was tested after having received various heat treatments. Each of the steels was found to contain approximately 0.40 per cent carbon. The machinability was estimated from the tool life. When the machinabilities at comparable tensile strengths were considered, it was found that the alloy steels were more easily machinable at all strengths than carbon steels, and that there was relatively little difference between the machinability of the various alloy steels. The chromium-molybdenum steel had the best machinability at a tensile strength of 100,000 lb. per sq. in. or less, and a chromium-vanadium steel had the best machinability at higher strengths. Surface finishes were also studied, and the various alloy steels were found to have about equivalent smoothness.

91. Welding Properties.—In a discussion at a meeting of the American Society for Testing Materials, Speller[142] asserted that phosphorus is one of the very few elements that can be added to welding steel without interfering with welding, and that molybdenum seemed to be another.

In their study of steels suitable for boiler construction, Prömper and Pohl[235] found that low-carbon steels containing several tenths of a per cent molybdenum could be welded satisfactorily. The yield strength of welds in a molybdenum steel at temperatures up to 500°C. (930°F.) is shown in Fig. 51 (page 126). The tensile properties and impact resistance at the welds of plates containing 0.15 per cent carbon and 0.34 per cent molybdenum are given in Table 32. After welding, the samples were normalized, the tensile samples being straightened prior to normalizing. The welded portion was slightly stronger than the normal material, but the impact resistance fell from 22 m-kg. per sq. cm. for the normal steel to 15 or 18 m-kg. per sq. cm. at the weld.

TABLE 32.—TENSILE AND IMPACT PROPERTIES OF WELDS IN MOLYBDENUM STEELS*
(Specimens tested at 20 and 500°C. [68 and 930°F.])

Number	Temperature		Tensile strength, lb./sq. in.	Yield strength, lb./sq. in.	Elongation in 8 in.,† per cent	Impact resistance, m-kg./sq. cm.‡
	°C.	°F.				
1	20	68	60,700	47,500	9.5	14.8
2	20	68	53,300	40,000	8.0	12.1
3	20	68	49,600	41,300	6.0	17.9
Average	...	...	54,600	43,000	7.9	14.6
1	500	930	36,600	28,200	3.0	9.5
2	500	930	41,300	27,300	7.0	13.4
3	500	930	41,500	31,400	8.0	13.3
Average	...	...	39,800	29,000	6.0	12.1

* Prömper and Pohl.[235]
† Specimens all broke partly in weld.
‡ Notch in weld.

Both Christmann[324] and Bailey, Dickenson, Inglis, and Pearson[422] found that molybdenum structural steels were easily welded. The latter stated that such steels can be welded by forging, with oxy-acetylene, or by electricity.

92. Forming Properties.—According to Gillett and Mack,[151] low-carbon molybdenum steels in the annealed condition are very ductile and are suitable for deep drawing and stamping.

The molybdenum steels recommended by Prömper and Pohl[235] were found by them to be almost as easily formed as carbon steel plate. These authors found that in the ability of the molybdenum steel to be bent in the quenched condition, and bent hot or cold, it was not inferior to carbon steel. Other forms of working, including flattening, and slitting followed by bending and drifting, also indicated that the steel could be worked as easily as carbon steel.

93. Carburizing Properties.—In a general discussion of carburizing, Guillet[49] reported that the effect of tungsten and molybdenum on carburizing properties is to increase the rate of carburization, and that their effect is similar to that of chromium. In steels carburized under the same conditions, he found a penetration of 1.1 mm. (0.044 in.) in a steel containing 2 per cent molybdenum, as compared with 0.9 mm. (0.036 in.) in a carbon steel. Detailed data on these tests were not reported. Molybdenum, according to Guillet, in 1911 was rarely used in carburizing steels.

Lake,[57] in a discussion of carburization by gases, stated that chromium increases the rate of penetration of carbon more than any other element except manganese, and that molybdenum has about the same effect as chromium.

The effect of various percentages of molybdenum on the depth of the penetration of carbon in a hexane-hydrogen mixture, as determined by Tammann,[117] is shown in Fig. 55. As shown

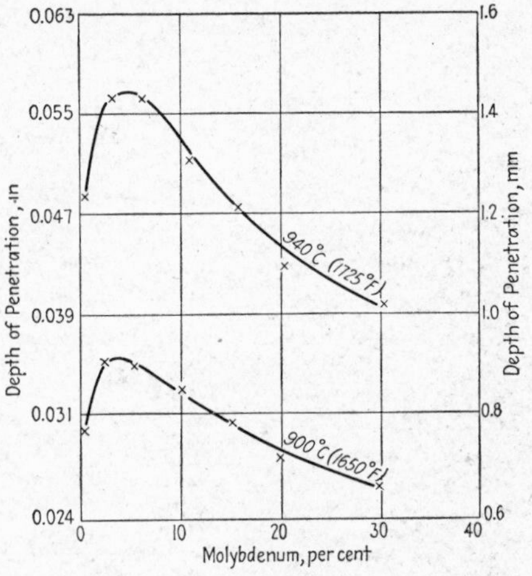

Fig. 55.—Effect of molybdenum on depth of carbon penetration in hexane-hydrogen mixture. (*Tammann.*[117])

by this figure, an increasing molybdenum content first increases and then decreases the depth of carbon penetration, the maximum depth resulting with 5 per cent molybdenum.

Tests on carburization of several alloy steels, including one containing 0.13 per cent carbon, 0.96 per cent chromium, and 0.48 per cent molybdenum, were made by Spalding,[116] who found that penetration of carbon in the chromium-molybdenum steel was equal to or better than that in any other steel, but that the case could not be refined by either a single or a double heat treatment.

The Studebaker Corporation, according to Dawe,[106] used a chromium-molybdenum steel for carburizing but discontinued its use because of difficulty in producing a tough core with a single quench. This company, at the time the article was prepared (1922), was experimenting with a nickel-molybdenum steel for carburizing, which showed considerable promise.

Shepherd[163] claims that a steel containing from 1.5 to 2.0 per cent nickel and from 0.15 to 0.25 per cent molybdenum is a good carburizing material. The use of molybdenum in chromium steels is not recommended by him because of the tendency of such steels to be distorted during the carburizing operation.

Carburizing tests were made by Oberhoffer, Hochstein, and Hessenbruch[286] on an oxygen-rich and a low-oxygen molybdenum steel containing, respectively, 0.25 and 0.34 per cent carbon. The former steel contained 1.22 and the latter 1.20 per cent molybdenum. The depth of case produced in both steels was less than that produced in other alloy steels. The depth of carbon penetration was decreased by the oxygen in the molybdenum as well as in the other alloy steels. The oxygen-rich steel was abnormal as judged by the McQuaid-Ehn[112] test.

The Society of Automotive Engineers has assigned the number 4615 to steels of the following composition, which, according to their "Handbook,"[295] are intended primarily for case hardening:

	Per Cent
Carbon	0.10 to 0.20
Manganese	0.30 to 0.60
Phosphorus	0.04 maximum
Sulphur	0.05 maximum
Nickel	1.50 to 2.00
Molybdenum	0.20 to 0.30

An extensive series of tests on various carburizing steels was reported by McQuaid and McMullan.[281] The steels tested included S.A.E. 4615, a chromium-molybdenum steel, a manganese-molybdenum steel, and a steel containing 3.44 per cent nickel with 0.34 per cent molybdenum. From these tests it was concluded that, where high surface hardness and high resistance to impact are desired together with a good strength, S.A.E. 4615 steel single quenched from above the upper critical range of the core gave the best results. Where extremely high load-carrying capacity and good impact resistance are desired and high surface hardness is not necessary, it was found the S.A.E. 2512 (5 per cent nickel steel) was the most satisfactory. The authors mentioned the need of further work on manganese-molybdenum steels.

The successful use of nickel-molybdenum carburizing steels in anti-friction bearings of all sizes has been mentioned by Langenberg and McKnight.[230] The use of a nickel-molybdenum steel for carburized races has also been mentioned by Davis.[435]

According to MacKenzie,[231] chromium-molybdenum steels are not satisfactory for carburizing because their deep hardening properties result in hardening of the core with consequent embrittlement. A nickel-molybdenum steel, however, is suitable for carburizing, and a very hard case can be produced on this steel by subjecting the carburized part to an oil quench.

An anonymous article in the *Vancoram Review*[308] claimed that chromium-molybdenum steels had been found unsuitable for carburized parts, and that manganese steels containing molybdenum yielded excellent results with the more complex of the usual heat treatments but failed to develop good properties with a simple heat treatment. A high core strength was obtained in a steel containing 3.5 per cent nickel and 0.25 per cent molybdenum.

Rowe[397] wrote that a steel containing 0.16 per cent carbon, 4.0 per cent nickel, 1.1 per cent chromium, and from 0.20 to 0.30 per cent molybdenum is becoming increasingly important as a carburizing steel. It is relatively difficult to machine even in the fully annealed condition, but after heat treatment the core has excellent properties, and a high hardness is developed in the case. He further asserted that the steel designated as S.A.E. 4615, containing 1.75 per cent nickel and 0.30 per cent molybdenum, is popular in the United States. It likewise yields a high-strength core and very hard case. This was claimed to be a "foolproof" steel. It has much to recommend it, particularly in competition with the standard 3 per cent nickel steel.

The "National Metals Handbook," 1930 edition, claims that the chief characteristic of the S.A.E. 4615 steel is the high degree of hardness obtainable with a comparatively mild quench, which, therefore, gives little distortion. Furthermore, good case and core conditions can be produced with a single quench.

94. Susceptibility to Embrittlement.—It has been shown by Jones[110, 176] and others that certain steels, particularly those containing nickel and chromium, may become brittle if slowly cooled from the tempering temperature. Such brittleness is usually referred to as temper-brittleness, and it has been found that a small quantity of molybdenum greatly decreases this tendency to become brittle. The effect of molybdenum on temper-brittleness will be discussed in the section dealing with the effect of molybdenum in nickel-chromium steels.

Another type of brittleness, usually observed in carbon steels, is "blue brittleness," which manifests itself during working or stressing at slightly elevated temperatures, or by cold-worked steel becoming brittle if heated to this temperature. The fact that there is no pronounced drop in impact values around temperatures of 100, 200, and 300°C. (210, 390, and 570°F.) in Table 26 (page 127), from Prömper and Pohl,[235] indicates that molybdenum tends to decrease blue brittleness in low-carbon steels.

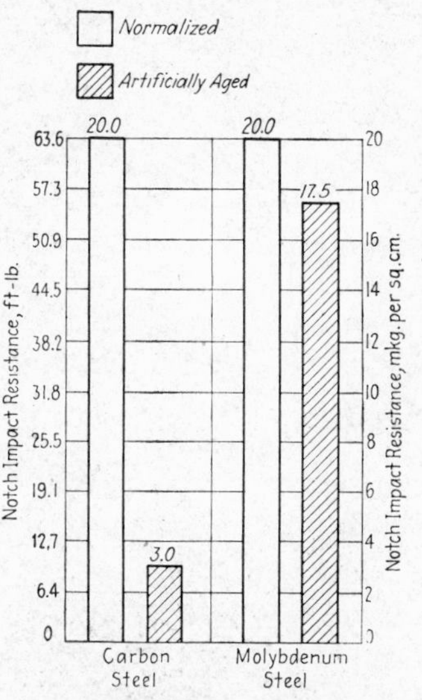

Fig. 56.—Effect of embrittling treatment on a molybdenum and a carbon steel. (*Prömper and Pohl.*[235])

In comparing the susceptibility to embrittlement of molybdenum steel with a carbon steel, Prömper and Pohl[235] used an ordinary carbon boiler-plate steel and a steel containing several tenths of 1 per cent molybdenum. Both steels were normalized, elongated 10 per cent, and "aged" at 200°C. (390°F.). The notched-bar impact strength of the carbon steel fell from 20 to 3.0 m-kg. per sq. cm. owing to this treatment, while the impact value of the molybdenum steel was lowered very little. These results are shown diagrammatically in Fig. 56.

95. Other Properties.—Honda and Takahasi[196] found that the addition of 1 per cent chromium or tungsten or 0.5 per cent molybdenum increased both the sharpness and life of cutlery knife blades.

According to Hildorf and McCollam,[351] molybdenum in low-carbon steel causes a characteristic spark by which the presence of molybdenum can be detected. In a high-carbon steel, however, the characteristic spark due to molybdenum is obscured, but an examination of the pellets or globules thrown from the grinding wheel will show whether or not molybdenum is present. Hildorf and McCollam gave detailed directions for the detection of molybdenum and other elements from the pellets produced in the spark test.

Mutchler and Buzzard[386] attempted to develop a simple and rapid test for separating chromium-molybdenum steel tubing from carbon steel tubing. After trying various tests, including hardness measurements, magnetic testing, spot testing, and spark testing, they found only the last to be satisfactory. The molybdenum in the chromium-molybdenum steel produced a characteristic "spear-head" spark, by which the steel could be readily separated from molybdenum-free steel.

Later work, according to Redmond,[512] has, however, resulted in the development of a rapid chemical test for the detection of chromium-molybdenum steel. In this test an orange-red compound, formed by the action of thiocyanate with quinquevalent molybdenum in a solution of drillings, offers a certain identification of molybdenum-bearing steel.

D. CHEMICAL PROPERTIES OF MOLYBDENUM STEELS

Malowan[378] pointed out that molybdenum lies between tungsten and chromium in the periodic arrangement of the elements, but that it is not so noble as tungsten and does not become passive like chromium. Consequently, molybdenum would not be expected to produce a marked increase in the resistance of steels to chemical attack.

96. Resistance to Chemical Attack.—The molybdenum steels made by Swinden[52] were used by Friend and Marshall[62] to determine the effect of molybdenum on corrosion resistance. These molybdenum steels contained from 1 to 4 per cent molybdenum and from 0.2 to 1.0 per cent carbon. Carbon steels were used for comparison. Small cylinders were corroded in tap water, in 3 per cent salt water, in 0.05 and 0.5 per cent sulphuric acid solutions, and by an alternate wet and dry test. The loss of weight was used as a measure of corrosion, the corrosion products being removed by scraping before weighing. In all but the wet and dry tests, molybdenum appeared to have no influence on the corrosion; but in this test it appeared to increase the corrosion. The author concluded that the alternate wet and dry test most nearly simulated service conditions, and the molybdenum was, therefore, an undesirable constituent with respect to corrosion in steels containing no other alloying element.

The loss of weight in various solutions of steels containing from 0.68 to 0.82 per cent carbon and as much as 20.70 per cent molybdenum was determined by Aitchison.[64] As his results shown in Fig. 57 indicate, molybdenum, in the solutions used,

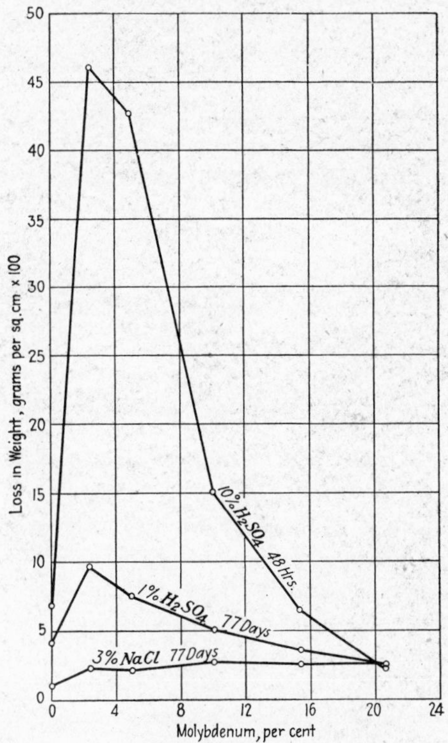

FIG. 57.—Loss of weight of molybdenum steels in various solutions. Carbon 0.68 to 0.82 per cent. (*Aitchison.*[64])

increased the rate of corrosion. Submersion of the samples in tap water for 77 days indicated a slight decrease of corrosion resistance due to molybdenum. Aitchison believed that the increased corrosion of the molybdenum steels resulted from the finer division of the constituents produced by the molybdenum.

Thompson[184] determined the relative attack of nitric acid solutions of various concentrations on molybdenum steels and found that molybdenum did not increase the resistance to either dilute or concentrated acid. Even ferromolybdenum, containing over 63 per cent molybdenum, would not withstand nitric acid.

Tests by Endo[213] indicated that the addition of 1 per cent molybdenum to a steel containing 0.3 per cent carbon slightly increases the loss in weight in both hydrochloric and sulphuric acid, but that with larger quantities of molybdenum the rate of attack decreases until it reaches an asymptotic value at approximately 5 per cent molybdenum. In a nitric acid solution the rate of attack decreased almost linearly with increasing molybdenum content.

97. Electrochemical Potential.—Tammann and Sotter[128] determined the electrochemical potential of a series of iron-molybdenum alloys after polarization in 0.1 normal sulphuric acid. The values determined were:

Molybdenum, Per Cent	Potential, Volts
2.5	−0.26
10	−0.24
20	−0.25
50	−0.21
60	−0.22
70	+0.23
80	+0.36
90	+0.28
100	+0.21

The exact analyses of the alloys were not given. As the above values indicate, alloys containing 60 per cent or less molybdenum are electronegative and have essentially the same value as iron. At approximately 60 per cent molybdenum the alpha phase disappears, and the alloys behave like molybdenum. According to these values of potential, copper could be precipitated from its solutions by alloys containing 60 per cent or less molybdenum, but not by alloys containing 70 per cent or more molybdenum.

E. USES OF MOLYBDENUM STEELS

Although molybdenum is used in a large tonnage of steel, it is generally used only in conjunction with some other alloying element, such as nickel, chromium, or manganese. The use of those steels containing molybdenum as the only alloying element is discussed below.

98. Early Uses and Proposed Uses.—According to a recent anonymous article in *Aciers Spéciaux*,[314] the Creusot works of Schneider et Cie. made a 400-kg. (882-lb.) heat of molybdenum steel in 1894 and a 35,000-kg. (77,000-lb.) heat in 1895. These steels were used for armor plate and evidently contained no alloying elements other than molybdenum, but the record given for subsequent production of armor plate indicated that the steels contained either nickel or chromium in addition to molybdenum. Other authors have asserted that molybdenum was used in ordnance steels, but no authentical reference to molybdenum steel for such uses has been found.

Thallner,[17] in 1901, suggested molybdenum as a substitute for tungsten in tool steels, and others have approved the use of molybdenum in high-speed steels, although such steels usually contain other alloying elements. The uses of molybdenum high-speed steel will be discussed in a subsequent chapter.

Curie[14] and Stogoff and Messkin[296] found that molybdenum steel made excellent permanent magnets, and several reviews mention the use of molybdenum in such steels, but no definite reports of the commercial use of these steels have been found.

In recent correspondence Mathews called attention to the considerable quantity of molybdenum high-speed steel produced about thirty years ago. This steel contained about 0.70 per cent carbon, from 9.0 to 9.5 per cent molybdenum, and no other alloying elements.

> At that time it constituted a fairly satisfactory high-speed steel but was abandoned a little later. It hardens at a lower temperature than the commercial high-speed steel, and the result of overheating is to bring about an incipient fusion and a eutectic constituent at grain boundaries. It also produces extensive volatilization.

Many reviews mention extensive uses of molybdenum steels, particularly of the structural type, but such steels usually contain either nickel or chromium in addition to molybdenum.

99. Contemporary Uses.—According to Prömper and Pohl,[235] Jungbluth,[357] and Christmann,[324] low-carbon steels containing several tenths of 1 per cent molybdenum are used for boiler construction in Germany because of the high strength of such steels at temperatures up to 500 or 600°C. (930 or 1110°F.) and their ease of welding. Bailey, Dickenson, Inglis, and Pearson[422] also recommend such steels for use at elevated temperatures.

Pohl[490] maintained that a molybdenum steel had been successfully used in the manufacture of locomotive and street railway tire wheels. Such a steel was claimed to be advantageous in that it has a high resistance to wear and, therefore, a long life; the surface is not appreciably work-hardened, which decreases the wear of the rails. The use in Löffler boilers of a steel containing 0.64 per cent molybdenum was mentioned by Rochel.[494] This steel was used on account of its strength at high temperatures.

F. CAST MOLYBDENUM STEEL

While an alloying element may have precisely the same effect on steel whether or not the steel is subjected to mechanical work, the factors governing the selection of a steel for castings differ sufficiently from those governing the selection for other purposes to warrant consideration of the effect of molybdenum in cast steel.

TABLE 33.—TENSILE PROPERTIES AND BRINELL HARDNESS OF CAST MOLYBDENUM STEEL*
(Tested in the as-cast condition)

Composition, per cent		Series	Tensile strength, lb./sq. in.	Yield strength,† lb./sq. in.	Elongation,‡ per cent	Reduction of area, per cent	Brinell hardness
C	Mo						
0.10	0.24	2	51,500	26,900	35	58	92
0.05	0.31	1	40,300	24,600	11	29	124
0.10	0.45	2	53,600	29,200	34	55	131
0.06	0.52	1	49,300	24,600	12	21	95
0.11	0.94	1	65,000	51,500	6	14	160
0.12	1.55	2	67,200	38,100	22	27	101
0.13	1.78	1	65,000	44,800	2	4	194
0.11	3.00	2	69,400	40,300	14	15	127
0.07	7.14	2	67,200	40,300	5	6	144
0.32	7.55	1	98,600	67,200	2	3	248
0.44	11.74	1	76,200	44,800	1	2	188
0.09	12.50	2	51,500	......	0	1	250
0.08	18.70	2	51,500	......	0.25	0	306
0.10	23.75	2	49,300	......	0	1	280

* Hadfield.[67]
† Reported as elastic limit.
‡ Gage length not stated.

100. Properties of Cast Molybdenum Steels.—The mechanical properties of cast specimens of two series of molybdenum steels were determined by Hadfield.[67] The properties as cast are listed in Table 33, and the properties after annealing at 800°C.

(1470°F.) are given in Table 34. Ferromolybdenum was used in preparing series 1, and molybdenum powder was used in the other series; consequently the carbon contents of the steels containing several per cent molybdenum are higher in series 1 than in series 2. Details of melting and casting were not given. From these results, Hadfield concluded that molybdenum did not have a marked effect on the properties of low-carbon cast steels.

TABLE 34.—TENSILE PROPERTIES AND BRINELL HARDNESS OF CAST MOLYBDENUM STEELS ANNEALED AT 800°C. (1470°F.)*

Composition, per cent		Series	Tensile strength, lb./sq. in.	Yield strength,† lb./sq. in.	Elongation,‡ per cent	Reduction of area, per cent	Brinell hardness
C	Mo						
0.10	0.24	2	49,300	26,800	37	66	84
0.10	0.45	2	49,300	26,600	42	66	92
0.06	0.52	1	51,500	24,600	25	34	87
0.11	0.94	1	62,700	42,560	8	20	126
0.12	1.55	2	62,700	31,400	30	66	97
0.13	1.78	1	51,500	38,100	5	11	131
0.11	3.00	2	65,000	31,400	36	67	125
0.07	7.14	2	80,600	40,300	15	16	156
0.32	7.55	1	96,300	60,500	5	5	196
0.44	11.74	1	76,200	42,560	2	2	212
0.09	12.50	2	58,200	......	0	0	263
0.92	17.40	1	76,200	......	0	0	300
0.08	18.70	2	51,500	......	0	0	306
0.10	23.75	2	26,800	......	0	0	280

* Hadfield.(67)
† Reported as elastic limit.
‡ Gage length not stated.

Prömper and Pohl(235) found that the properties of molybdenum cast steels were similar to those of rolled molybdenum steel plate, and that the castings were suitable for high-temperature service. Table 35 gives the tensile properties at temperatures up to 500°C. (930°F.) of a cast and annealed molybdenum steel, and the yield strength of this steel is plotted against the temperature in Fig. 58. The steel presumably contains approximately 0.15 per cent carbon and 0.3 per cent molybdenum.

The properties of heat-treated alloy steel castings have been studied at the Krupp laboratories and discussed at length by

Rys.[398] The steels investigated included one molybdenum steel and two chromium-molybdenum steels. From a determina-

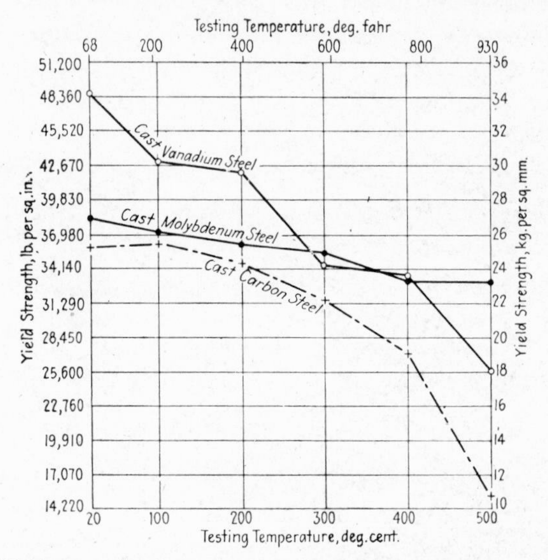

FIG. 58.—Yield strength of cast steels at elevated temperatures. (*Prömper and Pohl.*[235])

TABLE 35.—PROPERTIES OF CAST ANNEALED MOLYBDENUM STEEL AT VARIOUS TEMPERATURES*
(Load applied at 70 lb./sq. in./sec.)

Temperature		Tensile strength, lb./sq. in.	Yield strength, lb./sq. in.	Elongation in 8 in., per cent	Reduction of area, per cent	Impact resistance, m-kg./sq. cm.
°C.	°F.					
20	68	64,600	38,400	21.0	43.0	16.25
100	210	63,300	37,300	12.0	38.2	16.63
200	390	81,400	36,300	12.8	37.9	16.70
300	575	75,600	35,400	18.8	42.2	14.67
400	750	60,000	33,600	18.5	58.6	9.9
500	930	45,600	33,400	17.7	63.6	9.88

* Prömper and Pohl.[235]

tion of the properties of heat-treated bars varying in width from 40 to 400 mm. (1.58 to 15.8 in.), it was concluded that a nickel-chromium steel had the best combination of properties, and that a chromium-molybdenum steel was next best. Short-time tensile tests on a carbon steel, molybdenum steel, a chromium-molybdenum steel, and a vanadium steel indicated that the molybdenum steel (0.23 per cent carbon and 0.68 per cent molybdenum) had the highest strength at 500°C. (930°F.). Rys also reported that samples of steel containing 0.19 per cent carbon, 0.60 per cent manganese, and 0.33 per cent molybdenum taken from a thick-walled casting had the following properties:

Temperature		Tensile strength, lb./sq. in.	Yield strength, lb./sq. in.	Elongation, per cent
°C.	°F.			
20	68	69,700	42,700	25.5
500	930	57,000	21,400	30.0

A sample from a section from another thick-walled casting containing 0.37 per cent carbon, 0.75 per cent manganese, and 0.58 per cent molybdenum had the following properties:

Temperature		Tensile strength, lb./sq. in.	Yield strength, lb./sq. in.	Elongation, per cent
°C.	°F.			
20	68	92,500	44,200	18.0
500	930	71,100	38,000	29.6

The creep limits and tensile properties of two molybdenum cast steels as given by Stäger[408] are shown in Table 36. The creep limit represents the stress at which an elongation of 0.001 per cent per hour occurs between the one thousandth and two thousandth minute.[1] Carbon and nickel-chromium low-alloy steels were also tested, and it was found that the molybdenum steels had the highest creep limit.

A study of the properties of fifteen cast alloy steels at temperatures as high as 500°C. (930°F.) was recently reported by Körber and Pomp.[466A] Analyses of the steels studied are given in Table 37, from which it may be observed that steels *G, H, I, K, N*, and *O* contained 0.5 per cent molybdenum and steel *P* contained 0.3 per cent molybdenum. The specimens were cast in an intricate sand mold, which permitted the produc-

[1] This is, consequently, an accelerated creep test, and caution should be used in comparing these values with those obtained by more prolonged tests.

TABLE 36.—TENSILE PROPERTIES OF CAST MOLYBDENUM STEELS AT VARIOUS TEMPERATURES*

(*Steel* 1: 0.25 per cent carbon, 0.41 per cent molybdenum. *Steel* 2: 0.22 per cent carbon, 0.8 per cent molybdenum)

Steel number	Temperature		Tensile strength, lb./sq. in.	Yield strength, lb./sq. in.	Elongation, per cent	Impact resistance, m-kg./sq. cm.	Creep limit, lb./sq. in.
	°C.	°F.					
1	20	68	69,600	42,200	27.8	5.4	
2	20	68	78,100	46,800	25.0	4.2	
1	400	750	64,200	27,800	13.0	4.8	27,000
2	400	750	65,700	27,800	20.0	5.2	27,000
1	500	930	47,400	26,300	25.0	3.5	9,250
2	500	930	51,800	28,000	20.0	3.6	10,000
1	600	1110	33,900	24,300	31.0	3.8	2,100
2	600	1110	34,400	22,800	44.5	4.6	2,850

* Stäger.(408)

TABLE 37.—ANALYSES OF CAST STEELS TESTED AT ELEVATED TEMPERATURES*

Number	Kind	Composition, per cent									
		C	Si	Mn	P	S	Cr	Ni	Mo	V	W
A........	Mn	0.35	0.50	1.15	0.027	0.024					
B........	Mn	0.22	0.41	1.80	0.010	0.033					
C........	W	0.27	0.32	0.49	0.008	0.012	....	....	....	....	0.93
D........	W	0.32	0.31	0.56	0.012	0.009	....	....	....	....	0.87
E........	V	0.20	0.30	0.40	0.018	0.038	....	....	....	0.28	
F........	V	0.31	0.31	0.32	0.006	0.026	....	....	....	0.27	
G........	Mo	0.31	0.29	0.62	0.017	0.017	....	....	0.51		
H........	Mo	0.40	0.37	0.46	0.017	0.022	....	....	0.50		
I........	Mo-Mn	0.21	0.19	1.03	0.014	0.020	....	....	0.57		
K........	Mo-Mn	0.25	0.23	0.87	0.014	0.023	....	....	0.48		
L........	Ni-Cr	0.20	0.32	0.43	0.014	0.024	0.52	1.50			
M........	Ni-Cr	0.28	0.31	0.45	0.013	0.013	0.56	1.06			
N........	Cr-Mo	0.17	0.20	0.46	0.014	0.017	1.06	....	0.51		
O........	Ni-Mo	0.28	0.27	0.50	0.014	0.015	....	2.52	0.40		
P........	Ni-Cr-Mo	0.33	0.33	0.51	0.022	0.018	0.66	1.86	0.36		

* Körber and Pomp.(466A)

tion of vertically cast specimens free from a shrinkage cavity. All specimens were heat-treated by heating to 950°C. (1740°F.) for 3 to 4 hr., cooling rapidly to 550°C. (1020°F.), reheating to

650°C. (1200°F.), and then cooling in the furnace. Short-time tensile tests, and Charpy impact tests were made at temperatures between 20°C. (70°F.) and 500°C. (930°F.). The results of these tests are shown graphically in Figs. 59 and 60. As may be observed from these figures, the results are in agreement with

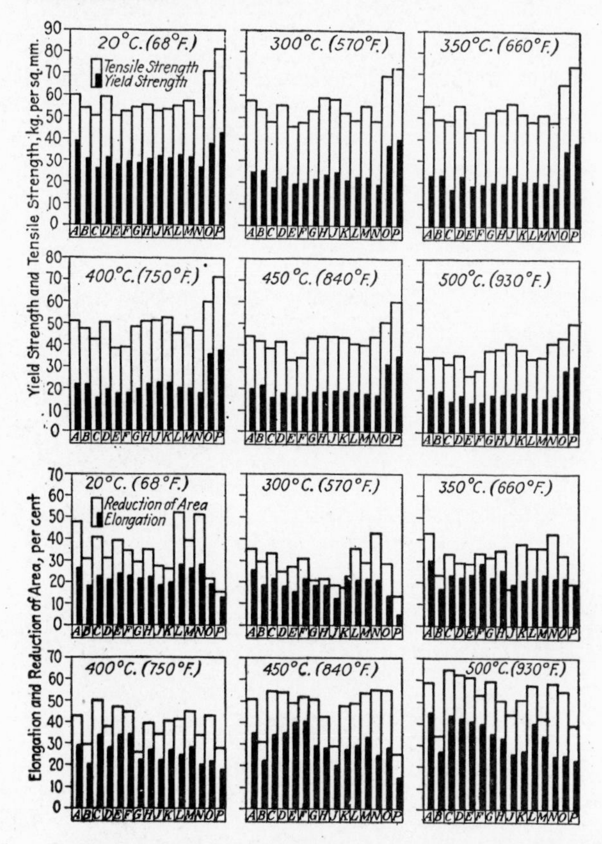

Fig. 59.—Tensile properties of cast steels of composition given in Table 37. (*Körber and Pomp.*[466A])

those of other investigators in that the seven molybdenum-containing steels have the higher strength at elevated temperatures. The yield strength represents the load required to give a permanent elongation of 0.2 per cent, and in determining this value each load at which the elongation was determined was maintained for 30 sec. Two sizes of Charpy impact specimens were used; the large one was 30 × 30 × 160 mm. (1.18 × 1.18

× 6.3 in.) and the notch was 15 mm. (0.59 in.) deep, while the small specimen, which was cut from one end of the large specimen, was 10 × 10 × 55 mm. (0.39 × 0.39 × 2.2 in.) and the notch was 2.5 mm. (0.098 in.) deep. The authors, in evaluating the suitability of the steels for use at elevated temperature, used the ratio of the yield strength at 500°C. (930°F.) to the tensile strength at 20°C. (70°F.). The highest ratio, 0.42, was observed for the nickel-molybdenum steel designated as *O*. The lowest ratio, 0.29, was observed in the nickel-chromium steel designated as *M*. Körber and Pomp pointed out that all of the steels had received the same heat treatment and that the order of merit of the steels might have been changed if a different heat treatment had been used.

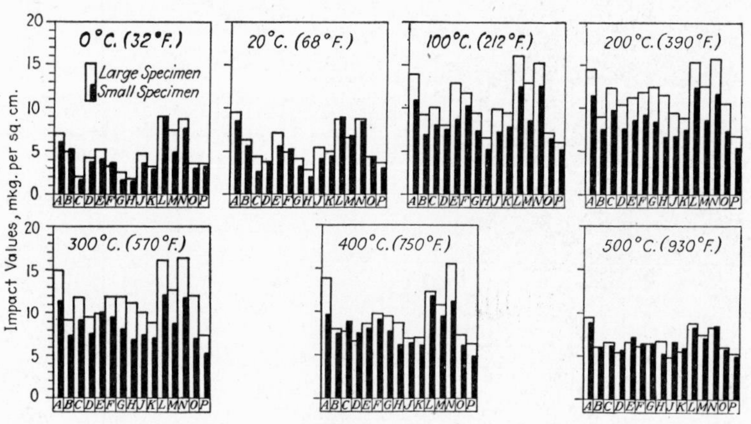

FIG. 60.—Charpy impact values of cast steels of composition given in Table 37. (*Körber and Pomp.*[466A])

101. Uses of Cast Molybdenum Steel.—Bratton[119] mentioned the use of molybdenum in cast-steel rolls. According to him, molybdenum was first used in rolls in 1920, and at the time the article was written (1923) it was used in all classes of rolls. The cast-steel rolls are heat-treated by first annealing to break up the casting structures and then hardening by an air quench.

Cast molybdenum steels, according to Grotts,[136] are used for hydroelectric work, turbines, and many other castings where high tensile properties are desired. In 1928, Frank[215] asserted that straight molybdenum steel was not commonly used in castings, and that molybdenum, when used, frequently was added in amounts from 0.20 to 0.40 per cent.

The use of molybdenum steel for castings used at medium-high temperatures is recommended by Prömper and Pohl[235] and by Rys.[398] The article by Rys contains a photograph of a large cast turbine housing made of molybdenum steel.

In 1930, Shaw[404] stated that molybdenum steel is not in common use for castings, but that it offers advantages in decreasing the tendency to crack.

Dickson[330] reported that guns are cast centrifugally from a steel containing 0.35 to 0.40 per cent carbon, about 0.40 per cent molybdenum, and occasionally a small percentage of vanadium.

G. AUTHOR'S SUMMARY

1. Molybdenum apparently has little effect on the mechanical properties of unheat-treated steels. In heat-treated steels containing more than 0.3 per cent carbon, however, molybdenum in quantities less than 1 per cent produces a substantial increase in tensile strength with possibly a slight decrease in elongation and reduction of area. The effect of molybdenum in steels containing less than 0.3 per cent carbon is less marked, although with several per cent of this element the tensile strength and yield strength are substantially increased, while elongation and reduction of area are slightly reduced.

2. The endurance limit of molybdenum steels is the same as for other steels of the same strength and hardness.

3. Molybdenum increases the strength at high temperatures, and several tenths of 1 per cent molybdenum added to a low-carbon steel increases the yield strength, tensile strength, and creep limit at temperatures of 500 to 600°C. (930 to 1110°F.).

4. Molybdenum in small amounts probably increases the machinability of steel.

5. The weldability is not adversely affected by molybdenum.

6. Molybdenum increases the rate of carbon penetration in carburizing.

7. The susceptibility to temper embrittlement and blue heat brittleness is decreased by molybdenum.

8. The rate of chemical attack is, in some cases, slightly increased by molybdenum. In general, molybdenum when present in quantities up to several per cent has little effect on the corrosion resistance.

9. The effect of small amounts of molybdenum on low-carbon cast steel is the same as its effects on wrought steel.

CHAPTER VI

MOLYBDENUM CAST IRON

Manufacture of Molybdenum Cast Iron—Influence of Molybdenum on Structure—Mechanical Properties of Molybdenum Cast Iron—Special Properties of Molybdenum Cast Iron—Effect of Temperature on Molybdenum Cast Iron—Uses of Molybdenum Cast Iron—Author's Summary

Alloy cast irons have only recently been studied or used to an appreciable extent, and until very recently nickel or nickel together with chromium were almost the only alloys commercially used in cast iron. As the results of investigations given below show, molybdenum produces very desirable effects in cast iron, and one is lead to believe that "high-test" molybdenum cast irons have real merit.

A. MANUFACTURE OF MOLYBDENUM CAST IRON

Much of the literature dealing with the effect of molybdenum in cast iron is based on results of laboratory tests that give little information as to the commercial melting and casting of cast iron containing molybdenum. The subject is treated in this section, however, from the point of view of the commercial or large-scale production of molybdenum cast iron.

102. Methods for Adding Molybdenum.—At the present time cast iron is melted in the cupola, electric arc furnace, air furnace, and, less frequently, in crucible or induction furnaces. In all processes except the cupola the partly melted or the molten iron is comparatively accessible and alloys can be added at almost any time, but in cupola practice additions can be made only as the materials are charged or after the iron is tapped from the furnace. A recent trade publication(431) recommended that ferromolybdenum be added in the cupola spout unless only part of the iron is to contain molybdenum, in which case the molybdenum alloy can be gradually added to the ladle as it is being filled. As previously mentioned, a special molybdenum-iron alloy having a lower melting point than standard ferromolybdenum is marketed and is recommended for use in cast iron.

A survey reported by Cone,[254] in 1929, showed that three alloying elements, nickel, chromium, and molybdenum, contribute to the bulk of the alloy iron castings produced in the United States. It was concluded that molybdenum had just come into extensive use, and that it was normally used without other alloying elements. In cupola practice ferromolybdenum is usually added to the ladle, and in air-furnace practice calcium molybdate is generally added to the furnace.

The introduction of molybdenum into cast iron by means of calcium molybdate has been discussed by Hardy.[344] Owing to the limited time for reduction, this salt cannot be successfully added to the ladle. It can, however, be satisfactorily used in the air furnace, but, owing to the low temperature, a longer time for reduction is required than in steel making. The use of calcium molybdate is alleged to be particularly advantageous in that it produces a uniform distribution of molybdenum and gives freedom from possible carbide segregations. It is reported that calcium molybdate is frequently employed in molybdenum iron melted in the air furnace. The present and best practice is to distribute the required number of bags throughout the charge. Calcium molybdate can be used in the cupola by adding it with each charge of coke. It is best used in briquetted form, which is commercially available, in order to prevent its loss as dust. It has been found that with briquettes an almost complete recovery of molybdenum results, but that it is not possible to work to the close chemical limits used in steel making. In general, calcium molybdate can be used satisfactorily only in a cupola producing nothing but molybdenum iron, but the practice of tapping one or two batches of molybdenum iron at the start of a regular run has worked out well.

C. H. Lorig of Battelle Memorial Institute found that calcium molybdate tends to oxidize part of the carbon, silicon, and manganese in cast iron, and that its use thereby makes it difficult to control the chemical composition.

Smith[407] recommended that the low-melting molybdenum-iron alloy be added to the ladle of iron melted in the cupola and stated that the use of calcium molybdate is permissible in the electric or air furnace.

The loss of molybdenum when ferromolybdenum was added to a small quantity of iron was determined by Challansonnet,[322] who added sufficient ferromolybdenum to a 20-kg. (44-lb.)

crucible melt of iron to yield 0.5 per cent molybdenum. After the addition of the ferroalloy, the temperature was raised to 1600°C. (2910°F.) and then lowered to 1500°C. (2730°F.) before casting. The resulting castings contained only 0.36 per cent molybdenum, which represented a 28 per cent loss of molybdenum, and the castings were covered with light-yellow powder, which was probably the oxide of molybdenum (MoO_3). It seems unlikely that so large a loss of molybdenum would occur in commercial melting practice. E. G. Brick, of the Cadillac Motor Car Co., in commenting on this said that the loss of molybdenum found by Challansonnet seemed to be excessive, for he had found only about a 10 per cent loss when ferromolybdenum was added to the cupola and less than half that loss when the addition was made to the ladle. He also found that trouble was experienced when a carbon-reduced ferromolybdenum was used, but that a silicon-reduced alloy readily dissolved in the iron. The greater ease with which the silicon-reduced alloy was dissolved was attributed to its lower melting point.

103. Effects of Molybdenum on Casting Properties.—According to Campion,[73] molybdenum, likewise boron, tungsten, and chromium, increase the shrinkage of cast iron. Smalley[115, 126] found, however, that molybdenum reduces sponginess and coarseness of texture. Stahl[245] asserted that molybdenum irons are free from cracks and hard spots. It has been reported, however, that sponginess has been experienced in molybdenum iron, which took the form of short cracks in a brake-drum flange. The use of a reducing agent tended to remedy this defect.

Castings of molybdenum iron of varying sections, according to Smith,[407] do not crack in the mold so readily as iron containing no molybdenum.

The Climax Molybdenum Co.[431] claimed that molybdenum "does not decrease the internal or fluid shrinkage of the iron," but that it produces a denser iron, and that it is, therefore, necessary to use large risers or feed heads to care for shrinkage resulting from solidification. It was further maintained that molybdenum iron has greater fluidity and pours from the ladle more cleanly than unalloyed iron. The author understands from conversation with E. G. Brick of the Cadillac Motor Car Co., however, that low-carbon iron containing one-half of 1 per cent molybdenum tends to be sluggish, and that additional phosphorus is introduced in "high-test" iron in order to mitigate the sluggishness produced by the molybdenum. There is, however, some room for conjecture as to how much of the sluggishness and excessive shrinkage is due to molybdenum and how much to the low total-carbon content.

It was found by Sherwin and Kiley[(498)] that molybdenum decreases solid contraction or patternmaker's shrinkage.

B. INFLUENCE OF MOLYBDENUM ON STRUCTURE

For the present discussion, cast iron may be considered as a steel containing either graphite or an exceptionally large quantity of cementite. Whether most of the carbon in an iron occurs as graphite or cementite depends both on its chemical composition and on the rate at which it was cooled. In practice, the quantity of graphite produced is regulated chiefly by the silicon and carbon contents; to produce a soft gray iron a relatively large amount of silicon is added and, if a white iron is desired, less silicon is used. Of course, other elements influence the tendency to graphitize and, in considering the effects of any element in cast iron, its effect on graphitization is of prime importance. An element may also influence the structure and, therefore, the properties of an iron by changing the form and distribution of the graphite, by changing the amount of carbon in the steel matrix, or by changing the structure of the matrix.

104. Amount of Graphite.—As a general rule, an element that forms carbides tends to prevent graphitization, while one that does not form carbides promotes graphitization. Molybdenum belongs to the former group and would, therefore, be expected to decrease graphitization, but, as the data cited below indicate, in general its effect in preventing graphitization is small.

Smalley[(115)] stated that, in steel, molybdenum combines preferentially with ferrite, but that it also forms a double carbide and may, therefore, play the dual rôle of both nickel and chromium. As the chemical analyses of Piwowarsky's irons[(161)] given in discussion of the mechanical properties indicate, a molybdenum content up to 1 per cent did not apparently increase the amount of combined carbon.

Brick[1] found that a molybdenum content below 1 per cent had little effect on the amount of combined carbon, and also that the beneficial effects to be gained by the use of from 0.50 to 1.00 per cent molybdenum as compared with from 0.35 to

[1] Private communication.

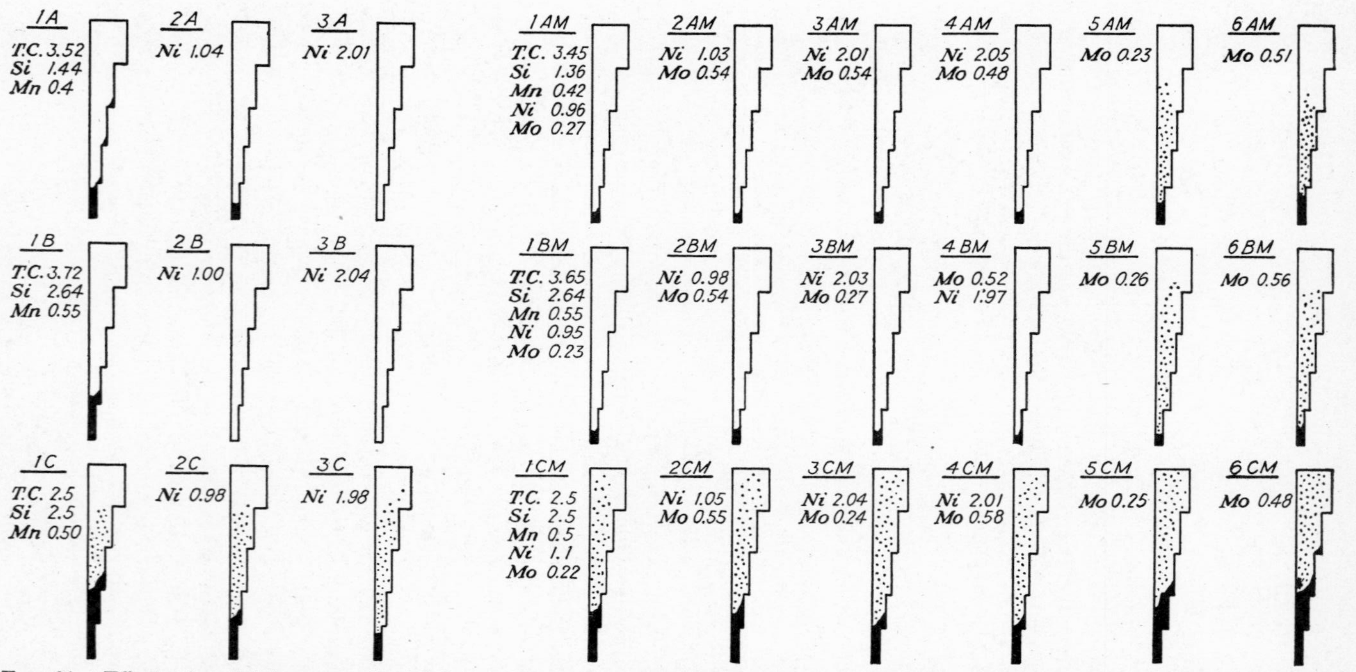

FIG. 61.—Effect of molybdenum and nickel on chill in cast iron. Black areas = white iron; dotted areas = mottled iron; white areas = gray iron. (*Challansonnet.*[322])

0.50 per cent were not sufficient to warrant the extra cost of the alloy.

The effects of molybdenum on an iron containing approximately 3 per cent carbon and 1.7 per cent silicon were studied by Musatti and Calbiani.(385) These authors apparently found no increase in combined carbon in irons containing less than 3.5 per cent molybdenum, but in irons containing this quantity of molybdenum ledeburite[1] was observed. The analyses of some of their alloys given under mechanical properties show that small amounts of molybdenum do not tend to produce a white iron.

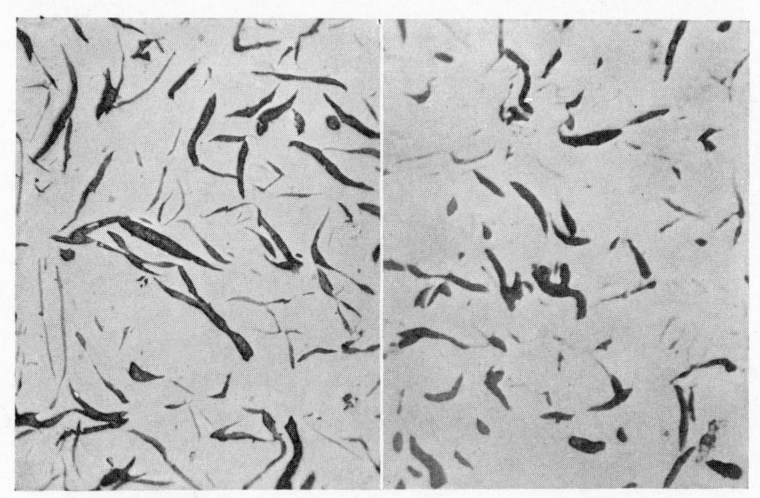

Fig. 62. Fig. 63.

Fig. 62.—Gray iron, molybdenum-free, 2.78 per cent total carbon, and 0.63 per cent combined carbon. Unetched. 100 ×. (*Dahle.*)

Fig. 63.—Gray iron, 0.83 per cent molybdenum, 2.75 per cent total carbon, and 0.48 per cent combined carbon. Unetched. 100 ×. (*Dahle.*)

Figure 61, from the work of Challansonnet,(322) shows the effect of molybdenum on graphitization of iron containing nickel. This figure represents the structures found in a stepped casting, the thickness of the five sections being 3, 6, 12, 18, and 31 mm. (0.12, 0.24, 0.47, 0.71, and 1.22 in.). The black areas represent white iron, the dotted areas mottled iron, and the white areas gray iron. In these specimens the chilling effect of molybdenum is apparent.

[1] Eutectic structure of austenite and cementite.

105. Form of Graphite.—In unalloyed gray cast iron, graphite usually occurs in flat plates, which under the microscope have the appearance shown in Fig. 62. Investigators of molybdenum cast iron, including Smalley,[126] Smith and Aufderhaar,[294, 406] Smith,[407] Musatti and Calbiani,[385] Challansonnet,[322] and the Climax Molybdenum Co.,[431] proved that molybdenum causes the graphite to separate either as globules or as small crumpled plates, which give microsections of the appearance shown in Figs. 63 to 65. Figure 62 shows the form and distribution of

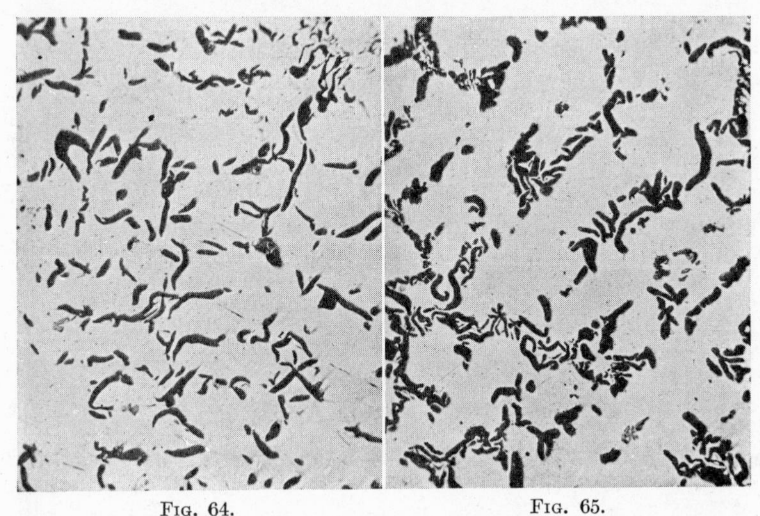

Fig. 64. Fig. 65.

Fig. 64.—Gray iron, 0.92 per cent molybdenum, 2.80 per cent total carbon, and 0.86 per cent combined carbon. Unetched. 100×. (*Dahle.*)

Fig. 65.—Gray iron, same composition as specimen shown in Fig. 64. Heat-treated. Unetched. 100×. (*Dahle.*)

graphite in an ordinary gray iron and Fig. 63 the same for an iron containing 0.83 per cent molybdenum; the relative amounts of graphite visible are without significance. Figures 64 and 65 show a type of dendritic segregation found in molybdenum gray iron, evidenced by the distribution of the graphite. Figure 65 represents a heat-treated specimen, and the graphite plates may have increased in size owing to decomposition of a portion of the carbide. The dendritic formation is believed to result from too high a pouring temperature. These micrographs were prepared by F. B. Dahle of Battelle Memorial Institute.

Merten[481] maintained that the production of a high-strength gray iron depends primarily upon preventing the precipitation of graphite in large flakes, and that molybdenum prevents such an occurrence.

106. Structure of the Matrix.—The structure of the matrix, or the non-graphitic portion, of a gray cast iron is largely dependent on the amount of combined carbon, which is dependent on the chemical composition, the maximum temperature to which the iron is heated, the time maintained at this temperature,

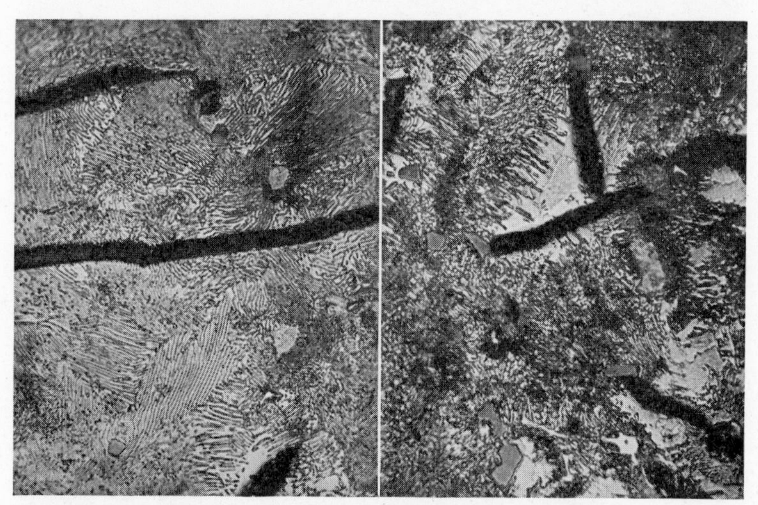

FIG. 66. FIG. 67.

FIG. 66.—Molybdenum-free gray iron, same composition as specimen shown in Fig. 62. Etched with alcoholic picric acid. 500×. (*Dahle.*)

FIG. 67.—Gray iron, same composition as specimen shown in Fig. 63. Etched with alcoholic picric acid. 500×. (*Dahle.*)

and the rate of cooling. As Swinden's previously discussed work has shown, molybdenum decreases the amount of carbon associated with the eutectoid, and consequently an entirely pearlitic matrix would be expected to occur with a lower combined carbon content in molybdenum iron than in an unalloyed iron. The tendency of molybdenum to produce an emulsified pearlite in steel should also be operative in cast iron.

Smith and Aufderhaar[294] found that molybdenum in gray cast iron induces a fine pearlitic or "sorbito-pearlitic" structure.

The studies of Musatti and Calbiani[385] indicated that the pearlite in molybdenum irons is much finer than in unalloyed irons, and that not much change in structure occurs with less than 1.5 or 1.6 per cent molybdenum, but that, as the molybdenum is increased to 2.5 per cent, a troosto-martensitic or a martensito-sorbitic structure is formed.

Challansonnet[322] found that molybdenum in cast iron produces a sorbitic structure, and that small brilliant spots or particles occur in the sorbite, which are probably complex carbides. These spots or particles could not be found in the irons containing nickel in addition to molybdenum.

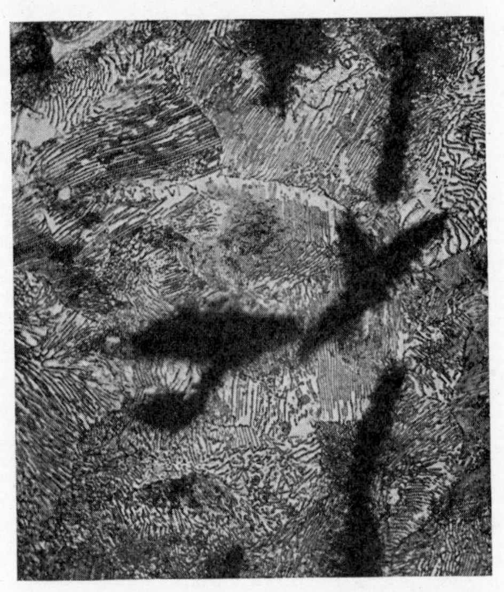

FIG. 68.—Gray cast iron of composition and properties shown in table, page 166. Etched. 500×. (*Boegehold.*)

Figure 66 at a magnification of 500×, shows the structure of an ordinary gray iron and Fig. 67 the structure of a comparable iron containing 0.83 per cent molybdenum. These micrographs were also prepared by Dahle of Battelle Memorial Institute. The molybdenum iron shown in Fig. 67 contains pearlite, ferrite, and an unidentified structure, which might be termed pseudo-martensite.

Some micrographs of molybdenum iron taken by Boegehold of the Cadillac Motor Car Co. are shown in Figs. 68, 69, and 70. These irons were melted in a cupola and duplexed in an electric furnace with steel additions to reduce the total carbon content. Low-carbon, silicon-reduced ferromolybdenum was added to the ladle. The iron was heated to 1565 to 1595°C. (2850 to 2900°F.) in the electric furnace, tapped at once, and cast at a temperature

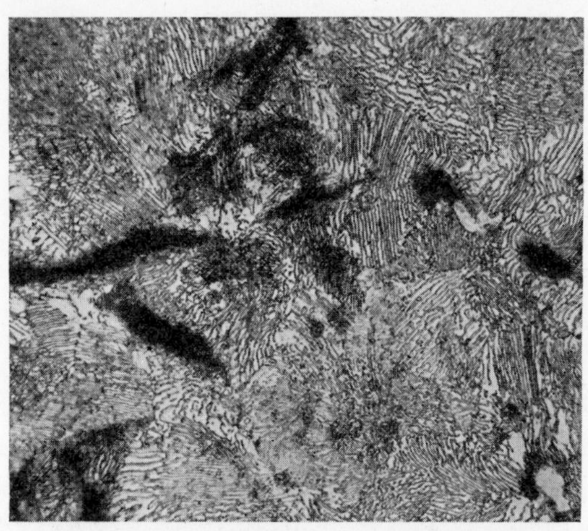

FIG. 69.—Gray cast iron of composition and properties shown in table, page 166. Etched. 500 ×. (*Boegehold.*)

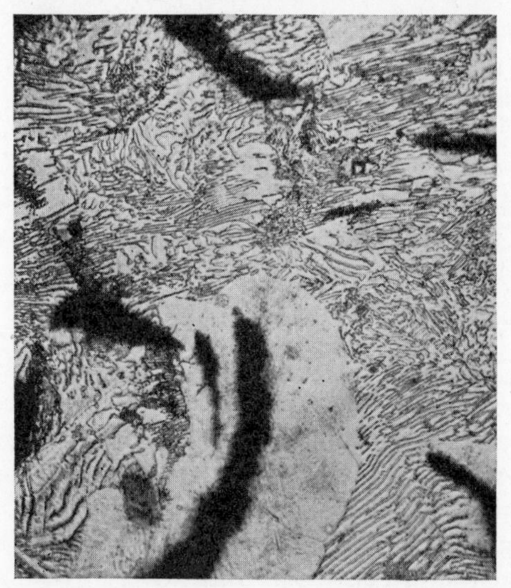

FIG. 70.—Gray cast iron of composition and properties shown in table, page 166. Etched. 500 ×. (*Boegehold.*)

between 1370 and 1425°C. (2500 and 2600°F.). The iron represented by the three figures mentioned above had the following properties and composition:

Figure	Composition, per cent							Tensile strength, lb./sq. in.	Brinell hardness
	Total C	Combined C	Si	S	P	Mn	Mo		
68	2.09	0.45	2.77	0.040	0.16	0.55	0.51	55,800	255
69	2.34	0.61	1.96	0.039	0.16	0.48	0.50	44,500	241
70	2.04	0.15	3.60	0.044	0.18	0.46	0.49	31,000	207

The properties and structure of the iron represented by Fig. 70 illustrate the effect of an excessive amount of silicon on an otherwise "high-test" iron.

C. MECHANICAL PROPERTIES OF MOLYBDENUM CAST IRON

In determining the effects of molybdenum on the mechanical properties of cast iron, great caution must be observed in comparing the results of one investigator with those of others, for differences in composition, melting practice, casting, or testing may produce large differences in the mechanical values reported. Therefore, in the following discussion the data are grouped in relation to the investigators, and, whenever possible, the properties of comparable unalloyed irons are given together with the properties of the molybdenum-bearing irons.

The value representing the transverse strength is usually reported in this country as the load required to break a bar of definite size supported on knife edges a definite distance apart. In Europe, however, it is customary to represent the transverse strength by the maximum fiber stress produced in the bar at fracture. This value is more commonly known as the "modulus of rupture." In the tables on transverse tests given below, the breaking load has been given when the results were reported in that form and the modulus of rupture has been given when reported as such. This procedure was adopted because it was feared that errors might be introduced in conversion.

107. Early Investigations.—In 1918, Campion[73] reported that experiments with gray iron indicated that the addition of 1 per cent molybdenum increases strength and lowers Brinell hardness. In later work, Campion[78] found that the addition of 1 per cent molybdenum to an iron containing 3.4 per cent carbon, 1.5 per cent silicon, and 0.5 per cent manganese increased the transverse strength on a 1-in. square section and a 12-in.

TABLE 38.—MECHANICAL PROPERTIES OF MOLYBDENUM CAST IRON*

No.	Composition, per cent							Transverse test†		Compressive strength, lb./sq. in.	Tensile strength, lb./sq. in.	Brinell hardness	Depth of chill, in.
	Total C	Combined C	Si	Mn	P	S	Mo	Load, lb.	Deflection, in.				
1A	3.32	0.41	1.94	0.62	0.93	0.076	Nil	2,812	0.12	110,900	27,330	207	0.09
1B	3.47	0.37	2.03	0.64	0.92	0.070	0.15	3,010	0.12	97,200	24,000	201	Nil
1C	3.47	0.46	2.05	0.62	0.90	0.067	0.26	3,240	0.13	107,700	26,700	201	0.3
1D	3.25	0.43	1.92	0.75	0.89	0.047	0.52	3,940	0.15	128,100	29,600	229	0.06
2A	3.42	0.87	1.10	0.85	0.51	0.114	Nil	3,940	0.12	132,000	31,400	217	0.17
2B	3.30	0.89	1.24	0.69	0.51	0.115	0.12	3,970	0.13	139,300	35,400	229	0.02
2C	3.30	0.91	1.26	0.66	0.52	0.096	0.24	3,950	0.13	128,000	39,900	229	0.031
3A	2.84	0.61	1.54	0.55	0.54	0.114	Nil	2,972	0.12	137,000	41,200	223	0.16
3B	2.78	0.60	1.68	0.66	0.62	0.082	1.55	3,233	0.10	168,000	51,500	269	0.19
4A	3.30	0.43	1.98	0.61	0.87	0.083	Nil	2,762	0.12	130,400	34,000	221	0.06
4B	3.26	0.38	2.00	0.60	0.87	0.076	1.49	3,122	0.116	143,100	36,500	223	0.04

* Smalley.[126]
† 1 × 2-in. bar; 12-in. span.

distance between supports from 2,136 to 2,730 lb. The tensile strength was increased from 30,200 to 39,400 lb. per sq. in.

In a discussion of structural steels containing molybdenum, Sargent[(92)] cited data on the effects of 2 and 4 per cent molybdenum in cast iron to prove that molybdenum increases both strength and hardness of the cast iron, but no details regarding analyses or preparation of the castings were given.

Smalley[(115)] added 0.11 per cent molybdenum to an iron containing 3.07 per cent carbon, 2.17 per cent silicon, and 0.56 per cent manganese. This quantity of molybdenum apparently had little effect on Brinell hardness; the other mechanical properties were not reported.

A more extended investigation of the effects of molybdenum in cast iron was described by Smalley[(126)] in a later report. The mechanical values given in this report are listed in Table 38.[1]

[1] In private discussion MacKenzie pointed out that molybdenum may interfere with the determination of sulphur by evolution of H_2S, and that the sulphur content of irons listed in this and subsequent tables may be in error. The sulphur in molybdenum-bearing iron should be determined gravimetrically.

Mr. R. S. MacPherson of the Allis Chalmers Mfg. Co., however, stated in a private communication that he had found the following volumetric method applicable for determining sulphur in gray irons containing 0.2 to 0.4 per cent molybdenum: Use the conventional volumetric apparatus and weigh a 5-gram sample of drillings into the flask. Use 60 cc. of cadmium chloride solution in absorption glass. Fill about three-fourths full with distilled water. Put thistle tube assembly in place tightly, and add 60 cc. concentrated HCl. Have delivery tube extend to bottom of absorption glass. When action slows down, bring low flame under flask and warm to complete solution. Raise flame until steam comes over in delivery tube and disconnect. Cool by standing beaker in cold water a few minutes in subdued light. Add about 30 cc. strong HCl to absorption glass with 2 or 3 cc. of starch. Titrate at once in iodine solution standardized to the theoretical value. It appears that the use of concentrated HCl and final boiling of same brings over the full amount of sulphur in sample.

Solutions

Cadmium Chloride Solution

Water	500 cc.
Cadmium chloride crystals	10 grams
Ammonium hydroxide c.p., sp. gr. 90	500 cc.

Starch Solution

Rub 14 grams of arrowroot starch to a thin cream with water and pour into a hot solution of 20 grams of Na OH in 1,000 cc. H_2O. Heat nearly to

The transverse bars[1] were 1 in. × 2 in. and were broken unmachined on a 12-in. span. The compression tests were made on cylinders 0.798 in. in diameter and 1 in. high. Smalley concluded that 0.5 per cent molybdenum slightly reduces chilling power and produces an all-round improvement.

108. Piwowarsky's Work.—A comprehensive study of the effects of molybdenum on cast iron was reported by Piwowarsky[(161)] in 1925. As indicated in Table 39, three series of irons were cast, containing, respectively, 1 per cent, 1.75 per cent, and 2.75 per cent silicon. The alloys were prepared from a Swedish pig iron of the following analysis:

	Per Cent
Total carbon	4.01
Silicon	0.04 to 0.06
Manganese	0.13 to 0.14
Phosphorus	0.018 to 0.02
Sulphur	0.011 to 0.02

The irons were melted in a gas-fired crucible furnace and were heated to 1400°C. (2550°F.) before addition of the ferroalloys, after which they were cooled to 1300°C. (2370°F.) for casting. The samples were cast in dry molds in the form of round bars 20 mm. (0.79 in.) in diameter and 650 mm. (25.6 in.) long. The transverse tests were made on unmachined samples, 20 mm. (0.79 in.) in diameter, with a 40-cm. (16.5-in.) span. The tensile test pieces were 10 mm. (0.39 in.) in diameter at the reduced section. Compression tests were made on cylinders 18 mm. (0.71 in.) in diameter and 18 mm. (0.71 in.) high. Impact specimens were unnotched and unmachined cylinders cut from the 20-mm. (0.79-in.) diameter transverse test pieces.

---

boiling and then cool and make up to 2,000 cc. Add 12 grams KI. This solution keeps for months.

Standard Iodine

Pure iodine	4 grams
KI	8 grams

Dissolve by digestion in small volume of water. Dilute to 1 liter and standardize.

[1] The transverse tests used in Great Britain have been discussed by Pearce.[(390)] Prior to 1928 tests were generally made on a rectangular bar 1 in. × 2 in., tested upright on 36-in. centers. The standard specifications now call for cylindrical test specimens of a diameter dependent on the size of the casting.

The results of Piwowarsky's tests are given in detail in Table 39. As may be observed, some of the alloys contained 0.25 per cent vanadium. Piwowarsky concluded from these results that 0.5 per cent molybdenum improves all of the mechanical properties, but increasing the amount of molybdenum to 1 per cent does not further improve the properties. He also found that 0.25 per cent vanadium has little effect on mechanical properties of the irons; but as indicated in the table, vanadium in the presence of molybdenum strengthens the irons.

109. Investigation of Smith and Aufderhaar.—A series of irons containing up to 3 per cent molybdenum was made and tested by Smith and Aufderhaar.(294) These irons were prepared in a crucible from a mixture of 42 per cent cast scrap, 50 per cent pig iron, and 8 per cent steel. The analysis of test bars was as follows:

	Per Cent
Silicon	2.18
Manganese	0.52
Sulphur	0.060
Phosphorus	0.37
Total carbon	3.32
Graphite	2.67
Combined carbon	0.65

Results of the tests on the irons studied are plotted in Fig. 71. The transverse tests were made on 1.20-in. diameter specimens with a 12-in. span. The breaking load was divided by the cross-sectional area and reported as pounds per square inch. Smith and Aufderhaar stated that a limited number of impact tests indicated that iron containing 1.77 per cent molybdenum has about double the shock resistance of the unalloyed iron, but no values were given.

In a later article Smith and Aufderhaar(406) reported that, in an iron containing 1.61 per cent silicon, 0.62 per cent manganese, and 3.66 per cent total carbon, the addition of 0.47 per cent molybdenum increased transverse strength from 3,150 to 3,425 lb., tensile strength from 24,200 to 28,410 lb. per sq. in., and Brinell hardness from 179 to 207.

The American Cast Iron Pipe Co., according to MacKenzie,[1] analyzed some of the samples used by Smith and Aufderhaar(294)

[1] Private communication.

TABLE 39.—EFFECT OF MOLYBDENUM ON PROPERTIES OF CAST IRON*

Series	Composition, per cent						Transverse test†		Com-pressive strength, lb./sq. in.	Tensile strength, lb./sq. in.	Impact resistance, m-kg./sq. cm.	Brinell hardness
	Si	Mo	V	Total C	Com-bined C	Graph-ite	Modulus of rupture, lb./sq. in.	Deflection, in.				
I	1.12	....	....	3.70	0.87	2.83	33,300	0.26	82,600	13,650	0.69	150
	1.16	0.19	....	3.89	0.83	3.06	33,900	0.34	82,500	13,400	0.83	162
	1.16	0.41	....	3.85	0.75	3.10	33,700	0.27	87,500	14,500	0.81	166
	1.09	1.10	....	4.00	0.80	3.20	32,900	0.26	86,800	15,900	0.59	164
	1.01	0.24	0.19	3.95	0.82	3.13	38,700	0.23	91,000	16,900	0.65	158
	1.11	0.47	0.21	4.00	0.80	3.20	40,800	0.25	94,300	18,900	0.74	154
	1.13	0.96	0.25	3.91	0.75	3.16	37,600	0.22	103,300	19,800	1.03	176
II	1.86	....	....	3.75	0.65	3.10	41,800	0.33	97,000	18,500	0.68	161
	1.77	0.29	....	3.73	0.59	3.14	40,000	0.30	108,800	22,600	0.98	200
	1.77	0.52	....	3.85	0.62	3.23	55,600	0.29	125,800	30,300	1.08	224
	1.82	1.12	....	3.54	0.57	2.97	51,500	0.28	119,800	27,300	0.80	216
	1.80	0.25	0.22	3.90	0.65	3.25	39,100	0.25	101,300	18,800	0.58	182
	1.88	0.57	0.20	3.40	0.48	2.92	64,000	0.31	152,200	35,300	1.17	238
	1.77	1.14	0.19	3.73	0.44	3.29	49,500	0.34	136,100	27,500	1.15	189
III	2.80	....	....	3.76	0.44	3.32	33,300	0.29	89,600	14,900	0.59	173
	2.72	0.31	....	3.81	0.49	3.32	37,400	0.37	92,800	15,600	0.63	190
	2.27	0.47	....	3.89	0.51	3.38	44,100	0.31	120,500	21,800	0.73	202
	2.78	0.95	....	3.63	0.50	3.13	42,250	0.24	116,800	18,500	0.75	191
	2.72	0.27	0.26	3.79	0.48	3.31	37,300	0.25	111,200	15,800	0.93	182
	2.87	0.56	0.28	3.54	0.37	3.17	55,200	0.33	137,700	26,700	0.75	219
	2.75	1.05	0.26	3.59	0.32	3.27	51,500	0.32	113,400	22,900	0.60	185

* Piwowarsky.[161]

† 20-mm. (0.79-in.) diameter specimens; 40-cm. (16.5-in.) span. Impact tests on same unnotched section.

and made transverse tests on small samples cut from these bars. Their analyses, as listed in Table 40 in which both carbon and silicon analyses are the average of three determinations, show that there is considerable variation in the sum of the carbon plus one-third of the silicon, which varies from 3.72 to 4.14 per cent. The results of transverse tests made on ½-in. diameter

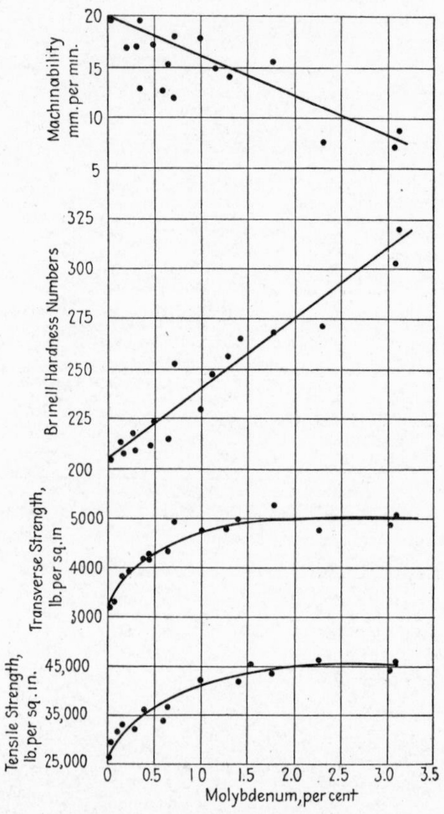

Fig. 71.—Effect of molybdenum on the properties of gray cast iron. (*Smith and Aufderhaar.*[294])

section with a 5-in. span are plotted in Fig. 72 together with the value carbon plus one-third silicon.

MacKenzie affirmed that the curves shown in the paper by Smith and Aufderhaar are probably approximately correct, but that, when individual results are considered, serious discrepancies result if a constant analysis is assumed. He also stated that the assumption of a constant analysis in crucible melts is a common source of error.

110. Investigation of Musatti and Calbiani.—A comprehensive study of the effects of molybdenum on cast iron was recently

TABLE 40.—ANALYSES OF IRONS TESTED BY SMITH AND AUFDERHAAR[294]
(As determined by J. T. MacKenzie of the American Cast Iron Pipe Co.)

Number	Composition, per cent			
	Mo	C	Si	C + ⅓Si
1	0.00	3.32	2.16	4.04
2	0.12	3.26	2.58	4.14
3	0.16	3.08	2.23	3.82
4	0.24	3.07	2.29	3.83
5	0.36	3.26	2.25	3.81
6	0.47	3.19	2.37	3.98
7	0.64	3.23	2.05	3.91
8	0.75	3.39	2.17	4.11
9	0.98	3.24	2.35	4.02
10	1.24	3.12	1.84	3.73
11	1.36	3.24	2.33	4.02
12	1.87	3.41	2.08	4.10
13	3.21	3.11	1.82	3.72

reported by Musatti and Calbiani.[385] The irons were melted in a small electric furnace, and the following materials were used:

	Per Cent
Pig Iron	
Total carbon	4.0
Manganese	0.09
Silicon	0.20
Phosphorus	0.017
Sulphur	0.03
Steel	
Carbon	0.5
Silicon	0.2
Manganese	1.0
Ferrosilicon	
Silicon	45
Ferromanganese	
Manganese	75
Ferromolybdenum	
Molybdenum	65 to 68

The heats were held at a temperature of 1500°C. (2730°F.) for 10 min. and cast at a temperature of 1450°C. (2640°F.) into bars 30 mm. (1.18 in.) in diameter and 650 mm. (25.6 in.) long. Transverse tests were made with a 60-cm. (23.6-in.) span. Tensile tests were made on specimens 20 mm. (0.79 in.) in diameter, and compression tests on 16 × 16-mm. (0.63 × 0.63-in.) cylinders. Brinell hardness determinations were made at the center of the samples.

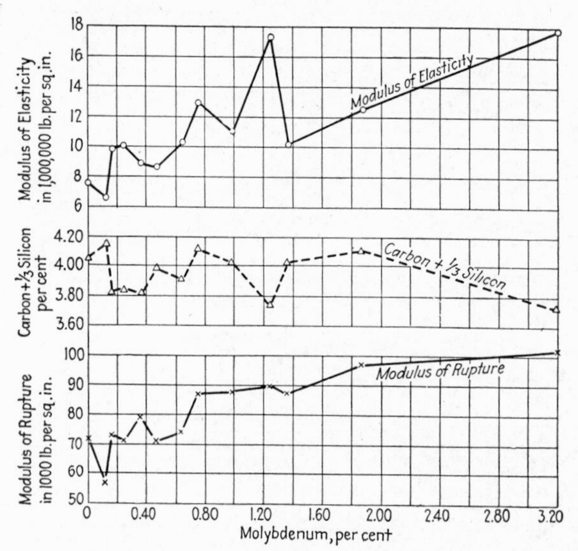

Fig. 72.—Transverse tests on small specimens. (*Irons made by Smith and Aufderhaar;*[294] *tests made by MacKenzie.*)

The analyses and mechanical properties of the irons are listed in Tables 41 and 42. Figure 73 shows the effect of various amounts of molybdenum on tensile strength and modulus of rupture of irons having definite carbon and silicon contents.

111. Challansonnet's Investigation.—The combined effects of molybdenum and nickel on the properties of three series of irons were recently studied by Challansonnet.[322] The alloys were prepared by melting in a plumbago crucible, 45 kg (100 lb.) of each alloy being prepared. The samples used in determining mechanical properties were 35 mm. (1.38 in.) in diameter and 500 mm. (19.7 in.) long. They were cast in dry sand molds.

The mechanical properties and analyses of the irons tested by Challansonnet are listed in Table 43. As may be observed from

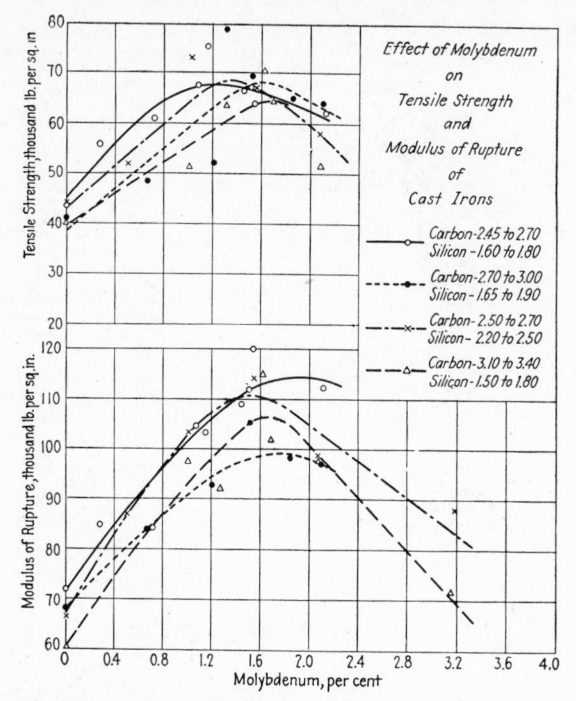

Fig. 73.—Effect of molybdenum on strength properties of cast irons. (*Musatti and Calbiani.*[385])

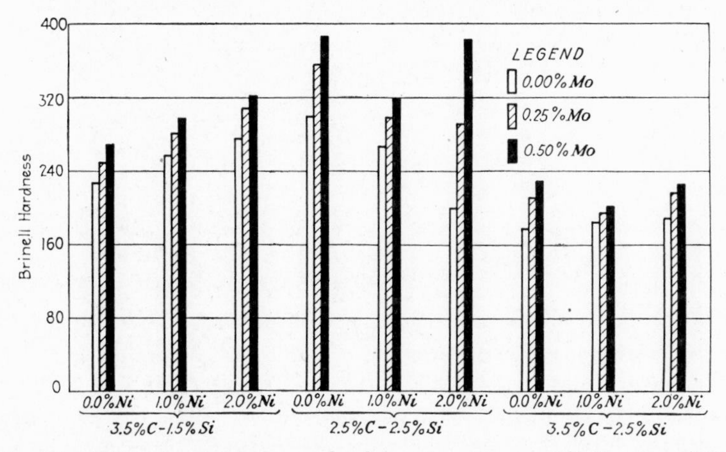

Fig. 74.—Effect of molybdenum on hardness of cast irons. (*Challansonnet.*[322])

TABLE 41.—MECHANICAL PROPERTIES OF MOLYBDENUM CAST IRON*

Number	Composition, per cent								Transverse test†		Com-pressive strength, lb./sq. in.	Tensile strength, lb./sq. in.	Brinell hardness
	Total C	Graph-ite	Com-bined C	Si	Mn	P	S	Mo	Modulus of rupture, lb./sq. in.	Deflection, in.			
1	2.54	1.57	0.97	1.78	0.52	0.033	0.039	....	71,800	0.413	130,100	43,700	239
2	2.74	2.06	0.68	1.70	0.32	0.020	0.040	....	68,000	0.354	142,200	41,200	228
3	2.69	1.90	0.79	2.18	0.39	0.022	0.039	....	66,300	0.480	144,400	43,800	201
4	2.48	1.53	0.95	1.74	0.50	0.041	0.033	0.28	84,800	0.496	176,400	55,900	242
5	2.54	1.62	0.92	2.28	0.47	0.029	0.034	0.51	86,900	0.520	176,400	52,100	232
6	2.72	1.99	0.73	2.53	0.35	0.025	0.027	0.55	93,200	0.689	140,200	42,800	199
7	2.85	2.07	0.78	1.73	0.36	0.027	0.026	0.67	83,900	0.453	197,700	48,600	228
8	2.55	1.67	0.88	1.67	0.31	0.043	0.025	0.72	84,100	0.370	214,800	61,200	267
9	2.62	1.73	0.89	2.46	0.49	0.023	0.018	1.02	103,300	0.488	296,000	72,800	271
10	2.61	1.80	0.71	1.78	0.45	0.025	0.031	1.08	104,500	0.480	224,000	67,600	237
11	2.60	1.82	0.78	1.76	0.44	0.026	0.039	1.16	103,200	0.445	....	75,400	243
12	2.88	1.86	1.02	1.89	0.54	0.031	0.025	1.21	92,900	0.472	204,900	52,100	290
13	2.79	1.93	0.76	1.74	0.39	0.032	0.027	1.31	72,100	0.323	310,000	78,800	262
14	2.53	1.57	0.96	1.89	0.43	0.027	0.021	1.41	111,800	0.453	224,800	68,400	289
15	2.63	1.88	0.75	1.68	0.46	0.028	0.018	1.45	108,800	0.449	241,800	66,600	256
16	2.62	1.78	0.80	1.77	0.53	0.035	0.036	1.51	111,900	0.457	192,000	67,100	260
17	2.89	1.98	0.91	1.68	0.40	0.025	0.023	1.52	105,300	0.614	249,000	69,300	256
18	2.57	1.86	0.71	1.70	0.35	0.022	0.044	1.54	120,200	0.531	....	64,000	233
19	2.69	1.82	0.87	2.48	0.46	0.023	0.020	1.55	114,200	0.665	212,000	66,900	265
20	2.77	2.02	0.75	1.68	0.38	0.026	0.021	1.85	98,300	0.571	250,300	64,900	249
21	2.52	1.48	1.04	2.24	0.48	0.033	0.029	2.07	98,800	0.551	186,500	57,900	294
22	2.59	1.49	1.10	1.55	0.30	0.022	0.034	2.12	112,300	0.453	....	62,200	295
23	2.78	1.67	1.09	1.65	0.55	0.027	0.029	2.10	97,200	0.472	232,600	64,000	286
24	2.62	....	....	2.22	0.52	0.035	0.041	3.19	88,300	0.217	....	......	388

* Musatti and Calbiani.[385]

† 30-mm. (1.18-in.) diameter specimens; 60-cm. (23.6-in.) span.

TABLE 42.—MECHANICAL PROPERTIES OF MOLYBDENUM CAST IRON*

Number	Composition, per cent								Transverse test†		Com-pressive strength, lb./sq. in.	Tensile strength, lb./sq. in.	Brinell hardness
	Total C	Graph-ite	Com-bined C	Si	Mn	P	S	Mo	Modulus of rupture, lb./sq. in.	Deflection, in.			
28	3.26	2.54	0.72	1.57	0.30	0.025	0.037	....	60,400	0.453	135,400	40,500	191
29	3.08	2.21	0 87	2.30	0.35	0.024	0.029	0.62	91,000	0.760	152,200	46,800	221
30	3.06	2.20	0.86	1.72	0.37	0.023	0.025	1.01	97,300	0.520	163,500	51,500	239
31	3.00	2.07	0.93	2.38	0.42	0.024	0.027	1.23	99,600	0.732	199,100	54,900	230
32	3.28	2.23	0.95	2.08	0.38	0.027	0.025	1.23	81,200	0.610	106,000	28,300	191
33	3.32	2.43	0.89	1.78	0.32	0.025	0.026	1.28	92,000	0.744	155,300	44,700	211
34	3.04	2.08	0.96	2.30	0.42	0.026	0.028	1.25	97,600	0.760	177,700	47,100	220
35	3.42	2.55	0.87	1.53	0.50	0.029	0.022	1.24	98,100	0.472	192,500	64,000	252
36	3.24	2.45	0.79	1.61	0.50	0.025	0.023	1.31	74,900	0.492	170,800	63,600	221
37	3.10	2.33	0.77	1.53	0.30	0.027	0.027	1.36	99,600	0.535	210,500	62,600	242
38	3.15	2.31	0.84	1.51	0.48	0.020	0.021	1.45	104,100	0.669	177,700	53,900	246
39	3.14	2.16	0.98	1.85	0.30	0.036	0.020	1.68	107,800	0.579	254,700	65,700	258
40	3.36	2.44	0.92	1.73	0.35	0.032	0.014	1.62	115,000	0.610	284,600	70,400	253
41	3.17	2.31	0.86	1.67	0.43	0.023	0.021	1.69	101,700	0.709	223,200	64,800	252
42	3.08	2.07	0.96	1.59	0.48	0.021	0.026	1.59	113,800	0.472	214,200	65,100	248
43	3.12	2.01	1.11	1.63	0.41	0.027	0.019	2.08	97,800	0.402	183,500	51,600	260
44	3.07	....	....	1.71	0.51	0.029	0.020	3.15	71,900	0.165	....	......	412‡

* Musatti and Calbiani.(385)

† 30-mm. (1.18-in.) diameter specimen; 60-cm. (23.6-in.) span.

‡ White fracture.

this table, one series contained 3.5 per cent carbon with 1.5 per cent silicon, another series the same amount of carbon with 1 per cent silicon, while the third series contained 2.5 per cent carbon with 2 per cent silicon. Each series consisted of alloys

TABLE 43.—MECHANICAL PROPERTIES OF MOLYBDENUM CAST IRON*

Number	Composition, per cent									Transverse test, breaking load, lb.†	Compressive strength, lb./sq. in.	Brinell hardness
	Total C	Combined C	Si	Mn	P	S	Ni	Mo	Ni/Mo			
1A	3.52	1.4	1.44	0.4	0.077	0.02	....	....	....	1625	145,400	228
2A	3.43	1.48	1.3	0.45	0.075	0.02	....	0.23	....	2000	203,400	250
3A	3.5	1.5	1.4	0.36	0.075	0.02	....	0.51	....	2121	204,800	269
4A	3.52	1.32	1.43	0.4	0.075	0.02	1.04	....	....	1670	146,800	258
5A	3.45	1.4	1.36	0.42	0.075	0.02	0.96	0.27	3.5	1900	153,600	281
6A	3.49	1.32	1.30	0.35	0.075	0.02	1.03	0.54	1.90	2205	175,000	297
7A	3.52	1.20	1.44	0.4	0.075	0.02	2.01	....	....	1720	157,800	262
8A	3.55	1.2	1.40	0.31	0.075	0.02	2.01	0.23	8.75	2396	206,300	309
9A	3.59	1.15	1.32	0.4	0.075	0.02	2.05	0.48	4.2	2480	207,700	322
1B	3.71	1.05	2.64	0.55	0.11	0.04	....	....	....	1378	72,500	278
2B	3.65	0.95	2.63	0.42	0.10	0.04	....	0.26	....	1571	93,200	212
3B	3.67	0.90	2.50	0.57	0.10	0.04	....	0.55	....	1615	93,200	230
4B	3.68	1.02	2.63	0.52	0.10	0.04	1.00	....	....	1289	79,600	186
5B	3.65	0.90	2.64	0.55	0.10	0.04	0.95	0.23	4.1	1790	81,100	196
6B	3.72	0.97	2.6	0.50	.....	.....	0.98	0.54	1.8	1889	85,300	202
7B	3.69	1.00	2.62	0.50	0.12	0.038	2.04	....	....	1442	82,800	192
8B	3.75	0.85	2.55	0.50	0.10	0.04	2.03	0.27	7.5	2094	91,000	217
9B	3.68	0.90	2.43	0.48	0.10	0.04	1.97	0.52	3.8	2176	91,300	226
1C	2.5	1.5	2.5	0.50	0.07	0.038	....	....	....	2396	159,600	301
2C	2.45	2.11	2.40	0.53	0.07	0.02	....	0.25	....	2833	179,200	359
3C	2.31	2.2	2.35	0.54	0.07	0.018	....	0.48	....	2646	182,800	389
4C	2.48	1.3	2.45	0.48	0.07	0.036	0.98	....	....	2302	179,200	251
5C	2.5	2.08	2.5	0.50	0.07	0.038	1.1	0.22	4.5	2480	184,900	301
6C	2.43	2.15	2.43	0.38	0.07	0.038	1.05	0.55	2.0	2811	193,400	320
7C	2.50	1.2	2.43	0.50	.....	.....	1.98	....	....	2278	180,600	277
8C	2.39	1.9	2.54	0.45	0.07	0.038	2.04	0.24	8.5	3086	196,300	293
9C	2.35	2.04	2.45	0.35	0.07	0.038	2.1	0.58	3.6	3031	200,600	385

* Challansonnet.(322)

† Sample 10 mm. (0.39 in.) high, 8 mm. (0.31 in.) wide, 30-mm. (1.18-in.) span.

containing 0, 1, and 2 per cent nickel with either 0.25 or 0.5 per cent molybdenum. The compression tests were made on 9 × 9-mm. (0.35 × 0.35-in.) cylinders. The transverse tests were made on samples 8 mm. (0.31 in.) wide and 10 mm. (0.39 in.) high with a 30-mm. (1.18-in.) span. Values of "double shear" were given by Challansonnet but are not included here.

TABLE 44.—MECHANICAL PROPERTIES OF MOLYBDENUM CAST IRON*

Number	Composition, per cent							Transverse test†		Tensile strength, lb./sq. in.	Brinell hardness	Shrinkage, in.	Drill,‡ per cent
	Total C	Combined C	Si	S	Mn	P	Mo	Load, lb.	Deflection, in.				
1	3.38	0.68	1.88	0.098	0.76	0.24	0	1994	0.25	30,300	196	0.135	− 5.6
2	3.46	0.80	1.80	0.10	0.80	0.22	0.19	2125	0.29	32,150	187	0.130	+ 7.2
3	3.49	0.67	1.82	0.10	0.73	0.26	0.38	2559	0.31	38,950	187	0.090	+ 6.0
4	3.45	0.77	1.85	0.096	0.81	0.23	0.73	2692	0.32	44,300	207	0.105	+13.6
5	3.41	0.81	1.89	0.096	0.80	0.25	0.82	2843	0.30	47,200	228	0.105	+19.3
6	2.97	0.82	2.92	0.162	1.07	0.10	0.82	3071	0.32	59,200	302	0.140	+70.0

* Sherwin and Kiley.[498]
† 1.20-in. diameter specimens, 18-in. span.
‡ See section on machinability.

The Brinell hardness values determined by Challansonnet are plotted in Fig. 74 and, as may be observed, the molybdenum in all cases causes a slight increase in hardness.

112. Investigation of Sherwin and Kiley.—The effects of molybdenum on the properties of cast iron as determined by Sherwin and Kiley(498) are shown in Table 44. As these authors observed, molybdenum increases hardness, tensile strength, transverse strength, and deflection. The transverse tests were made on standard A.S.T.M. bars, 1.20-in. diameter, with an 18-in. span. All of the irons were cupola-melted, and ferromolybdenum was added at the spout. In irons 1 to 5 inclusive 20 per cent steel was used, while iron 6 is described as "high-test," and the charge consisted of 75 per cent steel.

TABLE 45.—MECHANICAL PROPERTIES OF MOLYBDENUM CAST IRON*

Number	Composition, per cent							Transverse test		Tensile strength, lb./sq. in.	Brinell hardness
	Total C	Combined C	Si	Mn	P	S	Mo	Modulus of rupture, lb./sq. in.	Deflection, in.		
1	3.44	0.68	2.62	0.43	0.16	0.09	....	49,000	0.417	27,500	167
2	3.42	0.68	2.48	0.43	0.16	0.06	0.80	70,200	0.504	36,700	195
3	3.46	0.70	2.41	0.27	0.13	0.03	1.24	63,300	0.400	43,400	207
4	3.24	0.74	2.50	0.35	0.15	0.03	1.27	68,600	0.476	36,000	229
5	3.36	....	2.45	0.4	....	.....	1.91	......	......	36,300	223
6	3.30	0.92	2.48	0.4	0.16	.....	2.23	70,700	0.378	41,000	241
7	3.32	0.98	2.50	0.42	0.15	0.039	2.50	84,400	0.469	48,900	245

* Küster and Pfannenschmidt.(468)

113. Investigation of Küster and Pfannenschmidt.—Irons were prepared by Küster and Pfannenschmidt(468) by melting 2000 kg. (4400 lb.) of "hematite iron" and 400 kg. (880 lb.) of steel scrap in a Héroult furnace. The bath was superheated and then cooled to 1380°C. (2515°F.) after which test pieces were cast. Several additions of molybdenum were then made, test pieces being cast after each addition. The iron was not superheated between additions of molybdenum, and all bars were cast at 1380°C. (2515°F.). After testing, the bars were remelted in an air furnace; the remelted irons were Nos. 3 to 6 inclusive. The values reported by these authors are listed in

Table 45. The dimensions of neither castings nor test pieces were given. Küster and Pfannenschmidt observed that molybdenum increases all strength values.

114. Report of the Climax Molybdenum Co.—The data in Table 46, taken from the Climax Molybdenum Co.'s booklet,[(431)] are the results of tests on automotive irons obtained in daily practice by five different commercial foundries. The transverse tests in this and other tables were obtained with a 1.25-in. diameter bar on a 12-in. span. The following crushing tests[1] were reported on pistons:

	Total Load, Lb.
0.35 per cent molybdenum iron	20,000
0.80 per cent molybdenum iron	22,000
Other alloy iron	18,000

The analyses and transverse tests on some "wear-resistant" irons are listed in Table 47 and similar data for die irons are given in Table 48. The analyses and mechanical properties of some "high-test" irons are listed in Table 49. All of these irons were melted in electric furnaces.

The following data show the effect of molybdenum on the endurance limit and impact resistance of "cylinder" iron:

Iron	Endurance limit, lb./sq. in.	Charpy impact strength
Plain iron	18,000	2.2
0.35 % molybdenum iron	22,000 to 24,000	2.2
0.80 % molybdenum iron	....	4.1

115. Report of the Molybdenum Corporation of America.—A recently issued booklet[(482)] describes a study of the combined effects of molybdenum and chromium, and molybdenum and nickel, on the properties of a medium-strength cast iron, the objective being the determination of the effect of small amounts of these elements on the properties of an iron having a tensile strength of approximately 30,000 lb. per sq. in. Two acid electric-furnace heats were used in preparing twenty-one sets

[1] According to one of the reviewers the 0.80 per cent molybdenum iron also contains 0.35 per cent nickel. Without the nickel the pistons tend to show a tendency to chill on the skirts.

TABLE 46.—MECHANICAL PROPERTIES OF MOLYBDENUM AUTOMOTIVE IRONS FOR CYLINDER BLOCKS AND PISTONS*

Composition, per cent							Transverse test†		Tensile strength, lb./sq. in.	Brinell hardness
Total C	Combined C	Si	S	P	Mn	Mo	Load, lb.	Deflection, in.		
3.32	0.23	2.38	0.07	0.158	0.53	0.35	4,680 (Avg. 4)	0.115 (Avg. 4)	......	207
3.36	0.15	2.10	0.09	0.15	0.44	0.35	4,500	0.126	38,900	207
3.31	0.34	2.35	0.072	0.151	0.46	0.35	4,210	0.12	38,880	207
3.20	0.46	2.42	0.057	0.210	0.51	0.41	5,600	0.13		
3.23	0.33	2.10	0.079	0.21	0.58	0.30	4,500			
3.30	0.41	2.27	0.072	0.21	0.60	0.35	5,100	.....	......	207
3.29	....	2.20	0.09	0.15	0.65	0.35	4,060 (Avg. 5)	.....	34,800 (Avg. 4)	217
3.44	0.57	2.30	0.113	0.165	0.81	0.40	.....	.....	34,640	
3.30	0.62	1.90	0.146	0.18	0.90	0.38	4,450	.....	......	255
3.40	0.46	2.25	0.065	0.165	0.63	0.40	5,132	.....	......	202
3.28	0.46	2.14	0.066	0.171	0.63	0.35	5,000	0.145		

* Climax Molybdenum Co.[431]

† 1.25-in. diameter specimen; 12-in. span.

TABLE 47.—MECHANICAL PROPERTIES OF MOLYBDENUM WEAR-RESISTANT IRONS*

Composition, per cent							Transverse test†	
Total C	Combined C	Si	S	P	Mn	Mo	Load, lb.	Deflection, in.
3.30	0.54	2.36	0.047	0.314	0.54	0.52	5,650	0.12
3.52	0.46	2.05	0.060	0.210	0.52	0.54	5,550 5,460	0.14 0.14
3.20	0.35	2.23	0.049	0.154	0.60	0.54	5,370 6,080	0.11 0.13
3.21	0.50	2.19	0.046	0.169	0.56	0.54	6,160 6,140	0.14 0.14
3.22	0.44	2.34	0.041	0.214	0.64	0.54	5,990 5,350 5,730	0.15 0.13 0.15
3.38	0.42	2.35	0.051	0.210	0.54	0.57	5,500 5,790	0.12 0.13
3.24	0.52	2.20	0.050	0.162	0.62	0.57	5,720 6,440	0.14 0.15
3.20	0.48	2.27	0.045	0.173	0.57	0.58	6,000 5,360	0.15 0.12
3.15	0.54	2.14	0.038	0.238	0.60	0.58	5,680	0.14
3.36	0.47	2.21	0.050	0.154	0.54	0.58	5,590 6,190	0.12 0.13
3.13	0.58	2.13	0.046	0.164	0.59	0.59	5,940 5,760	0.13 0.14
3.29	0.56	1.96	0.050	0.215	0.60	0.60	5,520 5,310	0.12 0.12
3.32	0.58	2.08	0.040	0.168	0.59	0.60	5,800 5,660	0.13 0.11

* Climax Molybdenum Co.[431]

† 1.25-in. diameter specimens; 12-in. span.

TABLE 47.—(*Continued*)

Composition, per cent							Transverse test†	
Total C	Combined C	Si	S	P	Mn	Mo	Load, lb.	Deflection, in.
3.08	0.56	2.26	0.045	0.145	0.62	0.62	5,730 6,590 6,100 6,160	0.14 0.15 0.14 0.14
3.28	0.43	2.51	0.042	0.141	0.54	0.69	6,970	0.13
3.12	0.53	2.59	0.042	0.176	0.63	0.70	5,390	0.12
3.22	0.45	2.23	0.040	0.148	0.63	0.72	5,310 5,800	0.13 0.13
3.20	0.41	2.25	0.045	0.146	0.60	0.72	5,770	0.14
3.20	0.64	2.10	0.059	0.213	0.67	0.74	5,380	0.15
3.24	0.52	1.81	0.040	0.116	0.54	0.74	5,520 5,790	0.12 0.12
3.32	0.64	1.72	0.052	0.123	0.47	0.75	5,560 5,750 5,780 5,700 5,880 5,760	0.12 0.13 0.13 0.14 0.15 0.13
3.20	0.56	1.94	0.048	0.156	0.50	0.75	5,400 5,720	0.16 0.15
3.11	0.48	2.38	0.081	0.150	0.61	0.89	6,860 6,370	0.15 0.14

of test bars. The charges of 400 lb. each consisted of 50 per cent pig iron, 25 per cent scrap, 15 per cent railroad malleable scrap, and 10 per cent steel. The alloys used were 62.12 per cent ferromolybdenum, 70 per cent ferrochromium, and 92 per cent nickel shot.

Round transverse test bars 1.22 in. in diameter and 13 in. long were cast and broken on a 12-in. span. Tensile test bars were machined from the broken transverse specimens. Machinability tests were made by determining the depth of penetration of a 5/16-in. high-speed drill supporting a weight of 135 lb. and rotating at 400 r.p.m. The results of the tests are given in Table 50.

TABLE 48.—MECHANICAL PROPERTIES OF MOLYBDENUM DIE IRONS*

Composition, per cent							Transverse test†	
Total C	Combined C	Si	S	P	Mn	Mo	Load, lb.	Deflection, in.
3.32	0.46	2.35	0.040	0.144	0.62	1.25	6,430 6,700	0.14 0.14
3.55	0.70	2.10	0.061	0.247	0.56	1.36	5,600 5,900	0.13 0.13
3.18	0.67	1.88	0.060	0.375	0.51	1.51	5,600 5,470	0.13 0.14
3.09	0.76	1.55	0.066	0.237	....	1.23	5,800	0.15
3.18	0.49	2.06	0.029	0.259	0.50	1.60	6,000	
3.13	0.58	1.99	0.042	0.175	0.56	0.94	6,220	0.14
3.31	0.31	1.92	0.045	0.235	0.53	1.12	6,200	0.15

* Climax Molybdenum Co.[431]
† 1.25-in. diameter specimens; 12-in. span.

From these results it was concluded that where increased strengths and good machinability are desired the molybdenum-chromium and molybdenum-nickel irons offer splendid opportunities, and that the alloys can be added to ladle or furnace with excellent recoveries. It was pointed out that in one case the strength was increased 60 per cent by the use of the alloys.

116. Other Reports.—The possibility of improving malleable iron by addition of molybdenum was considered by Coonan.[255] He determined the effect of molybdenum in such iron by preparing bars containing as much as 1 per cent molybdenum and annealing them for 140 hr. at 845°C. (1550°F.), including the

TABLE 49.—MECHANICAL PROPERTIES OF MOLYBDENUM HIGH-TEST IRONS*

	Composition, per cent							Transverse test†		Tensile strength, lb./sq. in.	Brinell hardness
	Total C	Combined C	Si	S	P	Mn	Mo	Load, lb.	Deflection, in.		
Low molybdenum additions to electric furnace iron	3.10	0.55	2.30	0.10	0.10	0.64	0.35	5,150	0.15	......	241
	2.66	0.75	2.54	0.075	0.224	0.50	0.35	5,370	0.13	50,100	
	3.09	0.85	2.22	0.10	0.20	....	0.35	6,000	0.16	47,000	255
	3.10	0.70	2.35	.....	.....	....	0.35	5,500	.....	......	255
	2.93	....	2.48	0.106	0.18	0.65	0.35	5,650	0.155	......	269
								5,800	0.160		
	3.03	....	2.46	0.103	.....	0.74	0.35	5,500	0.155	......	255
								5,390			
	3.20	....	2.34	0.110	.....	0.72	0.35	5,600	0.17	......	
								5,700	0.17	......	241
Medium molybdenum additions to electric furnace iron	2.50	0.60	2.25	0.09	0.20	0.40	0.50	7,750	.....	63,000	260

* Climax Molybdenum Co.[431]

† 1.25-in. diameter specimens; 12-in. span.

TABLE 50.—MECHANICAL PROPERTIES OF MOLYBDENUM-CHROMIUM AND MOLYBDENUM-NICKEL CAST IRON*

Base† iron	Composition, per cent				Transverse test‡		Tensile strength, lb./sq. in.	Machinability, in./min.	Brinell hardness
	Combined C	Mo	Cr	Ni	Load, lb.	Deflection, in.			
A......	0.66	....	....	....	4,560	0.150	31,000	1.02	207
A......	0.68	0.13	....	....	4,910	0.155	32,000	0.94	212
A......	0.68	0.13	0.07	....	5,150	0.140	32,000	0.94	217
A......	0.68	0.13	0.14	....	5,500	0.170	39,000	0.94	223
A......	0.69	0.13	0.19	....	5,030	0.152	38,000	0.94	223
A......	0.72	0.13	0.31	....	4,450	0.141	31,000	0.87	241
A......	0.68	0.13	....	0.22	5,030	0.160	35,000	1.02	207
A......	0.66	0.13	....	0.55	4,680	0.175	35,500	1.10	212
A......	0.69	0.13	....	1.49	5,030	0.145	40,100	1.06	223
B......	0.68	....	....	....	4,620	0.160	31,250	1.02	212
B......	0.68	0.37	....	....	5,590	0.190	34,000	1.02	217
B......	0.68	0.37	0.06	....	7,100	0.181	42,750	1.10	223
B......	0.69	0.37	0.14	....	5,220	0.180	43,500	1.02	228
B......	0.70	0.37	0.19	....	4,970	0.144	49,250	0.94	228
B......	0.71	0.37	0.35	....	3,920	0.135	32,600	0.79	241
B......	0.70	0.37	....	0.31	5,560	0.180	33,000	1.26	228
B......	0.71	0.37	....	0.39	5,675	0.160	45,050	1.12	241
B......	0.72	0.37	....	0.59	5,620	0.170	40,500	0.94	241
B......	0.71	0.37	....	0.73	5,730	0.190	45,700	0.94	255
B......	0.72	0.37	....	0.94	5,770	0.185	44,200	0.87	248
B......	0.72	0.37	....	3.93	.....	.....	43,100	0.79	248

* Molybdenum Corporation of America.[482]
† Analyses of base irons are given in Table 50*A*.
‡ 1.22-in. diameter specimen; 12-in. span.

TABLE 50*A*.—ANALYSES OF BASE IRONS USED FOR TESTS REPORTED IN TABLE 50

Iron	Composition, per cent				
	Total C	Si	S	Mn	P
A...............	3.18	2.12	0.098	0.70	0.235
B...............	3.21	2.00	0.098	0.63	0.272

time of heating and cooling. The results of tensile tests on these samples are given in Table 51.

Examples were given by Lowry(373) to prove that a chromium-molybdenum iron has good mechanical properties.

TABLE 51.—TENSILE PROPERTIES OF MALLEABLE IRON CONTAINING MOLYBDENUM*

Number	Mo, per cent	Tensile strength, lb./sq. in.	Yield strength,† lb./sq. in.	Elongation in 2 in., per cent
1	0	44,200	31,600	7.5
2	0.25	48,500	35,100	8.0
3	0.50	54,300	35,100	8.5
4	0.75	58,300	40,200	8.0
5	1.00	60,000	44,000	7.0

* Coonan.(255)
† Reported as yield point.

In a discussion by Gebrüder Sulzer Aktiengesellschaft,(341) it was stated that the alloying elements frequently added to cast iron, including molybdenum, cause a marked increase in hardness, but that the strength does not rise above that of the best unalloyed irons.

Bromer(426) reported the summary of tests on four grades of iron made during two months (December and January, 1930–1931) at the Standard Foundry Co., Table 52. These tests were made on 1.20-in. diameter bars with a 12-in. span except where noted. The bars were cast in green sand. The exact analyses of the irons were not given. All of the irons probably contained some nickel and chromium because of the return of the scrap.

The results of tests on cast irons containing molybdenum made at Battelle Memorial Institute for the Worthington Pump and Machinery Co., through whose courtesy the data are made available here, are listed in Table 53. The tensile tests in this table made at 425°C. (800°F.) were made by the short-time method and do not indicate much, if any, difference due to the molybdenum. The test bars were cast 1.2 in. in diameter and 13 in. long. The transverse specimens were broken on a 12-in. span. The results of creep or flow tests, plotted in Fig. 75 and summarized in Table 54, indicate that 0.83 per cent molybdenum in an iron of the type tested markedly increases the load that can be maintained at a temperature of 370°C. (700°F.) without creep. Creep tests on iron 64 at 425°C. (800°F.)

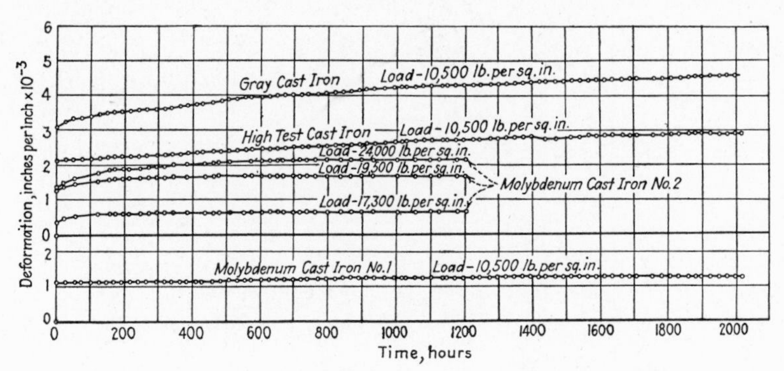

FIG. 75.—Creep (flow) of cast irons at 370°C. (700°F.). Gray cast iron is No. 0 of Table 53; molybdenum iron No. 1 is No. 25 of Table 53; and molybdenum iron No. 2 is No. 64 of Table 53. (*Battelle Memorial Institute.*)

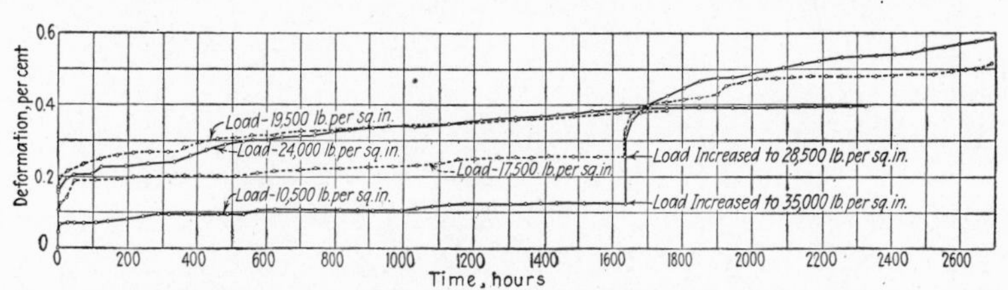

FIG. 76.—Creep (flow) of molybdenum cast iron at 425°C. (800°F.). Iron tested is No. 64 of Table 53. (*Battelle Memorial Institute.*)

are shown in Fig. 76. Results obtained on other irons by this method of testing have been considered by R. J. Allen in a discussion of a recent paper by Bolton and Bornstein.[425]

TABLE 52.—SUMMARY OF RESULTS OF TRANSVERSE TESTS* RUNNING TWO MONTHS AT STANDARD FOUNDRY CO.†

Iron	Number of bars tested	Average load, lb.	Average deflection, in.
Plain iron	88	4,738	0.128
Plain iron (18-in. span)	14	2,722	0.24
Nickel-chromium iron (low)	32	4,740	0.137
Nickel-chromium iron (high)	42	4,738	0.13
Molybdenum iron	41	5,400	0.157

* 1.20-in. diameter specimens; 12-in. span unless noted.
† Bromer.[426]

TABLE 53.—MECHANICAL PROPERTIES OF MOLYBDENUM CAST IRON*

Number	Composition, per cent								Transverse test†		Tensile strength, lb./sq. in.		Brinell hardness
	Total C	Graph-ite	Com-bined C	Si	Mn	P	S	Mo	Load, lb.	Deflection, in.	Room tem-perature	425°C. (800°F.)	
0	3.40	2.70	0.70	1.50	0.75	0.15	0.08	0	4,020	0.16	32,900	31,400	197
22	2.75	2.38	0.37	2.42	0.68	0.06	0.07	0.63	4,930	0.17	43,000	39,900	192
25	2.75	2.27	0.48	2.10	0.70	0.06	0.06	0.83	6,490	0.17	59,500	52,900	241
26	2.80	2.40	0.40	2.02	0.65	0.06	0.05	1.58	6,780	0.18	59,800	55,100	223
52	2.80	1.94	0.86	1.89	0.62	0.06	0.08	0.92	6,180	0.14	61,000	......	287
53	2.42	1.37	1.05	1.96	0.60	0.06	0.09	0.76					
55	2.78	2.15	0.63	2.16	0.67	0.05	0.08	0.81	5,920	0.13	64,900	......	260
64	2.72	2.06	0.66	2.50	0.66	0.054	0.071	0.83	5,970	0.145	52,500	......	241

* Battelle Memorial Institute.
† 1.20-in. diameter specimen; 12-in. span.

In discussion of the June, 1931, *Report* of the A.S.T.M. Committee A-3, MacKenzie presented the data given in Fig. 77, which show the uniform properties of molybdenum cast iron. Round bars 2 in. in diameter were machined from various loca-

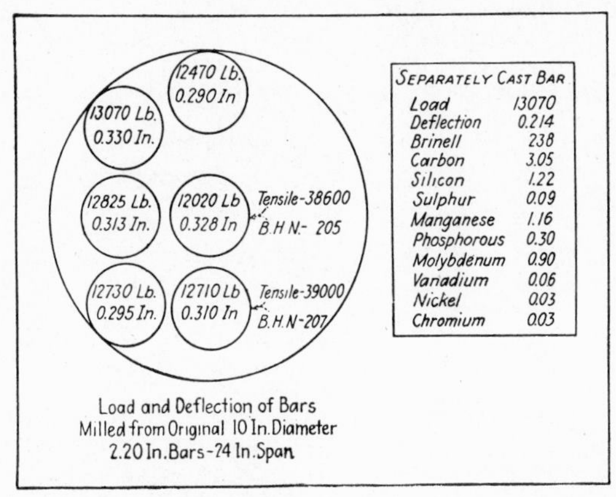

FIG. 77.—Properties of molybdenum cast iron as influenced by size of section Separately cast bar 2.2 in. in diameter. (*MacKenzie.*)

tions in a 10-in. round casting, and the properties of these bars compared with bars cast as 2-in. rounds. The iron was made in

TABLE 54.—CREEP OR FLOW OF CAST IRON AT 370°C. (700°F.)*

Number	Mo, per cent	Load, lb./sq. in.	Deformation, in./in./hr. $\times 10^{-7}$				
			1 to 150 hr.	150 to 450 hr.	450 to 900 hr.	900 to 1,200 hr.	1,200 to 2,000 hr.
0	0	10,500	12.1	12.1	5.9	3.4	3.0
x†	0	10,500	5.3	5.3	5.3	3.4	0‡
25	0.83	10,500	0.8	0.8	2.2	0	0
64	0.83	17,300	10.0	0	0	0	
64	0.83	19,500	16.7	3.7	0	0	
64	0.83	24,000	30.0	6.7	1.6	0	

* Battelle Memorial Institute.
† Special "high-test" iron.
‡ 1,850 to 2,000 hr.

a cupola from a mixture containing 70 per cent steel rails, and the molybdenum was added to the ladle in the form of ferromolybdenum. MacKenzie pointed out that the separately cast bar

(2-in. diameter) represents the strength fairly well, even of the 10-in. diameter bar, but that deflection on the separately cast bar is considerably lower and Brinell hardness higher. Tensile tests were made with the U. S. Ordnance standard specimen for cast iron, being machined to a diameter of 1.129 in. with a gage length of 1 in.

D. SPECIAL PROPERTIES OF MOLYBDENUM CAST IRON

It is usually necessary to produce castings that can be readily machined, as some machining is done on the majority of castings. Unfortunately, no very satisfactory test has been developed for machinability, and the effect of molybdenum on this property must be judged from reported observations of shop work and comparative drill tests. The wear resistance is another property that cannot be exactly estimated from laboratory tests, although the Amsler test probably indicates the relative wear resistance. Data on the effects of molybdenum on such properties as density, electric resistance, and magnetic permeability of cast iron are not available.

117. Machinability.—Sargent[92] gave Brinell hardness values and tensile-strength values for cast irons containing 2 and 4 per cent molybdenum in comparison with molybdenum-free iron. Although molybdenum increased the hardness and strength, Sargent claimed that the machinability of both irons containing molybdenum was better than for ordinary iron. In a discussion of this statement, Davis declared that experiments in which molybdenum was added to "semi-steel" mixtures also proved that molybdenum increases the machinability as well as hardness.

It was observed by Smalley[126] that as much as 0.5 per cent molybdenum does not affect the machining properties of cast iron, but that a larger quantity renders machining difficult.

In agreement with others, Cone[254] considered that molybdenum in cast iron increases hardness without decreasing machinability, but he stated that one foundry found that molybdenum-free castings could be more readily machined than castings containing molybdenum.

The results of machinability tests by Smith and Aufderhaar[294] on cast iron containing molybdenum, as measured by time of drilling, are shown in Fig. 71 (page 172). From these tests the authors concluded that molybdenum decreased machinability, but that machining does not become notably difficult until molybdenum has reached 1.5 per cent. With 3 per cent molybdenum drilling is difficult, and a bar containing 4.40 per cent molybdenum could not be drilled.

The effect of molybdenum on the machinability of cast iron has been determined by Sherwin and Kiley[498] by means of a drill test. The tests were made with a ¼-in. high-speed drill using a pressure of 12 lb., and the time required for the drill to penetrate to a depth of ¾ in. was noted. The time required to drill a standard bar was determined, and the increase or decrease in time for the sample investigated was recorded in per cent plus or minus. Results are listed in Table 44 (page 179). It was concluded that molybdenum increases the time of machining, as evidenced by the drill test, but that this is due to increased density or toughness, and not to hard spots or structures that would ruin a tool.

Merten[481] claimed that in non-magnetic irons molybdenum restores or retains machinability even at fairly high Brinell hardness.

Tests at Battelle Memorial Institute on the "drillability" of some of the irons listed in Table 51 are given below. The depth represents the depth in inches drilled in 2 min. at 415 r.p.m. with a ¼-in. high-speed steel drill.

Number	Depth	Brinell hardness
0	1.22	197
22	1.00	192
25	0.89	241
26	0.59	223

It is also claimed[431] that a molybdenum iron will machine better at the same Brinell hardness than an unalloyed iron.

118. Wear Resistance.—Smalley[126] reported that abrasive tests have shown that molybdenum in cast iron increases resistance to wear, and he suggested the use of molybdenum in parts subjected to abrasion. Smith[407] also claimed that molybdenum enhances the resistance to wear of cast iron, but he did not give data.

Amsler wear-resistance tests of molybdenum cast iron were made by Musatti and Calbiani,[385] using a type A 135 machine, specimens 40 mm. (1.57 in.) in diameter and 10 mm. (0.39 in.)

thick, 10 per cent slip, 150-kg. (330-lb.) load, and 166 r.p.m. Their results are given in the curves of Fig. 78. As may be observed from these curves, molybdenum increases the wear resistance, and the best results are obtained with 1.5 per cent of this element.

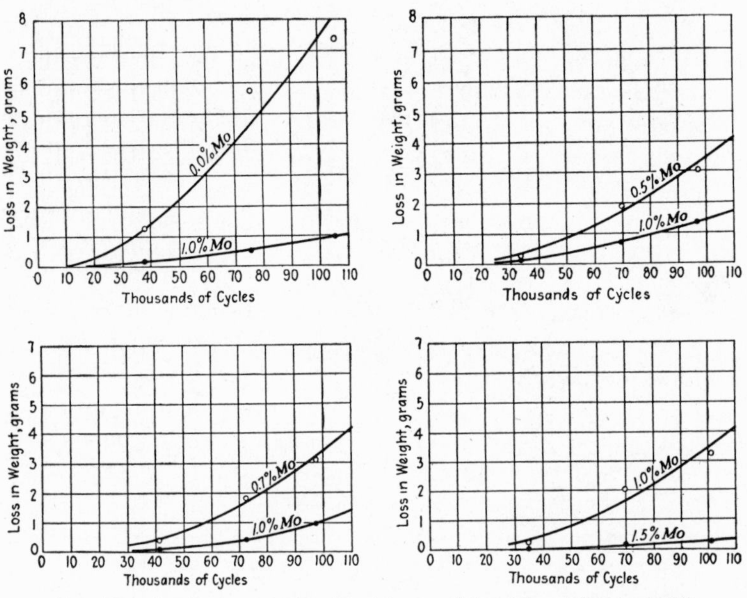

FIG. 78.—Amsler wear tests of cast iron. (*Musatti and Calbiani.*(385))

Mando S. Ariens[1] of the Brillion Iron Works obtained the values of wear resistance given below. Both the molybdenum iron and the unalloyed iron were made in an electric furnace. The wear tests were made on an Amsler wear-testing machine, and the results were reported as grams wear (loss in weight) per 1000 m-kg. of work. Each value represents the average of five tests:

Composition, per cent					Wear
C	Si	Mn	S	Mo	
3.15	2.21	0.63	0.125	....	0.0028
3.05	2.37	0.83	0.071	0.60	0.0022

[1] Private communication.

Resistance to abrasion is a service characteristic,[431] and general numerical values for increased resistance to wear of molybdenum irons cannot be given. However, some service tests have shown that molybdenum irons have superior wear resistance.

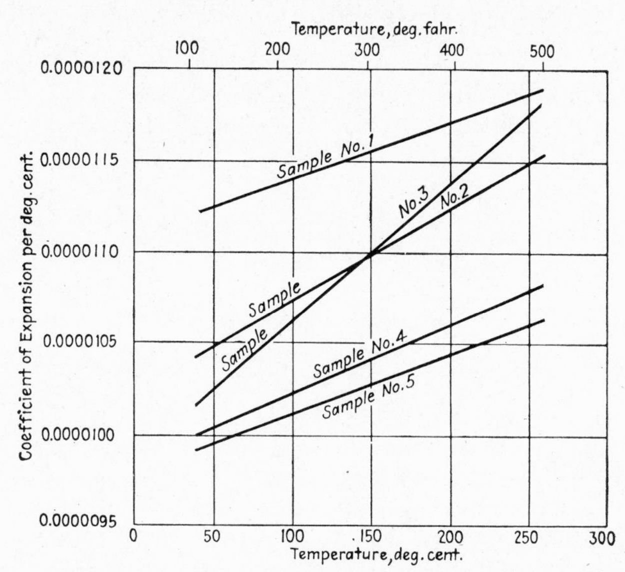

FIG. 79.—Expansion of alloy cast irons. Composition given in table below. (*Boegehold.*[319])

119. Coefficient of Expansion.—The values of the coefficients of expansion for the several irons given in Fig. 79 were reported by Boegehold.[319] The irons were as follows:

Number	Composition, per cent						
	C	Mn	P	S	Si	Mo	Ni
1	0.20	(Steel)					
2	3.25	0.59	0.09	0.09	2.22		
3	3.32	0.44	0.13	0.06	1.93	0.37	
4	3.26	0.43	0.12	0.06	1.89	0.73	
5	3.14	0.40	0.13	0.08	1.99	....	1.41

It was pointed out that molybdenum irons 3 and 4 have low coefficients, and that the increase of the coefficient with temperature for iron 4 containing 0.73 per cent molybdenum is very low.

120. Resistance to Corrosion.—The paucity of data on corrosion resistance of molybdenum cast iron was noted by Vanick.[300]

Smith[407] maintained that molybdenum cast iron withstands atmospheric corrosion better than ordinary cast iron.

The effect of molybdenum on the corrosion of cast iron in tenth normal solutions of sulphuric acid, nitric acid, hydrochloric acid, acetic acid, and in sodium hydroxide, potassium hydroxide, sea water, distilled water, and air were studied by Musatti and Calbiani.[385] These authors stated that no beneficial effects of molybdenum were observed but did not give any data.

"Corrosion tests" (or more correctly, a study of the solubility when immersed in chemical solutions, and having no bearing on any other conditions than those existing in those particular solutions) on a gray iron containing no molybdenum and on one containing 0.83 per cent molybdenum were made at Battelle Memorial Institute for the Worthington Pump and Machinery Co. Loss of weight was determined in a 5 per cent solution of sulphuric acid and in a 3 per cent solution of sodium chloride. The loss of weight for both irons was practically the same.

According to the Climax Molybdenum Co.,[431] a molybdenum content of 0.35 per cent noticeably increases the resistance to atmospheric corrosion and rusting of cast iron.

E. EFFECT OF TEMPERATURE ON MOLYBDENUM CAST IRON

In the more common gray cast iron it is frequently desirable to have an alloy whose structure or volume will not be changed by heating, while in malleable cast iron an almost complete decomposition of the cementite must occur on annealing. The effects of temperature on molybdenum cast irons are here discussed from the point of view both of the influence of molybdenum on graphitization and of its influence on structural and chemical changes producing growth. Gray cast irons are frequently annealed, either at low temperatures to relieve casting stresses and to prevent change of dimension on aging or at higher temperatures in order to soften the material. Such irons are in rare instances heat-treated by quenching and tempering in order to better the mechanical properties.

121. Graphitization.—The effect of molybdenum on graphitization of white cast iron on reheating was studied by Sawamura,[179, 495] who cast 5-mm. (0.20-in.) specimens in thick-walled steel molds and determined their temperature of graphitization by means of the dilatometer. The irons contained 2 8 per cent carbon, 0.8 per cent silicon, and from 0.46 to 3.14 per cent molybdenum. Molybdenum did not influence the graphitization temperature, as graphitization began at 840 to 850°C. (1540 to 1560°F.), and the maximum expansion occurred at 930 to 940°C. (1710 to 1725°F.) in all samples. It was observed, however, that the amount of undecomposed cementite increased with increasing molybdenum content.

An investigation to determine the effects of alloying elements, including molybdenum, on the graphitization treatment of malleable iron was made by Schwartz and Guiler.[181] They found that molybdenum has a detectable effect in hindering commercial graphitization, but that its effect is noticeable only when several per cent are present.

The effect of molybdenum in malleable iron was also studied by Coonan,[255] who found that molybdenum tends to prevent graphitization. After annealing, an alloy with 1 per cent molybdenum contained a relatively large amount of pearlite and a few particles of undecomposed cementite.

The effect of molybdenum on graphitization of iron of the type used for producing malleable iron was studied by Henderson.[456] From 1 to 5 per cent molybdenum was added to iron of the approximate composition 2.6 per cent carbon, 0.8 per cent silicon, and 0.2 per cent manganese. Castings ⅝ in. in diameter were made from each composition and these bars heated for various periods at 705°C. (1300°F.) and 930°C. (1710°F.). The amount of graphitization was judged by microscopic examination, and, as Fig. 80 indicates, molybdenum tended to increase the time required for graphitization. It was also observed that molybdenum refined the structure. Irons containing chromium and chromium plus molybdenum were also made, but it was found that chromium completely suppressed graphitization in all of the alloys.

In U. S. Patent 1,707,753, Apr. 2, 1929, Boegehold claimed that the addition of 0.5 per cent molybdenum to a white cast iron which is to be converted into malleable iron tends to prevent the formation of graphite during cooling, thus making it possible to increase the silicon content and to produce thoroughly malleablized iron by a relatively short annealing time. A malleablized iron containing 2.27 per cent carbon, 1.50 per cent silicon, 0.50

per cent molybdenum had a tensile strength of 71,800 lb. per sq. in. and an elongation of 10.5 per cent.

A series of "synthetic" cast irons containing either nickel or molybdenum, or both, was prepared by Challansonnet[322] from electrolytic iron, carbon, and the requisite quantity of nickel and molybdenum. Transformation temperatures and the temperature of the beginning of graphitization were determined by means of the dilatometer. As Table 55 indicates, molybdenum has a

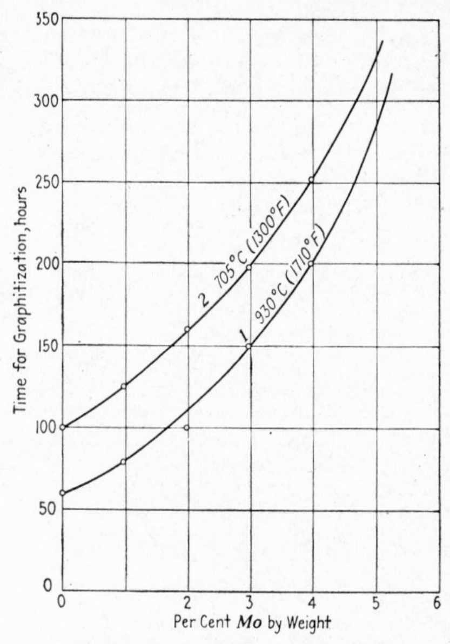

FIG. 80.—Effect of molybdenum on time required for complete graphitization of white cast iron. Annealed at 705°C. (1300°F.) and 930°C. (1710°F.) (*Henderson.*[456])

tendency to raise the temperature of graphitization or to repress completely the decomposition of cementite; the samples were heated to 1100°C. (2010°F.), and it was suggested by the author as possible that graphitization might have occurred above this temperature in some of the irons in which it was not observed. Dilatometric studies were also made on molybdenum irons containing approximately 2.6 per cent silicon and 0.5 per cent manganese, the results of which are given in Table 56. In common with steels, the presence of molybdenum in both series of irons increased the difference between the transformation temperature observed on heating and that observed on cooling.

122. Growth.—Andrew and Hyman[131] found that 0.58 per cent molybdenum in an iron containing 3.33 per cent total carbon, 0.32 per cent combined carbon, and 1.31 per cent silicon has no detectable effect on growth or increase in volume on heating.

TABLE 55.—TRANSFORMATION TEMPERATURES OF CAST IRON CONTAINING NO SILICON*

Composition, per cent			Cementite Curie point, °C.	*Ac*, °C.	*Ar*, °C.	*Ac* − *Ar*, °C.	Beginning of graphitization, °C.
Total C	Ni	Mo					
3.72	....	....	200	700	630	70	1000
3.68	1.03	....	200	660	575	95	1000
3.7	2.00	....	200	665	550	115	975
3.65	1.05	0.28	200	725	600	125	1000
3.74	0.97	0.53	200	725	500	225	None
3.68	1.98	0.23	200	725	525	200	1050
3.7	2.03	0.55	200	725	450	275	1070
3.62	....	0.26	200	725	625	100	None
3.74	....	0.50	200	725	575	150	None

* Challansonnet.[322]

TABLE 56.—TRANSFORMATION TEMPERATURES OF CAST IRON CONTAINING 2.6 PER CENT SILICON AND 0.5 PER CENT MANGANESE*

Composition, per cent			Cementite Curie point, °C.	*Ac*, °C.	*Ar*, °C.	*Ac* − *Ar*, °C.	Beginning of graphitization, °C.
Total C	Ni	Mo					
3.65	0.95	0.23	None	700	600	100	600
3.72	0.98	0.54	None	750	625	125	600
3.75	2.03	0.27	None	750	600	150	
3.68	1.97	0.52	None	700	600	100	550
3.65	....	0.26	150	800	650	150	None
3.67	....	0.55	150	800	500	300	None

* Challansonnet.[322]

According to Vanick,[300] deterioration at high temperatures is usually a form of oxidation in which graphite is oxidized, dissolved carbon is graphitized, and finally the residual matrix is oxidized.

Furthermore, graphitizing elements such as nickel and silicon would be expected to contribute to this effect, while carbide-forming elements such as molybdenum would retard decomposition by resisting expulsion of dissolved carbon.

Musatti and Calbiani[385] heated several of the irons listed in Table 40 (page 173) at a temperature of 800°C. (1470°F.) for 24 hr. and determined the increase in volume. The samples were cylinders 20 mm. (0.78 in.) in diameter and 100 mm. (3.93 in.) long. The results were as follows:

Number	Per Cent Increase
1 (no molybdenum)	8.0
2 (no molybdenum)	7.8
8 (0.74% molybdenum)	6.1
10 (1.08% molybdenum)	5.8
18 (1.54% molybdenum)	1.75

On heating for 100 hr. at 800°C. (1470°F.) all five of these irons increased in volume approximately 30 per cent.

Dilatometric curves obtained by Crosby of the Studebaker Corporation proved that for several heating cycles molybdenum and low-alloy nickel-chromium irons show less growth than unalloyed cast iron. Although these curves were cited as evidence that molybdenum cast iron is resistant to growth,[431] they should not be interpreted as indicating any marked resistance to growth for many heating cycles or for a prolonged sojourn at high temperatures.

123. Heat Treatment.—According to Lowry,[373] the machinability of a high-strength iron containing nickel, chromium, and molybdenum can be increased by proper annealing without appreciably lowering the hardness or strength. An annealing temperature of 510°C. (950°F.) was recommended for an iron containing 3.35 per cent total carbon, 0.64 per cent combined carbon, 1.70 per cent silicon, 1.46 per cent nickel, 0.63 per cent chromium, and 0.75 per cent molybdenum.

The effect of quenching from various temperatures on the hardness of cast irons containing both chromium and molybdenum was studied by Walls and Hartwell.[504] A marked increase in hardness was observed in bars quenched from 815°C. (1500°F.) or above. Transverse and tensile tests were also made on several quenched and tempered samples.

Results obtained on heat treating two of the irons listed in Table 53 (page 190) are shown in Table 57. This work was done by F. B. Dahle of Battelle Memorial Institute, who considered that the data obtained were too sketchy to warrant conclusions on the effect of molybdenum on the properties of heat-treated cast iron.

F. USES OF MOLYBDENUM CAST IRON

In all probability the use of molybdenum in many instances has not been reported in the literature, and as the following discussion is based largely on uses suggested or mentioned in the literature it must suffer from incompleteness.

124. Suggested Uses of Molybdenum Cast Iron.—Sargent[92] stated that the use of molybdenum in malleable iron seems to offer some promise. The use of molybdenum in malleable iron was also considered by Coonan,[255] whose experiments, however, did not indicate that molybdenum was a desirable constituent of such iron.

In his discussion of molybdenum cast iron Kothny[364] concluded that molybdenum has desirable effects, but that it is too costly for many applications.

TABLE 57.—HEAT TREATMENT OF MOLYBDENUM CAST IRON*
(Analysis given in Table 53)

Treatment	Transverse test†		Tensile strength, lb./sq. in.	Brinell hardness
	Load, lb.	Deflection, in.		
Melt 52:				
As cast	6,000	0.14	61,000	287
2 hr. at 870°C. (1595°F.), furnace cooled	.....	....	36,700	151
2 hr. at 870°C. (1595°F.), furnace cooled to 760°C. (1400°F.), and air quenched	.....	....	51,000	212
Melt 55:				
As cast	5,750	0.13	64,900	260
6 hr. at 870°C. (1595°F.), furnace cooled	4,000	0.12	37,300	147
6 hr. at 870°C. (1595°F.), furnace cooled to 760°C. (1400°F.), and air quenched	5,200	0.13	50,700	227

* Battelle Memorial Institute.

† 1.20-in. diameter specimens—12-in. span.

125. Actual Uses of Molybdenum Cast Iron.—It has been reported[431] that regular applications of molybdenum cast iron include:

INDUSTRIAL

Gas engine cylinders.
Clutch plates.
Pistons.
Gears.
Forming dies.
Stamping dies.
Heavy machinery bushings.
Machine-tool tables.
Machine-tool saddles.
Molding-machine pistons.
Paper-mill rolls.
Steel-mill rolls.
Chilled car wheels.

AUTOMOTIVE

Cylinder blocks.
Cylinder heads.
Pistons.
Air-cooled cylinders.
Valve-stem guides.
Clutch plates.
Brake drums.
Small gears.
Valve-seat inserts.

Mention of the use of molybdenum in cast-iron rolls was made by Bratton,[119] Stahl,[245] and Cazaud.[252] Stahl also mentioned the use of molybdenum in automotive irons.

A survey reported by Cone,[254] in 1929, indicated that molybdenum was used in cast-iron rolls and also in certain types of castings for automobiles and airplanes. The quantity of molybdenum used varies from 0.3 to 1 per cent. It was found that, although the use of molybdenum in cast iron is a comparatively recent development, it has passed beyond the experimental stage.

Vanick[300] reported that nickel and chromium, and to a lesser extent molybdenum, are added to cast iron to improve resistance to wear which is encountered in sizing, screening, conveying, and crushing equipment.

In reviewing the work of Musatti and Calbiani, Neath[(387)] contended that, even though molybdenum benefits cast iron, its use is too costly. His conclusions, however, were based on the use of 1.5 per cent molybdenum.

The Cadillac Motor Car Co., according to Danse,[1] found that severe brake application, when driving the heavier cars at speeds of 90 to 100 m.p.h., results in heating the brake drums to 510 to 540°C. (950 to 1000°F.). A series of experiments indicated that a pearlitic high-strength molybdenum gray cast iron makes the most satisfactory drum. It has been suggested that the applicability of this iron is due in part to its superior wear resistance. The iron used contained approximately 0.5 per cent molybdenum, and this same iron is used for clutch plates on the Cadillac. An iron containing 0.35 per cent molybdenum is used for other parts of these automobiles.

Merten[(481)] found that molybdenum, molybdenum-manganese, and nickel-molybdenum alloy irons are becoming important, and that, combined with nickel or manganese, the improvement resulting from molybdenum is more marked than from any other alloying element.

In a trade bulletin the United Engineering and Foundry Co. mentioned as one of their accomplishments "the patented use of molybdenum in low-phosphorus alloy-iron rolls."

The advantages of using molybdenum in automotive gray irons were discussed in a pamphlet recently issued by a producer of molybdenum.[(510)]

In reply to discussion of a paper on the characteristics of alloy cast irons, Shipley[(515)] gave some comparative tests on several alloy cast irons, which included an iron containing 3.30 per cent carbon, 2.10 per cent silicon, 1.35 per cent nickel, and 0.37 per cent molybdenum. This iron had a tensile strength of 42,450 lb. per sq. in. and had an "ideal structure," but its cost was considered to be too high to warrant its use.

A recent note in *Steel*[(508)] stated that a cast-iron cam shaft containing 3.15 per cent total carbon, 0.54 per cent combined carbon, 2.34 per cent silicon, 2.25 per cent molybdenum, and 1.70 per cent nickel had been run for 500 consecutive hours in

[1] Private communication. Owing to a small amount of nickel in the scrap the brake-drum iron will run about 0.10 per cent nickel. Metallurgists of the Cadillac Motor Car Co. believe that the effect of this small amount of nickel is negligible.

an automotive engine developing 100 hp. with the throttle wide open. The only detectable wear was at the gear operating the oil-pump shaft.

G. AUTHOR'S SUMMARY

1. Molybdenum can be introduced into cast iron made in an electric or air furnace by adding either calcium molybdate or ferromolybdenum to the charge in the furnace. In cupola practice, however, ferromolybdenum—with the lowest possible melting point—is probably the only satisfactory addition agent; it can be added to the charge or to the iron as it is being tapped.
2. There is considerable uncertainty regarding the effect of molybdenum on the casting properties of cast iron.
3. Molybdenum has a slight tendency to prevent graphite formation in gray iron.
4. Molybdenum decreases the size of the graphite plates in gray cast iron and tends to give them a characteristic crumpled appearance.
5. The matrix of a gray iron is refined by molybdenum.
6. Molybdenum increases the tensile and transverse strength of gray cast iron. It also increases its hardness, but with the increased hardness resulting from one-half of 1 per cent or less molybdenum, machinability is not markedly decreased. Molybdenum likewise increases endurance limit. Sufficient data are not available to determine the effect of molybdenum on the impact strength of cast iron.
7. It has been claimed that for the same hardness molybdenum iron machines more readily than an unalloyed iron, but the information available is not sufficient to affirm or to contradict this statement.
8. Molybdenum increases the wear resistance of gray cast iron, which follows reasonably from the increased Brinell hardness, though there are no data on which to gage the probable increased resistance to wear in different types of actual service.
9. Molybdenum probably has little influence on the corrosion resistance of cast iron.
10. Molybdenum has some tendency to prevent graphitization on reheating cast iron.
11. Molybdenum may have a slight tendency to prevent growth at elevated temperatures.

12. Molybdenum improves the high-temperature properties of gray iron.

13. Molybdenum makes the properties less dependent on size of section, as is indicated by MacKenzie's work, and, according to MacKenzie, this is one of the most important effects of molybdenum in cast iron.

14. Molybdenum is beginning to find an extensive use in cast iron.

CHAPTER VII

CHROMIUM-MOLYBDENUM STEELS

Mechanical Properties of Chromium-molybdenum Structural Steels—Other Properties of Chromium-molybdenum Structural Steels—Properties of Miscellaneous Chromium-molybdenum Steels—Uses of Chromium-molybdenum Steels—Author's Summary

Commercial molybdenum steels usually contain at least one other alloying element in addition to molybdenum. At present chromium-molybdenum steels of the low-alloy or structural type are extensively used, and the properties of such steels have been the subject of many recent articles. In this chapter, and in subsequent chapters which also deal with more complex alloys, division is, in general, made with respect to types of steel. Little more can be done other than list the properties of molybdenum-bearing steels and in some cases compare the properties of these steels with other steels having similar characteristics.

A. MECHANICAL PROPERTIES OF CHROMIUM-MOLYBDENUM STRUCTURAL STEELS

The extensive use of steels containing small amounts of chromium and molybdenum in automotive and related industries has caused the Society of Automotive Engineers[295] to set forth the following numbers and chemical specifications for such steels:

S.A.E. steel number	Composition, per cent					
	C	Mn	P	S	Cr	Mo
4130	0.25 to 0.35	0.40 to 0.70	0.04 max.	0.05 max.	0.50 to 0.80	0.15 to 0.25
4140	0.35 to 0.45	0.40 to 0.70	0.04 max.	0.05 max.	0.80 to 1.10	0.15 to 0.25
4150	0.45 to 0.55	0.40 to 0.70	0.04 max.	0.05 max.	0.80 to 1.10	0.15 to 0.25

Recently, a steel differing from 4130 only in that it contains from 0.80 to 1.10 per cent chromium has been designated as 4130X. It is extensively used in aircraft construction.[356]

Only those steels containing less than 2 per cent chromium are discussed in this division; other steels are considered in a subsequent division.

126. S.A.E. Steel 4130X.—The mechanical properties of three chromium-molybdenum steels in the annealed and in the quenched and tempered conditions were reported by McAdam;[122] of these steels, No. 2 has a composition corresponding to S.A.E. 4130X, No. 1 corresponds to 4140 except for the low chromium content, and No. 3 corresponds to 4150. Compositions, heat treatments, and endurance limits of these steels are given in Table 58, tensile and impact properties in Table 59, and torsional

TABLE 58.—ENDURANCE LIMIT, COMPOSITION, AND HEAT TREATMENT OF CHROMIUM-MOLYBDENUM STEELS*

Number	Composition, per cent							Cooled from 870°C. (1600°F.)	Tempering temperature,		Endurance limit, lb./sq. in.
	C	Mn	P	S	Si	Cr	Mo		°C.	°F.	
1A	0.39	0.49	0.034	0.035	0.195	0.76	0.18	Water	480	900	68,000
1B								Water	590	1100	68,500
1C								Furnace	...	....	38,500
2A	0.31	0.44	0.034	0.035	0.22	0.85	0.20	Water	480	900	72,500
2B								Water	590	1100	63,500
2C								Furnace	...	....	36,500
3A	0.50	0.48	0.030	0.039	0.24	1.03	0.19	Water	480	900	88,000
3B								Water	590	1100	77,000
3C								Furnace	...	....	49,500

* McAdam.[122]

properties in Table 60. The endurance tests were made on a rotating cantilever machine, and the results are based on ten million revolutions. The bars, when heat-treated, were ⅞ or 1 in. in diameter.

TABLE 59.—TENSILE AND IMPACT PROPERTIES OF CHROMIUM-MOLYBDENUM STEELS*

Number	Tensile strength, lb./sq. in.	Yield point, lb./sq. in.	Yield strength,† lb./sq. in.	Elongation in 2 in., per cent	Reduction of area, per cent	Charpy impact, ft-lb.
1A	121,570	86,220	85,220	12.7	55.3	11.4
1B	136,630	108,500	107,500	17.3	61.3	10.5
1C	85,750	48,250	47,250	29.0	49.3	8.1
2A	164,750	124,250	122,500	13.3	52.3	18.0
2B	139,880	116,500	115,500	16.0	62.3	12.5
2C	82,430	43,130	42,100	27.5	51.7	12.5
3A	172,000	128,500	127,500	12.3	41.7	12.2
3B	157,000	129,000	128,000	16.3	55.5	20.7
3C	111,350	50,850	49,900	21.0	41.0	4.8

* McAdam.(122)
† Reported as proportional limit.

TABLE 60.—TORSION PROPERTIES OF CHROMIUM-MOLYBDENUM STEELS*

Number	Nominal torsional strength, lb./sq. in.	Yield strength,† lb./sq. in.	Angle of twist per linear inch at yield strength, minimum	Angle of twist per linear inch at break, deg.
1A	101,890	99,015	82	4
1B	73,053	55,545	46	140
1C	65,190	31,830	26	236
2A	104,150	94,180	77	107
2B	86,040	72,450	60	115
2C	62,950	26,560	19	110
3A	125,510	111,960	81	83
3B	103,370	81,950	66	103
3C	76,700	36,960	30	172

* McAdam.(122)
† Reported as proportional limit.

In a discussion of materials used in aircraft construction, Johnson,(175) in 1926, mentioned the use of a steel similar to 4130X for tubing; it had a tensile strength of 95,000 lb. per sq. in. and a yield strength of 60,000 lb. per sq. in. In 1928, Johnson[225] stated that a steel conforming to S.A.E. 4130X was called for in the U. S. Army specifications, and that it was used almost exclusively for aircraft tubing. It was found by several investigators that a tensile strength of 95,000 lb. per sq. in. results on cooling this steel from a welding heat, and a unit stress of 80,000 lb. per sq. in. for sections close to welds is generally used in design. The steel, normalized by cooling in air from 885°C. (1625°F.), has a tensile strength and elongation equivalent to those obtained by quenching and tempering at 650°C. (1200°F.). The strength after normalizing is 95,000 lb. per sq. in. Johnson also asserted that the chromium-molybdenum sheet steel has been found to be even superior to chromium-vanadium steel, for it is more easily welded and bending operations can be performed with greater ease. Normalized sheet material can be bent 180 deg. without cracking over a radius equal to the thickness of the sheet. Annealing the steel or quenching followed by tempering at 650 to 705°C. (1200 to 1300°F.) increases workability and permits 180-deg. bends over a radius equal to one-half the thickness in sections up to 3/8 in. thick.

The properties of sheets rolled from steel 4130X were also discussed by Johnson.[354] The sheets were produced by hot-rolling 16 × 20-in. ingots into bars 12 in. wide and from 2 to 4 in. thick. The bars were then cross-rolled hot to a thickness of about 5/16 in., after which they were reheated and rolled to the desired thickness, the rolling direction being at 90 deg. to the previous direction of rolling. After rolling, the sheets were annealed. The tensile properties of sheets, presumably annealed, are listed in Table 61, and the properties of these materials after quenching and tempering are given in Table 62. It was claimed that an air-quench will give a tensile strength greater than 150,000 lb. per sq. in., but the values are not so uniform as those resulting from a quench in a liquid.

In two recent articles Johnson[354, 356] discussed the properties of chromium-molybdenum steel used for aircraft construction. In one of these articles[354] he cited data to prove that the endurance limit of tubing made from 4130X steel is noticeably lowered by internal die marks and showed that the effect of such marks is accentuated in tubes heat-treated and tempered below 370°C. (700°F.).

The properties and heat treatment of chromium-molybdenum steel used in aircraft were also discussed by Knerr,[228, 229, 278, 362] whose conclusions are essentially in agreement with those of Johnson. It was claimed that the 4130X steel may be machined after having been heat-treated to give a strength of 150,000 or even 175,000 lb. per sq. in. Richardson[238] in a discussion of this steel declared that fatigue resistance and toughness are particularly high, and that it is uniform in quality. Beams made from 4130X steel, according to an article in *The Iron Age*,[315] are heat-treated to give a tensile strength of 140,000 to 150,000 lb. per sq. in.

TABLE 61.—TENSILE PROPERTIES OF CHROMIUM-MOLYBDENUM STEEL SHEET, No. 4130X*
(Specimens ½ in. wide)

Thickness, in.	Composition, per cent				Tensile strength, lb./sq. in.	Yield strength,† lb./sq. in.	Elongation in 2 in., per cent
	C	Mn	Cr	Mo			
0.039L	0.33	0.58	0.91	0.24	102,000	88,000	14.0
0.062L	0.31	0.58	0.92	0.28	100,000	80,500	16.0
0.124L	0.30	0.58	0.96	0.25	98,000	76,000	19.5
0.250L	0.31	0.59	0.98	0.21	94,500	61,500	26.5
0.039X	....	....	....	....	99,000	87,000	12.0
0.062X	....	....	....	....	102,000	87,000	14.5
0.124X	....	....	....	....	102,000	77,000	18.5
0.250X	....	....	....	....	100,000	66,000	23.0

L = axis of specimen parallel to direction of final rolling.
X = axis of specimen perpendicular to direction of final rolling.
* Johnson.[354]
† Reported as yield point.

According to Lake,[368] 4130X tubing has a tensile strength of 95,000 lb. per sq. in. and a yield strength of 60,000 lb. per sq. in., while corresponding values for carbon-steel tubing are only 55,000 and 36,000 lb. per sq. in. The 4130X tubing was reported to have nearly double the tensile strength and yield strength of duralumin tubing and to have much more than double its resistance to vibrational or torsional stresses.

The manufacture of hollow airplane propellers from 4130X steel was described by Lampton,[469] who stated that the steel is quenched by replacing the reheated propellers in a water-cooled forming die. The tensile strength is 225,000 lb. per sq. in. after quenching and is reduced to 200,000 lb. per sq. in. by tempering.

The tensile properties of sheets made from 4130X steel, and the effects of heat treatment on these sheets, were determined

TABLE 62.—PROPERTIES OF HEAT-TREATED CHROMIUM-MOLYBDENUM STEEL SHEET, No. 4130X*
(Specimens ½ in. wide)

Thickness, in.	Tempered		Tensile strength, lb./sq. in.	Yield point, lb./sq. in.	Yield strength,† lb./sq. in.	Elongation in 2 in., per cent	Rockwell *C* hardness	Rockwell *B* hardness
	°C.	°F.						
Quenched in oil from 885°C. (1625°F.)								
0.039	345	650	210,500	192,000	160,000	2.5	47	120
0.039	480	900	166,500	150,000	140,000	5.5	37	117
0.039	595	1100	150,000	140,000	130,000	7.0	32	114
0.064	345	650	215,000	194,000	165,000	4.5	44	118
0.064	480	900	168,000	156,500	135,000	6.5	37	117
0.064	595	1100	146,500	134,500	110,000	9.0	34	114
0.124	345	650	222,000	206,000	150,000	6.0	47	122
0.124	480	900	169,000	156,000	130,000	8.0	40	118
0.124	595	1100	148,000	139,000	120,000	11.0	35	115
0.250	345	650	222,000	204,000	140,000	9.0	47	122
0.250	480	900	175,000	160,000	110,000	12.0	39	118
0.250	595	1100	150,000	141,000	110,000	14.5	35	115
Quenched in water from 885°C. (1625°F.)								
0.039	345	650	210,000	199,000	170,000	2.5	45	120
0.039	480	900	168,000	157,000	130,000	5.5	36	117
0.039	595	1100	153,000	143,000	125,000	6.5	32	114
0.064	345	650	212,000	195,000	160,000	4.0	46	120
0.064	480	900	168,000	157,500	140,000	6.5	37	117
0.064	595	1100	151,000	138,000	130,000	8.5	34	114
0.124	345	650	202,000	191,000	140,000	6.0	45	120
0.124	480	900	170,000	157,000	125,000	7.0	39	117
0.124	595	1100	146,000	134,000	120,000	10.0	33	114
0.250	345	650	229,000	204,000	170,000	9.0	44	121
0.250	480	900	178,000	165,000	150,000	12.5	39	117
0.250	595	1100	149,000	141,000	130,000	14.5	34	114

* Johnson.[354]
† Reported as proportional limit.

by Sisco and Warner.[243] The tests were made on sheets varying in thickness from 0.0375 to 0.25 in., and all material used was believed to be from the same heat. The heavier-gage specimens were machined to a width of ¾ in. and the lighter-gage specimens to ½ in. The normalizing treatment consisted in maintaining

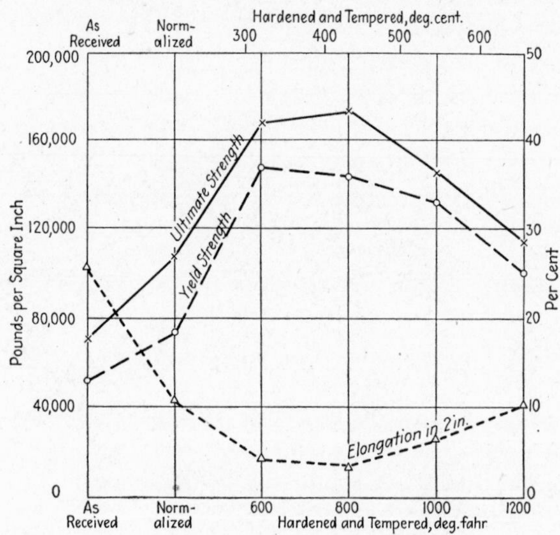

FIG. 81.—Properties of 4130X steel sheet 0.0375 in. thick. (*Sisco and Warner*.[243])

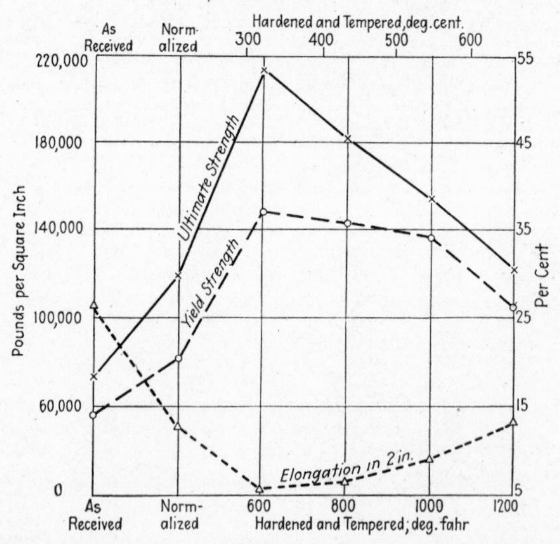

FIG. 82.—Same as Fig. 81. Sheet 0.063 in thick. (*Sisco and Warner*.[243])

the materials at 925°C. (1700°F.) for 1 hr. and cooling in still air. Quenching was done in water from a temperature of 870°C.

(1600°F.), and, in tempering, the specimens were maintained at the indicated temperature for ½ hr. and cooled in still air. Chemical analyses of the sheets of each gage indicated an extremely uniform composition. Carbon varied from 0.32 to 0.36 per cent, manganese from 0.55 to 0.56 per cent, chromium from 0.86 to 0.91 per cent, molybdenum from 0.22 to 0.25 per cent. Results of the tensile tests are shown in Figs. 81 to 84. Attention was called to the slight differences in properties for tempering temperatures of 315 and 425°C. (600 and 800°F.). The tensile properties were found to be practically independent of the direction of rolling. Tests in which the strips were bent over a mandrel equivalent to twice the thickness of the sheets were also reported. In general, it was found that the sheets as received, after normalizing and after tempering at 540 or 650°C. (1000 or 1200°F.), withstood this test.

The average-strength values of aircraft tubing ranging in outside diameter from ¾ to 2 in., as determined by Whittemore and Brueggeman[414] preparatory to testing welds made with these tubes, are as follows:

Tension	
Strength, lb./sq. in.	105,100
Yield point, lb./sq. in.	98,000
Yield strength,* lb./sq. in.	50,600
Modulus of elasticity, lb./sq. in.	28.4 million
Elongation in 2 in., per cent	19
Compression	
Strength, lb./sq. in.	100,200
Yield strength,* lb./sq. in.	65,100
Modulus of elasticity, lb./sq. in.	29.1 million

* Reported as proportional limit.

In a discussion of a paper by Knerr,[363] Clayton stated that normalized 4130X steel frequently has a tensile strength above 150,000 lb. per sq. in.

127. Steels Containing Less than 0.25 Per Cent Carbon.—The properties of steels containing from 0.80 to 0.90 per cent chromium, from 0.35 to 0.45 per cent molybdenum, and from 0.15 to 0.45 per cent carbon in steps of 0.05 per cent were listed by Barton,[118] but as the source of the data and exact compositions are not known these values will not be given here.

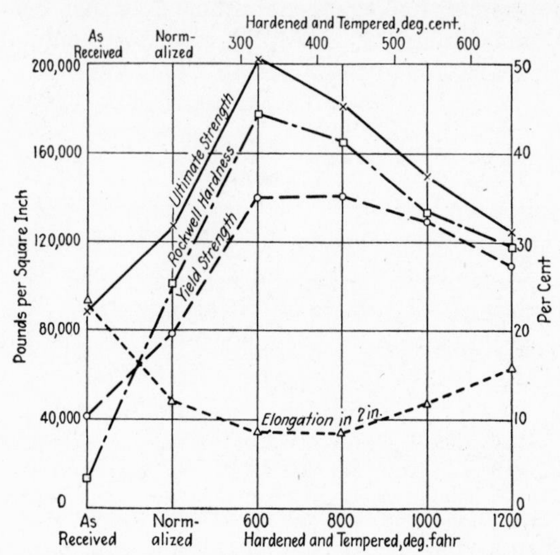

FIG. 83.—Same as Fig. 81. Sheet ⅛ in. thick. (*Sisco and Warner.*[243])

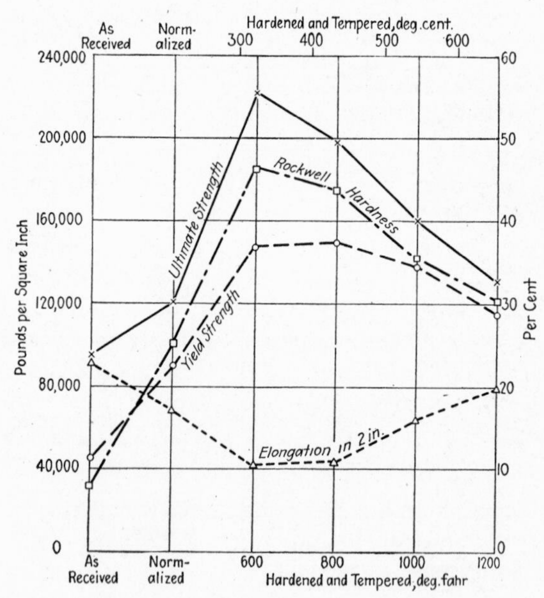

FIG. 84.—Same as Fig. 81. Sheet ¼ in. thick. (*Sisco and Warner.*[243])

The properties of a steel containing 0.19 per cent carbon, 0.95 per cent chromium, and 0.53 per cent molybdenum as determined by Swinden[61] are listed in Table 63.

TABLE 63.—MECHANICAL PROPERTIES OF A STEEL CONTAINING 0.19 PER CENT CARBON, 0.95 PER CENT CHROMIUM, AND 0.53 PER CENT MOLYBDENUM*

Quenched		Quenching medium	Tempered		Tensile strength, lb./sq. in.	Yield strength,† lb./sq. in.	Elongation in 2 in., per cent	Reduction of area, per cent	Brinell hardness
°C.	°F.		°C.	°F.					
As rolled		....	...	....	86,000	68,500	25.0	61.6	170
900	1650	Air	...	....	71,700	49,700	34.5	68.0	141
900	1650	Oil	500	930	109,600	90,500	19.5	67.0	222
900	1650	Oil	550	1020	111,000	92,500	21.0	66.0	238
900	1650	Oil	600	1110	110,000	89,600	22.5	63.0	235
850	1560	Water	500	930	130,000	107,000	16.0	60.4	294
850	1560	Water	550	1020	127,800	110,000	19.0	59.2	285
850	1560	Water	600	1110	127,900	111,000	20.0	63.6	289
850	1560	Water	650	1200	107,400	85,500	19.5	56.0	235

* Swinden.[61]
† Reported as elastic limit.

The properties of a steel containing 0.15 per cent carbon, 0.73 per cent chromium, and 0.28 per cent molybdenum were given by Gillett and Mack[151] and are listed in Table 64. The endurance values reported by these investigators were obtained on an Upton-Lewis machine. Izod tests were made with 0.45-in. diameter round test pieces with the regular V-notch having an angle of 45 deg. and a 0.01-in. radius at the base of the notch.

An extensive series of tests on tubing containing 0.15 per cent carbon, 0.86 per cent chromium, and 0.30 per cent molybdenum was described by Christmann,[253] but the results do not allow an appraisal of the effects of molybdenum.

128. Steels Containing from 0.25 to 0.35 Per Cent Carbon.— The properties of some heat-treated chromium-molybdenum steels, as determined by Jones,[176] are shown in Table 65. From a consideration of these results in comparison with results obtained on chromium steels, Jones concluded:

Marked improvement in the properties of steels containing approximately 1.0, 1.5, and 2.0 per cent respectively of chromium resulted from the addition of 0.5 per cent of molybdenum. In the case of the 1.0

TABLE 64.—MECHANICAL PROPERTIES OF CHROMIUM-MOLYBDENUM STEELS*

Number	Composition, per cent			Quenched		Quenching medium	Tempered		Tensile strength, lb./sq. in.	Yield strength,† lb./sq. in.	Elongation in 2 in., per cent	Reduction of area, per cent	Brinell hardness	Izod impact, ft-lb.	Endurance limit, lb./sq. in.
	C	Cr	Mo	°C.	°F.		°C.	°F.							
47	0.15	0.73	0.28	925	1700	Water	425	800	155,500	125,000	14.0	55.5	320	53	61,000§
47				925	1700	Water	525	975	126,250	105,000	18.5	63.9	285	79	69,000
47				925	1700	Water	630	1165	97,000	77,500	25.5	78.6	215	117	52,000
46	0.22	0.79	0.34	850	1560	Water	425	800	137,000	124,000‡	13.5	52.0	330	32	80,000
46				850	1560	Water	525	975	135,500	110,250	18.0	63.0	320	56	75,000
46				850	1560	Water	625	1155	116,000	90,000	22.5	69.1	260	81	57,000
46				900	1650	Air	...	....	98,000	86,000‡	21.5	60.0	205		
49	0.25	0.95	0.73	925	1700	Oil	425	800	187,750	150,000	15.0	56.4	400	33	86,000
49				925	1700	Oil	530	985	165,250	140,000	19.0	62.2	365	59	
49				925	1700	Oil	525	975	175,000	155,000	19.0	57.5	385	....	81,000
49				925	1700	Oil	600	1110	150,000	131,000	20.0	66.0	320	....	72,000
49				925	1700	Oil	630	1165	119,500	100,000	22.0	71.3	250	95	
45	0.40	0.88	0.30	820	1510	Oil	425	800	202,500	170,000	12.0	47.6	420	8	98,000
45				820	1510	Oil	525	975	166,250	143,000	15.0	52.8	330	26	87,000
45				820	1510	Oil	625	1155	133,500	111,500	21.0	65.5	290	58	70,000
45				900	1650	Air	...	....	127,000	60,000	17.3	50.1	245		
10	0.40	0.95	0.68	900	1650	Oil	425	800	219,000	170,000	12.0	43.3	425	19	97,000
10				900	1650	Oil	525	975	203,500	165,000	13.0	46.2	390	33.5	85,000§
10				900	1650	Oil	625	1155	174,000	145,000	15.0	51.9	350	43	89,000
10				900	1650	Air	...	....	160,000	47,500	5.0	4.5	320	7.5	
10				820	1510	Air	...	....	148,500	38,500	15.0	20.0	285	6	67,000
11	0.41	0.89	0.36	900	1650	Oil	425	800	201,500	170,000	12.0	49.1	395	22	
11				900	1650	Oil	525	975	178,200	155,000	14.7	51.9	375	33.5	85,000
11				900	1650	Oil	625	1155	140,250	112,000	19.0	62.3	265	71	
11				900	1650	Air	...	....	129,500	57,500	18.0	45.5	280	7.5	
11				840	1550	Air	...	....	129,500	57,500	16.5	44.0	250	12	65,000
48	0.42	0.55	0.39	925	1700	Oil	425	800	207,000	187,500	14.0	51.5	420	21	95,000
48				925	1700	Oil	530	985	174,750	162,500	17.0	55.3	365	51	92,000
48				925	1700	Oil	525	975	184,500	170,000	14.0	41.5	385		
48				925	1700	Oil	630	1165	130,000	122,500	20.0	64.7	255	95	79,000
48				900	1650	Air	...	....	122,250	72,500	17.0	45.5	250	20	
48				825	1515	Anneal	...	....	97,000	57,500	24.5	43.3	180	30.5	
50	0.52	0.95	0.39	815	1500	Oil	425	800	209,250	170,000	13.0	47.9	400	16	100,000
50				815	1500	Oil	525	975	188,250	155,000	17.5	53.9	365	19	92,000§
50				815	1500	Oil	625	1155	135,000	100,000	19.5	55.7	285	72	60,000
50				900	1650	Air	...	....	153,500	50,000	12.0	28.0	300	5	

* Gillett and Mack.[151]
† Reported as yield point.
‡ From drop of beam; others from extensometer.
§ Approximate value.

per cent chromium steel the properties were further improved by the addition of molybdenum up to 1.0 per cent, but no advantage was gained by increasing the molybdenum content beyond this amount. The results also illustrate the influence of chromium on a steel containing 0.5 per cent of molybdenum. Great improvement of properties was effected by the addition of 1 per cent of chromium and this continued with additions of chromium up to 1.5 per cent; but no advantage was gained by further increasing the chromium except for steels of high tensile strength (135,000 lb. per sq. in.).

In a discussion of a paper by Hunter,[99] Mathews reported that surprisingly low Izod impact values were sometimes obtained for tempered chromium-molybdenum steels. The following data show the effect of tempering on the Izod values of three chromium-molybdenum steels which were reported to be normal in all respects except the low impact values obtained at certain tempering temperatures:

Analyses

Steel	1	2	3
Carbon, per cent	0.31	0.34	0.44
Manganese, per cent	0.63	0.48	0.73
Chromium, per cent	1.01	0.46	0.92
Molybdenum, per cent	0.34	0.30	0.41
Izod Values, Ft-lb.			
Tempered at 205°C. (400°F.)	27	24	15
Tempered at 315°C. (600°F.)	9	18	9
Tempered at 425°C. (800°F.)	15	46	15
Tempered at 540°C. (1000°F.)	52	61	42
Tempered at 650°C. (1200°F.)	78	82	77
Tempered at 705°C. (1300°F.)	99	104	89

In private correspondence Mathews has pointed out that the decrease in impact resistance at tempering temperatures in the neighborhood of 315°C. (600°F.) is not peculiar to chromium-molybdenum, as stated in his discussion, "but is a much neglected feature of many of the structural alloy steels and, in fact, many curves are presented showing the Izod curves to be just as smooth as the tensile or yield-point curves, which is far from being the case." Grossmann[135] attributed this drop in impact resistance to the decomposition of retained austenite.

TABLE 65.—PROPERTIES OF CHROMIUM-MOLYBDENUM STEELS*

No.	Composition, per cent			Oil-quenched,		Tempered, 2 hr.,		Tensile strength, lb./sq. in.	Elastic limit, lb./sq. in.	Yield strength,† lb./sq. in.	Elongation in 2 in., per cent	Reduction of area, per cent	Izod impact, ft-lb.	Brinell hardness
	C	Cr	Mo	°C.	°F.	°C.	°F.							
9	0.26	1.08	....	900	1650	500	930	95,000	58,200	68,500	26	64	63	204
9	....	....	....	900	1650	600	1110	87,600	53,500	63,200	28	70	78	183
9	....	....	....	900	1650	650	1200	83,100	49,300	60,200	31	72	82	174
9	....	....	....	900	1650	670	1235	81,300	44,800	54,600	32	70	86	172
9	....	....	....	900	1650	700	1290	80,200	44,800	54,600	35	75	89	168
10	0.33	1.08	0.57	900	1650	550	1025	151,000	98,600	127,000	19	52	20	329
10	....	....	....	820	1510	550	1025	152,300	100,800	128,800	18	52	21	330
10	....	....	....	900	1650	600	1110	141,800	94,100	119,000	17	56	23	310
10	....	....	....	900	1650	650	1200	127,500	91,800	106,500	19	64	58	274
10	....	....	....	900	1650	670	1235	116,000	80,600	92,800	21	65	67	247
10	....	....	....	820	1510	670	1235	117,400	85,100	96,300	23	66	66	250
10	....	....	....	900	1650	700	1290	109,600	73,900	88,200	26	67	74	232
11	0.33	1.07	1.04	900	1650	550	1025	181,000	134,400	158,600	16	52	18	394
11	....	....	....	820	1510	550	1025	181,000	136,600	156,800	17	55	20	385
11	....	....	....	900	1650	600	1110	159,700	116,500	136,600	18	55	23	339
11	....	....	....	900	1650	650	1200	141,100	114,200	124,000	20	62	49	299
11	....	....	....	900	1650	670	1235	133,000	103,000	116,300	21	64	58	285
11	....	....	....	820	1510	670	1235	125,200	103,000	112,000	23	62	61	270
11	....	....	....	900	1650	700	1290	118,100	98,600	105,300	25	66	70	248
12	0.25	1.10	1.38	900	1650	600	1110	155,600	109,800	138,000	19	57	15	341
12	....	....	....	900	1650	650	1200	126,600	103,000	111,700	21	62	54	275
12	....	....	....	900	1650	670	1235	118,500	94,100	102,400	22	63	60	250
12	....	....	....	900	1650	700	1290	111,600	87,300	95,200	25	66	66	236

TABLE 65.—(*Continued*)

No.	Composition, per cent			Oil-quenched,		Tempered, 2 hr.,		Tensile strength, lb./sq. in.	Elastic limit, lb./sq. in.	Yield strength,† lb./sq. in.	Elongation in 2 in., per cent	Reduction of area, per cent	Izod impact, ft-lb.	Brinell hardness
	C	Cr	Mo	°C.	°F.	°C.	°F.							
13	0.26	1.58	0.64	900	1650	600	1110	131,700	96,300	113,400	21	62	25	287
13	....	....	....	900	1650	650	1200	114,500	85,100	97,400	23	65	54	245
13	....	....	....	900	1650	670	1235	106,800	78,400	88,700	23	67	58	230
13	....	....	....	900	1650	700	1290	100,200	69,400	80,400	25	69	68	216
14	0.33	2.03	0.54	900	1650	550	1025	189,500	147,800	173,700	16	50	19	412
14	....	....	....	820	1510	550	1025	189,100	150,100	173,800	16	50	20	411
14	....	....	....	900	1650	600	1110	164,000	116,500	147,000	17	55	32	350
14	....	....	....	900	1650	650	1200	141,600	105,300	124,500	20	59	46	293
14	....	....	....	900	1650	670	1235	134,400	100,800	116,500	22	64	51	283
14	....	....	....	820	1510	670	1235	128,600	98,600	109,800	23	64	56	273
14	....	....	....	900	1650	700	1290	116,700	82,900	98,600	25	66	63	250

* Jones.[176]
† Reported as yield point.

The properties of steel 1 mentioned above, after quenching in oil from 855°C. (1575°F.) and tempering at various temperatures, are plotted in Fig. 85. In the Izod curve the minimum in the neighborhood of 315°C. (600°F.) is indicated.

Table 66 gives properties of a chromium-molybdenum steel containing 0.32 per cent carbon as determined by Swinden.[61] Table 64, previously mentioned (page 215), includes the prop-

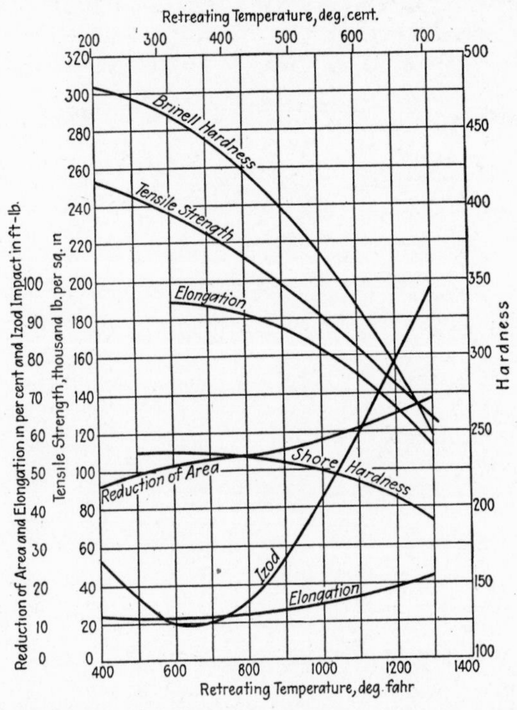

FIG. 85.—Properties of a 0.31 per cent carbon, 1.01 per cent chromium, 0.34 per cent molybdenum steel, quenched in oil from 855°C. (1575°F.) and tempered at indicated temperatures. (*Mathews.*[99])

erties determined by Gillett and Mack[151] of a chromium-molybdenum steel containing 0.22 per cent carbon.

Figure 86, given by Sargent,[102] compares properties of a water-quenched chromium-molybdenum steel containing 0.32 per cent carbon with those of an oil-quenched chromium-vanadium steel containing 0.39 per cent carbon.

The effect of various heat treatments on a steel containing 0.27 per cent carbon, 1.01 per cent manganese, 0.88 per cent

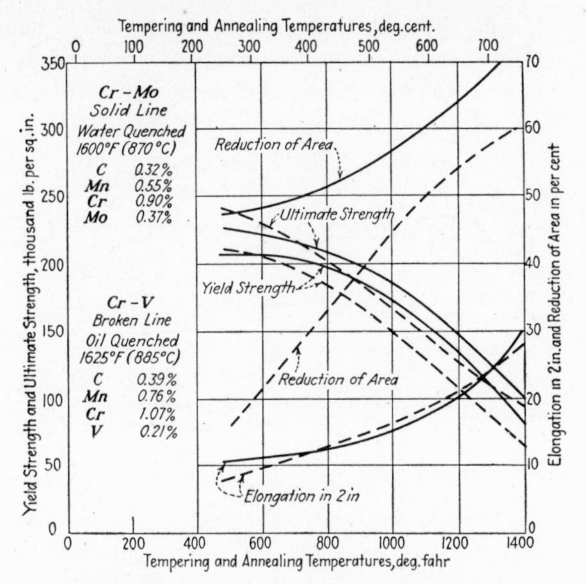

FIG. 86.—Tensile properties of chromium-molybdenum and chromium-vanadium steel. Treated as $1\frac{1}{4}$-in. square bars and machined to 0.505-in. specimens. (*Sargent.*[102])

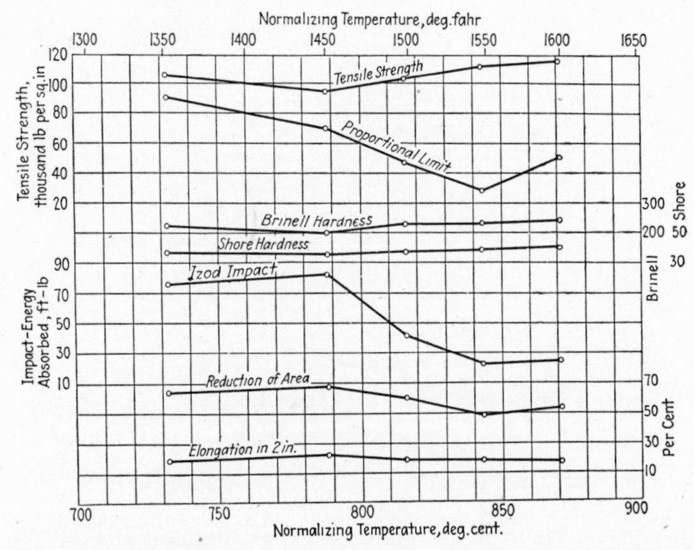

FIG. 87.—Properties of a 0.27 per cent carbon, 1.01 per cent manganese, 0.88 per cent chromium, 0.52 per cent molybdenum steel, air-cooled from indicated temperature. (*French.*[107])

chromium, and 0.52 per cent molybdenum was exhaustively studied by French.(107) The sections treated were ½ in. round. Round impact specimens with 45-deg. notches 0.019 in. deep

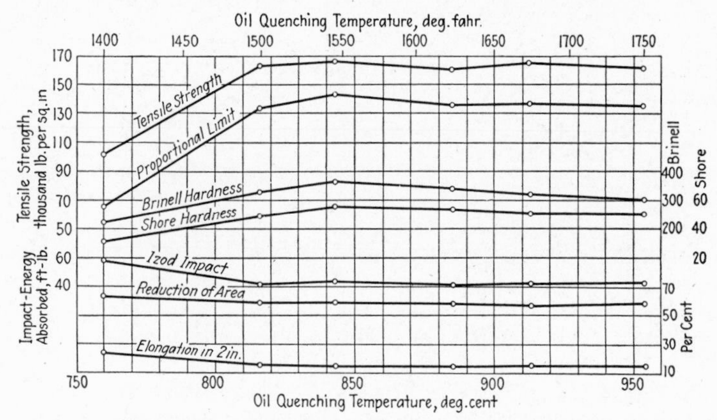

Fig. 88.—Same steel as in Fig. 87. Quenched in oil from indicated temperature and tempered at 540°C. (1000°F.). (*French.*(107))

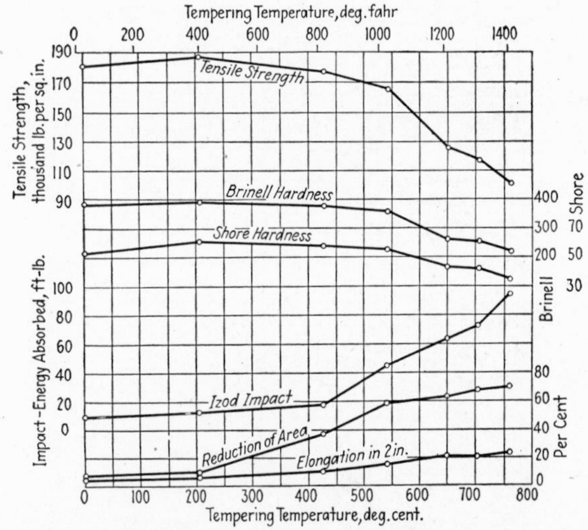

Fig. 89.—Same steel as in Fig. 87. Quenched in oil from 845°C. (1550°F.) and tempered at indicated temperature. (*French.*(107))

were used. Figure 87 shows the properties of the steel after having been normalized by holding at the indicated temperatures for 30 min. and cooling in air. Figure 88 gives the properties of the steel, oil-quenched from various temperatures and tempered at 540°C. (1000°F.). The properties after quenching in oil from 845°C. (1550°F.) and tempering at various temperatures are shown in Fig. 89.

TABLE 66.—MECHANICAL PROPERTIES OF STEEL CONTAINING 0.32 PER CENT CARBON, 0.91 PER CENT CHROMIUM, AND 0.46 PER CENT MOLYBDENUM*

Quenched		Quenching medium	Tempered		Tensile strength, lb./sq. in.	Yield strength,† lb./sq. in.	Elongation in 2 in., per cent	Reduction of area, per cent	Brinell hardness
°C.	°F.		°C.	°F.					
As rolled		....	...	....	125,400	90,500	16.0	52.4	255
900	1650	Air	...	....	98,000	68,700	23.5	57.2	241
900	1650	Oil	500	930	148,000	129,200	14.5	51.6	321
900	1650	Oil	550	1020	156,100	133,400	16.0	53.6	336
900	1650	Oil	600	1110	146,000	125,200	18.0	51.0	311
850	1560	Water	500	930	183,500	159,800	13.0	42.0	364
850	1560	Water	550	1020	178,200	159,000	17.5	54.8	382
850	1560	Water	600	1110	179,600	162,200	15.0	51.0	364
850	1560	Water	650	1200	155,600	116,500	18.0	62.6	321

* Swinden.(61)
† Reported as elastic limit.

TABLE 67.—TENSILE PROPERTIES OF STEEL CONTAINING 0.32 PER CENT CARBON, 0.60 PER CENT MANGANESE, 1.01 PER CENT CHROMIUM, AND 0.43 PER CENT MOLYBDENUM AT NORMAL AND LOW TEMPERATURES*
(Tested in form of 0.025-in. wire)

Quenched in water from		Tempered		Tensile strength, lb./sq. in.		Elongation in 2 in., per cent		Reduction of area, per cent	
°C.	°F.	°C.	°F.	+25°C. (+75°F.)	−180°C. (−290°F.)	+25°C. (+75°F.)	−180°C. (−290°F.)	+25°C. (+75°F.)	−180°C. (−290°F.)
Annealed 20 min. at 850°C. (1560 °F.)..				88,100	150,700	8.23	11.71	65	52
850	1560	...	....	261,000	306,500	0.75	.....	59	25
850	1560	300	570	207,700	257,000	1.60	1.95	68	61
850	1560	450	840	193,500	245,000	2.07	2.35	66	57
850	1560	600	1110	183,300	231,000	3.10	3.12	66	60
850	1560	700	1290	129,500	189,000	5.10	7.90	72	68

* Sykes.(143)

The properties of a chromium-molybdenum steel at room temperature and a temperature of −180°C. (−290°F.) as determined by Sykes(143) are given in Table 67. Sykes also made tests on a 0.29 per cent carbon steel and on a nickel steel containing 0.25 per cent carbon and 3.50 per cent nickel. The maximum tensile strength was found in the chromium-molybdenum steel, either as hardened, hardened and tempered, or annealed, when tested at −180°C. (−290°F.), but the nickel steel possessed the highest elongation in all conditions.

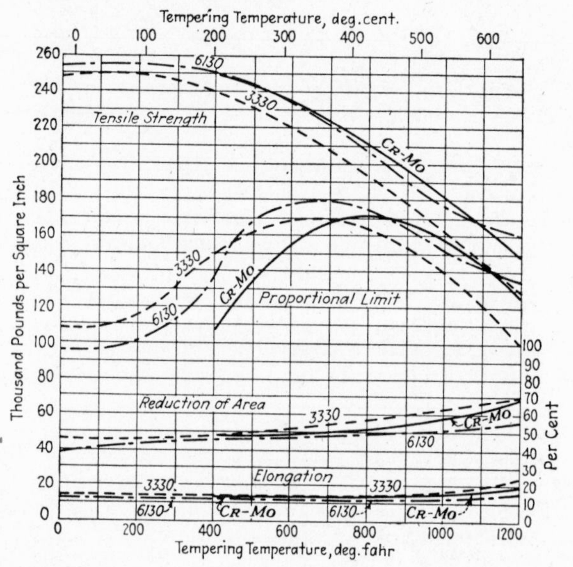

Fig. 90.—Tensile properties of three alloy steels. Composition and quenching temperature given in table below. Tempered at indicated temperatures. (*Moore and Schaal.*[123])

The properties of a nickel-chromium (S.A.E. 3330), a chromium-vanadium (S.A.E. 6130), and a chromium-molybdenum steel were compared by Moore and Schaal.[123] The steels and the heat treatments were:

Steel	Composition, per cent						Oil-quenched from	
	C	Mn	Ni	Cr	V	Mo	°C.	°F.
S.A.E. 3330	0.26	0.47	3.58	1.59	....	....	800	1475
S.A.E. 6130	0.27 to 0.29	0.66	....	1.02	0.17 to 0.20	....	910	1675
Chromium-molybdenum	0.28	0.67	....	1.18	....	0.70	870	1600

TABLE 68.—IMPACT VALUES* OF STEELS QUENCHED IN OIL AND TEMPERED AT THE INDICATED TEMPERATURE†

Tempered		Izod			Charpy		
°C.	°F.	6130	3330	Cr-Mo	6130	3330	Cr-Mo
None	None	14.9	18.5	....	20.7	25.6	
95	200	13.8	17.0	....	21.6	21.1	
205	400	14.8	20.8	21.5	22.5	22.7	22.7
315	600	9.6	16.3	17.4	22.5	21.9	20.6
425	800	13.5	22.3	18.9	14.5	26.6	19.1
540	1000	21.4	37.8	46.3	18.5	34.9	31.0
650	1200	18.6	88.5	88.5	20.7	54.6	48.9

* A reviewer pointed out that the ratio of Izod to Charpy is strange. The units of impact were not stated.

† Moore and Schaal.[123]

TABLE 69.—TENSILE PROPERTIES OF A STEEL CONTAINING 0.26 PER CENT CARBON, 0.57 PER CENT MANGANESE, 0.80 PER CENT CHROMIUM, AND 0.36 PER CENT MOLYBDENUM*

(Quenched in water from 840 to 900°C. (1550 to 1650°F.) and tempered at indicated temperatures)

Size quenched	Tempered		Tensile strength, lb./sq. in.	Yield strength,† lb./sq. in.	Elongation in 2 in., per cent	Reduction of area, per cent
	°C.	°F.				
7/8-in. round....	540	1000	158,500	146,800	21.2	55.6
1-in. round....	540	1000	162,200	153,900	19.4	55.9
1½-in. round....	540	1000	157,600	147,900	20.3	57.0
2-in. square...	540	1000	125,400	108,500	27.6	62.0
7/8-in. round....	595	1100	137,000	122,700	22.5	60.7
1-in. round....	595	1100	129,000	112,400	24.7	64.7
1½-in. round....	595	1100	131,900	118,500	24.0	64.4
2-in. square...	595	1100	117,200	100,500	25.4	66.5
7/8-in. round....	650	1200	118,900	101,000	26.5	68.4
1-in. round....	650	1200	117,400	99,300	27.1	66.7
1½-in. round....	650	1200	112,400	92,900	26.9	68.8
2-in. square...	650	1200	100,600	78,800	29.0	70.0

* Dawe.[106]

† Reported "yield point as elastic limit."

Tensile, torsional, impact, and hardness tests were made on these steels after various heat treatments. The tensile values are plotted in Fig. 90, and the impact values are given in Table 68. The notch in the Izod specimens was a 45-deg. "V," 0.079 in. deep and rounded to a radius of 0.01 in. at the bottom. The specimen was 0.394 in. square. The distance from the notch to the striking edge of the hammer was 0.866 in. The Charpy specimens were 0.394 in. square, 2.16 in. long, and tested with 1.575 in. between the edges of the anvil supports. The notch was cut in the center of the specimen 0.197 in. deep, 0.079 in. wide, with a radius of 0.0395 in. at the bottom.

TABLE 70.—MECHANICAL PROPERTIES OF CHROMIUM-MOLYBDENUM STEEL CONTAINING 0.31 PER CENT CARBON, 0.58 PER CENT CHROMIUM, AND 0.22 PER CENT MOLYBDENUM*

(Specimens 0.352 × 1.5 × 12 in.; quenched in water)

Quenched		Tempered		Tensile strength, lb./sq. in.	Yield strength,† lb./sq. in.	Elongation in 2 in., per cent	Reduction of area, per cent	Brinell hardness	Izod impact, ft-lb.
°C.	°F.	°C.	°F.						
As rolled		....		102,200	72,700	22.0	44.4	207 to 228	
900	1650	Air-cool		95,700	66,000	28.6	45.6	196 to 207	49
870	1600	480	900	163,500	150,900	15.6	38.1	302 to 351	
870	1600	540	1000	149,800	134,900	19.5	44.1	311 to 321	47
870	1600	595	1100	129,200	119,400	21.2	47.7	262 to 267	53
870	1600	650	1200	114,800	102,400	23.8	49.9	241 to 248	74

* Bremmer.(320)

† Reported as yield point.

The properties of a chromium-molybdenum steel containing 0.26 per cent carbon after heat treatment of various-sized sections were reported by Dawe.(106) Some of his values are given in Table 69.

In a study of steel suitable for deep-well casings, Bremmer(320) determined the properties of a chromium-molybdenum steel containing 0.31 per cent carbon. The samples studied were cut from a seamless tube. The impact specimens were obtained after upsetting the tube in order to obtain a standard Izod specimen. The values reported are given in Table 70.

TABLE 71.—MECHANICAL PROPERTIES OF STEELS OF THE FOLLOWING ANALYSES*

Carbon: 0.45 per cent carbon, 0.57 per cent manganese. *Chromium:* 0.33 per cent carbon, 0.41 per cent manganese, 0.72 per cent chromium. *Chromium-molybdenum:* 0.32 per cent carbon, 0.72 per cent manganese, 0.80 per cent chromium, 0.27 per cent molybdenum.

Steel	Water-quenched		Tempered		Tensile strength, lb./sq. in.	Yield strength,† lb./sq. in.	Elongation in 2 in., per cent	Reduction of area, per cent	Brinell hardness	Izod impact, ft-lb.
	°C.	°F.	°C.	°F.						
Carbon	As rolled		...	...	82,100	50,100	28.3	48.8	...	16.5
Chromium	As rolled		...	...	82,850	52,000	30.6	59.7	...	20.3
Chromium-molybdenum	As rolled		...	...	113,700	86,100	19.6	59.6	230	5.0
Carbon	Annealed‡		...	...	77,100	41,900	28.1	44.9	...	10.5
Chromium	Annealed‡		...	...	78,200	46,700	28.9	52.6	...	15.3
Chromium-molybdenum	Annealed§		...	...	96,930	64,100	24.0	51.9	189	11.8
Carbon	860	1580	400	750	127,350	100,450	12.3	33.5	...	27.3
Chromium	845	1550	415	775	138,500	118,100	12.7	39.4	...	10.5
Chromium-molybdenum	845	1550	400	750	190,125	171,300	12.8	56.4	381	37.5
Carbon	860	1580	450	840	117,800	81,750	13.0	35.4	...	29.0
Chromium	845	1550	450	840	113,350	98,800	14.7	45.7	...	14.5
Chromium-molybdenum	845	1550	450	840	185,375	161,600	14.3	57.5	372	38.3
Carbon	860	1580	500	930	114,650	81,150	16.5	42.1	...	26.5
Chromium	845	1550	500	930	127,400	99,800	16.8	51.0	...	21.0
Chromium-molybdenum	845	1550	500	930	172,300	150,350	15.8	58.5	355	49.3
Carbon	860	1580	550	1020	107,200	74,400	19.8	47.0	...	27.5
Chromium	845	1550	550	1020	115,450	93,530	20.6	61.2	...	78.0
Chromium-molybdenum	845	1550	550	1020	162,100	144,500	16.8	62.0	331	57.3
Carbon	860	1580	600	1110	101,300	70,500	22.8	54.9	...	30.0
Chromium	845	1550	600	1110	109,250	87,500	22.1	64.6	...	85.0
Chromium-molybdenum	845	1550	610	1130	141,900	122,200	19.8	65.2	292	76.0

* Camp and Francis.(146)
† By drop of beam.
‡ 870°C. (1600°F.).
§ 860°C. (1580°F.).

Tests made at Carnegie Steel Co. comparing the properties of chromium-molybdenum steel with those of a carbon steel and a chromium steel were described by Camp and Francis.(146) The analyses of the steels used and the properties obtained are listed in Table 71. The chromium steel was in the form of 1⅛-in.

rounds and the two other steels in the form of ⅞-in. rounds. After treating, standard test specimens 0.5 in. in diameter were machined. Each value given represents the average of four determinations. Yield strength was obtained by drop of beam. All three steels were rolled on the same mill from 4 × 4-in. billets.

Table 72, from Camp and Francis,[146] compares the properties of a chromium-molybdenum steel with other steels heat-treated to give approximately the same strength. In a discussion of these results the authors wrote:

> From these data it is evident that molybdenum has the effect of markedly increasing the ratio of the elastic limit to the ultimate strength as compared with carbon steel but only slightly so when compared with other alloy steels of similar mechanical properties, otherwise. In ductility, as shown in both the tensile and bend tests, the chromium-molybdenum steel is superior to all others, while its ability to withstand impact, as indicated by the Izod test, is very remarkable. In all these features, these tests but corroborate the results obtained by a great number of other investigators.

129. Steels Containing over 0.35 Per Cent Carbon.—The properties of five steels containing from 0.40 to 0.52 per cent carbon as determined by Gillett and Mack are given in Table 64 (page 216). Tables 58, 59, and 60 (pages 207–208) giving the results of work by McAdam[122] also contain values for steels containing 0.39 and 0.50 per cent carbon.

The properties of some heat-treated S.A.E. 4140 steels are shown in Table 73. The data given in this table were obtained at the laboratory of a producer of this type of steel and were made available through the courtesy of the metallurgist in charge of the physical laboratory. Partial analyses are shown in the table; other elements always present in steel were within the following limits:

	Per Cent
Manganese	0.59 to 0.74
Phosphorus	0.011 to 0.028
Sulphur	0.003 to 0.014
Silicon	0.20 to 0.30

Table 74, from Liebig,[81] lists the properties of a steel containing 0.39 per cent carbon.

TABLE 72.—MECHANICAL PROPERTIES OF STEELS HAVING APPROXIMATELY THE SAME TENSILE STRENGTH*

(*Carbon:* 0.62 per cent carbon, 0.45 per cent manganese. *Chromium:* 0.49 per cent carbon, 0.53 per cent manganese, 0.60 per cent chromium. *Nickel:* 0.40 per cent carbon, 0.65 per cent manganese, 3.60 per cent nickel. *Nickel-chromium:* 0.43 per cent carbon, 0.57 per cent manganese, 1.60 per cent nickel, 0.46 per cent chromium. *Chromium-molybdenum:* 0.32 per cent carbon, 0.72 per cent manganese, 0.80 per cent chromium, 0.27 per cent molybdenum.)

Steel	Tempered		Tensile strength, lb./sq. in.	Yield strength,† lb./sq. in.	Elongation in 2 in., per cent	Reduction of area, per cent	Brinell hardness	Izod impact, ft-lb.	Bend test	
	°C.	°F.							Load, lb.	Deg.
Carbon	Annealed		103,050	62,400	19.0	29.9	196			
Chromium	Annealed		116,250	74,100	20.0	41.2	217			
Nickel	Annealed		104,750	71,000	21.7	40.8	205			
Nickel-chromium	Annealed		111,750	70,300	22.3	49.5	212			
Chromium-molybdenum	Annealed		109,450	89,400	20.8	52.9	217			
Carbon	565	1050	126,200	84,400	18.0	43.6	235	5.0	1,225	15
Chromium	610	1130	125,300	107,200	18.0	56.5	228	66.5	1,300	25
Nickel	540	1000	128,000	112,500	18.8	51.4	248	54.5	1,355	19
Nickel-chromium	600	1110	128,000	111,000	19.8	60.3	248	54.0	1,320	22
Chromium-molybdenum	615	1140	125,700	112,250	21.0	68.0	235	90.0	1,365	30

All air-cooled from 775°C. (1425°F.). Tempered samples oil-quenched from 845°C. (1550°F.).

* Camp and Francis.[146]

† Reported as elastic limit.

TABLE 73.—PROPERTIES OF HEAT-TREATED S.A.E. 4140 STEELS*

Diameter, in.	Number of tests	Composition, per cent			Tempered		Tensile strength, lb./sq. in.	Yield strength,† lb./sq. in.	Elongation in 2 in., per cent	Reduction of area, per cent	Brinell hardness
		C	Cr	Mo	°C.	°F.					
Quenched in oil from 845°C. (1550°F.)											
5/8	3	0.38	0.98	0.20	610	1130	144,300	133,500	20.0	63.6	308
3/4	6	0.41	0.95	0.20	605	1120	147,700	141,200	18.8	59.5	308
3/4	3	0.40	1.01	0.17	605	1120	142,500	133,000	20.3	63.2	311
7/8	1	0.39	0.95	0.19	565	1050	145,750	131,900	17.5	55.5	311
7/8	1	0.39	0.95	0.19	595	1100	135,350	115,750	18.5	62.1	298
7/8	6	0.39	0.95	0.19	625	1155	132,100	119,700	19.1	62.0	297
1	3	0.39	0.95	0.21	600	1110	131,800	113,300	18.8	60.8	303
1	3	0.41	0.95	0.20	600	1110	135,400	117,200	18.8	61.1	308
1 1/8	3	0.41	0.94	0.20	580	1075	138,000	119,600	18.3	56.3	305
1 1/8	4	0.38	0.85	0.21	595	1100	131,900	112,100	22.2	61.2	291
1 1/8‡	3	0.39	0.98	0.21	565	1050	132,300	117,300	18.5	61.0	305
1 1/8	6	0.38	0.85	0.21	595	1100	131,900	115,900	20.8	58.3	311
1 1/4	3	0.39	0.91	0.20	630	1170	135,600	115,300	18.7	57.8	296
1 1/2	4	0.41	0.87	0.20	650	1200	132,300	122,500	20.7	61.8	289
1 1/2	2	0.41	0.88	0.19	650	1200	126,900	113,200	20.7	60.0	285
1 1/2	2	0.41	0.87	0.20	565	1050	130,600	108,200	19.8	54.8	297
1 9/16	2	0.41	0.88	0.19	565	1050	130,600	111,100	21.3	58.8	297
1 3/4	4	0.41	0.88	0.19	650	1200	133,600	119,500	21.0	61.7	294
1 3/4	2	0.39	0.91	0.20	570	1060	130,700	108,300	19.5	59.0	289
1 3/4	3	0.41	0.88	0.19	565	1050	126,200	107,300	21.5	58.2	288
1 3/4	3	0.41	0.88	0.19	650	1200	121,400	106,200	22.7	61.4	268
Quenched in water from 805 or 815°C. (1480 or 1500°F.)											
1 1/2	3	0.41	1.03	0.22	620	1150	143,100	130,750	16.5	54.0	305
1 13/16	2	0.40	0.91	0.21	620	1150	134,800	121,700	19.7	61.4	297
1 13/16	1	0.41	0.98	0.20	620	1150	148,850	131,300	17.0	51.4	302
2 1/2	2	0.41	0.95	0.20	580	1075	154,100	142,150	18.2	57.7	336
2 1/2	2	0.41	0.95	0.20	600	1110	145,600	133,400	18.7	57.3	302
Normalized at 870°C. (1600°F.)											
1 5/8	4	0.42	0.95	0.20	...	....	124,100	95,100	21.2	55.5	241
Annealed at 870°C. (1600°F.)											
1 5/8	4	0.42	0.95	0.20	...	....	100,400	70,000	25.0	50.7	200

* *Private communication.*

† Reported as yield point.

‡ Quenched from 870°C. (1600°F.).

Angell[306] suggested the possibility of quenching alloy steels below the Ac_3 transformation and above the Ar_3 transformation and determined the properties of a number of steels so treated,

TABLE 74.—PROPERTIES OF A STEEL CONTAINING 0.39 PER CENT CARBON, 0.83 PER CENT MANGANESE, 1.10 PER CENT CHROMIUM, AND 0.40 PER CENT MOLYBDENUM AFTER COOLING IN FURNACE FROM INDICATED TEMPERATURES*

Temperature		Tensile strength, lb./sq. in.	Yield strength,† lb./sq. in.	Elongation in 4 in., per cent	Brinell hardness
°C.	°F.				
735	1350	104,900	81,500	11.7	194
745	1375	96,200	66,100	14.1	182
760	1400	94,700	76,800	14.8	182
775	1425	101,800	58,400	12.5	187
785	1450	109,700	51,400	13.3	201
815	1500	124,800	76,100	7.8	247

* Liebig.[81]

† Reported as yield point.

TABLE 75.—PROPERTIES OF S.A.E. 4140 STEEL*

(Quenched in water from 885°C. (1625°F.) and tempered for 4 hr. at indicated temperatures. Treated as hollow cylinders, 8 in. O.D. and 3 in. I.D. Composition: 0.39 per cent carbon, 0.56 per cent manganese, 0.86 per cent chromium, and 0.17 per cent molybdenum.)

Tempered		Tensile strength, lb./sq. in.	Proportional limit, lb./sq. in.	Yield strength, lb./sq. in.	Elongation in 2 in., per cent	Reduction of area, per cent	Brinell hardness
°C.	°F.						
260	500	210,900	127,000	165,800	6.5	31.8	388
370	700	137,200	79,000	121,500	18.0	59.4	287
400	750	163,300	110,000	143,800	13.8	47.8	321
480	900	120,700	83,000	96,300	18.5	59.5	255
595	1100	108,800	70,000	76,600	26.5	63.1	204
735	1350	93,700	48,000	54,300	30.0	60.7	179
840	1550	89,000	35,000	41,000	28.0	43.7	166

* Digges.[436]

including one containing 0.53 per cent carbon, 0.80 per cent chromium, and 0.35 per cent molybdenum. The steels were heated above the Ac_3 transformation and then cooled slowly to just above the Ar_3 temperature before quenching. The properties of the chromium-molybdenum steel treated by quenching in this manner and by quenching from the normal high temperature are given in Table 76.

In a report of the machinability of several common alloy steels heat-treated to various strengths, Digges[436] gave the properties of a chromium-molybdenum S.A.E. 4140 steel. This steel was heat-treated in the form of hollow cylinders 8-in. outside diameter and 3-in. inside diameter. The properties of the heat-treated steel are given in Table 75.

TABLE 76.—PROPERTIES OF A HEAT-TREATED STEEL CONTAINING 0.53 PER CENT CARBON, 0.73 PER CENT MANGANESE, 0.80 PER CENT CHROMIUM, AND 0.35 PER CENT MOLYBDENUM*

Treatment†	Tensile strength, lb./sq. in.	Yield strength,‡ lb./sq. in.	Elongation in 2 in., per cent	Reduction of area, per cent	Izod impact, ft-lb.	Brinell hardness
A........	213,900	163,000	2.5	13.5	18.5	415
B........	213,900	163,000	8.0	19.7	20	415

* Angell.[306]

† *A*, quenched in water from 815°C. (1500°F.) and tempered at 480°C. (900°F.). *B*, heated to 815°C. (1500°F.), cooled in furnace to 705°C. (1300°F.), quenched in water, and tempered at 480°C. (900°F.).

‡ Reported as proportional limit.

Impact values for steels containing approximately 0.50 per cent carbon, 0.85 per cent chromium, and 0.30 per cent molybdenum after quenching and tempering at various temperatures were given by Grossmann.[135] The slight drop in impact values produced by tempering at 345°C. (650°F.) together with the length changes were interpreted as being due to the decomposition of austenite retained at quenching.

B. OTHER PROPERTIES OF CHROMIUM-MOLYBDENUM STRUCTURAL STEELS

Even though steels of the type discussed are used primarily because of their mechanical properties, other characteristics may be of great importance in the selection of a steel for a particular use. This is illustrated by the extended use of the 4130X steel in aircraft construction, for its general use is due chiefly to its welding properties or, more properly, the ability of the steel to maintain its strength in sections adjacent to a weld. Within the past eight years much has been written on welding this type of steel, but inasmuch as a large part of this literature is of interest only from the standpoint of welding the work has not been discussed in detail.

In a previous section data were presented which showed that molybdenum when added to carbon steels increased creep resistance at temperatures in the neighborhood of 500°C. (930°F.) and in absence of definite evidence to the contrary it could be assumed that molybdenum would also be effective in increasing the creep resistance of chromium steels.

The mass effect or the dependence of hardening on the size of the piece treated is often of extreme importance but is a characteristic which has not been frequently studied.

130. Welding Properties.—In a discussion of welding in aircraft construction, Daniels[168] stated that chromium-molybdenum steel welds satisfactorily with a carbon-steel welding wire, and that chromium-vanadium steel parts can be easily welded to chromium-molybdenum steel tubing. The welding can be done either by the oxy-acetylene method or by the metallic-arc method. The air-hardening properties of chromium-molybdenum steels result in a joint having a tensile strength as high as the unwelded tube. Welds in chromium-molybdenum tubing quenched in water from 885°C. (1625°F.) and tempered from 425 to 675°C. (800 to 1250°F.) have given tensile strength values from 155,000 to 110,000 lb. per sq. in. with an elongation in 2 in. of from 4 to 17 per cent.

Many recent articles have discussed the welding of S.A.E. 4130X steel in airplane construction; included are those by Sisco and Boulton,[165] Johnson,[197, 225] Knerr,[228] Hackett,[265, 266] Mock,[284] Downes,[332] Perkins,[391] Herb,[347] Whittemore and Brueggeman,[414] McManus,[473] George,[444] and Zeyen.[506]

The recent investigation of Whittemore and Brueggeman[414] may be used to show the strength expected from welded butt joints made in 4130X tubing. Some of their results on gas welds in variously sized tubing are given in Figs. 91 to 93. Figure 91 shows tensile strength in pounds per square inch and as a percentage of the original strength, while Fig. 92 gives compressive strength of the welded tubing expressed in the same manner. Practically all failures occurred about ½ in. from the weld. The divisions in inches in these figures represent diameters and thicknesses of the tubes. Figure 93 gives Vickers hardness values for points adjacent to the welds, and, as may be observed, minimum-hardness values occur at a distance of ½ in. from the middle of the weld.

The use of a chromium-molybdenum steel welding rod for welding 4130X tubing was studied by Sisco and Boulton.[165] They compared the behavior during welding and the resulting welds for a low-carbon steel welding wire and a wire containing 0.28 per cent carbon, 0.61 per cent manganese, 1.14 per cent

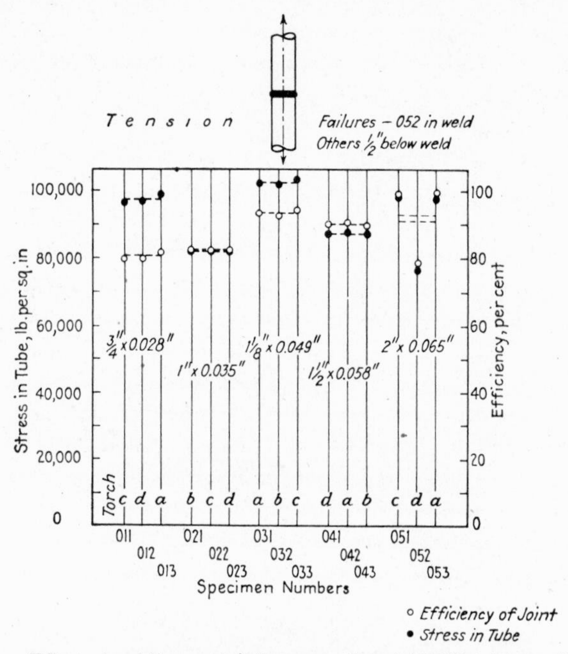

Fig. 91.—Effect of welding on tensile properties of 4130X tubing. Efficiency of 100 per cent represents strength equivalent to unwelded tubing. Results of tensile tests. (*Whittemore and Brueggeman.*[414])

chromium, and 0.95 per cent molybdenum. It was observed that the alloy welding rod did not flow so well as the low-carbon steel rod. Tensile tests were made on the welded joint, both with and without heat treatment subsequent to welding, but the fractures normally occurred outside the welds, thereby rendering a comparison of the weld strength impossible. Daniels,[168] however, considered that the use of a chromium-molybdenum welding rod might be justified if the welds are to be heat-treated.

The results of tests using various kinds of welding rods in arc welding nickel steels were reported by McManus,[473] who found that a chromium-molybdenum steel rod produced the best welds with respect to all mechanical properties.

Endurance properties of welded chromium-molybdenum steel tubing were studied by Beissner.[423] The tubing was of American manufacture and corresponded to 4130X, and the two sections used had wall thicknesses of 0.59 in. (1.5 mm.) and 0.12 in. (3.0 mm.), respectively. In the best welds the endurance limit

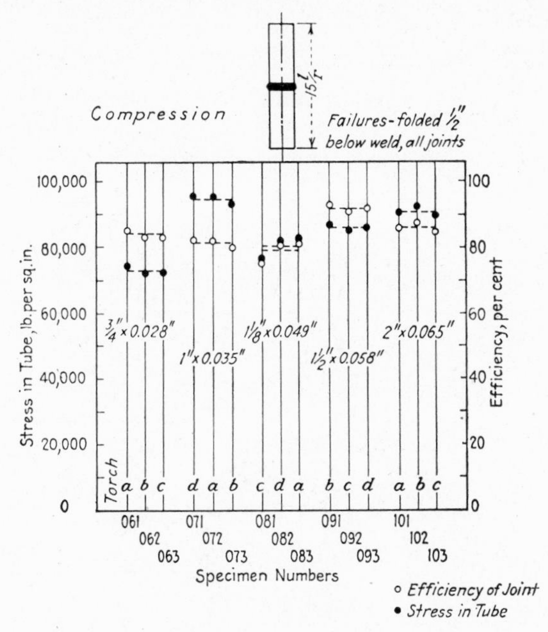

FIG. 92.—Same as Fig. 91. Results of compression tests. (*Whittemore and Brueggeman.*[414])

was approximately 60 per cent of the endurance limit of the unwelded tubing. The fatigue breaks occurred outside of the welds except in faulty welds. The use of an ingot iron welding rod resulted in welds of higher strength in the thin-walled tubing, while a chromium-molybdenum steel rod produced welds with the higher endurance limit in the thick-walled tubing. No explanation for this anomaly was given.

131. Properties at High Temperatures.—The short-time tensile properties of a series of steels, including a chromium-molybdenum steel, at elevated temperatures were determined by MacPherran.[100] The chromium-molybdenum steel contained 0.38 per cent carbon, 0.62 per cent manganese, 0.86 per cent chromium, and 0.34 per cent molybdenum. It was quenched in water from 925°C. (1700°F.) and tempered at 705°C. (1300°F.), after which its tensile strength was approximately 150,000 lb. per sq. in. at room temperature. On heating, the tensile strength fell gradually to 140,000 lb. per sq. in. at a temperature of 370°C. (700°F.), after which it fell rapidly.

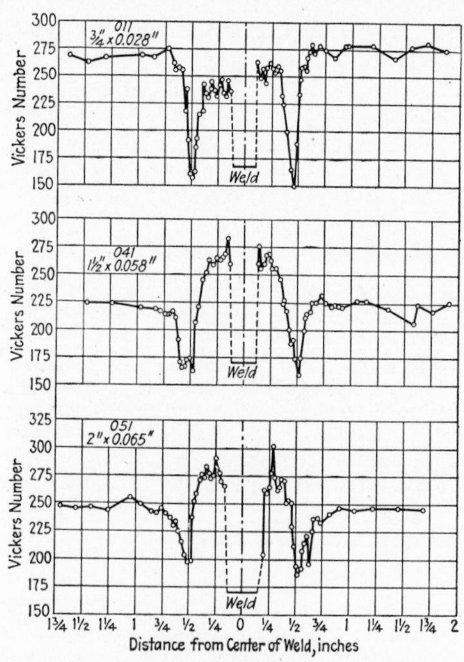

Fig. 93.—Vickers hardness in and adjacent to welds in 4130X tubing. (*Whittemore and Brueggeman.*[414])

Short-time tensile tests on a steel containing 0.27 per cent carbon, 0.62 per cent manganese, 0.99 per cent chromium, and 0.41 per cent molybdenum were reported by French and Tucker,[120] who compared its properties with those of other steels. Tensile properties at temperatures up to 550°C. (1020°F.) are plotted in Fig. 94. Other steels tested included carbon, chromium, nickel-uranium, and chromium-vanadium steels. The yield strength at all temperatures of the chromium-molybdenum steels was higher than that of any other steel. From their work the authors concluded that the strength or load-carrying capacity of steels at elevated temperatures is improved by such elements as chromium, cobalt, uranium, molybdenum, and vanadium, but that nickel appears to "soften" rather than strengthen steels at elevated temperatures, particularly at and above 550°C. (1020°F.).

Short-time tensile tests made by four laboratories on a chromium-molybdenum steel were given by a committee of the A.S.T.M.(191) The steel contained 0.39 per cent carbon, 0.51 per cent manganese, 0.87 per cent chromium, and 0.21 per cent

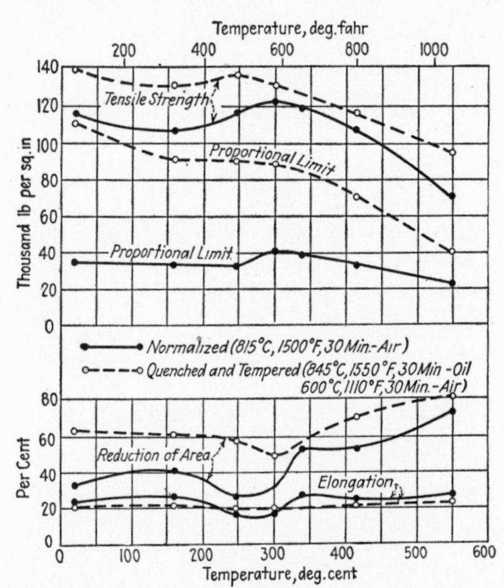

FIG. 94.—High-temperature tensile properties of chromium-molybdenum steel, normalized or quenched and tempered. Composition: 0.27 per cent carbon, 0.62 per cent manganese, 0.99 per cent chromium, 0.41 per cent molybdenum. (*French and Tucker.*(120))

molybdenum. It was tested after having been normalized at 885°C. (1625°F.), oil-quenched from 845°C. (1550°F.), and tempered at 705°C. (1300°F.). Results of the tests by the four laboratories are plotted in Fig. 95.

The materials used in short-time tensile tests at elevated temperatures by Freeman and Quick(336) included a chromium-molybdenum and a manganese-molybdenum steel. The behavior of these steels was not essentially different from that of the carbon steels.

A recent article by Spooner and Foley(499) included a table listing high-temperature properties of various steels. The values given in Table 77 are from this table; the strength at elevated temperatures is expressed as the stress that will just fail to produce an elongation of 1 per cent in 100,000 hr. Part of these data was credited to Kanter and Spring[358] and French, Kahl-

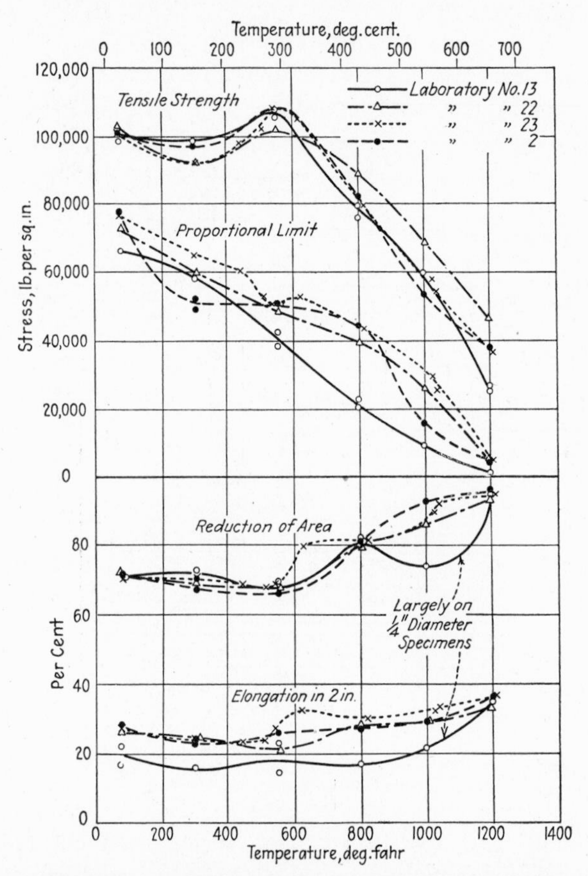

FIG. 95.—Short-time tensile properties of a 0.39 per cent carbon, 0.51 per cent manganese, 0.87 per cent chromium, 0.21 per cent molybdenum steel at various temperatures. Quenched in oil and tempered at 705°C. (1300°F.). (*A.S.T.M.*[191])

baum, and Peterson.[338] No attempt was made by the writers to analyze the data to determine the effect of molybdenum in these steels.

From creep tests on a steel containing 0.39 per cent carbon, 0.51 per cent manganese, 0.87 per cent chromium, and 0.21 per cent molybdenum, normalized at 885°C. (1625°F.), quenched in oil from 840°C. (1550°F.), and tempered at 705°C. (1300°F.), French, Cross, and Peterson[193] constructed the charts given in Fig. 96. The steel under discussion was found to be "structurally unstable at 650°C. (1200°F.); it showed decarburization and grain growth."

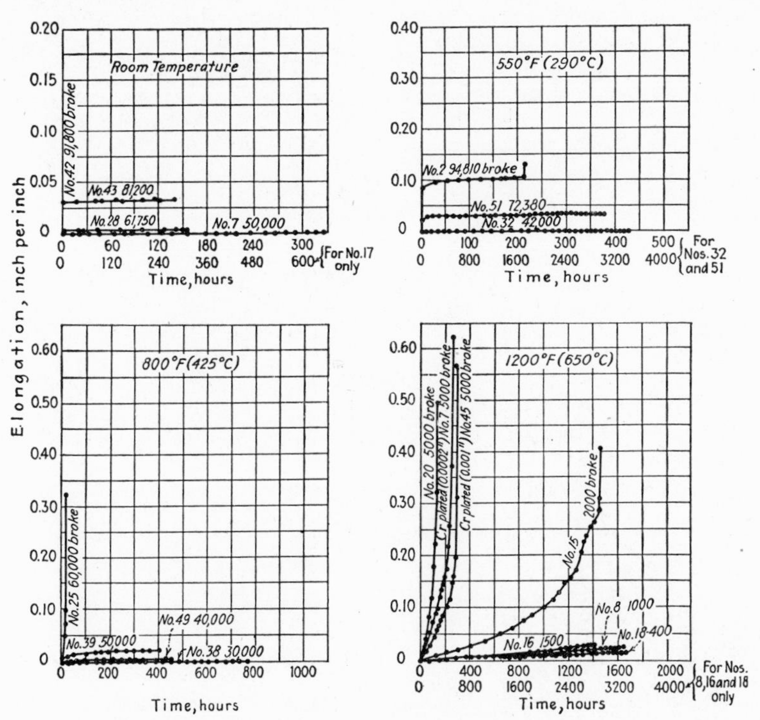

FIG. 96.—Time-elongation curves of chromium-molybdenum steel, of analysis and treatment given in Fig. 95. (*French, Cross, and Peterson.*[193])

From a consideration of published values on creep resistance of low-alloy steels, Tapsell[501] concluded that molybdenum either alone or in combination with nickel and chromium considerably improves resistance to creep at elevated temperatures, and further that chromium-molybdenum steels have very good creep resistance at temperatures up to about 500°C. (930°F.).

Creep results reported by Spring[500] for a chromium-molybdenum, a nickel-chromium, and a nickel-chromium-molybdenum steel are shown in Fig. 97. The analyses of the samples which were obtained from castings were:

Samples	Composition, per cent					
	C	Mn	Si	Ni	Cr	Mo
Chromium-molybdenum......	0.37	0.48	0.24	....	0.91	0.24
Nickel-chromium............	0.41	0.58	0.29	2.00	0.87	
Nickel-chromium-molybdenum	0.40	0.57	0.28	2.03	0.82	0.23

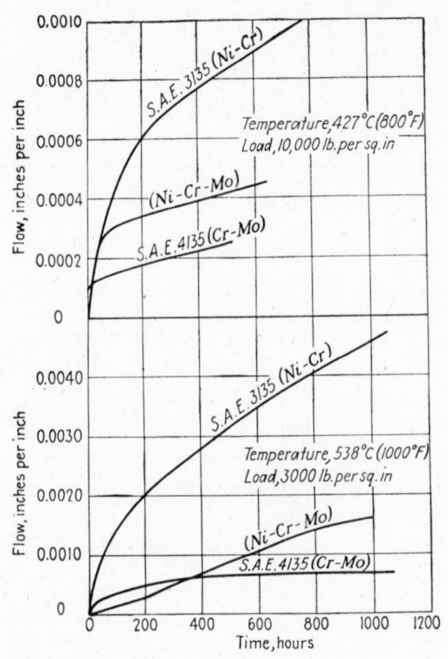

Fig. 97.—Creep in cast nickel-chromium and chromium-molybdenum steels. (*Spring.*[500])

In a discussion at the recent symposium on Effect of Temperature on the Properties of Metals, Mathews[477] stated that

. . . an addition of chromium alone to steel does not give high creep strength. Creep values for a 4 to 6 per cent chromium steel are lower than for a plain carbon tube steel at 480°C. (900°F.), but approximately equal at 540°C. (1000°F.). Resistance to creep in this steel can be very materially improved by small additions of either tungsten or molybdenum.

The development of heat-resistant steels at the Krupp works was discussed by Jungbluth and Müller[463] who concluded that

TABLE 77.—CREEP TESTS OF MOLYBDENUM STEELS*
(Strength is the highest stress that will not produce a deformation to exceed 1 per cent in 100,000 hr.)

Number	Composition, per cent							Strength, lb./sq. in.			
	C	Mn	Si	Ni	Cr	V	Mo	425°C. (800°F.)	450°C. (840°F.)	460°C. (860°F.)	540°C. (1000°F.)
47	0.48	0.63	0.20	3.38	0.08	....	0.32	22,000			
48	0.48	0.63	0.20	3.38	0.08	....	0.32	15,000			
49	0.20	0.41	0.14	....	0.87	0.22	0.29	....	......	44,000	
50	0.34	0.80	0.29	2.77	1.09	....	0.78	....	13,500		
51	0.34	0.80	0.29	2.77	1.09	....	0.78	....	18,000		
52	0.34	0.60	....	2.74	0.61	....	0.25	....	25,600		
53	0.34	0.60	....	2.74	0.61	....	0.25	....	13,000		
54	0.39	0.73	1.24	2.78	0.84	....	0.48	....	22,000		
55	0.34	0.80	0.79	2.76	1.09	....	0.78	....	15,100		
56	0.54	1.18	0.23	....	0.51	....	0.22	....	14,400		
57	0.54	1.18	0.23	....	0.51	....	0.22	....	14,400		
58‡	0.37	0.48	0.24	....	0.91	....	0.24	50,000	......	......	7,500
60§	0.53	0.95	0.23	....	1.07	....	0.44	....	......	......	23,000
61§	0.75	0.52	0.31	0.15	1.45	0.27	0.54	....	......	......	12,000
62§	0.39	0.51	0.19	....	0.87	....	0.21	41,000†	......	......	18,000

Number	Heat treatment of specimens, °C. (Temperatures in parenthesis, °F.; O.Q., oil quench; A.C., air cool; F.C., furnace cool)
47	900 (1650) A.C., 800 (1475) F.C., 650 (1200) F.C.
48	900 (1650) A.C., 825 (1520) O.Q., 650 (1200) O.Q., 425 (800) F.C.
49	950 (1740) O.Q., 610 (1130) F.C.
50	950 (1740) A.C., 800 (1475) A.C., 650 (1200) F.C.
51	950 (1740) A.C., 750 (1380) A.C., 650 (1200) F.C.
52	835 (1530) O.Q., 625 (1155) O.Q., 400 (750) F.C.
53	825 (1520) F.C., 625 (1155) O.Q., 425 (800) F.C.
54	950 (1740) A.C., 815 (1500) A.C., 625 (1150) A.C., 600 (1110) F.C.
55	900 (1650) A.C., 835 (1530) O.Q., 625 (1150) O.Q., 400 (750) F.C.
56	900 (1650) A.C., 835 (1530) O.Q., 625 (1150) O.Q., 425 (800) F.C.
57	900 (1650) A.C., 835 (1530) F.C., 675 (1250) O.Q., 425 (800) F.C.
58‡	Annealed
60§	840 (1550) O.Q., 650 (1200) F.C.
61§	840 (1550) O.Q., 595 (1100) Slow Cool
62§	885 (1625) A.C., 840 (1550) O.Q., 705 (1300) O.Q.

* Spooner and Foley.[499]
† At 370°C. (700°F.).
‡ From Kanter and Spring.[358]
§ From French, Kahlbaum, and Peterson.[338]

a chromium-molybdenum and a chromium-molybdenum-silicon steel containing about 1 per cent chromium have a high creep resistance and a high resistance to scaling at temperatures of 600 or 650°C. (1110 or 1200°F.). A molybdenum-bearing steel containing about 6 per cent chromium and 1.5 per cent silicon has a slightly lower creep limit but is resistant to scaling at temperatures up to 800°C. (1470°F.).

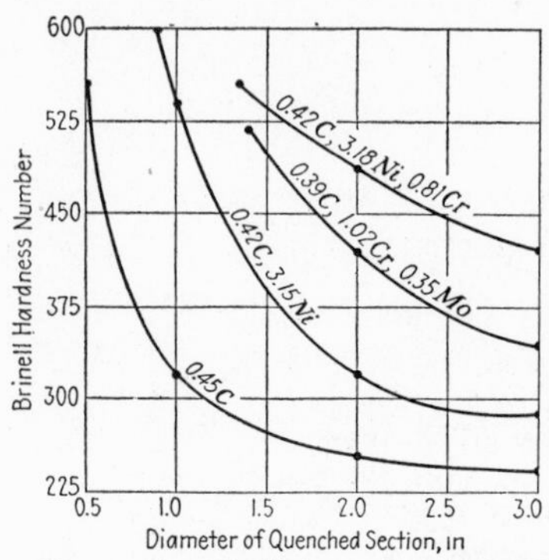

FIG. 98.—Variation in Brinell hardness at center of section as influenced by diameter of specimen. Quenched in water. Composition given in table below. (*Janitzky*.[109])

132. Mass Effect.—The values obtained by Dawe[106] and listed in Table 69 (page 225) give the properties of a chromium-molybdenum steel heat-treated in various sections and suggest some indication of the mass effect in steel of this composition.

Figure 98, by Janitzky,[109] gives the hardness and shows the relative mass effect of four types of structural steel of the following composition:

Type	Cr-Ni	Cr-Mo	Ni	C
Carbon, per cent	0.42	0.39	0.42	0.45
Manganese, per cent	0.30	0.53	0.61	0.78
Nickel, per cent	3.18	....	3.15	
Chromium, per cent	0.81	1.02		
Molybdenum, per cent	....	0.35		

In this illustration the Brinell hardness at the center of the section is plotted against the diameter of the section quenched.

Recently Kallen and Schrader[465] studied the effect of size and alloying elements on the hardening of structural steels. Sections, 20, 50, 100, and 200 mm. (0.79, 1.97, 3.94, and 7.87 in.) in diameter, were heat-treated, and the mass effect was judged by the difference in properties between edge and core of each section and by the effect of the size of specimen on properties. The two steels of the following compositions are of interest in the present discussion:

Steel	Composition, per cent			
	C	Mn	Cr	Mo
F	0.31	0.66	0.86	
G	0.33	0.75	0.91	0.26

Tensile and impact tests indicated that the 0.26 per cent of molybdenum in steel *G* had an appreciable effect in tending to produce hardening throughout the sections 50 mm. (1.97 in.)

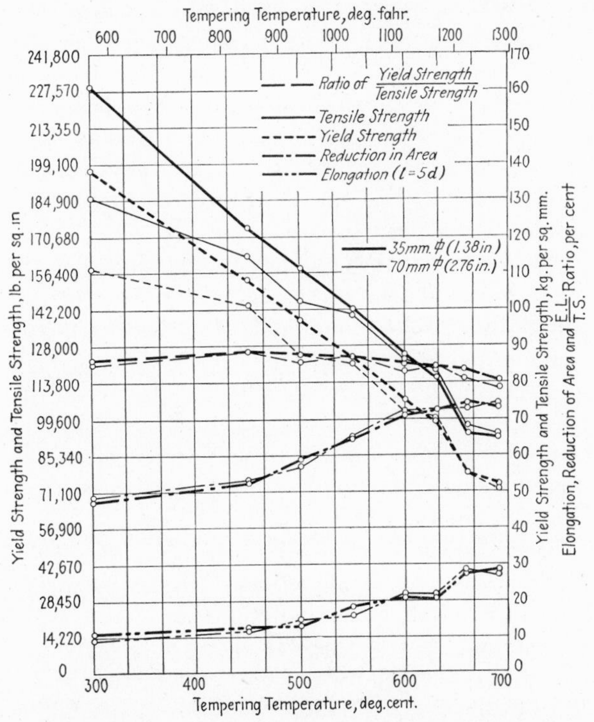

Fig. 99.—Properties of a chromium-molybdenum steel quenched in water from 830°C. (1525°F.) and tempered as shown. Specimens as quenched 35 mm. (1.38 in.) and 70 mm. (2.76 in.) in diameter. (*Kallen and Schrader.*[465])

and 100 mm. (3.94 in.) in diameter, but that it was unable to prevent marked differences in properties between the surface and core of specimens 200 mm. (7.87 in.) in diameter. A steel similar to *G* except for the presence of 0.32 per cent vanadium besides the chromium and molybdenum was also studied, and it was found that its ability to harden throughout a heavy section was greater than that of steel *G*. The properties of steel *G*, water-quenched in 35-mm. (1.38-in.) and 70-mm. (2.76-in.) sections and tempered at various temperatures were also obtained and are shown in Fig. 99.

133. Microstructures.—The microstructures of a quenched and tempered steel containing 0.46 per cent carbon, 1.07 per cent chromium, and 0.35 per cent molybdenum were discussed by Pulsifer and Greene(125) and were compared with those of a nickel-chromium steel. The quenched and tempered nickel-chromium steel appeared as uniform cellular martensite after etching with picric acid. The structure of the chromium-molybdenum steel was quite difficult to develop, and the boundaries of the cells were hazy. No troostite was observed in the nickel-chromium steel, but there was apparently some in the other steel. It was suggested that the better physical properties of the chromium-molybdenum steel were in part explained by the indistinctness of the structure.

Zieler(507) decreased the number of non-metallic inclusions in a chromium-molybdenum structural steel by adding a zirconium-silicon alloy to the molten steel. The usual zirconium addition amounted to about 0.15 per cent, and analyses indicated that the steel contained from 0.01 to 0.09 per cent zirconium. The inclusions in forged bars were counted, the large inclusions being counted two times and the very large inclusions four times. It was found that the zirconium addition decreased the number of inclusions to less than half.

134. Miscellaneous Properties.—Jominy(462) studied the surface decarburization of a high-carbon chromium-molybdenum steel and a carburized nickel-molybdenum steel in a gas-fired furnace. The analyses of these steels were not given, and his results are of interest with respect to the subject of decarburizing rather than to the effect of molybdenum on the behavior of the steel.

C. PROPERTIES OF MISCELLANEOUS CHROMIUM-MOLYBDENUM STEELS

Although most commercial chromium-molybdenum steels are of the low-alloy or structural type just discussed, the properties of some steels containing these two elements and intended for use as corrosion-resistant alloys or for ball bearings have been determined. The corrosion-resisting alloys discussed below are of the types containing at least 10 per cent chromium and are commonly designated as stainless steels or irons.

135. Properties of Corrosion-resistant Alloys.—From an investigation of a series of iron-chromium-molybdenum alloys containing as much as 60 per cent chromium and as much as 5.7 per cent molybdenum, Monnartz[(50)] concluded that molybdenum refines the structure of iron-chromium alloys and increases their strength. Furthermore, in alloys containing over 20 per cent chromium several per cent of molybdenum greatly increase the resistance to acids. The effect of molybdenum on the acid resistance of alloys containing less than 20 per cent chromium was not marked. Benner,[(54)] an anonymous article,[(53)] and Duisberg[(58)] mentioned the high resistance to acids of an alloy containing 60 per cent chromium, 35 per cent iron, and 2 or 3 per cent molybdenum, and German Patent 246,035, Jan. 22, 1910, by Borchers and Monnartz[(55)] claims that such an alloy has the strength and workability of soft steel but is resistant to dilute nitric acid and alkali chlorides and is completely insoluble in boiling aqua regia. Tests by Rohn,[(178)] however, indicated that an alloy containing 70 per cent iron, 25 per cent chromium, and 5 per cent molybdenum is not so resistant to acids as nickel-chromium-iron alloys.

In a discussion of corrosion-resistant steels Armstrong[(132)] maintained that the addition of molybdenum to iron-chromium alloys does not increase their workability, and that there is a tendency for molybdenum-bearing iron-chromium alloys to form seams, but that molybdenum adds appreciably to their acid resistance.

The action of copper sulphate solution on a number of ferrous alloys was studied by Kurtz and Zaumeyer[(156)] by placing a drop of a copper sulphate solution on a clean surface of the alloy to be tested and observing whether or not copper was deposited. It was found that alloys containing chromium were most resistant to the copper sulphate, and that molybdenum did not have an appreciable effect on alloys containing less than 10 per cent chromium, but that the addition of 5 to 10 per cent molybdenum to a 10 per cent chromium alloy greatly increased its resistance. Two alloys containing, respectively, 10 per cent chromium with 5 per cent molybdenum, and 10 per cent chromium with 10 per cent molybdenum, were exposed to the action of the solution for 5 days. The alloy containing only 5 per cent molybdenum was attacked, but the one containing 10 per cent molybdenum was not even etched.

French[169] maintained that the addition of molybdenum to a high-chromium steel increases the resistance to acids and cited the following two types of steel as being typical of molybdenum-bearing corrosion-resistant alloys: (1) 0.50 per cent carbon, 8.0 per cent chromium, 1.5 per cent silicon, 0.75 per cent molybdenum and (2) 0.60 per cent carbon, 17.0 per cent chromium, 1.0 per cent silicon, and 0.5 per cent molybdenum.

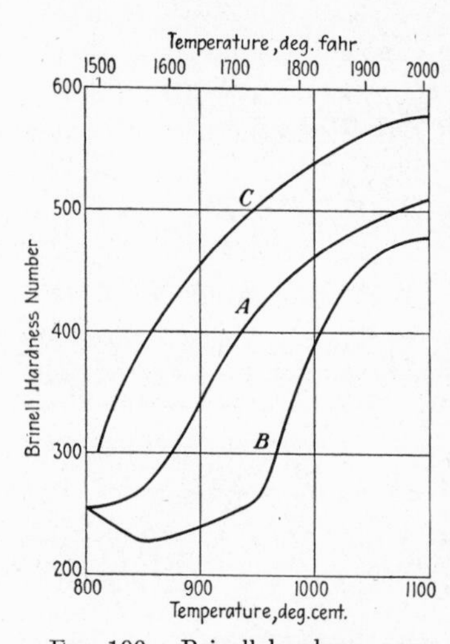

FIG. 100.—Brinell hardness numbers obtained from chromium-molybdenum steel containing 0.24 per cent carbon, 12.8 per cent chromium, 2.28 per cent molybdenum after water-quenching (curve A) or air-cooling (curve B) from the temperatures indicated. Curve C gives typical results obtainable on air-cooling a steel free from molybdenum, but otherwise similar in analysis. (*Monypenny.*[177])

The data listed in Table 78 were given by Monypenny[177] to show the increased resistance to acids effected in stainless steels by the addition of molybdenum. Steels from which these data were obtained were in the hardened and tempered condition. It was claimed that the addition of 2 per cent molybdenum to a stainless steel containing 12 per cent chromium raises the Ac_1 transformation and reduces the air-hardening capacity when cooled from 100°C. (180°F.) or so above the Ac_1 temperature. The curves given in Fig. 100 illustrate the effects of molybdenum on a steel quenched from various temperatures. If a suitable hardening temperature is used in treating a molybdenum-bearing stainless steel, its mechanical properties after tempering are similar to those of an ordinary stainless steel except that in the fully tempered condition the molybdenum steel is harder.

Free-cutting stainless steels are sometimes produced by adding molybdenum to the more common steels and increasing the sulphur content. Such steels, however, are naturally found to

TABLE 78.—ACID RESISTANCE OF STAINLESS STEEL*
(*Steel A:* 0.32 per cent carbon, 12.2 per cent chromium. *Steel B:* 0.23 per cent carbon, 11.6 per cent chromium, 2.3 per cent molybdenum)

Acid	Strength, per cent	Duration of test	Loss, per cent		Loss, mg./sq. cm./hr.	
			A	*B*	*A*	*B*
Nitric	Normal	6 hr.	0.54	0.206	1.76	0.67
Hydrochloric	10	24 hr.	2.59	0.24	2.15	0.20
Sulphuric	5	24 hr.	4.90	1.65	4.09	1.37
Sulphuric	35	6 hr.	3.16	0.525	20.5	1.72
Acetic	5	8 days	0.785	0.045	0.079	0.0045
Acetic	33	10 days	1.15	0.109	0.093	0.0089
Citric	6	7 days	2.08	0.071	0.24	0.008
Tartaric	25	13 days	0.68	0.34	0.043	0.022

* Monypenny.(177)

TABLE 79.—PROPERTIES OF A FREE-CUTTING STAINLESS STEEL PERPENDICULAR TO ROLLING DIRECTION*
(0.12 per cent carbon, 0.35 per cent manganese, 0.40 per cent silicon, 0.133 per cent sulphur, 13.91 per cent chromium, and 0.30 per cent molybdenum; 0.357-in. diameter specimens; specimens from 5¾-in. round.)

Location of specimen	Tensile strength, lb./sq. in.	Yield strength,† lb./sq. in.	Elongation in 1.4 in., per cent	Reduction of area, per cent
Annealed steel				
Close to outer diameter	76,500	50,000	3.2	3.5
Midway between surface and center	75,500	47,000	4.0	2.5
Through center	77,000	48,000	5.0	4.4
Oil-quenched from 995°C. (1825°F.), tempered at 650°C. (1200°F.)				
	83,000	50,000	0	0
Oil-quenched from 1065°C. (1950°F.), tempered at 650°C. (1200°F.)				
	98,000	70,000	3.0	3.4

* Watertown Arsenal.
† Reported as proportional limit.

have a very low ductility in a direction perpendicular to the rolling direction as is shown by data obtained at Watertown Arsenal and given in Table 79.

Boston[319A] determined the machinability of a chromium "stainless iron" and a similar alloy containing a high sulphur content and a small amount of molybdenum by means of planing, drilling, and milling tests. The partial analyses of the alloys were:

Alloy	Composition, per cent				
	C	Mn	S	Cr	Mo
Chromium iron	0.06	0.31	0.022	13.35	
Free-machining iron	0.09	0.30	0.46	15.15	0.25

The steel with molybdenum and a high sulphur content had decidedly better machining properties than the normal stainless iron, and, in fact, its machinability approached that of screw-machine steel.

The effects of silicon and molybdenum on the mechanical properties and corrosion resistance of steels containing 15 per cent chromium were studied by Oertel and Würth.[202] The molybdenum content of these alloys was as high as 1.4 per cent, and the carbon content varied from 0.2 to 0.6 per cent. The addition of molybdenum did not decrease the ductility. Molybdenum increased the resistance to attack in acetic acid and sea water, and the alloys containing molybdenum scaled less at high temperature than those free from this element.

The short-time tensile properties at temperatures up to 600°C. (1110°F.) and the creep limits at temperatures of 400, 500, and 600°C. (750, 930, and 1110°F.) for a steel containing 0.64 per cent carbon, 16.0 per cent chromium, and 1.83 per cent molybdenum were given by Stäger.[408] This steel had a decidedly higher creep limit as determined by an accelerated creep test than steels containing no molybdenum, and Stäger attributed this high resistance to deformation at temperatures from 400° to 600°C. (750 to 1110°F.) to the presence of the molybdenum.

136. Ball-bearing Steels.—The following types of ball-bearing steels were studied by Robinson:[206]

Type	Composition, per cent				
	C	Cr	Mn	Mo	V
Chromium	1.00 to 1.10	1.30 to 1.50	0.20 to 0.40		
Chromium-molybdenum	1.00 to 1.10	1.10 to 1.30	0.20 to 0.40	0.30 to 0.50	
Chromium-vanadium	1.00 to 1.10	1.30 to 1.50	0.20 to 0.40	....	0.20 to 0.40

Samples from two lots of each type were used, and the specimens were hardened by quenching in oil from 820°C. (1510°F.) and tempering at 175°C. (350°F.) for 20 min. The endurance limit, bending strength, and Rockwell hardness of these steels are listed in Table 80. Endurance tests were made on a rotating-beam machine. The bending tests were made on a round specimen ½ in. in diameter, and the maximum fiber stress was calculated. From a microscopic examination of the various specimens, it was concluded that the endurance limit was dependent on carbide distribution, for a segregation or a nonuniformity in size of carbide particles apparently caused low endurance values.

TABLE 80.—PROPERTIES OF BALL-BEARING STEELS*

Steel	Endurance limit, lb./sq. in.	Maximum bending stress, lb./sq. in.	Rockwell *C* hardness
Chromium 1	84,000	233,000	60.5
Chromium 2	88,000	220,000	59.5
Chromium-molybdenum 1	75,000	164,000	61.5
Chromium-molybdenum 2	83,000	218,000	61.5
Chromium-vanadium 1	94,000	290,000	59.5
Chromium-vanadium 2	95,000	285,000	60.5

* Robinson.[206]

Two bearing steels, both containing chromium and one containing 0.21 per cent molybdenum, were examined by Kjerrman,[198] who attempted to use electric-resistivity values to determine the effectiveness of the alloying elements. Hardness tests were also made on the steels subjected to various treatments, but no clear conclusions were drawn from the work.

137. Other Steels.—Together with other steels, Dowdell[133] studied the magnetic properties of a chromium-molybdenum steel and a steel containing cobalt, chromium, and molybdenum, but the properties of these steels are significant only when considered in relation to the other steels investigated.

In an anonymous article, illustrating the application of physics to metallurgy,[316] experience with a track chisel made from a chromium-molybdenum steel is described. It was found that properly heat-treated chisels made from a steel containing 0.50 per cent carbon, 1 per cent chromium, and 0.25 per cent molybdenum withstood service conditions, but that chisels manufactured in mass production failed by cracking. X-ray diffraction patterns from failed chisels revealed the presence of untransformed austenite, which was considered to be responsible for the brittleness of the chisels.

TABLE 81.—PROPERTIES OF HEAT-TREATED CHROMIUM-MOLYBDENUM STEEL CASTINGS*

(Approximate composition: 0.27 per cent carbon, 0.94 per cent manganese, 1.0 per cent chromium, and 0.50 per cent molybdenum. Annealed at 900°C. (1650°F.), held 2 hr. at 855°C. (1575°F.), and quenched in water.)

Tempered		Tensile strength, lb./sq. in.	Yield strength,† lb./sq. in.	Elongation,‡ per cent	Reduction of area, per cent
°C.	°F.				
565	1050	141,500	132,800	8.0	30.8
565	1050	153,900	141,500	10.5	28.7
620	1150	124,900	107,400	18.0	47.9
620	1150	131,800	115,600	14.0	37.3
680	1250	104,000	81,500	20.0	50.3
680	1250	110,400	88,900	20.0	43.0
705	1300	99,400	75,900	22.0	52.7
705	1300	103,000	76,400	18.5	52.8
730	1350	100,000	66,600	21.0	54.1
730	1350	98,900	65,800	21.0	51.1

* *Iron Age.*[94]

† Reported as elastic limit.

‡ Gage length not given.

It was maintained in an anonymous article in *Zeitschrift für die gesamte Giessereipraxis*[210] that the addition of from 0.2 to 0.4 per cent molybdenum to a cast steel containing from 0.7

to 1.1 per cent chromium increases yield strength and tensile strength without appreciably lowering elongation.

The properties of some heat-treated chromium-molybdenum steel castings, as given in *The Iron Age*[94] are shown in Table 81. These results are from bars of various sizes, and a number of the castings were 3-in. diameter shafts.

Tests comparing the life of chromium-steel balls for use in a Marcy mill with the life of chromium-molybdenum steel balls were reported by Clapp and Devereaux,[147] who found that the molybdenum-containing balls had the longer life. Analyses of the steels used were not given.

The properties of a number of steels suitable for air-hardening rivets were studied by Herschman[195] with the object of finding a steel that would have good ballistic properties when used as rivets. Such a steel should have a Brinell hardness of from 375 to 425 and an elongation of 10 per cent or more when cooled in air. The alloys studied consisted of a number of nickel-chromium steels, containing from 0.23 to 0.42 per cent carbon, and the following molybdenum-bearing steels:

Number	Composition, per cent				
	C	Mn	Ni	Cr	Mo
925	0.26	1.00	....	....	1.22
926	0.25	0.82	....	0.78	0.81
927	0.33	0.92	1.41	0.62	0.49

Shearing tests on rivets made from these molybdenum steels indicated that they ranked among the highest-strength alloys, but, owing to the few experiments and the lack of ballistic data, it was difficult to judge their suitability. "Nevertheless, the data which are made available by these few tests show promise for these steels."

D. USES OF CHROMIUM-MOLYBDENUM STEELS

As is evident from the data presented, chromium-molybdenum low-alloy or structural steels have properties similar to other alloy steels and may be used interchangeably with other types of steel. The extended use of the 4130X steel in airplanes is evident from the preceding discussion and should need little further comment. This is apparently the only widely advertised use of chromium-molybdenum steels, although it is probable that there are other important uses less extensively advertised. An appreciable tonnage of chromium-molybdenum steel is used in the United States in bearings, but little mention is made of this use.

138. Structural Steels.—An anonymous article published in *Oesterreichische Zeitschrift für Berg- und Hüttenwesen*(11) maintains that the addition of from 0.2 to 0.3 per cent chromium with an equal quantity of molybdenum to an armor-plate steel produces an alloy which, after hardening, has great resistance against crushing and is not brittle. Such material was manufactured by Schneider et Cie. A recent article in *Aciers Spéciaux*(314) also mentions the early use of chromium-molybdenum steels for armor plate.

McKnight,(101) in 1920, mentioned the use of chromium-molybdenum steels in automobile parts. According to Sargent,(92) such steels are useful for gears, crankshafts, connecting rods, springs, cams, bearings, etc., in automobiles and airplanes. Schmid(103) stated that a large portion of the molybdenum steel manufactured is used in automotive forgings and pressed parts, but that its properties warranted an extension of its applications to railroad forgings, track bolts, armor plate, air flasks, agricultural implements, shovels, machinery forgings, piston rods, various edge tools, etc.

Molybdenum steels (probably chromium-molybdenum) are stated to have been used for light fighting turrets during the World War.(86) The same article mentions the use of chromium-molybdenum steels in chassis springs, heavy gears, forgings, and rivet sets.

A steel containing 0.25 per cent carbon, 0.75 per cent manganese, 0.75 per cent chromium, and 0.75 per cent molybdenum, according to Guertler(98) in 1921, was used as a bridge steel in Germany.

The *Scientific American*,(95) in 1921, mentioned the use of chromium-molybdenum steels in automobiles, and Cutter(104) also wrote of such uses.

Dawe(106) described the type of chromium-molybdenum steels used in automobiles by the Studebaker Corporation of America. A steel containing from 0.23 to 0.30 per cent carbon, 0.70 to 0.90 per cent chromium and from 0.30 to 0.40 per cent molybdenum gave satisfactory results and could be quenched in water without cracking.

In discussing the subject of Alloys in Machine Tools at the Conference on Metals and Alloys at Case School of Applied Science in November, 1931, D. G. Gurney of the Warner-Swasey Co. made the following statement in reference to chromium-molybdenum steels:

> S.A.E. 4140 steels find their application for parts that are to be machined after heat treatment. Chromium-molybdenum steels are unique in that they possess exceptional machining qualities at higher Brinell hardness values than any of the usual alloys. It is not uncommon to machine this grade of steel at Brinell values ranging from 321 to 418.
>
> This steel is used for intricate parts requiring high hardness and high physical properties that would be difficult to obtain without undue distortion using some of the other steels, heat-treated subsequent to machining.

The use of chromium-molybdenum steel for case hardening was mentioned by Tupholme.(166)

The use of chromium-molybdenum steels in aircraft construction was discussed by Daniels,(168) Johnson,(175, 197, 225, 354, 355, 356) French,(216) Knerr,(228, 229, 278, 362, 363) Richardson,(238) Sisco and Warner,(243) Hackett,(266) Hardecker,(267) Herrick,(272) Phillips,(288, 289) Kindelberger,(276) Mock,(284) Downes,(332) Moore,(383) Perkins,(391) Sisco,(405) Gabel and Knerr,(340) Thum,(410) Cone,(327) Lake,(368) Hartmann,(455) and Lampton.(469)

An article in *Journal of the Society of Automotive Engineers*,(167) in 1926, reports the recommendation that S.A.E. numbers be assigned to molybdenum steels because of their use in actual practice.

Rolf(240) stated that a chromium-molybdenum steel is used for automobile drive shafts. The steel flows well in the dies and rejections due to cracks, seams, laps, and burns are fewer than with any other steel tried.

Others who mentioned the use of chromium-molybdenum steels in the automotive industry include MacKenzie,(231) Watson,(505) and McCloud.(472)

A recent article in *Metal Progress*(311) speaks of the use of chromium-molybdenum steel in a yacht. A mast, of strength equal to a spruce mast, was constructed from chromium-molybdenum steel tubing.

In discussing splined shafts for automobiles, Davis[434] mentioned the use of the chromium-molybdenum steel S.A.E. 4140. This steel is characterized by excellent hardness but is more difficult to straighten than chromium steel unless the carbon is on the low side of the specification.

The use of chromium-molybdenum (S.A.E. 4130 and 4140) steels in producing hollow wire is mentioned in *Steel.*[310] One use for this hollow wire is in hypodermic needles.

According to a private communication from E. Pugsley, the barrels of Winchester double-barrel shotguns are made from a chromium-molybdenum steel containing from 0.30 to 0.40 per cent carbon. The barrels are heat-treated to give the following properties: 115,000 to 125,000 lb. per sq. in. tensile strength; 95,000 to 100,000 lb. per sq. in. yield strength; 25 to 30 per cent elongation; and 50 to 60 per cent reduction of area. The frame of the gun is made from a chromium-molybdenum steel heat-treated to give a tensile strength of approximately 200,000 lb. per sq. in.

Three molybdenum-bearing steels listed by Goerens[447] as being used in automobile and aircraft construction are listed in Table 82 together with the properties of the heat-treated steels.

139. Other Steels.—The Michigan Steel Castings Co.[94] has used cast chromium-molybdenum steels for shafts and hammer blocks. From 0.2 to 0.4 per cent molybdenum has been used together with 1 per cent chromium in cast-steel rolls.[210]

According to a private communication from Mr. K. H. Langguth, the Western Crucible Steel Casting Co. produces a cast steel containing 0.50 per cent carbon, 1.50 per cent chromium, and 0.60 per cent molybdenum for parts subjected to wear, such as dipper teeth. As normalized this steel has a Brinell hardness of 400 on a section 2 or 3 in. thick.

The use of chromium-molybdenum steel in a wrench, according to an article in *American Machinist*,[145] made possible a refinement in design with decrease in weight.

French[169] mentioned the use of acid-resisting steels containing molybdenum.

Tests by Kjerrman[198] and Robinson[206] on chromium-molybdenum ball-bearing steels were reported. An article in *Machinery*[187] speaks of the use of chromium-molybdenum steels in both balls and bearing rings of ball-bearing assemblies.

TABLE 82.—MOLYBDENUM STEELS USED IN AUTOMOBILE AND AIRCRAFT CONSTRUCTION*

Composition, per cent						Tensile strength, 1,000 lb./sq. in.	Yield strength, 1,000 lb./sq. in.	Elongation, per cent		Reduction of area, per cent	Charpy impact, m-kg./sq. cm.	
C	Mn	Ni	Cr	Mo	V			$L = 5D$	$L = 10D$		Longitudinal	Transverse
0.3 to 0.4	0.7	...	1.0	0.25	...	120 to 157	92 to 128	22 to 14	16 to 10	55 to 45	16 to 10	6 to 3
0.4	0.7	...	1.4	0.25	0.2	157 to 200	128 to 170	16 to 9	12 to 7	55 to 40	12 to 6	8 to 4
0.2 to 0.3	...	4.0	1.0	0.25†	...	164 to 200	135 to 170	16 to 10	12 to 8	50 to 40	12 to 6	8 to 5

* Goerens.[447]
† 0.8 per cent tungsten may be substituted for 0.25 per cent molybdenum.

According to Davis,[435] in 1930, American manufacturers were using a chromium-molybdenum steel for ball bearings.

Chromium-molybdenum steel is used successfully as a liner in extrusion dies working with copper alloys.

A steel containing 0.45 to 0.55 per cent carbon, 0.70 to 0.90 per cent manganese, 0.70 to 0.90 per cent chromium, and 0.20 to 0.30 per cent molybdenum, according to Davis,[434] has a high resilience and makes a dependable spring but is not used to any great extent.

The proper treatment for a chromium-molybdenum steel die block was discussed by Keeney.[359]

E. AUTHOR'S SUMMARY

1. The low-chromium structural alloy steels have improved properties in the quenched and tempered condition if the alloying effect of the chromium is intensified by the presence of other alloying elements such as 1 to 3.5 per cent of nickel, 0.20 per cent of vanadium, or 0.30 per cent of molybdenum. Among such ternary steels, those containing molybdenum have found considerable favor. In the earlier days of experience with molybdenum, the tendency was toward the use of approximately 0.75 per cent of this element, but a smaller amount, 0.15 to 0.50 per cent, is now generally used. Chromium-molybdenum structural steels are noteworthy for high reduction of area and impact resistance.

2. Chromium accentuates the air-hardening tendency conferred by molybdenum. With too high a content of carbon, chromium, and molybdenum, the air-hardening properties become too great to give good results on normalizing, so that such steels need to be fully quenched and tempered; but with a properly restricted amount of these three elements, especially carbon, chosen in proper relation to the cross-section of the piece to be normalized, the properties of the normalized steel are excellent. This fact, coupled with the good welding properties, has made the S.A.E. 4130 and 4130X steels almost without a rival for aircraft tubing.

3. The depth-hardening properties conferred by molybdenum on low-chromium steels make them of value for use in large parts to be quenched and tempered, up to sections of about 3-in. diameter. Beyond that, it is customary to introduce larger

amounts of the alloying elements, especially nickel, to bring about hardening throughout the section.

4. The resistance to tempering, which is one of the pronounced characteristics of all molybdenum steels, is markedly shown in chromium-molybdenum steels. The mechanism responsible for this phenomenon is probably also the cause for the increase of high-temperature strength, an effect characteristic of molybdenum and its near relation tungsten.

5. The high-temperature "creep strength" of low-chromium steels up to 550 to 600°C. (1020 to 1110°F.) is very markedly raised by the addition of molybdenum. Without it, chromium steels are very little different in high-temperature properties from carbon steels. This effect is probably lost at very high temperatures, for at a sufficiently high tempering temperature a hardened chromium-molybdenum steel will soften as a chromium steel does; but the range of temperature, before creep begins or before material softening starts on tempering, is notably increased.

6. Superior machinability of the chromium-molybdenum steels even at high hardness is claimed, but there is insufficient evidence to support a categorical affirmation or denial.

7. Molybdenum lowers, and splits, the Ar_1 point; hence chromium-molybdenum steels, if heated high enough initially, may be quenched from a lower temperature than similar steels containing no molybdenum. There is evidence that, in addition to decreasing the tendency to crack on quenching of parts with uneven sections, this treatment may affect the mechanical properties favorably. However, the method seems, as yet, to have found little application.

8. Low chromium-molybdenum steel, in the quenched and tempered condition, competes with nickel-chromium and chromium-vanadium steel as a structural material. It is chosen when cost, depth-hardening or air-hardening properties, and toughness for a given strength give it a marked advantage. For normalizing, the chemical composition should be controlled closely, there probably not being so much leeway as in the chromium-vanadium composition.

9. In the high-chromium, "stainless" type of steel, molybdenum improves creep resistance. Data are lacking to show whether it tends to overcome the tendency of high-chromium steels to embrittlement in a certain temperature range, though

there is evidence that it is a helpful addition for this purpose to the "18-8" type.

10. Corrosion resistance to weather and acids, as well as resistance to oxidation at high temperature, of high-chromium steels is claimed to be enhanced by rather large amounts (5 or 10 per cent) of molybdenum. Further evidence of this and data on the effect of molybdenum on the cold-working and deep-drawing properties of high-chromium steels are needed.

11. Relatively little commercial use has yet been made of molybdenum in high-chromium steels, but the low chromium-molybdenum structural type is now well established for a very wide variety of commercial applications. The greatest tonnage of heat-treated molybdenum steel is in the low chromium-molybdenum compositions.

CHAPTER VIII

NICKEL-MOLYBDENUM AND NICKEL-CHROMIUM-MOLYBDENUM STEELS

Nickel-molybdenum Steels—Nickel-chromium-molybdenum Structural Steels—Miscellaneous Nickel-chromium-molybdenum Steels—Author's Summary

While neither nickel-molybdenum nor nickel-chromium-molybdenum steels are at present so extensively used as chromium-

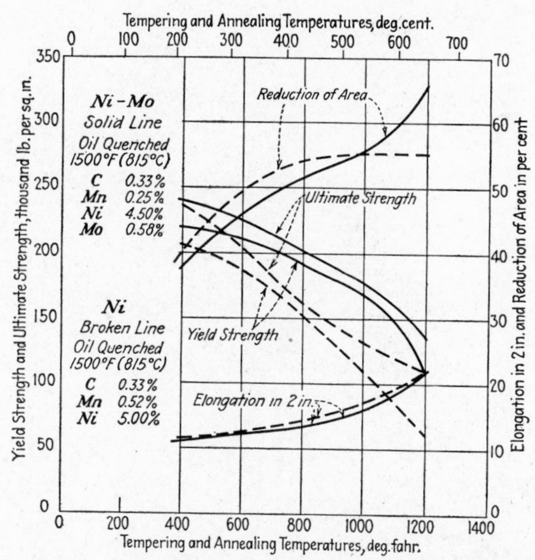

FIG. 101.—Tensile properties of a nickel and a nickel-molybdenum steel. Heat-treated as 1¼-in. square bars and machined to 0.505-in. specimens. (*Sargent.*[102])

molybdenum steels, they both have found certain applications, and published reports have proved that molybdenum betters the mechanical properties of both nickel and nickel-chromium steels.

A. NICKEL-MOLYBDENUM STEELS

The nickel-molybdenum steels that have been used and with which most of the literature deals contain from 1 to 5 per cent nickel and less than 1 per cent of molybdenum.

TABLE 83.—MECHANICAL PROPERTIES OF NICKEL-MOLYBDENUM STEELS*

Composition, per cent			Tensile strength, lb./sq. in.	Yield strength,† lb./sq. in.	Elongation,‡ per cent	Reduction of area, per cent	Brinell hardness	Impact test,§ m-kg.
C	Ni	Mo						
As rolled								
0.17	6.0	0.51	130,100	113,100	12.0	68.7	248	15
0.10	6.40	1.23	127,300	113,100	11.0	44.2	223	15
0.15	5.92	2.04	151,300	122,300	14.0	46.1	293	9
0.24	5.80	5.13	175,000	122,300	10.0	44.2	248	9
0.54	3.60	0.63	163,600	146,600	9.0	22.9	269	6
0.35	3.52	1.02	129,400	93,200	12.5	46.1	228	8
0.50	3.24	2.02	179,300	137,200	10.0	68.7	293	6
0.47	2.96	4.36	169,300	122,300	11.0	58.9	277	6
Annealed 1000°C. (1830°F.)								
0.17	6.0	0.51	127,400	111,400	10.0	55.6	235	13
0.15	5.92	2.04	146,800	122,600	10.0	44.2	293	8
0.35	3.52	1.02	126,600	92,200	11.0	43.6	223	4
Quenched from 850°C. (1560°F.)								
0.17	6.0	0.51	232,000	196,000	9.0	10.0	375	10
0.10	6.40	1.23	185,000	169,000	11.0	9.5	286	9
0.15	5.92	2.04	226,000	202,000	7.5	10.5	321	7
0.24	5.80	5.13	239,000	239,000	3.0	0	411	5
0.54	3.60	0.63	....	....	Broke badly	....	460	2
0.35	3.52	1.02	....	....	Broke badly	....	430	2
0.50	3.24	2.02	....	....	Broke badly	....	532	1
0.47	2.96	4.36	246,000	246,000	0	1.0	512	4

* Guillet.[32]
† Reported as elastic limit.
‡ Gage length not given.
§ Reported as "Shock test."

140. Mechanical Properties.—In a discussion of the applications of molybdenum, in 1903, Ohly[20, 21] made the surprising statement that the addition of 0.25 per cent molybdenum to a nickel steel increased the elongation from 4 per cent to 45 per cent.

The properties of some rather unusual nickel-molybdenum steels reported by Guillet,[32] in 1906, are listed in Table 83.

TABLE 84.—MECHANICAL PROPERTIES OF NICKEL-MOLYBDENUM STEELS*
(*Steel A:* 0.15 per cent carbon, 0.98 per cent nickel, 0.53 per cent molybdenum. *Steel B:* 0.30 per cent carbon, 0.99 per cent nickel, 0.45 per cent molybdenum.)

Steel	Quenched		Quenching medium	Tempered		Tensile strength, lb./sq. in.	Yield strength,† lb./sq. in.	Elongation in 2 in., per cent	Reduction of area, per cent	Brinell hardness
	°C.	°F.		°C.	°F.					
A	As rolled		......	...	....	72,600	56,400	33.5	68.0	132
	900	1650	Air	...	....	71,600	50,200	33.0	62.6	135
	900	1650	Oil	500	930	90,600	72,800	23.5	68.0	187
	900	1650	Oil	550	1020	92,200	73,800	27.0	70.8	192
	900	1650	Oil	600	1110	90,600	72,600	27.0	71.6	187
	850	1560	Water	500	930	98,900	83,300	24.0	67.0	217
	850	1560	Water	550	1020	99,000	82,500	22.5	63.6	199
	850	1560	Water	600	1110	101,400	84,600	23.0	66.0	228
	850	1560	Water	650	1200	97,700	73,000	24.5	70.0	213
B	As rolled		......	...	....	98,600	78,800	21.0	57.2	204
	900	1650	Air	...	....	86,000	60,000	25.0	59.2	166
	900	1650	Oil	500	930	110,400	90,900	20.0	62.6	241
	900	1650	Oil	550	1020	113,700	88,800	22.5	62.4	235
	900	1650	Oil	600	1110	108,100	85,100	23.0	60.9	235
	850	1560	Water	500	930	152,600	132,200	17.0	54.8	321
	850	1560	Water	550	1020	144,800	123,000	20.0	59.2	321
	850	1560	Water	600	1110	142,500	121,200	18.0	57.3	302
	850	1560	Water	650	1200	124,600	91,400	20.5	60.3	228

* Swinden.[61]
† Reported as elastic limit.

Details regarding testing methods were not given. Guillet did not believe that such steels had advantageous properties.

Two low-alloy nickel-molybdenum steels were tested by Swinden, and his results are presented in Table 84.

Figure 101, comparing the properties of a nickel steel with those of a nickel-molybdenum steel, was given by Sargent[102] in a general discussion of molybdenum steels.

Burgess and Woodward[97] listed the properties of several heat-treated nickel-molybdenum steels, but their results are of little general interest because of the extremely low temperature, 175°C. (345°F.), used in tempering. From their study they concluded that molybdenum did not improve the properties of nickel steels that had been quenched and tempered at very low temperatures. It appears to the reviewer that this would be true of almost any alloying element.

Data from Norris and from McKnight on three nickel-molybdenum steels were reported by Gillett and Mack,[151] and are listed in Table 85.

According to Camp and Francis[146] several different types of nickel-molybdenum steels containing less than 0.40 per cent carbon are produced, and the nickel-molybdenum steels "may be considered as a worthy substitute for chrome-nickel steels to which they are said by some to be superior in resistance to shock." Data shown in Table 86 were given as being indicative of the properties obtainable in such steels. The samples used were 1-in. rounds and were turned to ½-in. diameter specimens subsequent to heat treatment.

The properties of several nickel-molybdenum steels reported by Jones[176] are listed in Table 87. In reference to the effect of molybdenum on nickel steels Jones concluded:

> Although a plain nickel steel was not included in this series, it is evident from results obtained previously on a steel of slightly higher nickel content that the addition of molybdenum to a steel containing 3 per cent of nickel raises the elastic limit, yield point, maximum load, and impact figure without serious decrease of elongation and reduction of area. This improvement in properties was very marked with the addition of 0.6 per cent of molybdenum, but, except for very high tensile strength, little further improvement resulted from additions of molybdenum above this amount.
>
> A steel containing 4.5 per cent of nickel with 0.5 per cent of molybdenum is suitable only when high tensile strength (over 125,000 lb. per sq. in.) is required and there appears to be no advantage in exceeding 0.5 per cent of molybdenum.
>
> A steel with 3 per cent of nickel and 1 per cent of molybdenum was found to be similar in properties to one containing 4.5 per cent of nickel and 0.5 per cent of molybdenum when tempered to the same hardness, but the steel with the higher molybdenum content required a higher tempering temperature and had a slightly better impact figure.

The properties and uses of nickel-molybdenum steels were discussed by Langenberg and McKnight,[230] who gave Fig. 102

TABLE 85.—MECHANICAL PROPERTIES OF NICKEL-MOLYBDENUM STEELS*
(Data for No. 1 from Norris, and for Nos. 2 and 3 from McKnight)

Number	Composition, per cent				Quenched		Quenching medium	Tempered		Tensile strength, lb./sq. in.	Yield strength,† lb./sq. in.	Elongation in 2 in., per cent	Reduction of area, per cent	Brinell hardness
	C	Mn	Ni	Mo	°C.	°F.		°C.	°F.					
1	0.30	0.29	5.01	0.62	800	1475	Air	...	....	232,500	221,000	13	44	419
					815	1500	Air	...	....	241,000	180,000	12	45	
					815	1500	Air	315	600	221,500	207,500	12	53.5	
					815	1500	Air	650	1200	169,000	168,000	17	57.5	421
					850	1560	Oil	540	1000	179,000	172,000	16.5	53.5	364
					800	1475	Oil	430	800	192,000	181,000	14	52	385
					800	1475	Oil	540	1000	175,000	165,500	16.5	54	351
					800	1475	Oil	650	1200	136,000	104,000	21.5	54.5	267
					800	1475	Oil							
					750	1380	Water	450	840	189,000	186,000	14.5	54	382
2	0.29	0.60	2.48	0.52	As forged			...	....	124,000	108,500	12	28.5	255
					845	1550	Water	205	400	261,000	206,000	12.5	46	460
					845	1550	Water	315	600	224,500	196,000	12	47	445
					845	1550	Water	425	800	203,000	189,000	12.5	50	385
					845	1550	Water	540	1000	168,500	158,500	16	55.5	365
					845	1550	Water	595	1100	152,500	145,000	18.5	60	320
					845	1550	Water	650	1200	121,000	116,000	22	62	260
					845	1550	Water	675	1250	114,000	102,500	23	65.5	255
					845	1550	Oil	...	....	268,000	236,000	10.5	31.5	600
					845	1550	Oil	205	400	250,500	227,500	13	41	530
					845	1550	Oil	315	600	254,000	198,000	12.5	42.5	530
					845	1550	Oil	425	800	195,500	188,500	13.5	51.5	420
					845	1550	Oil	540	1000	173,500	164,500	16.5	57	385
					845	1550	Oil	595	1100	140,000	124,500	20.5	60	320
					845	1550	Oil	650	1200	122,000	96,500	23	57.5	255
					845	1550	Oil	675	1250	118,000	99,500	23	62	250

TABLE 85.—(*Continued*)

Number	Composition, per cent				Quenched		Quenching medium	Tempered		Tensile strength, lb./sq. in.	Yield strength,† lb./sq. in.	Elongation in 2 in., per cent	Reduction of area, per cent	Brinell hardness
	C	Mn	Ni	Mo	°C.	°F.		°C.	°F.					
3	0.20	0.40	3.48	0.51	As forged			...	....	110,000	94,000	13	23.5	240
					845	1550	Water	205	400	214,500	191,500	13	45.5	445
					845	1550	Water	315	600	181,000	156,000	12.5	51.5	385
					845	1550	Water	425	800	163,500	156,500	14	55	365
					845	1550	Water	540	1000	154,000	147,500	17	48.5	340
					845	1550	Water	595	1100	145,000	141,000	18	57	330
					845	1550	Water	650	1200	113,500	105,000	21	57	240
					845	1550	Water	675	1250	113,000	94,500	25	60.5	230
					845	1550	Oil	...	....	212,500	193,500	12.5	45.5	475
					845	1550	Oil	205	400	209,000	194,500	12	47.5	460
					845	1550	Oil	315	600	208,500	200,000	12.5	46	445
					845	1550	Oil	425	800	166,500	158,500	13	53	375
					845	1550	Oil	540	1000	153,500	144,500	16.5	59.5	340
					845	1550	Oil	595	1100	132,000	123,000	21	62	300
					845	1550	Oil	650	1200	117,500	88,000	24.5	62	255
					845	1550	Oil	675	1250	113,500	87,000	24.5	59.5	240

* Gillett and Mack.[151]

† Reported as elastic limit.

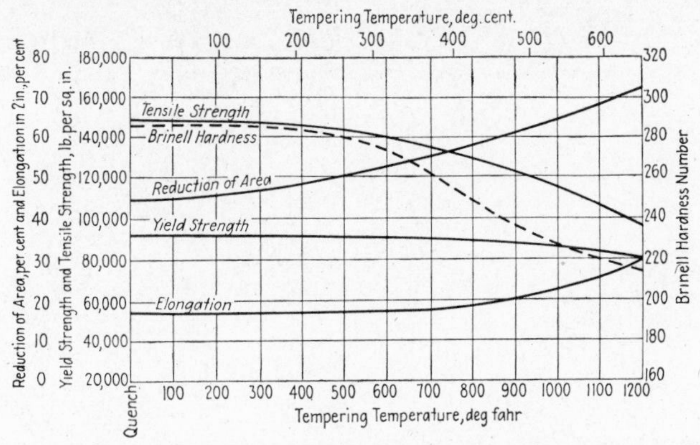

FIG. 102.—Properties of core of a carburized nickel-molybdenum steel. (*Langenberg and McKnight.*[230])

TABLE 86.—MECHANICAL PROPERTIES OF A NICKEL-MOLYBDENUM STEEL*

(0.39 per cent carbon, 0.45 per cent manganese, 0.20 per cent silicon, 1.60 per cent nickel, 0.40 per cent molybdenum. Quenched from 815°C. [1500°F.].)

Quenching medium	Tempered		Tensile strength, lb./sq. in.	Yield strength,† lb./sq. in.	Elongation in 2 in., per cent	Reduction of area, per cent	Brinell hardness	Charpy impact
	°C.	°F.						
As rolled			119,000	88,000	18.0	38.8	262	10.17
Annealed 760°C. (1400°F.)			98,000	62,000	23.5	43.0	187	8.08
Oil	425	800	190,000	171,000	12.5	46.0	352	12.93
Oil	480	900	180,000	160,000	13.0	44.0	352	15.24
Oil	540	1000	185,000	163,000	16.5	45.4	363	17.06
Oil	595	1100	150,000	138,000	16.0	49.7	321	18.95
Oil	650	1200	115,000	100,000	25.0	59.6	241	27.09
Oil	705	1300	100,000	71,000	26.0	47.1	201	11.79
Water	425	800	190,000	175,000	12.0	49.2	388	17.67
Water	480	900	195,000	170,000	13.0	40.4	388	14.06
Water	540	1000	183,500	169,000	16.0	49.7	341	16.44
Water	595	1100	150,000	138,000	18.5	47.2	285	21.65
Water	650	1200	123,500	110,000	21.5	59.8	255	28.53
Water	705	1300	101,000	75,000	26.0	55.5	207	22.00

* Camp and Francis.[146]

† By drop of beam.

TABLE 87.—MECHANICAL PROPERTIES OF NICKEL-MOLYBDENUM STEELS*

Number	Composition, per cent			Oil-quenched		Tempered, 2 hr.		Tensile strength, lb./sq. in.	Elastic limit, lb./sq. in.	Yield strength,† lb./sq. in.	Elongation in 2 in., per cent	Reduction of area, per cent	Izod impact, ft-lb.	Brinell hardness
	C	Ni	Mo	°C.	°F.	°C.	°F.							
4	0.26	2.78	0.64	900	1650	550	1020	142,200	100,800	121,200	19	57	34	314
				820	1510	550	1020	146,700	105,300	130,200	20	57	33	323
				900	1650	600	1110	142,900	107,500	128,600	17	58	35	295
				900	1650	650	1200	114,200	96,300	103,100	23	64	63	245
				900	1650	670	1240	106,200	78,400	89,600	26	67	72	227
				820	1510	670	1240	102,600	67,200	86,500	25	67	75	223
5	0.28	2.76	1.04	900	1650	550	1020	188,400	152,400	177,000	16	52	21	398
				820	1510	550	1020	190,200	159,000	181,700	16	52	21	399
				900	1650	600	1110	180,700	154,500	174,000	16	52	21	373
				900	1650	650	1200	124,100	107,500	115,200	20	59	53	264
				900	1650	670	1240	118,300	96,300	109,800	23	64	61	247
				820	1510	670	1240	118,000	100,800	111,200	21	65	65	252
6	0.28	4.57	....	900	1650	500	930	94,300	53,500	71,700	25	62	58	195
				900	1650	550	1020	91,800	60,500	70,100	30	62	65	189
				900	1650	600	1110	90,300	58,200	67,900	30	65	73	189
				900	1650	650	1200	83,800	44,800	59,200	35	68	78	172
7	0.26	4.54	0.51	900	1650	550	1020	160,200	127,700	150,100	18	55	25	338
				900	1650	600	1110	145,400	121,000	138,900	19	57	29	312
				900	1650	650	1200	118,700	85,100	99,000	25	59	52	250
8	0.30	4.50	0.86	900	1650	550	1020	188,400	161,300	178,500	16	52	16	388
				900	1650	600	1110	163,400	136,700	155,700	17	52	19	349
				900	1650	650	1200	128,800	85,100	107,600	21	58	41	266

* Jones.[176] † Reported as yield point.

as representative of the properties of the core of a case-hardened steel. The steel contained 0.15 per cent carbon, 0.58 per cent manganese, 1.62 per cent nickel, and 0.29 per cent molybdenum. Table 88, from the same article, lists the properties of a heat-

TABLE 88.—PROPERTIES OF A HEAT-TREATED NICKEL-MOLYBDENUM STEEL AT VARIOUS TEMPERATURES*

Tempered		Tested		Tensile strength, lb./sq. in.	Yield strength,† lb./sq. in.	Elongation in 2 in., per cent	Reduction of area, per cent	Charpy impact, ft-lb.
°C.	°F.	°C.	°F.					
480	900	25	75	140,450	105,000	17.5	64.7	25.61
		25	75	143,950	108,000	16.5	62.3	
		315	600	144,500	123,000	27.0	75.5	
		540	1000	71,500	53,000	24.0	87.5	
540	1000	25	75	130,450	104,000	20.5	67.0	31.34
		315	600	132,500	102,000	25.5	64.7	
		540	1000	74,500	52,000	23.0	37.5	
595	1100	25	75	123,600	102,000	21.0	69.2	38.48
		315	600	117,500	85,000	23.5	73.5	
		540	1000	75,000	54,000	24.5	88.7	
650	1200	25	75	107,300	89,000	25.0	75.5	49.01
		315	600	109,000	76,000	24.5	64.7	
		540	1000	70,000	56,000	30.0	85.8	
		540	1000	69,500	55,000	28.0	94.3	
705	1300	25	75	92,900	76,000	29.5	75.5	53.67
		315	600	98,500	57,000	31.0	71.4	
		540	1000	59,500	41,000	35.0	88.7	

* Langenberg and McKnight.(230)
† Reported as yield point.

treated nickel-molybdenum steel at several temperatures. This steel contained 0.31 per cent carbon, 0.51 per cent manganese, 1.14 per cent nickel, and 0.14 per cent molybdenum. It was normalized at 900°C. (1650°F.), quenched in water from 785°C. (1450°F.), and tempered at the temperatures indicated. The authors considered that this steel had a much higher impact resistance for the same physical properties as regards yield strength and tensile strength than other types of alloy steels.

TABLE 89.—PROPERTIES OF SOME FORGED NICKEL-MOLYBDENUM AND NICKEL-CHROMIUM-MOLYBDENUM STEELS*
(Quenched in oil from 825 or 850°C. (1515 or 1560°F.) and tempered at indicated temperatures; section treated 3 × 4 in.)

Steel number	Composition, per cent						Tempered		Tensile strength, lb./sq. in.	Yield strength,† lb./sq. in.	Elongation in 2 in., per cent	Reduction of area, per cent	Charpy round impact, ft-lb.	Brinell hardness
	C	Mn	Ni	Cr	Mo	V	°C.	°F.						
1	0.35	0.54	3.13	....	0.29	....	200	390	125,500	79,000	18.5	54.6	38.6	255
2	0.40	0.60	3.07	....	0.28	....	200	390	152,000	87,000	16.5	49.1	41.2	269
3	0.30	0.44	4.51	....	0.47	....	650	1200	137,500	110,000	23.5	62.3		
4	0.33	0.75	3.37	0.59	0.38	....	650	1200	130,000	104,000	24.0	62.3		
5	0.38	0.48	3.54	0.78	0.35	....	450	840	195,500	169,000	12.0	46.2		
6	0.38	0.68	3.35	0.84	0.31	....	650	1200	119,500	86,000	25.0	64.7		
7	0.38	0.68	3.31	1.02	0.35	....	650	1200	127,500	100,000	24.5	64.7		

* Watertown Arsenal.
† Reported as proportional limit.

The strength at elevated temperatures was also regarded as exceptional.

TABLE 90.—PROPERTIES OF A STEEL AT VARIOUS TEMPERATURES CONTAINING 0.30 PER CENT CARBON, 0.51 PER CENT MANGANESE, 1.14 PER CENT NICKEL, AND 0.14 PER CENT MOLYBDENUM*
(After water-quenching from 785°C. (1450°F.) and tempering as shown)

Tempered		Tensile strength, lb./sq. in.	Yield strength,† lb./sq. in.	Elongation in 2 in., per cent	Reduction of area, per cent	Charpy impact, ft-lb.
°C.	°F.					
Tested at 23°C. (74°F.)						
480	900	142,200	106,500	17.0	63.5	25.6
540	1000	130,450	104,000	20.5	67.0	31.3
595	1100	123,600	102,000	21.0	69.2	38.5‡
650	1200	107,300	89,000	25.0	75.5	49.0‡
705	1300	92,900	76,000	29.5	75.5	53.7‡
Tested at 315°C. (600°F.)						
480	900	144,500	123,000	27.0	75.5	
540	1000	132,500	102,000	25.5	64.7	
595	1100	117,500	85,000	23.5	73.5	
650	1200	109,000	76,000	24.5	64.7	
705	1300	98,500	57,000	31.0	71.4	
Tested at 540°C. (1000°F.)						
480	900	71,500	53,000	24.0	87.5	
540	1000	74,500	52,000	23.0	87.5	
595	1100	75,000	54,000	24.5	88.7	
650	1200	69,700	55,500	29.0	90.0	
705	1300	59,500	41,000	35.0	88.7	

* Watertown Arsenal.
† Reported as proportional limit.
‡ Failed to break.

The properties of some quenched and tempered nickel-molybdenum and nickel-chromium-molybdenum steels as determined at Watertown Arsenal are shown in Table 89. As may be noted from the table, pieces of comparatively large cross-section were treated (3 × 4 in.). The properties of a nickel-molybdenum steel tested at 23°C. (74°F.), 315°C. (600°F.), and 540°C. (1000°F.) are shown in Table 90. From these tests it was found that small additions of molybdenum to a nickel gun steel raised the yield strength, tensile strength, elongation, and reduction of area, and that the Charpy impact values were increased from about 15 ft-lb. to not less than 25 ft-lb.

Curves indicating the properties expected from quenched and tempered cast nickel-molybdenum steels were given by Mitchell,[379] but the composition of the steels was not stated.

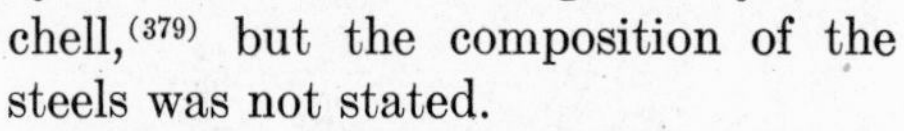

141. Properties at Elevated Temperatures.—As mentioned in the preceding section, Langenberg and McKnight[230] cited data which indicated that nickel-molybdenum steels had good properties at temperatures up to 540°C. (1000°F.).

In a discussion of a paper by Miller,[321] Carty said that he understood that nickel-molybdenum steels would withstand fatigue in boilers.

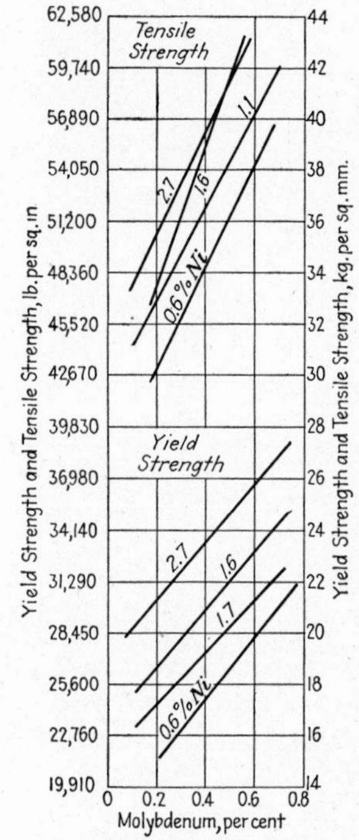

Fig. 103.—Effect of molybdenum on tensile and yield strength of cast nickel steel. Temperature of test 500°C. (930°F.). *Liestmann and Salzmann.*[369])

The effects of molybdenum and nickel on properties of cast steels at a temperature of 500°C. (930°F.) were studied by Liestmann and Salzmann.[369] Prior to testing, the castings were annealed at a temperature between 900 and 950°C. (1650 and 1740°F.). Five series of alloys were prepared, containing, respectively, 0.4, 0.6, 1.0, 1.5, and 2 per cent nickel with molybdenum in each series varying from 0.2 to 0.6 per cent. Analyses of the alloys and tensile properties at 500°C. (930°F.) are listed in Table 91, where each tensile test value is the average of two determinations. The tensile tests were made on an Amsler machine on 15-mm. (0.59-in.) diameter specimens. The yield strength is based on a permanent elongation of 0.2 per cent. The effect of molybdenum on tensile strength and yield strength of nickel steel at 500°C. (930°F.) was summarized by Fig. 103. From this work the authors concluded that for the temperature of test the addition of nickel and molybdenum to a cast carbon steel raises the tensile strength and yield strength but decreases the elongation and reduction of area. The addition of each 0.1 per cent molybdenum increases the yield strength about 1,500

TABLE 91.—TENSILE PROPERTIES OF CAST NICKEL-MOLYBDENUM STEELS AT 500°C. (930°F.)*

Number	Composition, per cent					Tensile strength, lb./sq. in.	Yield strength, lb./sq. in. (0.2)†	Elongation in 5.9 in. (150 mm.), per cent	Reduction of area, per cent
	C	Si	Mn	Ni	Mo				
1	0.09	0.20	0.66	2.11	0.62	53,300	29,800	16.5	51.5
2	0.18	0.21	0.97	2.10	0.56	60,200	36,300	11.0	20.5
3	0.11	0.19	0.68	2.05	0.35	50,600	27,000	19.3	57.8
4	0.29	0.23	0.92	2.05	0.28	61,400	38,200	12.7	31.8
25	0.20	0.30	0.80	2.10	0.19	51,600	30,100	19.8	41.2
5	0.21	0.18	0.68	1.62	0.51	55,000	30,900	17.1	25.3
6	0.25	0.18	0.85	1.62	0.49	58,500	32,900	13.5	20.8
7	0.19	0.22	0.81	1.59	0.43	49,200	29,700	14.3	23.9
8	0.21	0.25	0.85	1.56	0.30	51,800	28,300	19.4	29.7
24	0.20	0.29	0.81	1.58	0.23	48,600	27,500	20.6	35.3
9	0.20	0.27	0.83	1.12	0.52	55,300	29,400	15.1	40.5
10	0.19	0.26	0.82	1.15	0.47	53,500	28,200	16.7	44.2
11	0.19	0.28	0.80	1.13	0.40	50,200	27,000	19.6	47.3
12	0.21	0.30	0.80	1.13	0.33	48,200	26,200	27.0	43.2
23	0.19	0.28	0.81	1.08	0.22	47,900	25,900	17.5	31.4
13	0.24	0.33	0.81	0.63	0.62	55,000	29,300	23.6	33.5
14	0.22	0.29	0.71	0.58	0.53	51,100	26,500	24.1	48.4
15	0.17	0.30	0.83	0.62	0.39	48,100	24,750	30.0	57.2
16	0.18	0.28	0.81	0.61	0.28	46,200	22,700	28.0	59.5
22	0.18	0.29	0.79	0.63	0.24	41,600	22,500	29.3	59.0
17	0.15	0.30	0.80	0.45	0.51	51,100	28,200	20.1	44.9
18	0.25	0.31	0.81	0.43	0.45	50,500	27,400	24.7	49.1
19	0.21	0.31	0.79	0.42	0.35	54,300	25,700	23.4	59.6
20	0.18	0.30	0.81	0.43	0.26	47,100	23,700	23.9	41.5
21	0.18	0.28	0.80	0.45	0.20	44,000	23,600	26.8	35.0

* Liestmann and Salzmann.[369]
† Permanent set, 0.2 per cent.

lb. per sq. in. and the tensile strength about 3,000 lb. per sq. in. Correspondingly, 0.5 per cent nickel increases the yield strength

3,000 lb. per sq. in. and the tensile strength about 2,700 lb. per sq. in. With increasing quantities of molybdenum the ratio of yield strength to tensile strength decreases, while with increasing amounts of nickel it increases slightly.

142. Special Properties.—The carburizing properties of molybdenum steels containing nickel were discussed in Chap. V (page 141).

The addition of 5 per cent molybdenum to iron-nickel alloys used in bimetal strips was claimed by Rohn[290] to render the alloys less susceptible to variations in heat treatment. Curves were given to show the coefficient of expansion for such alloys at temperatures up to 600 or 800°C. (1110 or 1470°F.). Molybdenum was stated to be particularly effective in alloys containing from 22 to 27 per cent nickel.

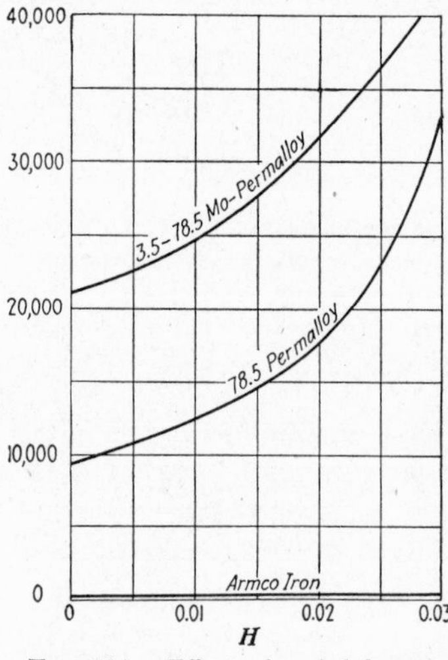

FIG. 104.—Effect of molybdenum on magnetic permeability of permalloy. (*Elmen.*[258])

According to Hiemenz,[349] iron-nickel alloys exhibit irregularities in their thermal expansion which the addition of 5 per cent molybdenum tends to suppress. In alloys containing 5 per cent molybdenum the variation in thermal expansion between room temperature and 100°C. (210°F.) amounts to only 2 or 3 per cent. The molybdenum, however, increases the thermal coefficient of expansion in the 22 to 27 per cent nickel alloy by approximately 50 per cent.

Permalloy is an iron-nickel alloy, which after proper heat treatment has an extremely high magnetic permeability at low magnetizing forces. Elmen[258, 439] found that the addition of chromium or molybdenum to permalloy increases permeability at low magnetizing forces. Figure 104 indicates the increase in permeability resulting from the addition of 3.5 per cent molybdenum to an alloy containing 78.5 per cent nickel.

Recently, Luerssen and Greene[470] studied the possibility of hardening steels that are normally non-magnetic (austenitic) at room temperatures by cooling to low temperatures. They used various nickel-chromium steels, nickel steels, a nickel-silicon steel, and a nickel-molybdenum steel. The last-named steel contained 0.12 per cent carbon, 24.95 per cent nickel, and 4.02 per cent molybdenum. The results obtained with this steel will not be discussed in detail, as this can be adequately done only with detailed consideration of the results obtained with the other steels. It was observed that the molybdenum apparently lowered the *Ar* point, for at −180°C. (−290°F.) only part of the transformation took place. A maximum Brinell hardness of 387 occurred in this steel by cooling to −180°C. (−290°F.) and reheating to 400°C. (750°F.). At this hardness the Izod impact value was 22 ft-lb.

Sergeson[496] determined the impact values of some low-alloy steels for temperatures as low as −75°C. (−100°F.). He found that properly heat-treated nickel-molybdenum steels, as well as nickel steels, had "excellent notched impact resistance at subzero temperatures." The high impact values at subzero temperatures were apparently due to the nickel rather than to molybdenum.

143. Uses.—Ohly,[20, 21] in 1903, recommended the use of nickel-molybdenum steels for large crank and propeller shafts, wire-drawing dies, plates for high-pressure boilers, and boilers of torpedo boats.

During the World War, according to McKnight,[101] nickel-molybdenum steel was used as armor for baby tanks, and the alleged use of this steel in large gun tubes by Germany was taken to show that it has high resistance to erosion.

The trial of nickel-molybdenum steel in rails was mentioned by Sargent, in discussion of a paper by Mathews.[111]

The use of nickel-molybdenum steels in bearings was discussed by Guillet[217] and Langenberg and McKnight.[230, 376] In such cases the steel is carburized.

McQuaid and McMullan,[281] among others, discussed the use and properties of nickel-molybdenum carburizing steel. The steel S.A.E. 4610 or 4615 is commonly used for carburizing.

Nickel-molybdenum steels, according to McKnight,[375] are suitable forging steels, for they forge readily and exhibit uniform properties. Because a high yield strength together with great toughness can be produced in nickel-molybdenum steels, according to Allen,[303] they are used in the manufacture of saws for wood-working.

The drawing of carbon and nickel-molybdenum steel into cups was discussed by Morton,[384] whose data indicate that the nickel-molybdenum steel can be successfully drawn.

It was reported by Watson[505] that nickel-molybdenum steels (S.A.E. 4615) are used for automobile transmissions containing carburized gears.

According to Sergeson,[496] the Canadian National Railway recently replaced some carbon steel springs by nickel-chromium-molybdenum steel springs because of the high impact resistance of the latter steel at subzero temperatures. Data given by Sergeson show the impact strength of these steels.

B. NICKEL-CHROMIUM-MOLYBDENUM STRUCTURAL STEELS

The preceding discussions prove that valuable low-alloy or structural steels result from the addition of molybdenum to

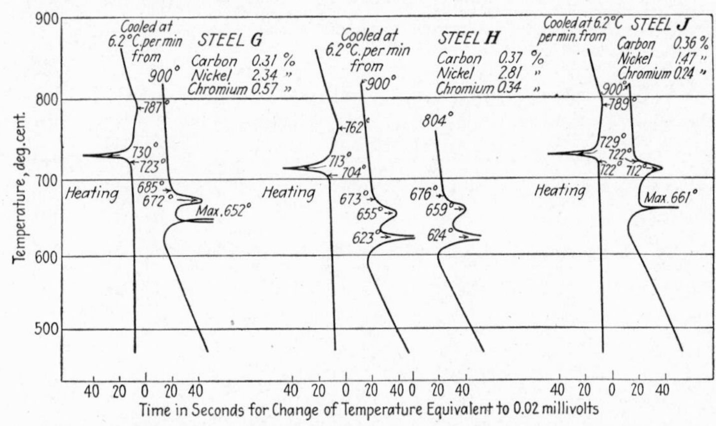

FIG. 105.—Heating and cooling curves for nickel-chromium steels. (*Jones.*[110])

either chromium or nickel steel. It now remains to consider the properties of steels containing small amounts of all three of these alloying elements. Experience with simpler alloy steels indicates that the most efficient utilization of molybdenum results from the addition of a small quantity (less than 1 per cent) of molybdenum to steels containing at least 0.75 per cent of other alloying elements, consequently, the nickel-chromium-molybdenum steels produced generally contain appreciable quantities of nickel and chromium and only small amounts of molybdenum.

144. Critical Points.—Heating and cooling curves for nickel-chromium and nickel-chromium-molybdenum steels reported by

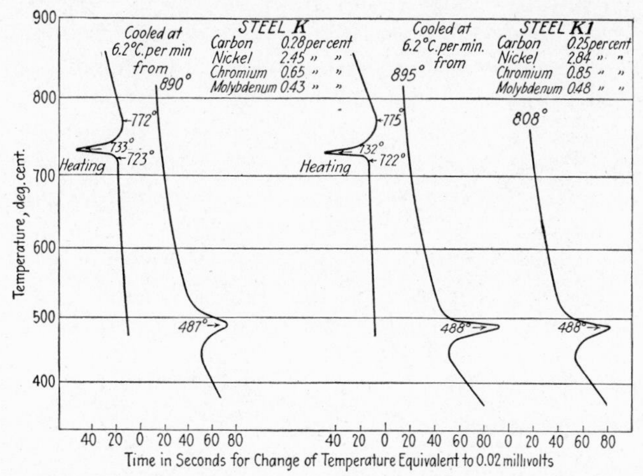

Fig. 106.—Heating and cooling curves for nickel-chromium-molybdenum steels. (*Jones.*[110])

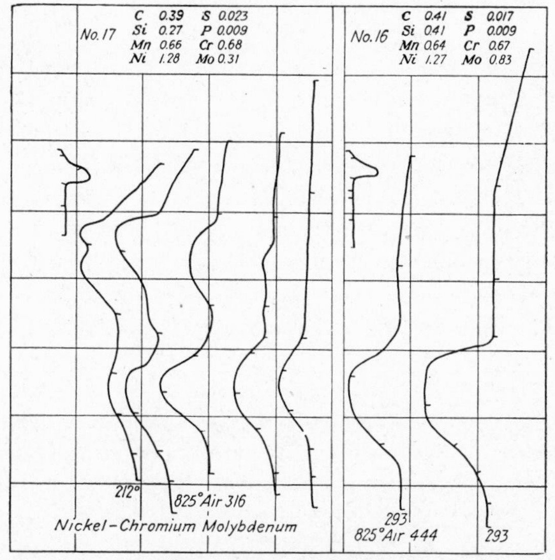

Fig. 107.—Heating and cooling curves for nickel-chromium-molybdenum steels. (*Gillett and Mack.*[151])

Jones[110] showed that approximately 0.5 per cent molybdenum has a marked effect in lowering the temperature of transformation found on cooling. Heating and cooling curves for steels with and without molybdenum are shown in Figs. 105 and 106. These inverse-rate curves were obtained by heating at a rate of 10°C. (18°F.) per minute and cooling at an average rate of 6.2°C. (11°F.) per minute between 845 and 580°C. (1550 and 1075°F.). The steels were cooled from 900°C. (1650°F.) in obtaining the *Ar* points. It was found that the critical points in the steels containing molybdenum were "hardly affected by initial temperature."

The cooling curves for two nickel-chromium-molybdenum steels obtained by Gillett and Mack,[151] and given in Fig. 107, show, in agreement with Jones, that molybdenum tends to suppress the *Ar′* transformation. The curves in Fig. 108, also from Gillett and Mack, likewise show this effect of molybdenum. From the cooling curves just mentioned, it is apparent that the addition of a small amount of molybdenum has more effect in suppressing the *Ar′* transformation than the addition of larger quantities of nickel and chromium.

The transformation temperatures occurring in six nickel-chromium-molybdenum steels were studied by Andrew, Fisher, and Robertson.[186] All of these steels contained a practically constant amount of molybdenum (0.8 per cent) and do not directly indicate the effects of molybdenum.

145. Mechanical Properties.—The properties of 32 nickel-chromium-molybdenum steels and several nickel-chromium steels in the heat-treated condition, as reported by Jones,[176] are listed in Table 92. The Izod impact tests were made with specimens conforming to the British Engineering Standards Association specification. From his work Jones concluded that molybdenum in nickel-chromium steels improves elastic properties, yield strength, elongation, and impact values. Furthermore:

> Nickel-chromium-molybdenum steels provide the best all-round combination of properties but they are closely approached by certain nickel-molybdenum and chromium-molybdenum steels, each of which type shows some advantages and some disadvantages. For example, the chromium-molybdenum steels are distinguished by a high notched-bar impact figure, though the elastic limit and yield point are slightly lower than those of nickel-chromium-molybdenum steels of the same hardness. Nickel-molybdenum steels, on the other hand, show higher yield ratios with considerably lower impact figures than nickel-chromium-molybdenum steels. Moreover, they are difficult to machine

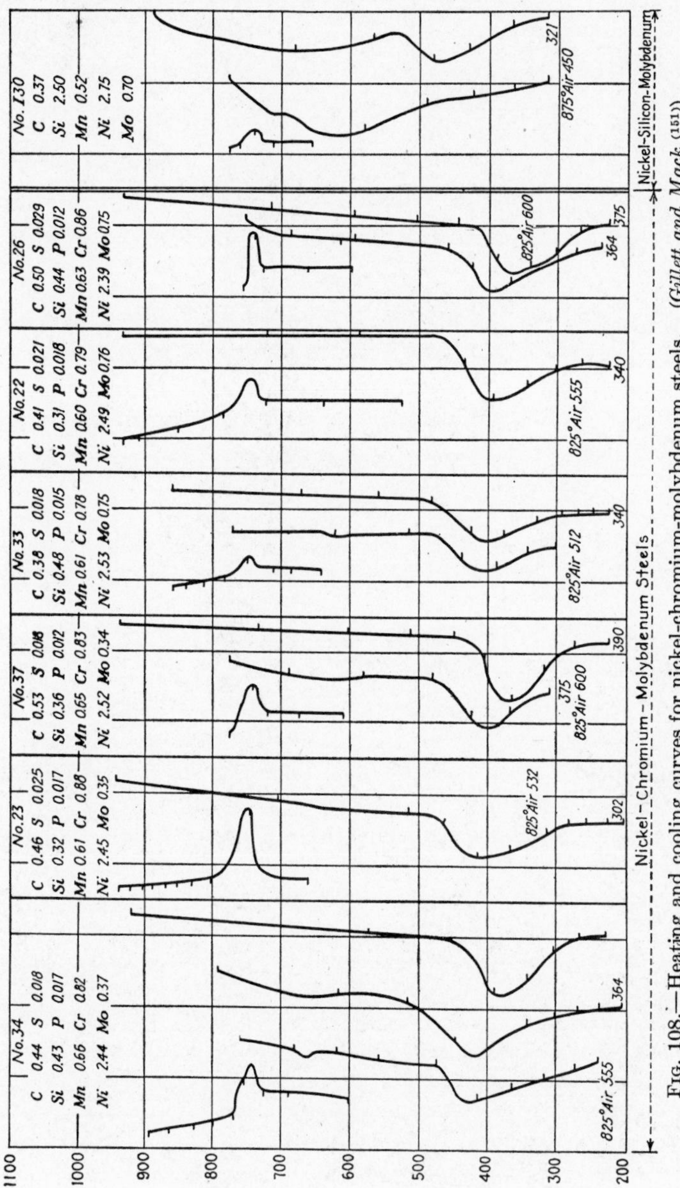

FIG. 108.—Heating and cooling curves for nickel-chromium-molybdenum steels. (Gillett and Mack.[151])

TABLE 92.—MECHANICAL PROPERTIES OF NICKEL-CHROMIUM-MOLYBDENUM STEELS*

Number	Composition, per cent				Oil-quenched		Tempered 2 hr.		Tensile strength, lb./sq. in.	Elastic limit, lb./sq. in.	Yield strength,† lb./sq. in.	Elongation in 2 in., per cent	Reduction of area, per cent	Izod impact, ft-lb.	Brinell hardness
	C	Ni	Cr	Mo	°C.	°F.	°C.	°F.							
15	0.36	1.74	1.08	....	900	1650	550	1020	139,300	94,100	121.000	20	58	45	291
					820	1510	550	1020	136,200	98,600	118,300	19	57	48	291
					900	1650	600	1110	121,800	87,300	106,000	22	64	59	260
					900	1650	650	1200	112,000	78,400	90,500	25	66	68	235
					900	1650	670	1240	110,700	78,400	89,300	26	66	72	229
					820	1500	670	1240	106,200	76,200	83,800	26	67	73	226
16	0.34	1.72	1.08	0.61	900	1650	550	1020	189,500	152,300	176,200	16	52	23	395
					820	1510	550	1020	190,000	156,800	176,200	17	54	24	396
					900	1650	600	1110	166,700	125,400	154,500	18	58	32	357
					900	1650	650	1200	137,500	107,500	120,500	21	62	51	284
					900	1650	670	1240	127,900	98,600	109,500	23	64	56	268
					820	1510	670	1240	130,200	103,000	113,800	22	64	54	270
					900	1650	700	1290	114,800	89,600	97,200	26	67	68	238
17	0.37	1.69	1.08	1.06	900	1650	550	1020	218,700	174,700	204,200	15	50	17	451
					820	1510	550	1020	214,100	177,000	199,300	15	50	18	441
					900	1650	600	1110	200,300	159,000	185,900	16	52	20	416
					900	1650	650	1200	149,300	125,400	134,400	20	56	42	309
					900	1650	650	1200	135,600	114,200	121,000	21	61	52	287
					900	1650	670	1240	138,900	110,000	122,300	20	61	49	290
					820	1510	670	1240	141,100	114,200	129,900	21	63	49	291
					900	1650	700	1290	122,300	96,300	106,800	23	64	60	255
18	0.22	2.09	0.78	....	900	1650	500	930	100,200	71,700	79,700	25	66	67	217
					900	1650	600	1110	93,700	65,000	76,100	26	69	77	204

					900	1650	650	1200	88,200	62,700	71,700	29	72	82	189
					900	1650	670	1240	86,800	60,500	69,400	29	72	89	187
					900	1650	700	1290	84,000	49,280	62,000	32	72	89	178
19	0.26	2.06	0.84	0.63	900	1650	600	1110	144,700	114,200	130,800	19	57	35	311
					900	1650	650	1200	118,300	91,900	102,400	22	65	53	251
					900	1650	670	1240	116,700	94,100	102,200	25	67	57	248
					900	1650	700	1290	108,400	76,200	88,600	26	66	63	232
20	0.24	2.14	0.85	0.87	900	1650	600	1110	155,300	125,400	143,400	19	57	33	338
					900	1650	650	1200	121,000	98,600	106,900	22	64	54	257
					900	1650	670	1240	118,500	96,300	104,000	24	67	57	252
					900	1650	700	1290	109,800	82,900	93,300	26	67	66	233
21	0.24	2.05	0.88	1.10	900	1650	600	1110	164,700	129,900	155,700	18	55	26	356
					900	1650	650	1200	128,800	103,000	115,400	22	61	47	280
					900	1650	670	1240	124,200	100,800	109,400	22	63	52	265
					900	1650	700	1290	114,200	80,600	94,900	26	66	56	235
22	0.40	2.73	0.56	....	900	1650	550	1020	129,800	94,100	108,900	21	59	43	277
					820	1510	550	1020	129,800	94,100	108,900	21	61	45	279
					900	1650	600	1110	123,800	87,300	101,800	21	59	52	257
					900	1650	650	1200	106,300	76,200	82,000	25	65	67	225
					900	1650	650	1200	102,700	65,000	77,600	26	67	70	215
					900	1650	670	1240	105,400	73,900	81,700	26	67	68	219
					820	1510	670	1240	106,300	76,200	83,000	26	68	68	222
23	0.27	2.53	0.66	0.37	900	1650	600	1110	121,800	89,600	104,500	20	62	44	268
					900	1650	650	1200	107,500	80,600	88,700	23	65	56	231
					900	1650	670	1240	105,300	76,200	85,100	23	64	59	226
					900	1650	700	1290	103,000	67,200	79,700	26	66	63	218
24	0.33	2.70	0.58	0.57	900	1650	550	1020	183,500	150,100	170,700	16	55	23	385
					820	1510	550	1020	182,800	152,300	170,200	15	54	24	382
					900	1650	600	1110	171,100	132,200	159,000	17	55	27	363

TABLE 92.—(*Continued*)

Number	Composition, per cent				Oil-quenched		Tempered ½ hr.		Tensile strength, lb./sq. in.	Elastic limit, lb./sq. in.	Yield strength,† lb./sq. in.	Elongation in 2 in., per cent	Reduction of area, per cent	Izod impact, ft-lb.	Brinell hardness
	C	Ni	Cr	Mo	°C.	°F.	°C.	°F.							
					900	1650	650	1200	134,000	112,000	120,300	21	63	52	285
					900	1650	650	1200	120,000	91,900	104,800	24	64	61	252
					900	1650	670	1240	125,000	100,800	108,800	23	64	57	261
					820	1510	670	1240	123,800	98,600	109,500	23	65	59	258
25	0.30	2.72	0.61	0.61	900	1650	600	1110	164,400	132,200	155,000	18	57	30	348
					900	1650	650	1200	130,100	105,300	116,300	22	65	51	277
					900	1650	670	1240	122,500	100,800	109,100	23	67	57	259
					900	1650	700	1290	115,600	71,700	90,800	26	66	65	240
26	0.25	2.48	0.68	0.67	900	1650	600	1110	150,000	121,000	139,400	20	61	37	329
					900	1650	650	1200	119,800	96,300	106,200	24	68	58	255
					900	1650	670	1240	115,300	91,800	99,600	25	67	63	248
					900	1650	700	1290	113,100	44,800	78,800	24	63	62	238
27	0.32	2.65	0.56	0.71	900	1650	600	1110	167,300	132,200	156,800	17	57	33	358
					900	1650	650	1200	132,800	105,300	117,400	23	66	54	278
					900	1650	670	1240	123,400	96,320	106,200	24	67	61	261
					900	1650	700	1290	116,000	69,400	88,500	25	66	71	240
28	0.29	2.71	0.56	0.77	900	1650	600	1110	171,600	141,100	160,800	17	57	30	363
					900	1650	650	1200	131,300	103,000	117,400	22	66	53	278
					900	1650	670	1240	123,500	98,600	109,300	24	67	60	261
					900	1650	700	1290	116,500	69,400	90,500	25	66	67	244

29	0.35	2.67	0.59	1.01	900	1650	550	1020	200,800	161,300	188,100	15	50	18	415
					820	1510	550	1020	199,000	168,000	186,300	15	47	20	417
					900	1650	600	1110	191,700	154,600	179,400	16	52	22	401
					900	1650	650	1200	140,900	116,500	127,400	20	59	45	289
					900	1650	650	1200	127,500	100,800	110,500	23	64	54	264
					900	1650	670	1240	131,500	109,800	117,600	21	62	51	278
					820	1510	670	1240	129,300	109,800	116,500	21	64	53	270
					900	1650	700	1290	123,700	78,400	98,600	23	61	56	252
30	0.29	2.68	0.60	1.04	900	1650	600	1110	182,800	147,800	172,500	17	55	25	385
					900	1650	650	1200	138,500	112,000	122,500	21	62	49	287
					900	1650	670	1240	129,500	100,800	113,800	24	64	55	274
					900	1650	700	1290	123,700	71,700	93,600	23	59	59	253
31	0.28	2.67	0.82	0.60	900	1650	600	1110	156,200	125,400	144,300	18	59	37	328
					900	1650	650	1200	129,300	105,300	114,300	22	65	57	272
					900	1650	670	1240	120,600	96,300	104,900	24	67	63	256
					900	1650	700	1290	116,100	62,700	85,400	26	66	71	240
32	0.27	2.59	0.85	0.86	900	1650	600	1110	163,800	127,700	153,000	17	59	34	346
					900	1650	650	1200	130,600	103,000	114,900	23	66	56	273
					900	1650	670	1240	123,200	96,300	106,900	24	67	61	260
					900	1650	700	1290	116,800	60,500	84,400	25	65	69	241
33	0.31	2.80	1.15	....	900	1650	550	1020	142,300	109,800	128,600	19	62	41	295
					820	1510	550	1020	142,700	112,000	129,200	19	62	42	298
					900	1650	600	1110	132,900	98,600	116,500	22	63	52	273
					900	1650	650	1200	119,300	89,600	100,800	24	66	64	249
					900	1650	670	1240	116,100	85,100	97,400	24	67	66	242
					820	1510	670	1240	116,800	89,600	98,200	24	66	67	243
34	0.23	2.51	1.15	0.23	900	1650	600	1110	130,200	96,300	114,200	22	66	51	280
					900	1650	650	1200	111,700	85,100	96,100	24	69	64	239
					900	1650	670	1240	109,400	82,900	92,700	24	67	67	236
					900	1650	700	1290	104,500	58,200	78,000	27	68	71	219

TABLE 92.—(*Continued*)

Number	Composition, per cent				Oil-quenched		Tempered 2 hr.		Tensile strength, lb./sq. in.	Elastic limit, lb./sq. in.	Yield strength,† lb./sq. in.	Elongation in 2 in., per cent	Reduction of area, per cent	Izod impact, ft-lb.	Brinell hardness
	C	Ni	Cr	Mo	°C.	°F.	°C.	°F.							
35	0.31	2.67	1.03	0.38	900	1650	600	1110	149,300	114,200	136,700	18	58	43	315
					900	1650	650	1200	130,700	105,300	116,300	23	66	57	270
					900	1650	670	1240	123,800	98,600	110,300	24	67	63	260
					900	1650	700	1290	116,900	62,700	89,200	25	65	70	240
36	0.33	2.81	1.18	0.58	900	1650	550	1020	193,300	161,300	178,400	18	54	21	404
					820	1510	550	1020	190,200	161,300	175,000	17	55	23	402
					900	1650	600	1110	171,100	138,900	156,800	17	55	28	362
					900	1650	650	1200	140,400	114,200	124,000	21	59	44	289
					900	1650	670	1240	134,900	109,800	118,100	22	62	48	280
					820	1510	670	1240	135,100	114,200	121,500	21	59	48	279
					900	1650	700	1290	122,800	67,200	91,800	24	62	57	254
37	0.23	2.55	1.09	0.59	900	1650	600	1110	148,000	116,500	137,500	19	59	40	324
					900	1650	650	1200	119,400	94,100	104,500	24	68	57	255
					900	1650	670	1240	114,900	87,300	98,600	24	67	62	250
					900	1650	700	1290	110,900	60,500	83,800	26	66	65	233
38	0.32	2.67	1.02	0.61	900	1650	600	1110	161,700	127,700	149,000	16	51	35	331
					900	1650	650	1200	136,700	112,000	119,900	22	63	51	281
					900	1650	670	1240	128,200	103,000	111,400	23	66	57	264
					900	1650	700	1290	120,800	56,000	86,900	23	61	61	246
39	0.26	2.78	1.17	1.00	900	1650	550	1020	199,400	150,100	180,600	16	52	18	411
					820	1510	550	1020	197,200	154,600	181,300	17	51	19	412

					900	1650	600	1110	184,600	143,400	170,800	16	52	23	386
					900	1650	650	1200	140,500	112,000	124,400	21	59	46	294
					900	1650	650	1200	128,800	100,800	112,700	23	64	54	273
					900	1650	670	1240	134,700	107,500	117,900	21	62	50	281
					820	1510	670	1240	134,000	112,000	119,500	21	63	49	281
					900	1650	700	1290	122,300	69,400	98,100	23	65	57	251
40	0.30	3.10	1.10	....	900	1650	600	1110	127,900	98,600	113,800	21	62	46	271
					900	1650	650	1200	117,800	85,100	102,000	23	64	57	249
					900	1650	670	1240	108,700	78,400	88,200	24	64	62	226
41	0.33	3.09	1.08	0.36	900	1650	600	1110	158,800	129,900	145,600	17	57	27	329
					900	1650	650	1200	138,000	112,000	123,200	21	59	39	287
					900	1650	670	1240	130,800	103,000	166,300	22	64	45	279
					900	1650	690	1275	121,800	69,400	93,200	24	62	52	254
42	0.31	3.10	1.08	0.49	900	1650	600	1110	160,500	125,400	147,800	17	55	29	332
					900	1650	650	1200	137,500	112,000	122,200	21	59	43	286
					900	1650	670	1240	130,000	96,300	113,500	22	64	51	273
					900	1650	690	1275	121,900	60,500	89,600	25	62	55	247
43	0.27	3.14	1.18	0.83	900	1650	600	1110	160,700	125,400	149,800	18	57	22	331
					900	1650	650	1200	133,500	109,800	118,800	21	59	38	280
					900	1650	670	1240	127,000	103,000	112,000	22	64	42	270
					900	1650	690	1275	120,100	71,700	96,400	24	65	49	249
44	0.34	3.18	1.07	0.84	900	1650	600	1110	173,500	138,900	160,400	17	56	20	359
					900	1650	650	1200	141,400	114,200	125,200	21	56	34	295
					900	1650	670	1240	134,700	103,000	117,800	21	61	40	278
					900	1650	690	1275	128,000	56,000	93,700	23	59	44	257
45	0.29	3.68	0.65	....	900	1650	500	930	128,200	96,300	112,100	20	55	34	270
					900	1650	600	1110	116,100	80,600	98,500	23	64	51	245
					900	1650	650	1200	105,800	71,700	87,100	24	66	61	221
					900	1650	670	1240	102,200	58,200	77,500	25	66	64	211

TABLE 92.—(*Continued*)

Number	Composition, per cent				Oil-quenched		Tempered 2 hr.		Tensile strength, lb./sq. in.	Elastic limit, lb./sq. in.	Yield strength,† lb./sq. in.	Elongation in 2 in., per cent	Reduction of area, per cent	Izod impact, ft-lb.	Brinell hardness
	C	Ni	Cr	Mo	°C.	°F.	°C.	°F.							
46	0.28	3.72	0.64	0.35	900	1650	600	1110	152,000	123,200	142,400	18	57	29	324
					900	1650	650	1200	131,800	103,000	117,400	21	59	42	282
					900	1650	670	1240	125,000	91,900	104,400	23	64	47	264
					900	1650	680	1255	122,500	51,500	85,100	24	59	49	253
47	0.29	3.76	0.67	0.48	900	1650	600	1110	160,200	123,200	149,200	18	57	24	336
					900	1650	650	1200	132,100	98,600	117,400	20	59	40	279
					900	1650	670	1240	127,900	80,600	107,500	22	64	44	264
					900	1650	680	1255	126,300	53,500	87,300	22	57	42	255
48	0.26	3.75	0.68	0.77	900	1650	600	1110	167,700	134,400	157,600	17	56	22	351
					900	1650	650	1200	135,000	109,800	120,700	21	59	41	285
					900	1650	670	1240	129,700	91,900	112,900	22	64	46	270
					900	1650	680	1255	127,000	58,200	91,500	21	61	45	257
49‡	0.25	2.60	0.66	0.62	900	1650	600	1110	147,100	116,500	136,600	19	59	37	321
					900	1650	650	1200	121,000	94,100	107,000	24	67	57	265
					900	1650	670	1240	117,100	91,900	102,100	25	67	60	252
					900	1650	700	1290	112,000	62,700	84,200	25	64	63	234
50§	0.27	2.55	0.68	0.62	900	1650	600	1110	150,300	123,200	140,200	19	58	38	326
					900	1650	650	1200	125,700	98,600	112,000	24	67	55	273
					900	1650	670	1240	116,500	91,900	100,800	25	57	60	249
					900	1650	700	1290	118,700	51,500	81,500	24	58	60	244
51‖	0.25	2.55	0.66	0.63	900	1650	600	1110	148,700	121,000	138,900	19	57	38	324
					900	1650	650	1200	123,700	96,300	109,500	24	67	55	270
					900	1650	670	1240	117,100	91,900	101,900	25	67	60	253
					900	1650	700	1290	119,400	44,800	79,700	24	58	58	248

* Jones.(176)
† Reported as yield point.
‡ No. 49: 0.33 per cent manganese.
§ No. 50: 0.57 per cent manganese.
‖ No. 51: 0.64 per cent manganese.

when the nickel content exceeds 3 per cent, which it must do to enable a tensile strength of 135,000 lb. per sq. in. to be obtained, and tests made after different rates of cooling indicate that they are more susceptible to mass effect than the nickel-chromium-molybdenum steels.

In papers on molybdenum steels Sargent(92, 102) and Schmid(103) discussed the properties of nickel-chromium-molybdenum steels, and Sargent(102) gave the curves shown in Fig. 109 to show the effects of molybdenum on heat-treated nickel-chromium steels.

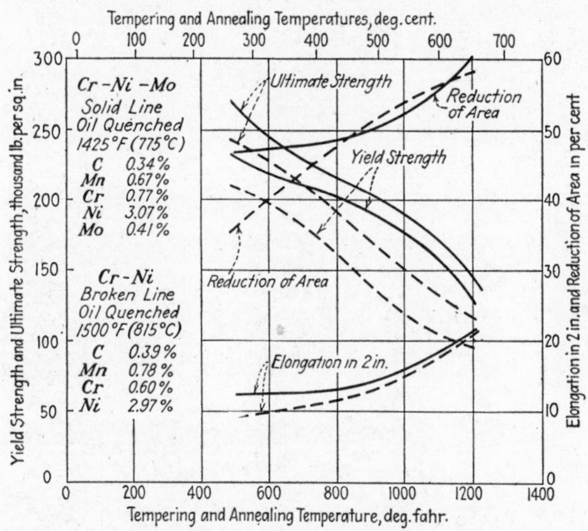

FIG. 109.—Tensile properties of a nickel-chromium and a nickel-chromium-molybdenum steel. (*Sargent.*(102))

It was reported by Dreibholz and Guertler(134) that the addition of 0.6 per cent molybdenum to a steel containing 0.3 per cent carbon, 3.5 per cent nickel, and 0.65 per cent chromium increased the yield strength and tensile strength without appreciably affecting the elongation.

The properties of five nickel-chromium-molybdenum steels, including endurance properties, as reported by Gillett and Mack,(151) are given in Table 93. These authors also made longitudinal and transverse tests of nickel-chromium-molybdenum steel rolled into plates, which proved that molybdenum did not adversely affect the properties in the direction at right angles to the direction of rolling.

The properties of six steels reported by Andrew, Fisher, and Robertson(186) are listed in Table 94. Two rates of cooling from

TABLE 93.—MECHANICAL PROPERTIES OF NICKEL-CHROMIUM-MOLYBDENUM STEELS*

Number	Composition, per cent				Oil-quenched		Tempered		Tensile strength, lb./sq. in.	Yield strength,† lb./sq. in.	Elongation in 2 in., per cent	Reduction of area, per cent	Brinell hardness	Izod impact, ft-lb.	Endurance limit, lb./sq. in.
	C	Ni	Cr	Mo	°C.	°F.	°C.	°F.							
17	0.39	1.28	0.68	0.31	825	1520	425	800	199,500	170,000	13.0	46.2	400	27	
					825	1520	525	975	168,500	155,000	15.0	54.5	355	37	88,000
					825	1520	625	1150	145,750	135,000	19.0	60.6	315	57.5	
16	0.41	1.27	0.67	0.83	825	1520	425	800	224,000	180,000	12.5	46.2	460	16	100,000
					825	1520	525	975	202,500	170,000	14.0	43.3	420	25.5	
					825	1520	625	1150	182,500	165,000	14.5	51.9	380	34	74,000
23	0.46	2.45	0.88	0.35	810	1490	425	800	214,000	185,000	13.0	49.1	420	20	
					810	1490	525	975	182,500	155,000	15.5	51.9	385	34	
					810	1490	625	1150	157,500	140,000	19.0	59.8	325	54	80,000
22	0.41	2.49	0.79	0.76	810	1490	150	300	312,000	187,500	11.2	29.6	530	....	135,000 ±
					805	1480	225	430	280,000	185,000	11.5	39.3	495		
					805	1480	325	620	246,000	200,750	11.5	40.3	475	....	100,000 ±
					810	1490	425	800	220,000	175,000	12.0	40.3	445	16	96,000
					805	1480	425	800	223,000	195,000	12.2	40.4	420		
					810	1490	475	885	203,000	172,500	13.2	43.1	420		
					810	1490	525	975	204,250	165,500	14.5	45.0	410	23	100,000
					805	1480	550	1020	198,500	170,000	15.0	46.0	410		
					805	1480	540	1000	200,000	175,000	15.5	48.0	400	....	84,000
					805	1480	625	1150	181,000	155,000	17.0	52.0	365		
					805	1480	600	1110	184,000	157,500	16.5	47.1	360		
					810	1490	625	1150	169,000	145,000	16.7	54.5	340	32	83,000
					810	1490	650	1200	157,500	146,500	18.0	55.0	320	....	72,000
					810	1490	675	1240	146,000	133,000	19.0	55.4	295		
					810	1490	750	1380	132,000	100,000	25.0	55.8	270		
26	0.50	2.39	0.86	0.75	790	1450	430	800	237,750	207,000	10.0	34.0	465	15	102,000
					790	1450	525	975	209,750	190,000	11.5	37.2	425	18	87,000
					790	1450	630	1170	163,750	150,000	16.0	49.1	335	34	70,000

* Gillett and Mack.[151]
† Reported as yield point by extensometer.

the tempering temperature were used to determine whether or not these steels were subject to temper-brittleness, and the negligible effect of this rate on impact values indicated that temper-brittleness was absent.

TABLE 94.—MECHANICAL PROPERTIES OF NICKEL-CHROMIUM-MOLYBDENUM STEELS*

Number	Composition, per cent				Tensile strength, lb./sq. in.	Elongation in 2 in., per cent	Izod impact, ft-lb.
	C	Ni	Cr	Mo			
Oil-quenched 860°C. (1580°F.), tempered 3 hr. at 650°C. (1200°F.) and water-cooled							
1	0.37	2.02	1.42	0.785	144,700	19.0	46
2	0.41	3.53	1.67	0.89	144,800	26.3	38
3	0.39	5.02	1.59	0.87	146,100	26.0	
4	0.78	2.04	1.61	0.87	169,700	8.1	23
5	0.80	3.42	1.68	0.865	193,600	3.1	6
6	0.87	4.52	1.69	0.87	191,300	6.0	3
Oil-quenched 860°C. (1580°F.), tempered 3 hr. at 650°C. (1200°F.) and slowly cooled							
1	0.37	2.02	1.42	0.785	136,300	18.5	46
2	0.41	3.53	1.67	0.89	146,500	17.5†	41
3	0.39	5.02	1.59	0.87	154,100	19.9†	28
4	0.78	2.04	1.61	0.87	188,300	8.9	19
5	0.80	3.42	1.68	0.865	192,600	2.7	6
6	0.87	4.52	1.69	0.87	186,300	3.3	4

* Andrew, Fisher, and Robertson.(186)
† Necked close to gage mark. True elongation is greater than value shown.

In his recent book "Overstrain of Metals and Its Application to the Auto-frettage Process of Cylinder and Gun Construction," Macrae(374) discussed the effects of overstrain on nickel-chromium-molybdenum steels, and, in fact, much of the work reported was performed on such steels. The data given, however, are of interest with respect to strengthening of materials by overstraining rather than with respect to properties of alloy steels.

In private correspondence, M. R. Chase, of A. Finkl and Sons Co., stated that nickel-chromium-molybdenum steels are well suited for use as large, highly stressed forgings ranging from 6 to 50 in. in section, which cannot be quenched or when quenching is not desired. Such parts are used in either the annealed or normalized and tempered condition. A typical analysis of such a steel is 0.55 per cent carbon, 0.50 per cent manganese, 1.50 per cent nickel, 0.75 per cent chromium, and 0.30 per cent molybdenum. A crankshaft made from this type of steel is shown in Fig. 110. Test pieces cut from midway of the 17-in. diameter

FIG. 110.—Nickel-chromium-molybdenum steel crankshaft. Journals 17-in. diameter, webs 37 × 22 in., length 14 ft. 6 in., finished weight 11,655 lb. Normalized and tempered. (*A. Finkl and Sons Co.*)

section of the normalized and tempered shaft had the following properties, which illustrate its deep-hardening characteristics:

Tensile strength, lb./sq. in.	120,600
Yield strength, lb./sq. in.	90,500
Elongation in 2 in., per cent	20.0
Reduction of area, per cent	42.0

The properties of a steel of a somewhat lower carbon content, as determined by Chase, are shown in Fig. 111.

146. Temper-brittleness.—It has been found that some quenched and tempered nickel-chromium steels become brittle when cooled slowly from the tempering temperature. This brittleness is manifested by a low impact resistance. The susceptibility of steels to such "temper-brittleness" is particularly serious in the manufacture of large parts, for it is difficult to cool them from the tempering temperature other than slowly.

As will be evident from the following discussion, a few tenths of 1 per cent of molybdenum in steels of the type subject to temper-brittleness prevent the occurrence of the phenomenon.

In testing steels for temper-brittleness, Jones[110] determined the Izod impact values of several steels after cooling from the tempering temperature at various rates. The steels were first quenched in oil from 900°C. (1650°F.). As his results given in Table 95 indicate, the impact values of the two steels containing approximately 0.5 per cent molybdenum were independent

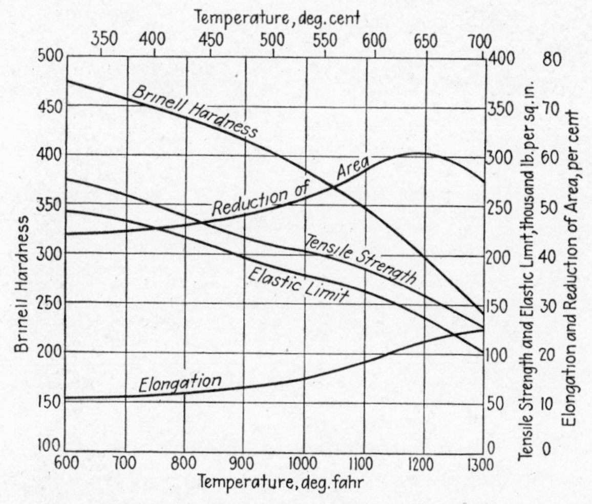

FIG. 111.—Properties of a 0.45 per cent carbon, 2.00 per cent nickel, 0.94 per cent chromium, 0.36 per cent molybdenum steel, normalized 830°C. (1525°F.), annealed 790°C. (1450°F.), and quenched from 790°C. (1450°F.). Heat-treated as 1-in rounds. (*A. Finkl and Sons Co.*)

of the cooling rate, while the impact values of the five other steels became quite small when the samples were slowly cooled. Expressed in other words, the molybdenum-bearing steels were quite unsusceptible to temper-brittleness, while the five other steels were obviously susceptible.

In a later publication, Jones[176] reported a study of the steels described in the preceding section to ascertain their susceptibility to temper-brittleness. In this study the steels were cooled from the tempering temperature of 650°C. (1200°F.) by quenching in water and by cooling in the furnace at a rate of approximately 0.3°C. (0.54°F.) per minute. He found that the chromium and nickel-chromium steels were slightly but distinctly susceptible to temper-brittleness, but that in every case steels containing as much as 0.3 per cent molybdenum were free from temper-brittleness. The nickel-chromium-molybdenum steels were even cooled at the extremely slow rate of 0.1°C. (0.2°F.) per minute without exhibiting temper-brittleness.

TABLE 95.—IZOD IMPACT VALUES OF STEELS COOLED AT DIFFERENT VELOCITIES FROM TEMPERING TEMPERATURE AT 650°C. (1200°F.)*
(Specimens quenched in oil from 900°C. [1650°F.]).

Steel	Composition, per cent				Cooling rate			
	C	Ni	Cr	Mo	In water	2½°C. per min.	1°C. per min.	0.3°C. per min.
A	0.43	1.96	2.15	....	45	4	3	3
B	0.42	2.02	1.04	....	57	8	5	4
C	0.37	1.93	0.62	....	49	20	11	7
D	0.35	3.00	1.49	....	43	4	3	2
E	0.23	3.72	0.92	....	44	13	7	6
K	0.28	2.45	0.65	0.43	58	..	..	57
*K*1	0.25	2.84	0.85	0.48	37	..	..	35

* Jones.[110]

A thorough study of the effect of composition on the temper-brittleness of nickel-chromium steels was reported by Greaves and Jones,[152] who found that the addition of 0.3 or more per cent molybdenum to these steels completely eliminated the susceptibility to temper-brittleness, unless the manganese or phosphorus content was high. When the manganese content was 0.8 per cent or the phosphorus content 0.07 per cent, the addition of molybdenum did not entirely eliminate susceptibility to temper-brittleness, but it reduced the tendency to embrittlement. In steels with normal manganese and phosphorus contents, there was no advantage in adding over 0.5 per cent molybdenum so far as temper-brittleness was concerned.

The absence of temper-brittleness in nickel-chromium-molybdenum steels was commented on by the following authors, some of whom gave definite data to indicate its absence; Dreibholz and Guertler,[134] Andrew,[130] Guillet and Ballay,[174] Andrew, Fisher, and Robertson,[186] Rowe,[242] Monypenny,[382] Maita,[476] and Goerens.[447]

Monypenny,[482A] however, spoke of the embrittlement of very strong structural steel when maintained at a temperature of 400 or 450°C. (750 or 840°F.) and continued as follows:

Many alloy steels, for example the ordinary nickel-chromium and chromium-vanadium steels used so largely in engineering work, are affected in this way, and it has been reported that even certain types of nickel-chromium-molybdenum steels, which appear from tests lasting a few hours to be free from temper brittleness, have been found to have their toughness greatly reduced by several months' exposure at 400 to 450°C. (750 to 840°F.).

Recent results obtained by Bailey and Roberts[509] support Monypenny's statement. These authors held specimens at a temperature of 400 or 500°C. (750 or 930°F.) while under a stress of from 1,100 to 22,400 lb. per sq. in. for as long as 250 hr. and compared the impact strengths of specimens treated in this manner with those of the untreated specimens. Many of the steels studied, which included nickel, nickel-chromium, and nickel-molybdenum types, were appreciably embrittled by this treatment, and the authors concluded that:

a. When the molybdenum is under 0.70 per cent, 1.5 to 3.5 per cent of nickel results in a steel liable to embrittlement.

Steels with 5 per cent nickel appear to be free from this defect.

b. An effect similar to that of nickel in *a* is produced by 1 to 2 per cent manganese; there are no data regarding the effect of molybdenum or other elements in inhibiting this condition.

c. Copper in small quantities, of the order of 0.5 per cent, certainly involves a liability to embrittlement.

147. Mass Effect.—Jones[110] found that the properties of a steel containing approximately 0.5 per cent molybdenum, treated in the form of a specimen 1 × 1⅓ × 5 in., were not essentially different from the properties of samples cut from a large gun forging. Other tests also indicated that the properties of this steel were to a considerable extent unaffected by variations in initial temperature and rates of cooling in oil. Table 96 shows Brinell hardness of rods of three different diameters, air-cooled from 900°C. (1650°F.), and gives some indication of the effect of size of section on hardening as well as the air-hardening properties of the various steels. As may be noted, the steel containing molybdenum has the least amount of carbon and is not directly comparable with the other steels. In a later work Jones[176] stated:

The same property of complete hardening with moderate rates of cooling is revealed in the relative absence of mass effect in nickel-chromium-molybdenum steels as compared with the nickel-chromium steels, shown by the uniformity of properties throughout the walls of large forgings after treatment. This property makes it more justifiable in the case of nickel-chromium-molybdenum steels than in most other alloy steels to make direct use of the results of treatment on a small scale to forecast properties of large forgings after treatment.

Andrew, Fisher, and Robertson[186] maintained that their cooling curves, which indicated a depression of *Ar* points by molybdenum, proved that molybdenum in nickel-chromium steels had a high efficiency in producing deep hardening.

TABLE 96.—BRINELL HARDNESS OF BARS AIR-COOLED AND WATER-QUENCHED FROM 900°C. (1650°F.)*

Steel	Composition, per cent				Hardness			
	C	Ni	Cr	Mo	Water-quenched	1-in. round,† air-cooled	2-in. round,† air-cooled	3-in. round,† air-cooled
A	0.43	1.96	2.15	...	555	545	544	535
D	0.35	3.00	1.49	...	493	405	370	355
B	0.42	2.02	1.04	...	538	420	385	370
E	0.23	3.72	0.92	...	440	320	295	285
F	0.31	3.62	0.82	...	522	380	350	335
K	0.28	2.45	0.65	0.43	459	295	285	275
C	0.37	1.93	0.62	...	511	265	250	245

* Jones.[110]

† Cooling rates for centers of rods: 1 in., 110°C. (200°F.) per min.; 2 in., 45°C. (80°F.) per min; 3 in., 33°C. (60°F.) per min.

The following statement by Hadfield[452] is of interest in reference to the depth-hardening properties of the steels under discussion:

The use of molybdenum as an addition to nickel-chromium steel has been found to confer further advantage by enabling the same degree of toughness to be obtained in parts of comparatively large section, as in the smaller sections. Thus in bars 4 in. in diameter of this nickel-chromium-molybdenum steel, and with a Brinell hardness of 330, tensile characteristics are obtainable as follows: yield point 134,000 lb. per sq. in. and maximum stress 156,800 lb. per sq. in., with an elongation of 20 per cent and a reduction of area of 60 per cent. These figures are accompanied by an Izod impact value as high as 50 ft-lb. With plain nickel-chromium steel there is some falling off in toughness in the larger sections as compared with the smaller ones.

The cooling curves shown in the section on the critical points in nickel-chromium-molybdenum steels show quite definitely that molybdenum tends to suppress the *Ar′* transformation, which means that molybdenum-containing steels can be hardened by a less rapid quenching rate than molybdenum-free steels, and that, therefore, the mass effect is decreased.

148. Properties at High Temperatures.—Results of accelerated creep tests reported by Guillet, Galibourg, and Samsoen[262, 264] indicate that nickel-chromium-molybdenum steels have a higher creep limit at 450°C. (840°F.) than the other low-alloy steels tested. The steel having the highest strength at this temperature contained 0.30 per cent carbon, 2.78 per cent nickel, 0.75 per cent chromium, and 0.33 per cent molybdenum. Inasmuch as exact heat treatments were not reported for the steels studied, the values obtained are not reported here. Chevenard[430] referred to these tests and emphasized the value of such steels for service up to 500°C. (930°F.).

According to Bailey, Dickenson, Inglis, and Pearson,[422] nickel-chromium-molybdenum steels containing 2.5 per cent nickel, 0.7 per cent chromium, and 0.30 per cent molybdenum have excellent properties up to 500°C. (930°F.), but their strength decreases rapidly at higher temperatures.

In discussing the high-temperature properties of low-alloy steels, Hatfield[268] stated that a nickel-chromium-molybdenum steel treated to give a tensile strength between 135,000 and 145,000 lb. per sq. in. has a "time-yield" value at 500°C. (930°F.) of only 17,900 or 20,100 lb. per sq. in., which falls to 4,480 lb. per sq. in. at 600°C. (1110°F.). A steel containing 0.30 per cent carbon, 2.38 per cent nickel, 0.61 per cent chromium, and 0.59 per cent molybdenum was listed as having a tensile strength of 126,300 lb. per sq. in. at room temperature and only 17,200 lb. per sq. in. at 800°C. (1470°F.). The time-yield value was defined by Hatfield[269] as the static stress which will just fail to produce an elongation of 0.5 per cent between the twenty-fourth and seventy-second hour of test. The steel just described (0.30 per cent carbon, etc.), after quenching in oil from 850°C. (1560°F.) and tempering at 625°C. (1155°F.), had a time-yield value at 350°C. (660°F.) of 37,600 lb. per sq. in. and at 550°C. (1020°F.) a value of only 6,700 lb. per sq. in.

A nickel-chromium-molybdenum steel sold under the trade name "Hecla 116," according to Hatfield, has the following creep stress limits: 38,000 lb. per sq. in. at 450°C. (840°F.), 17,900 lb. per sq. in. at 500°C. (930°F.), and 13,400 lb. per sq. in. at 550°C. (1020°F.). The tensile strength of this steel at room temperature was found to be 143,300 lb. per sq. in.

Table 77 (page 241), in the preceding chapter, includes creep properties of several nickel-chromium-molybdenum steels as given by Spooner and Foley.[499] These data were also published by Coffin and Swisher.[432]

TABLE 97.—EFFECT OF MOLYBDENUM ON TEMPERING TEMPERATURE OF NICKEL-CHROMIUM STEEL*

Description of test	Brinell hardness	Tempered		Tensile strength, lb./sq. in.	Yield strength† lb./sq. in.	Elongation in 2 in., per cent	Reduction of area, per cent
		°C.	°F.				
Tested at 20°C. (70°F.):							
Without molybdenum	232	495	925	120,700	81,700	21.0	47.0
With molybdenum	234	700	1290	118,600	85,100	20.1	43.4
Gain	...	205	365	....	4 per cent		
Tested at 540°C. (1000°F.):							
Without molybdenum	...	495	925	53,300	37,600	28.0	56.5
With molybdenum	...	700	1290	69,000	50,200	25.5	71.0
Gain	...	205	365	29 per cent	34 per cent	....	26 per cent

* Spring.[500]
† Reported as yield point.

The fact that molybdenum raises the tempering temperature of steels is taken by Spring[500] as evidence that it will also increase the strength at temperatures in the neighborhood of 500°C. (930°F.). Table 97, which was corrected as advised by private correspondence with Spring, lists the properties of two cast steels that were heat-treated to give substantially the same strength and Brinell hardness values. One of these steels contained 0.40 per cent carbon, 0.59 per cent manganese, 2.07 per cent nickel, 0.80 per cent chromium, and 0.29 per cent molybdenum; the other steel differed only in that it contained no molybdenum. As indicated by the table, in order to obtain a Brinell hardness of 230 it was necessary to temper the molybdenum steel at a temperature 200°C. (360°F.) higher than the other steel, and, furthermore, the molybdenum-bearing steel, as judged by the short-time tensile test, was much stronger at 540°C. (1000°F.) than the steel containing no molybdenum—in fact the molybdenum had apparently increased the tensile strength by 29 per cent and the yield strength by 34 per cent. Figure 97 (page 240), also by Spring, shows that molybdenum increases the creep resistance of nickel-chromium steel.

The tensile properties of a nickel-chromium-molybdenum steel at elevated temperatures as reported by Kahlbaum, Dowdell, and Tucker[464] are listed in Table 98. The impact values between −80°C. (−110°F.) and 900°C. (1650°F.) for a nickel-chromium-molybdenum steel were determined by Greaves and Jones,[152] but they need not be discussed here because they were not essentially different from those of other steels.

TABLE 98.—SHORT-TIME TENSILE TESTS AT ELEVATED TEMPERATURES ON STEELS CONTAINING 0.32 PER CENT CARBON, 0.70 PER CENT MANGANESE, 2.35 PER CENT NICKEL, 0.62 PER CENT CHROMIUM, AND 0.31 PER CENT MOLYBDENUM*

(Treatment *A*: oil-quenched from 850°C. [1560°F.]; treatment *B*: air-quenched from same temperature; all tempered at 620°C. [1150°F.])

Testing temperature		Treatment	Tensile strength, lb./sq. in.	Yield strength,† lb./sq. in.	Elongation in 2 in., per cent	Reduction of area, per cent	Brinell hardness
°C.	°F.						
20	70	*A*	156,000	126,000‡	17.0	59.4	325
425	800	*A*	123,000	52,500	16.5	61.1	
425	800	*A*	132,000	52,500	15.0	57.5	
480	900	*A*	109,500	35,000	17.5	69.7	
480	900	*A*	111,500	34,000	17.0	68.3	
540	1000	*A*	98,000	12,000	20.0	75.6	
20	70	*B*	135,500	96,000‡	17.6	54.9	281
425	800	*B*	110,500	42,000	16.5	57.5	
425	800	*B*	113,000	39,000	16.0	55.6	
480	900	*B*	101,000	32,000	17.0	61.5	
480	900	*B*	101,000	30,000	16.5	63.5	
540	1000	*B*	86,250	9,000	17.5	70.7	
540	1000	*B*	87,000	9,000	18.0	72.0	

* Kahlbaum, Dowdell, and Tucker.[464]

† Reported as proportional limit.

‡ Reported as elastic limit.

From some short-time tests at 800°C. (1470°F.) Hatfield[219] concluded that the addition of molybdenum to nickel-chromium steels increased the strength at elevated temperatures.

149. Miscellaneous Properties.—The erosion of various steels used in guns, including a nickel-chromium-molybdenum steel, was studied by Greaves, Abram, and Rees,[263] who found that erosion was dependent on the melting point of the material and that, consequently, Armco iron had a greater resistance to erosion than a nickel-chromium-molybdenum steel.

Andrew and Binnie[249] determined the liquidus and solidus temperatures for a number of alloy steels, including two nickel-chromium-molybdenum steels, and found that nickel plus chromium lowered the liquidus but not the solidus, but that the addition of molybdenum to nickel-chromium lowered the solidus. They concluded that, owing to the wider temperature range of solidification, nickel-chromium-molybdenum steels will have a more marked carbide segregation than molybdenum-free steels.

150. Uses.—Discussions of Sargent[92, 102] and Schmid[103] indicate that nickel-chromium-molybdenum steels are used in applications requiring high-strength materials.

The reports by Jones[110, 176] prove that the steels under discussion have been used in the manufacture of guns.

In a discussion of steels suitable for aircraft construction Richardson[238] mentioned the use of a nickel-chromium-molybdenum steel in the fuselage frame. This steel can be treated to give a tensile strength of 265,000 lb. per sq. in., a yield strength of 240,000 lb. per sq. in., and an elongation of 12.5 per cent. A similar use was also mentioned by Py.[236]

In the *Third Report of the Gas Cylinders Research Committee*[251] a nickel-chromium-molybdenum steel was recommended for the manufacture of small gas tanks.

A steel sold under the name "Vibrac," and containing 0.3 per cent carbon, 2.5 per cent nickel, 0.6 per cent chromium, and 0.6 per cent molybdenum, according to Johnson[275] is used in locomotive coupling and connecting rods.

The use of nickel-chromium-molybdenum steels in crankshafts and gears in automobiles is mentioned.[250]

According to McKnight,[376] in 1930, nickel-chromium steels for heavy forgings are being supplanted by nickel-molybdenum and nickel-chromium-molybdenum steels.

An anonymous article in *Aciers Spéciaux*[314] claims that a low-carbon nickel-chromium-molybdenum steel is used in motors on account of its high magnetic permeability. Another article[420] in the same journal also mentions this use.

The use of nickel-chromium-molybdenum steels in tractors is discussed in *The Iron Age*.[312] The use of such steels in motorcycles is mentioned in the *Nickel Bulletin*.[313] A pamphlet[461] discussing the materials of construction used in the Bluebird (an automobile that was driven 245 m. p. h.) states that many parts were made from nickel-chromium-molybdenum steels.

The use of nickel-chromium-molybdenum steel bolts subjected to medium-high temperatures has been recommended by Baumann.[318] Allen[417] claimed that a highly stressed cylinder for use at 480°C. (900°F.) could be made from a steel containing 0.3 per cent carbon, 2.1 per cent nickel, 0.8 per cent chromium, and 0.3 per cent molybdenum.

Table 82 (page 255) from Goerens[447] lists one nickel-chromium-molybdenum steel used for automobile and aircraft construction. From this table Goerens apparently regards 0.25 per cent molybdenum as equivalent to 0.8 per cent tungsten in this type of steel.

As a material for the manufacture of high-speed turbo-generator fans Sharp[497] recommended Vibrac V.30 steel, which contains 0.3 per cent carbon, 2.5 per cent nickel, 0.6 per cent chromium, and 0.6 per cent molybdenum. The use of several nickel-chromium-molybdenum steels in high-temperature steam turbines was recently mentioned by Van Duzer.[502]

C. MISCELLANEOUS NICKEL-CHROMIUM-MOLYBDENUM STEELS

Some of the corrosion-resistant or "stainless" alloys in use at the present time contain, in addition to chromium, sufficient nickel to render the alloys austenitic at room temperature. The most widely used alloy of this type contains approximately 18 per cent chromium and 8 per cent nickel with as small a carbon content as can be economically obtained. In some instances several per cent molybdenum are added to such an alloy, and it is therefore desirable to consider the function of molybdenum in this and related alloys.

Other nickel-chromium-molybdenum steels on which a very limited amount of data is available include die steels, steels used for rolls, and steels used in the cast condition.

151. Corrosion Resistance of Austenitic Alloys.—Data from Monypenny[177] showing the loss in weight in sulphuric acid of two austenitic nickel-chromium steels, one of which contained molybdenum, are given in Table 99. Monypenny mentioned the production of an alloy of the KA2 type (18 per cent chromium, 8 per cent nickel), with molybdenum, which is supposed to be resistant to sulphurous acid at high temperatures.

In other work Monypenny[381] again mentioned the use of molybdenum in austenitic chromium-nickel alloys to improve corrosion resistance.

The solubility of several steels in sulphuric acid, hydrochloric acid, and nitric acid was reported by Sauvageot and Lauprète.[400]

TABLE 99.—LOSS OF WEIGHT OF STEELS OF THE FOLLOWING ANALYSES IN SULPHURIC ACID*

(*Steel A:* 0.34 per cent carbon, 20.4 per cent chromium, 8.6 per cent nickel. *Steel B:* 0.44 per cent carbon, 20.5 per cent chromium, 6.5 per cent nickel, 3.8 per cent molybdenum.)

Strength of acid, per cent	Temperature		Time, hr.	Loss, mg./sq. cm./hr.	
	°C.	°F.		*A*	*B*
5	18	65	48	0.087	nil
10	18	65	48	0.098	nil
15	18	65	48	0.13	0.09
20	18	65	48	0.13	0.14
25	18	65	48	0.20	0.27
35	18	65	48	0.30	0.71
50	18	65	48	0.39	0.61
10	60/65	140/150	6	4.2	nil
20	60/65	140/150	6	11.9	15.8
30	60/65	140/150	6	17.7	29.7

* Monypenny.[177]

Of two steels of the 18 per cent chromium, 8 per cent nickel type, one contained 1.90 per cent molybdenum, while the other contained no molybdenum. Very little difference was observed between the rate of attack of these two steels.

From their study of austenitic chromium-nickel steels Pomey and Voulet[394] concluded that molybdenum additions decrease the resistance to boiling phosphoric acid and boiling dilute nitric acid, but that they increase resistance to organic acids and very dilute boiling sulphuric and hydrochloric acids.

Schafmeister and Gotta[513] added 2.8 per cent molybdenum to steel of the 18 per cent chromium, 8 per cent nickel type and found that the molybdenum-containing steel, in the cold-worked condition, was more prone to stay passive, and that it was less attacked by cold sulphuric acid. The magnetic saturation of the molybdenum-containing alloy remained low even when cold-worked to a reduction of 60 per cent in area, while the magnetic saturation value of the molybdenum-free alloy increased rapidly with more than 10 per cent reduction by cold work.

Kreutzberg[365] and Aborn and Bain[416] have stated that the addition of several per cent (2 to 4) of molybdenum to steels of the 18 per cent chromium, 8 per cent nickel type renders them more resistant to the sulphurous acid liquors encountered in paper mills. Nelson[484] also stated that molybdenum has a direct bearing on the corrosion resistance of this type of steel.

A study of films on stainless alloys by Bannister and Evans[317] indicated that molybdenum improves the quality of the skin responsible for the resistance to attack.

British Patent 343,997, March 2, 1931, covers a nickel-chromium steel containing small amounts of copper and either tungsten or molybdenum, or both. The presence of tungsten or molybdenum is claimed to effect a decided improvement in corrosion and heat resistance. The use of molybdenum in an austenitic alloy of the 18-8 type in which the nickel is replaced by manganese is specified in Canadian Patent 315,915, Oct. 6, 1931.

152. High-temperature Properties of Austenitic Alloys.—In a discussion of high-temperature strength, Dickie[256] maintained that the addition of molybdenum or tungsten to austenitic steel increases the high-temperature strength because of the large atomic volume of either of these elements as compared with iron.

The stability of the 18 per cent chromium, 8 per cent nickel type of alloy against embrittlement at temperatures in the neighborhood of 650 or 750°C. (1200 or 1380°F.) was said by Aborn and Bain[416] to be increased by certain addition elements, which include tungsten and molybdenum, but embrittlement is delayed rather than entirely prevented. In British Patent 348,586, May 4, 1931, by Atkinson and Hagon it is claimed that small amounts of molybdenum, as well as other elements, inhibit the weld decay in austenitic nickel-chromium steel.

An extended study of deterioration in austenitic nickel-chromium steels of the 18-8 type was recently reported by Krivobok and coworkers.[467] Deterioration was studied by magnetic measurements and the rate of attack by acidified copper sulphate solution and a 10 per cent hydrochloric acid solution. Several of the steels studied contained small amounts of both molybdenum and copper, and it was found that the presence of these elements tended to inhibit deterioration. The alloys examined contained as much as 3 per cent copper and as much as 3 per cent molybdenum. Of the alloys containing approximately 0.10 per cent carbon, one containing 1.55 per cent molybdenum and 1.67 per cent copper was particularly immune to deterioration. The study is being continued, and it is proposed to determine whether or not molybdenum in the absence of copper is effective in preventing decomposition with accompanying loss in corrosion resistance.

In studying the effects of various elements on the deterioration of steels of the 18-8 type, Payson[511] found that molybdenum in amounts as high as 1.87 per cent had little effect, but that a steel containing 3.3 per cent molybdenum was highly resistant to deterioration.

153. Austenitic Alloys Used.—In a table giving the compositions of stainless (*rostfreien*) steels Houdremont[352] listed an austenitic steel of the following composition:

	Per Cent
Carbon	0.15
Silicon	0.30 to 0.50
Manganese	0.30 to 0.40
Chromium	16.7 to 17.5
Nickel	9.5 to 10
Molybdenum	2.5 to 4.5

A recent note in the *American Machinist*[309] states that the producers of chromium-nickel stainless steels licensed by the Krupp Nirosta Co. standardized the symbol for the KA2 (18 per cent chromium, 8 per cent nickel) group of steels, and that steels KA2-Mo, KA2-SMo and KA2-HMo were specified to contain from 2 to 4 per cent molybdenum.

The analysis of a type of cast steel resistant to heat and corrosion was given by Phillips[489] as less than 0.30 per cent carbon, 10 to 12 per cent chromium, 22 to 24 per cent nickel, and 1 to 1.5 per cent molybdenum.

154. Study of Valve Steels by Losana.—The results of some interesting studies on the oxidation of valve steels were recently reported in a series of articles by Losana.[372] This author has, in particular, shown that the addition of molybdenum to nickel-chromium steels greatly inhibits oxidation at temperatures of 1050°C. (1920°F.) or below. To determine the rate of oxidation, carefully polished cylindrical samples were heated at the desired temperatures for periods of from 2 to 24 hr., and the gain in weight was determined.

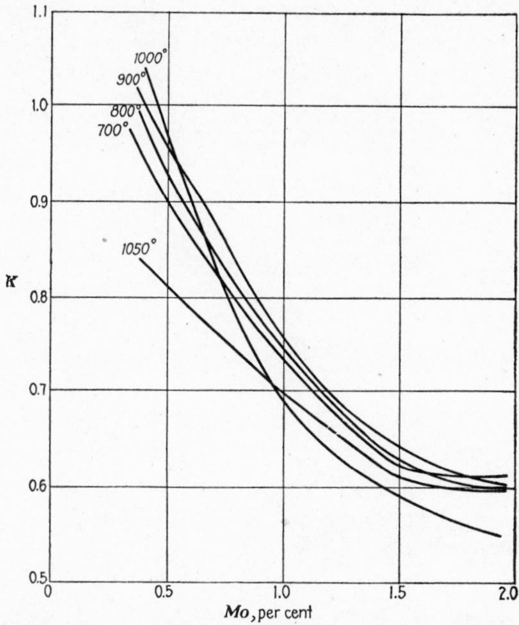

Fig. 112.—Effect of molybdenum on oxidation of 5 per cent nickel, 10 per cent chromium steels in air at indicated temperature. Testing time 24 hr. Ordinates represent ratio of gain in weight of molybdenum-containing steel to gain in weight of molybdenum-free steel. (*Losana.*[372])

In one of the early articles in the series, Losana studied eight valve steels of varying composition, three of which contained, respectively, 0.76, 0.51, and 0.74 per cent molybdenum. Although the compositions of the steels were not such as to furnish a definite and measurable effect of molybdenum, and the results of this study will not be given here in detail, it was found that those steels containing molybdenum had the greatest resistance to oxidation in air and in a mixture of gases representative of the exhaust gases from a gasoline engine.

From his studies of various steels Losana concluded that valve steels containing both nickel and chromium were much more resistant to oxidation than plain chromium steels. The latter type of steel is suitable for use below 800°C. (1470°F.), but with the simultaneous presence of nickel good resistance is obtained at temperatures up to 900°C. (1650°F.). After studying a wide range of nickel-chromium alloys, the author determined the effects of small amounts of molybdenum, tungsten, and vanadium on steels containing either 5 per cent nickel and 10 per cent

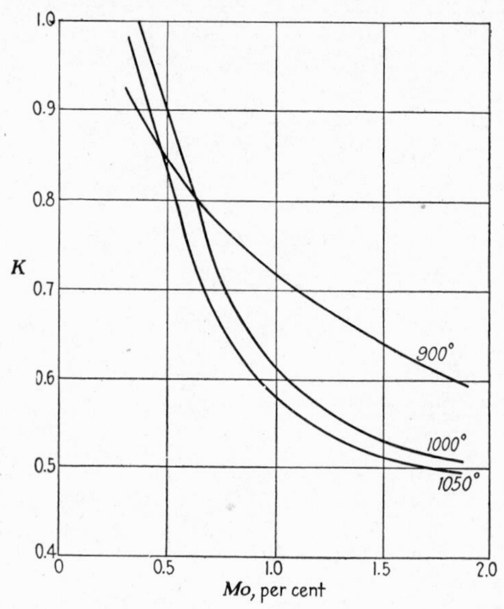

Fig. 113.—Effect of molybdenum on oxidation of 15 per cent nickel, 10 per cent chromium steel. Conditions of test same as given for Fig. 112. (*Losana.*[372])

chromium or 15 per cent nickel and 10 per cent chromium. The analyses of the steels used are given in Table 100, and the results of a 24-hr. test in air are listed in Table 101. The oxidation tests were made on polished cylinders 0.51 in. (13 mm.) in diameter and 0.69 in. (17.5 mm.) high, and, as stated in the table, the results are expressed as increase in weight per unit volume.

The effect of molybdenum in decreasing the loss in weight of steels containing 5 per cent nickel, 10 per cent chromium, and 0.4 per cent carbon is shown in Fig. 112, in which the ordinates represent the ratio of the increase in weight of the molybdenum-bearing steel to the molybdenum-free steel. Similarly, Fig.

113 indicates the effects of molybdenum in steels containing 15 per cent nickel, 10 per cent chromium, and 0.4 per cent carbon.

TABLE 100.—ANALYSES OF THE STEELS USED IN OBTAINING DATA GIVEN IN TABLE 101*

Number	Composition, per cent							
	Ni	Cr	Mn	Si	Mo	V	W	C
A	4.72	10.80	0.36	0.07	....	....	....	0.42
1	5.22	9.91	0.41	0.11	0.56	....	....	0.39
2	5.46	10.24	0.48	0.13	0.88	....	....	0.40
3	5.03	10.14	0.43	0.10	1.03	....	....	0.40
4	5.34	9.76	0.38	0.18	1.54	....	....	0.37
5	4.99	10.40	0.40	0.13	1.79	....	....	0.41
B	15.21	10.40	0.46	0.08	....	....	....	0.44
6	14.31	10.36	0.38	0.13	0.68	....	....	0.36
7	15.03	10.01	0.43	0.14	0.93	....	....	0.42
8	14.76	10.75	0.27	0.10	1.26	....	....	0.38
9	14.50	9.94	0.32	0.18	1.60	....	....	0.40
10	14.98	10.52	0.36	0.16	1.81	....	....	0.37
11	4.81	11.06	0.28	0.21	....	....	1.40	0.38
12	5.12	10.38	0.40	0.17	....	Trace	1.76	0.43
13	4.70	11.13	0.23	0.18	....	0.11	1.92	0.41
14	5.49	10.96	0.44	0.23	....	0.22	2.35	0.44
15	5.03	11.80	0.41	0.19	....	0.18	4.21	0.39
16	5.64	10.96	0.38	0.26	....	0.16	7.54	0.48
17	14.21	10.26	0.40	0.17	....	0.35	1.92	0.43
18	15.06	10.75	0.31	0.20	....	0.40	2.25	0.45
19	15.42	11.26	0.46	0.11	....	0.31	3.15	0.47
20	5.41	10.31	0.38	0.15	....	0.86	....	0.39
21	5.56	9.98	0.41	0.16	....	1.58	....	0.41
22	15.21	10.76	0.38	0.15	1.03	0.35	....	0.46
23	15.34	10.94	0.42	0.19	1.22	0.38	1.98	0.43
24	4.18	11.36	0.37	2.41	1.18	....	....	0.72

* Losana.(372)

TABLE 101.—OXIDATION OF THE STEELS DESCRIBED IN TABLE 100 IN AIR AT INDICATED TEMPERATURES*

Number	Increase in weight in 24 hr., mg./cu. cm.					
	600°C. (1110°F.)	700°C. (1290°F.)	800°C. (1475°F.)	900°C. (1650°F.)	1000°C. (1830°F.)	1050°C. (1925°F.)
A	0.10	0.21	0.50	1.03	12.86	36.80
1	0.08	0.19	0.47	1.00	12.34	36.02
2	0.08	0.18	0.45	0.92	11.21	33.40
3	0.07	0.15	0.37	0.80	8.32	26.20
4	0.06	0.13	0.31	0.67	7.21	22.52
5	0.06	0.13	0.30	0.64	6.89	20.80
B	....	....	0.09	0.21	3.27	18.30
6	....	....	Trace	0.18	2.98	17.0
7	....	....	....	0.13	2.02	14.3
8	....	....	....	0.12	1.91	13.6
9	....	....	....	0.12	1.90	13.0
10	....	....	....	0.11	1.88	12.7
11	0.09	0.20	0.48	0.96	12.0	36.4
12	0.08	0.18	0.45	0.94	11.36	35.0
13	0.08	0.19	0.43	0.93	11.12	34.12
14	0.07	0.19	0.44	0.96	11.3	34.0
15	0.09	0.18	0.44	0.91	11.0	34.8
16	0.08	0.17	0.41	0.93	11.8	33.2
17	....	....	0.06	0.19	3.02	17.5
18	....	....	0.05	0.16	2.86	13.9
19	....	....	0.05	0.15	2.60	12.0
20	0.09	0.20	0.46	0.96	12.02	35.4
21	0.10	0.23	0.53	1.12	13.8	37.9
22	....	....	....	0.15	1.98	14.0
23	....	....	....	0.10	1.54	11.2
24	0.05	0.13	0.38	0.79	8.86	30.91

* Losana.(372)

The increase in weight of the steels (compositions in Table 100) in a gas consisting by volume of 2 per cent oxygen, 10 per cent carbon dioxide, 4 per cent carbon monoxide, 84 per cent nitrogen, and traces of sulphur dioxide and hydrocarbons is given below. The values represent the increase in weight, expressed as milligrams per cubic centimeter, of samples of the dimensions mentioned above. They were maintained at temperature for 25 hr. The results are as follows:

Steel number	*A*	1	2	3	4	5
900°C. (1650°F.)	0.56	0.52	0.50	0.31	0.29	0.28
1000°C. (1830°F.)	7.96	7.6	7.0	4.6	3.34	2.9

Steel number	*B*	6	7	8	9	10
900°C. (1650°F.)	0.17	0.08	0.05	0.06	0.05	0.03
1000°C. (1830°F.)	2.10	1.9	1.9	1.2	1.16	1.09

Steel number	11	12	13	14	15	16
900°C. (1650°F.)	0.50	0.46	0.48	0.40	0.45	0.46
1000°C. (1830°F.)	7.6	6.9	6.7	7.2	6.9	7.0

From his investigation Losana concluded that molybdenum greatly increased the oxidation resistance of both the 5 per cent nickel, 10 per cent chromium, and the 15 per cent nickel, 10 per cent chromium steels. In contrast to molybdenum, tungsten had but slight effect on the oxidation, and its presence in valve steels is not justified. Steels containing both tungsten and molybdenum, however, are highly resistant to oxidation. Small amounts of vanadium are without effect, but larger quantities (1.1 per cent) promote oxidation. He further concluded that the behavior of the steels under discussion was the same in exhaust gases and in air, the oxidation in exhaust gases being less rapid than in air.

155. Miscellaneous Steels.—The use of nickel-chromium-molybdenum steels in die blocks was mentioned by Phillips,(287) who stated that the die-block material falls within the following limits: 0.40 to 0.70 per cent carbon, 1.50 to 1.75 per cent nickel, 0.65 to 0.75 per cent chromium, and 0.20 to 0.50 per cent molybdenum. Dies for heavy forgings are made from steels low in carbon and molybdenum in order to minimize cracking and chipping.

The use of nickel-chromium-molybdenum die steels was also discussed by Urquart,(299) Gill,(342) and Waehlert.(503)

Nickel-chromium-molybdenum steels, according to Hruska,(460) are finding some application in rolls.

According to M. R. Chase of A. Finkl and Sons Co., a nickel-chromium-molybdenum steel of the following composition has been extensively used in the drop-forging industry for die blocks, and, in fact, "the greater percentage of all die blocks used today are made from this steel or a slight variation of the same":

	Per Cent
Carbon	0.55
Manganese	0.50
Nickel	1.50
Chromium	0.75
Molybdenum	0.30

Little distortion resulting from heat treatment is observed in die blocks made from this steel and it hardens to a great depth.

The breakage of dies in the heat-treating operation and in service has been practically eliminated. These nickel-chromium-molybdenum steel dies can be machined at higher hardnesses than former die steels, they show more resistance to heat checking and give greater production. These dies range in size from 6-in. sections up to 20 × 45-in. sections and have weights ranging from a hundred to fourteen thousand pounds each. Great numbers of these dies are quenched and used at high hardnesses. It is essential that they be uniform in hardness from surface to center. This nickel-chromium-molybdenum steel will give all of these properties.

This type of steel is described in Finkl's patent, U. S. 1,464,174, Aug. 7, 1923.

A 6-in. square die block similar to the steel described above except in that it contains 0.75 per cent molybdenum is shown in Fig. 114. As may be observed from this figure, the Brinell hardness near the surface is 430 and at the center 402. Even though this higher molybdenum steel is more costly than the others, it is used extensively. It is used on special dies, hot-work tools, forging rolls, etc. It can be air- or oil-quenched to a hardness of 85 scleroscope or 652 Brinell. Air-hardened dies are exceptionally resistant to heat checking and will withstand the cooling action of water when they are in service.

Acid-resistant alloys containing molybdenum are discussed in the chapter on Miscellaneous Alloys Containing Molybdenum.

156. Cast Steels.—Shaw[(404)] claimed that the addition of molybdenum to cast nickel-chromium steel results in an alloy having all of the advantages of nickel-chromium steel, and which, in addition, hardens by quenching in air. Molybdenum also reduces distortion, internal strains, and fine cracks. Nickel-chromium-molybdenum steels are ideal for cast dies, and these dies are rapidly supplanting forged dies.

Anticipated properties of heat-treated cast nickel-chromium-molybdenum steels were given by Mitchell,[379] who maintained that such steels must be quenched and tempered to obtain the full benefit of the alloying elements.

FIG. 114.—Nickel-chromium-molybdenum die block, 6 in. square. Air-quenched and tempered at 540°C. (1000°F.). Split in half for Brinell hardness tests. (*A. Finkl and Sons Co.*)

The data given in Table 102 for the cast nickel-chromium-molybdenum steels were made available by the courtesy of K. H. Langguth of the Western Crucible Steel Casting Co. Blanks for the test bars were cast 1 in. wide, 3 in. deep, and 15 in. long with a header 3 × 3 × 15 in. Specimens were heat-treated when in the form of 1-in. squares and were then machined to the standard 0.505-in. tensile test pieces.

The use of the type of steels under discussion was recommended by Lorenz[371] for making intricate castings where high strength must be obtained without quenching in oil or water.

Some work was done at Battelle Memorial Institute on the properties of heat-treated cast steels containing molybdenum.

TABLE 102.—PROPERTIES OF CAST NICKEL-CHROMIUM-MOLYBDENUM STEELS*
(*Steel A:* 0.30 per cent carbon, 0.50 per cent manganese, 0.50 per cent nickel, 0.72 per cent chromium, and 0.30 per cent molybdenum. *Steel B:* 0.23 per cent carbon, 0.51 per cent manganese, 0.47 per cent nickel, 0.66 per cent chromium, and 0.22 per cent molybdenum.)

Steel cooled from 900°C. (1650°F.) in	Tempered		Tensile strength, lb./sq. in.	Yield strength,† lb./sq. in.	Elongation in 2 in., per cent	Reduction of area, per cent	Charpy impact, ft-lb.
	°C.	°F.					
A: Furnace	...	....	82,800	48,300	10.5	17.0	3.0
Furnace	...	....	82,100	45,500	18.0	24.1	6.0
Furnace	...	....	82,900	44,100	13.5	17.0	8.2
A: Air	675	1250	91,400	65,100	20.0	38.8	16.0
Air	675	1250	86,400	64,450	9.5	24.0	10.9
Air	675	1250	86,000	67,000	11.0	20.6	12.4
A: Oil	675	1250	102,500	83,550	7.5	18.8	13.9
Oil	675	1250	103,550	81,000	12.0	27.5	12.8
Oil	675	1250	105,750	83,900	15.5	27.5	21.0
A: Water	675	1250	108,200	85,000	8.5	22.3	9.0
Water	675	1250	111,300	90,350	12.0	27.5	12.8
Water	675	1250	113,800	93,300	13.0	30.8	10.0
A: Water	510	950	140,350	125,350	8.5	17.0	5.7
Water	510	950	134,200	119,900	4.5	14.2	6.0
B: Furnace	...	....	77,350	53,000	16.0	29.4	5.4
Furnace	...	....	74,600	41,900	20.5	34.1	5.4
Furnace	...	....	83,650	58,250	14.0	24.1	9.4
B: Air	705	1300	77,500	51,800	22.0	32.7	16.5
Air	705	1300	76,700	51,650	23.5	39.1	17.0
Air	705	1300	77,750	49,050	23.0	34.1	16.0
B: Oil	705	1300	86,900	63,650	20.5	37.3	14.0
Oil	705	1300	87,750	64,800	21.0	37.3	16.0
Oil	705	1300	87,500	63,750	18.0	34.1	16.0
B: Water	705	1300	87,600	62,500	19.5	37.3	13.0
Water	705	1300	93,550	72,150	16.5	27.5	13.0
Water	705	1300	90,950	69,350	17.5	34.1	14.0

* Western Crucible Steel Casting Co.
† Reported as yield point.

The work was done for the Ohio Steel Foundry Co., by whose courtesy it can be summarized here. The steels tested were cast into blocks 6 × 6 × 24 in. and had the following compositions:

Number	Composition, per cent						
	C	Mn	Si	Mo	Cr	Ni	V
*C*1	0.30	0.96	0.31	....	....	....	0.17
*C*2	0.35	1.19	0.36	0.23			
*C*3	0.24	0.46	0.37	0.35	0.84	2.76	
*C*4	0.33	1.08	0.40	....	....	1.18	
*C*5	0.26	1.28	0.37	0.26			
*C*6	0.23	0.64	0.32	....	....	1.98	

The Brinell hardness numbers of these steels as cast are shown in Figs. 115 and 116, where the variation in hardness values throughout one-fourth of the 6 × 6-in. cross-section is indicated. In Figs. 117 and 118 the Brinell hardness values of the steels quenched in water and tempered for 1 hr. at the indicated temperatures are shown. The Charpy impact values of the steels after various heat treatments are shown in Figs. 119 and 120 which indicate the treatments given.

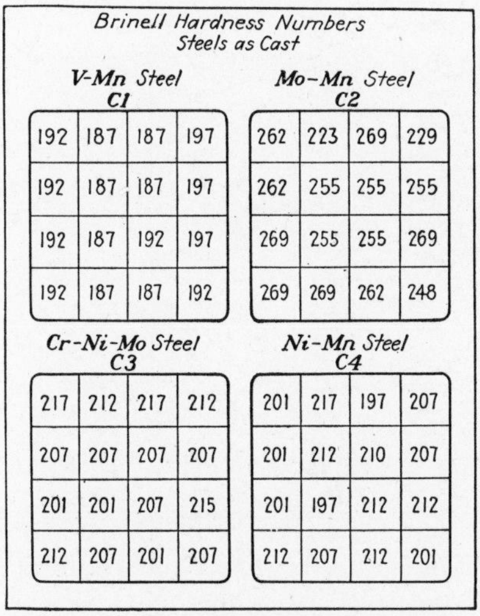

Brinell Hardness Numbers
Steels as Cast

V-Mn Steel C1

192	187	187	197
192	187	187	197
192	187	192	197
192	187	187	192

Mo-Mn Steel C2

262	223	269	229
262	255	255	255
269	255	255	269
269	269	262	248

Cr-Ni-Mo Steel C3

217	212	217	212
207	207	207	207
201	201	207	215
212	207	201	207

Ni-Mn Steel C4

201	217	197	207
201	212	210	207
201	197	212	212
212	207	212	201

Fig. 115.—Brinell hardness of cast alloy steels. (*Battelle Memorial Institute.*)

Brinell Hardness Numbers
Steels as Cast

Mo-Mn Steel C5

229	235	235	235
217	205	212	217
201	207	199	217
207	203	217	217

Ni Steel C6

179	179	179	164
159	156	159	187
174	170	156	179
163	170	170	179

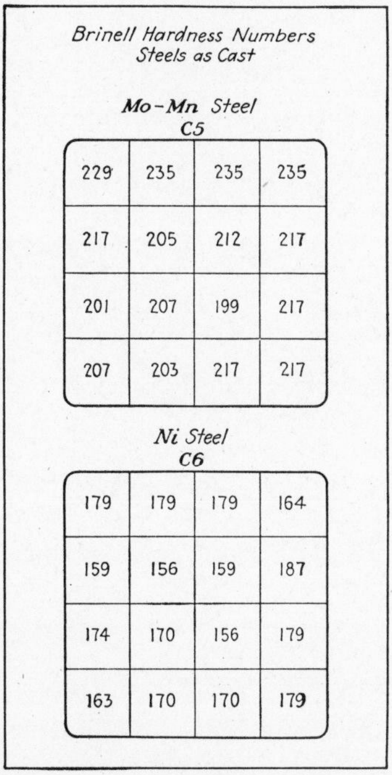

Fig. 116.—Brinell hardness of cast alloy steels. (*Battelle Memorial Institute.*)

The Charpy specimens were 0.39 × 0.39 × 2 in. and had a 45-deg. V-notch, 0.079 in. deep.

Figure 121, made available by courtesy of the Bonney-Floyd Company, gives properties of a heat-treated cast steel containing 0.25 to 0.35 per cent carbon, 1.75 to 2.25 per cent nickel, 0.65 to 0.90 per cent chromium, and 0.15 to 0.25 per cent molybdenum. The steel was cast into sections 1 in. square and heat-treated before machining the samples.

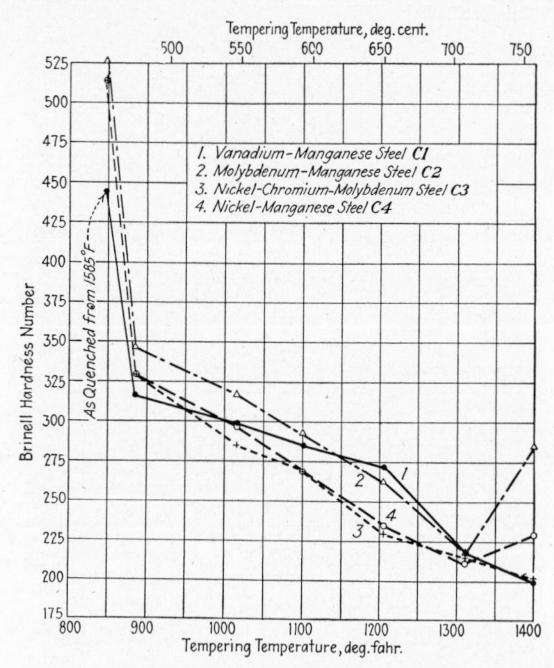

FIG. 117.—Brinell hardness of heat-treated alloy steels. (*Battelle Memorial Institute.*)

D. AUTHOR'S SUMMARY

1. The effects of molybdenum in low-alloy nickel or nickel-chromium steels are in general similar to its effects in chromium steels. These effects may be briefly summarized:

a. Molybdenum makes it possible to secure higher values of elongation, reduction of area, and impact resistance for a given tensile strength or Brinell hardness in heat-treated steels.

b. Molybdenum increases the ease of hardening. Molybdenum-bearing steels may therefore be hardened by a less drastic quench, and the hardening is less dependent on size of section quenched. More data on the mass effect in such steels containing molybdenum, however, would be welcome.

c. Molybdenum increases the strength at moderately high temperatures, *i.e.*, temperatures as high as 500°C. (930°F.).

2. Nickel-molybdenum steels have been found by actual use to be desirable carburizing steels. Their advantage lies in the good properties produced in the core by a single quench.

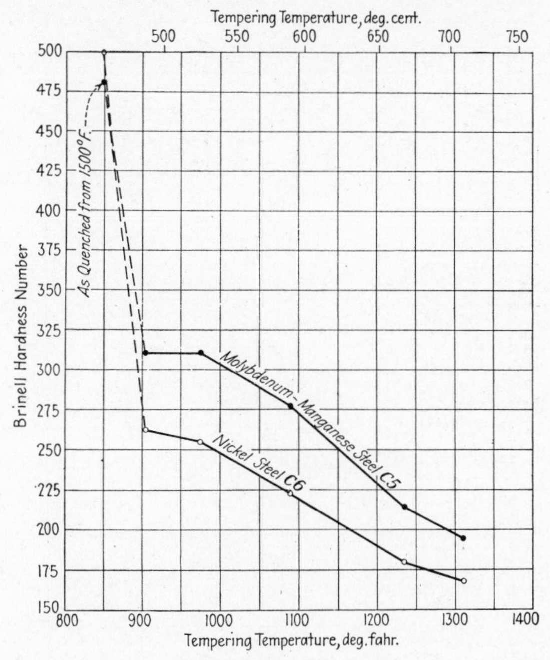

FIG. 118.—Brinell hardness of heat-treated cast alloy steels. (*Battelle Memorial Institute.*)

3. As Jones[176] pointed out, the mechanical properties of chromium, nickel, and nickel-chromium steels containing molybdenum are not dissimilar, but each type has its advantages and disadvantages. The chromium-molybdenum steels have a high impact resistance, but the yield strength is slightly lower than for nickel-chromium-molybdenum steels of the same hardness. Nickel-molybdenum steels, however, have a high ratio of yield strength to tensile strength, but their impact resistance is lower than that of nickel-chromium-molybdenum steels.

4. The use of nickel-chromium-molybdenum steels is to be recommended when one of the best steels of the structural type

is required, if by "best" is meant a material having the highest strength for a given ductility.

CHARPY IMPACT TESTS

Quenched and Tempered Normalized

V-Mn Steel

C1-2-2 C1-2-1

Quenched 1580°F (860°C) Tempered 1250°F (675°C)

34.9	27.2	25.1	35.4
24.0			31.5
29.7	48.5	58.4	28.0
31.7			37.8

21.0	21.7	21.9	24.4
24.6			26.2
24.5	21.2	24.5	25.3
25.4			28.6

1600°F (870°C)

Mo-Mn Steel

C2-2-2 C2-2-1

Quenched 1560°F (850°C) Tempered 1250°F (675°C)

49.8	55.0	53.8	52.9
52.2			54.8
51.6			59.5
50.6			52.5

4.2	3.8	4.6	3.7
4.2			4.0
4.4			4.2
4.1	8.4	11.0	4.1

1580°F (860°C)

Cr-Ni-Mo Steel

C3-2-2 C3-2-1

Quenched 1560°F (850°C) Tempered 1200°F (650°C)

23.7	22.5	24.9	23.4
25.3			21.5
25.0			23.0
23.8	27.8	27.5	23.5

22.3	22.2	21.1	21.9
19.4			15.2
20.3			16.6
20.8	25.7	23.2	16.5

1580°F (860°C)

Ni-Mn Steel

C4-2-2 C4-2-1

Quenched 1560°F (850°C) Tempered 1200°F (650°C)

36.3	35.5	47.5	46.1
38.7			46.8
36.5			43.2
40.7			30.2

25.8	24.3	18.0	18.7
24.9			16.2
22.5			16.5
17.0	24.5	22.6	16.0

1580°F (860°C)

FIG. 119.—Charpy impact values (foot-pounds) of heat-treated cast alloy steels. (*Battelle Memorial Institute.*)

Tempering temperatures for results given in cross-hatched areas.

	Quenched and tempered specimens	Normalized specimens
C1	1300°F. (705°C.)	1250°F. (675°C.)
C2	....	1250°F. (675°C.)
C3	1250°F. (675°C.)	1200°F. (650°C.)
C4	....	1200°F. (650°C.)

5. As was pointed out by Gillett and Mack,[151] the molybdenum-bearing steels, including nickel-molybdenum and nickel-

Mo–Mn Steel

C5-2

20.6	Oil Quenched 1525°F (830°C)		33.0
20.3	Tempered 1150°F (620°C)		28.5
19.3			27.0
24.8	23.5	25.8	29.1

46.2	59.6	64.5	57.7
49.3	Water Quenched 1525°F (830°C)		50.9
49.1	Tempered 1250°F (675°C)		58.0
50.6			48.1

15.8	10.5	13.3	9.0
19.2	Normalized 1550°F (845°C)		10.1
15.8			11.5
17.3			12.4

Ni Steel

C6-2

41.5	25.9	38.3	45.7
38.8	Water Quenched 1525°F (830°C)		43.5
40.6	Tempered 1150°F (620°C)		45.6
46.0			38.5

33.0	32.0	25.0	27.0
35.0	Normalized 1550°F (845°C)		28.4
29.8			23.4
29.2			24.5

FIG. 120.—Charpy impact values (foot-pounds) of heat-treated cast alloy steels. (*Battelle Memorial Institute.*)

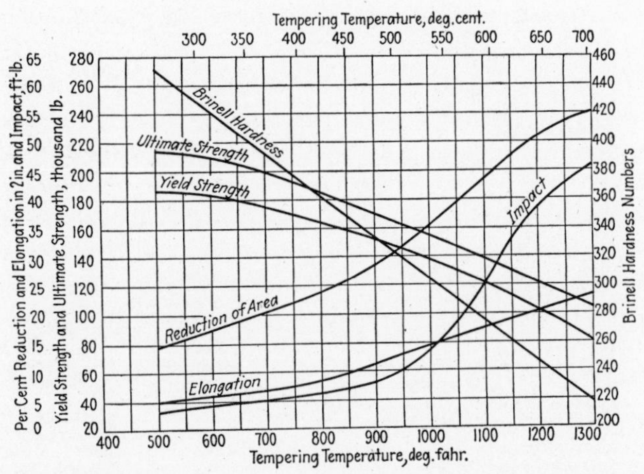

FIG. 121.—Properties of a cast nickel-chromium-molybdenum steel, quenched in water from 840°C. (1545°F.) and tempered at indicated temperatures. (*Bonney-Floyd Co.*)

chromium-molybdenum steels, can withstand a higher tempering temperature or a longer time at the tempering temperature than can comparable alloy steels. This permits of the relief of internal strains with an accompanying increase in ductility without a decrease in strength. Gillett and Mack showed that the endurance limit of nickel-chromium-molybdenum steels can be increased by increased soaking at the tempering temperature. In this instance not only the ratio of endurance limit to tensile strength but also the actual endurance limit increases.

6. Molybdenum, when present in amounts of 0.3 per cent, prevents temper-brittleness in nickel-chromium steels. Since this type of steel is otherwise prone to temper-brittleness, there is an increasing tendency to use molybdenum primarily for its specific effect as an antidote for temper-brittleness. Since the deep-hardening properties are also improved and very high strength can be obtained without too great a sacrifice in ductility, such complex steels, sometimes with the further addition of vanadium, are being used more and more in place of the older nickel-chromium steels. In general, when relatively high amounts of the three alloying elements are used, it is possible to obtain practically as high tensile-strength values after heat treatment with relatively low carbon contents as can be obtained in the nickel-chromium steels with higher carbon. By suitable lowering of the carbon content, the ductility can be kept relatively high.

7. It has been claimed that the nickel-chromium-molybdenum steels can be machined more easily than comparable steels of the same hardness, but, as indicated in the discussion on machinability in Chap. V, it is difficult to substantiate these claims.

8. Molybdenum in austenitic nickel-chromium steels increases the resistance to some types of corrosion and apparently stabilizes the austenite at elevated temperatures and decreases the scaling at such temperatures. More data on these effects, however, are decidedly needed.

CHAPTER IX

MOLYBDENUM IN HIGH-SPEED STEELS

Compositions of Molybdenum High-speed Steels—Mechanical Properties—Cutting Performance—Possible Limitations and Advantages in the Use of Molybdenum—Development Work at Watertown Arsenal—Author's Summary

Molybdenum as an alloying element in high-speed steels is used as an equivalent or as a partial replacing element for tungsten. In this rôle it exerts a proportionally greater effect than tungsten. Before reporting upon the investigations relating to molybdenum in molybdenum-bearing high-speed steels, it may be of interest to point out the relationship of molybdenum to other alloying elements with which it is frequently associated, namely, tungsten, chromium, vanadium, and cobalt. In considering the latter elements with respect to their effect on high-speed steels, Grossmann and Bain(450) group them, together with iron and carbon, as follows:

I. Tungsten, chromium, and vanadium.
II. Iron and cobalt.
III. Carbon.

In this scheme, chromium, vanadium, and molybdenum are regarded as increments of tungsten. Group I elements, including molybdenum, restrict the temperature range of the gamma phase and, when present in critical proportions and in the absence of carbon, eliminate the gamma form of iron completely. This is said to be due to the greater solubility of these body-centered cubic elements in alpha than in gamma iron. As a result of the observed relative effect in restricting the gamma region, Grossmann and Bain make the following assumption regarding the effectiveness of these elements as compared with tungsten:

Alloying Element	Equivalent to Percentage of Tungsten, Per Cent
Chromium	0.5
Vanadium	4.0
Molybdenum	1.3

A. COMPOSITIONS OF MOLYBDENUM HIGH-SPEED STEELS

Considering the quantitative effect of molybdenum as a tungsten-replacing element from other points of view, the figure varies from that given in the introductory paragraph, as will be evident from opinions of investigators quoted in the present chapter.

157. Molybdenum as a Partial Replacing Element for Tungsten.—That molybdenum can be considered a substitute for tungsten has been known for over thirty years. In a paper by Thallner,[17] in 1901, dealing with plant practice at the Bethlehem Steel Co., molybdenum was referred to as a substitute for tungsten in tool steel. This statement does not imply that this was the first recognition of molybdenum in this rôle. In 1904, Guillet[24] stated that only one-fourth the amount of molybdenum was required to replace a given amount of tungsten.

In a paper dealing with the development and use of high-speed steel, Gledhill[23] pointed out, in 1904, that less molybdenum than tungsten is required to produce an equivalent effect and also that a lower hardening temperature—under 1000°C. (1830°F.)—may be used to advantage. In a discussion of this paper, J. W. Richards said that molybdenum steels with carbon under 1 per cent possessed advantages equal to tungsten steels with higher carbon. Girod[45] stated that, when molybdenum is added to high-speed steels, the presence of carbon facilitates fusion of the alloy and its admixture with the steel.

Taylor,[35] in reviewing the patent of White and Taylor, stated that one part of molybdenum will produce approximately the same effect as two parts of tungsten. It was also stated in that paper that molybdenum renders chromium steel self-hardening. In 1903, a paper by Rossi[22] contained the statement that ferromolybdenum added to steel in such quantities as to incorporate 2 to 3 per cent of molybdenum in the resultant product imparts to it the property of "air-tempering" or "self-tempering." Smith[46] gave the ratio of 1 to 4 as the effective replacing value of molybdenum for tungsten. Along with several other writers of this period, he stated that its cost was prohibitive in replacing tungsten. Such does not appear to be the case at the present time, however. Giesen[39] gave the ratio as 1 to 2.225; Swinden[52] as 1 to 2 or 3; and Arnold and Ibbotson[76] as 1 to 2.3 In 1920, Arnold[87] stated that less than one-third the amount of molybdenum was required as compared with tungsten.

Hohage and Grützner[155] stated that a steel containing 14 to 16 per cent tungsten with 1.5 per cent molybdenum was equal to one containing 23 per cent tungsten and about 0.5 per cent vanadium. Molybdenum to the extent of 0.6 per cent was equivalent to 1 per cent of tungsten. Gill and Frost[171] believed that molybdenum can replace tungsten in high-speed steels in the ratio of 1 to 2.5.

Thus it will be seen that the effect of molybdenum on the properties of high-speed steel is more pronounced than that of tungsten, although the opinions of the various investigators differ as to the magnitude of the effect. This lack of agreement is evidently due to the fact that the methods of gaging the effect differed and, also, that in many cases the suggested replacing ratio was arrived at indirectly, *i.e.*, by comparison of steels not directly comparable in themselves with regard to the ultimate composition and other factors. In view of these considerations, the agreement of estimates by various investigators is to be considered good.

Concerning the underlying reasons for the greater effectiveness of molybdenum, Pokorny[205] called attention to the fact that the differences in atomic-weight percentages of molybdenum and tungsten must be taken into account. The atomic weights are: molybdenum 96, tungsten 184, thus a given atomic per cent of molybdenum in a high-speed steel can be obtained with a smaller weight per cent addition than with tungsten.

158. Compositions of High-speed Steels Containing Molybdenum.—The early molybdenum-bearing steels varied widely with respect to molybdenum content as well as to percentages of other alloying elements. Indeed, even at the present time it is difficult to give a classification on the basis of molybdenum content. However, certain limitations in the use of molybdenum have been recognized, and the molybdenum content is held within somewhat narrower limits. Tabulation of the published compositions of some molybdenum-bearing steels will bring out this point.

In Table 103 due to Gillett and Mack[151] in 1925, some typical high-speed steels containing molybdenum are listed. The compositions agree with those used in the first quarter of the twentieth century.

It will be noted that molybdenum was used in quantities ranging from 0.25 to 1.00 per cent to 10.00 per cent depending upon the type of steel in which it was employed. The steels might for convenience be classified as either tungsten or non-tungsten steels, containing chromium, vanadium, or cobalt usually to a lesser degree. In the non-tungsten steels molybdenum may be considered to have been substituted *in toto* for tungsten, but a smaller percentage of molybdenum than tungsten was, of course, required. In the high-tungsten steels molybdenum was present in smaller percentages, from 0.25 to 1.56 per cent.

TABLE 103.—COMPOSITIONS OF TYPICAL HIGH-SPEED STEELS*

Composition, per cent					
C	Mo	Cr	V	Co	W
0.50 to 1.00	6.00 to 10.00	1.00 to 7.00	0.10 to 1.00		
0.70	0.75	5.00	1.00	4.00	18.00
0.50	1.56	5.04	0.82	....	18.54
0.65	8.00	4.00	1.50	5.00	
0.65	7.50	3.25	1.25		
1.50	8.50	21.00	0.50	....	8.50
Up to 1.85	4.00 to 6.00	1.00 to 2.00			
0.20 to 0.75	0.25 to 1.00	3.00 to 5.00	1.10 to 1.50	....	12.00 to 18.00

* Gillett and Mack.[151]

In surveying the journal literature, an even greater variety of compositions was encountered. Some of these are listed in Table 104. The molybdenum contents ranged from 0.074 to 15.0 per cent, though admittedly some of these compositions were experimental. The steels listed include those containing tungsten up to approximately 25 per cent, chromium up to 14 per cent, vanadium up to 2.5 per cent, manganese up to 3.75 per cent, cobalt up to 18 per cent; carbon was usually under 1 per cent (in the neighborhood of 0.75 per cent), but it sometimes exceeded this amount. A few of the steels contained nickel, usually in smaller percentages. In the non-tungsten steels molybdenum was carried higher than in the tungsten steels, which is quite as would be expected. One steel in which tungsten was wholly replaced by molybdenum contained about 7 per cent molybdenum, and one in which tungsten was partially replaced con-

TABLE 104.—COMPOSITION OF VARIOUS MOLYBDENUM-BEARING TOOL STEELS

Composition, per cent												Type of steel	Date mentioned	Mentioned by*	Reference
Ni	V	W	Cr	Co	Mo	C	Mn	Si	P	S	Cu				
......	....	2.0	....	......	0.50	0.90	0.20	0.18	.....	0.03	....	Self-hardening crucible	1902	Kern	18
					9.65	0.66	....	0.046	0.016	....	....	High-speed tool	1904	Metcalf	26
......	....	......	2.99	......	4.29	0.47	....	0.15	....	....	....	High-speed tool	1906	Carpenter	31
					0.56	1.05	0.20	0.12	....	....	....	Tool	1907	Taylor	35
......	....	......	3.75	......	4.60	1.84	1.79	0.156	....	....	....	Tool	1907	Taylor	35
......	0.67	16.00	3.55	4.25	0.80	0.60	....	....	....	....	....	"Iridium"	1913	Hess	56
......	1.5	8 to 18	2.5 to 6.5	5	2	0.45 to 0.85	0.1 to 0.5	0.2	....	....	....	High-speed	1914–1915	Lantsberry	63
......	1.04	14.62	3.58	......	0.54	0.60	0.04	0.30	....	....	....	"Ultra" steels	1914–1915	Lantsberry	63
......	....	1.0	14.76	4.27	1.22	0.63	....	....	....	....	....	"Ultra" steels	1914–1915	Lantsberry	63
......	0.80	16.05	4.46	4.72	0.72	0.55	Trace	0.23	0.04	0.02	....	High-speed tool	1915	Hibbard	70
0.18	0.88	15.50	4.25	4.72	0.67	0.70	Trace	0.18	0.02	0.01	....	High-speed tool	1915	Hibbard	70
......	....	......	1 to 2	......	4 to 6	1.85	....	....	....	....	....	High-speed tool	1916	Horton	71
......	....	16 to 18	4 to 4.5	......	1.5 to 2	0.6	....	....	....	....	....	High-speed tool	1916	Horton	71
......	....	16 to 18	....	4 to 5.5	0.25 to 1.5	....	....	....	....	....	....	High-speed tool	1916	Horton	71
......	0.67	16	3.55	4.25	0.80	0.60	Low	Low	Low	Low	....	High-speed tool	1916	Horton	71
......	1.29	0	2.79	......	5.79	0.75	0.18	0.47	0.016	0.061	....	High-speed	1919	Arnold and Ibbotson	76
......	0	0	2.79	......	5.72	0.72	0.18	0.41	0.015	0.061	....	High-speed	1919	Arnold and Ibbotson	76
......	1.28	12.12	2.82	......	2.06	0.76	0.19	0.60	0.015	0.059	....	High-speed	1919	Arnold and Ibbotson	76
......	0	12.00	2.79	......	2.06	0.62	0.20	0.43	0.016	0.060	....	High-speed	1919	Arnold and Ibbotson	76
......	1.16	15.93	2.62	......	0	0.55	0.20	0.34	0.017	0.058	....	High-speed	1919	Arnold and Ibbotson	76
......	0	15.54	2.78	......	0	0.60	0.21	0.44	0.016	0.058	....	High-speed	1919	Arnold and Ibbotson	76
......	....	......	13.57	3.66	0.84	1.48	0.19	0.80	....	....	....	Cobalteron (similar to high-speed)	1919	Mathews	82
Trace	....	18.18	4.99	......	1.15	0.51	Trace	0.08	0.030	0.004	....	High-speed	1919	Poliakoff	83
......	0.82	18.54	5.04	......	1.56	0.50	Trace	0.10	0.020	0.003	....	High-speed	1919	Poliakoff	83
......	1	......	....	......	6	....	....	....	....	....	....	High-speed	1920	Arnold	87
			4.43	5.25	4.90	0.70	0.18	0.41	0.026	0.024	....	High-speed	1921	d'Arcambal	96
......	1.97	12.88	3.52	......	0.71	0.69	....	....	....	....	....	High-speed	1922	French and Strauss	108
......	1.10	16.65	3.58	......	0.71	0.64	....	....	....	....	....	High-speed	1922	French and Strauss	108
......	1.20	15.50	4.00	......	0.50	0.60	....	....	....	....	....	High-speed	1922	French and Strauss	108
......	1.00	17.70	4.25	4.88	1.07	0.65	....	....	....	....	....	High-speed	1922	French and Strauss	108
					Trace to 3.50	....	....	....	....	....	....	High-speed crucible	1922	Nelson	113
					6.00	....	....	....	....	....	....	High-speed crucible	1922	Nelson	113

TABLE 104.—(*Continued*)

Composition, per cent												Type of steel	Date mentioned	Mentioned by*	Reference
Ni	V	W	Cr	Co	Mo	C	Mn	Si	P	S	Cu				
......	....	....	3.75 to 4.25	.....	3.75 to 4.25	1.75 to 2.0	....	....	....	....	...	Mushet steel	1921	Mathews, quoted by Oertel	114
......	....	....	....	.....	9 to 15	....	....	....	....	....	...	Molybdenum	1921	Oertel	114
......	....	....	....	.....	6	....	....	....	....	....	...	Mathews high-speed (1905)	1922	Oertel	114
......	....	....	....	.....	7 to 8	....	....	....	....	....	...	"Blitz"	1922	Oertel	114
......	....	12	3	.....	2 to 6	0.6 to 0.7	....	....	....	....	...	Arnold's	1922	Oertel	114
......	0.75 to 0.85	17 to 18	4	.....	0.50	0.60	....	....	....	....	...	High-speed	1923–1924	Woodward	129
0.50	....	....	12 to 14	1 to 3	0.60	1.50	....	....	....	....	...	Special	1923–1924	Woodward	129
1.0	1.0	....	4.5	5.0	6.10	0.65	....	0.50	....	....	...	Special	1923–1924	Woodward	129
......	1.40	20.3	4.5	.....	0.5	0.70	0.30	0.25	....	....	...	High-speed	1924	Oertel and Pölzguter	140
			5.06	.....	6.37	0.80	0.32	0.32	....	....	...	High-speed	1924	Oertel and Pölzguter	140
......	1.37	....	4.70	6.76	7.27	1.06	0.40	0.36	....	....	...	High-speed	1924	Oertel and Pölzguter	140
......	0.40	18.76	4.76	.....	....	0.81	0.32	0.31	....	....	...	High-speed	1924	Oertel and Pölzguter	140
......	0.44	13.13	4.47	.....	....	0.83	0.36	0.27	....	....	...	High-speed	1924	Oertel and Pölzguter	140
......	0.54	....	4.74	.....	7.07	0.71	0.33	0.48	0.013	0.019	...	High-speed (W wholly replaced)	1925	French and Digges	149
......	1.04	11.95	3.40	.....	3.41	0.53	0.31	0.27	0.017	0.023	...	High-speed (W partially replaced)	1925	French and Digges	149
......	1.27	18.11	4.72	5.01	0.75	0.68	....	....	....	....	...	High-speed tool	1925	Guillet	154
......	1.28	18.08	5.32	4.90	0.89	0.78	0.11	0.35	Trace	Trace	...	High-speed tool	1925	Guillet	154
......	0.52	12.40	3.18	.....	3.98	0.79	....	....	....	....	...	High-speed	1925	Hohage and Grützner	155
......	0.49	18.70	3.14	.....	....	0.63	....	....	....	....	...	High-speed	1925	Hohage and Grützner	155
......	0.80	14.10	3.03	.....	4.60	0.67	....	....	....	....	...	High-speed	1925	Hohage and Grützner	155
......	1.60	13.80	4.00	.....	4.00	0.65	....	....	....	....	...	High-speed	1925	Hohage and Grützner	155
......	0.69	23.90	4.27	.....	....	0.79	....	....	....	....	...	High-speed	1925	Hohage and Grützner	155
					4.25	0.74	....	....	....	....	...	High-speed	1925	Maurer and Schilling	158
					7.50	0.66	....	....	....	....	...	High-speed	1925	Maurer and Schilling	158
......	1.0	10.0	5.0	5.0	0.8	0.58	0.10	0.20	....	....	...	High-speed	1925	Sasagawa	162
......	0.15	18.0	5.0	.....	1.6	0.5	....	....	....	....	...	High-speed	1927	Lantsberry	200
......	1.2	18.0	5.1	.....	0.6	0.90	....	....	....	....	...	High-speed	1927	Lantsberry	200
......	0.5	14.3	5.0	.....	....	0.7	....	....	....	....	...	High-speed	1927	Lantsberry	200
......	1.12	16.0	4.3	5.19	0.70	0.64	....	....	....	....	...	High-speed	1927	Lantsberry	200
......	0.6	19.0	3.8	5.43	0.75	0.8	....	....	....	....	...	High-speed	1927	Lantsberry	200

TABLE 104.—(*Continued*)

Composition, per cent												Type of steel	Date mentioned	Mentioned by*	Reference
Ni	V	W	Cr	Co	Mo	C	Mn	Si	P	S	Cu				
......	1.3	16.2	4.0	....	1.1	0.68	....	....	....	....	....	High-speed	1927	Lantsberry	200
0.11	1.10	18.0	3.07	....	0.91	0.57	0.15	0.26	....	....	0.01	High-speed	1927	Okochi and Okoshi	203
......	1.5	18	4.5	....	0.5	0.8	....	....	....	....	....	High-speed	1928	Hohage and Rollett	222
......	1.4	18	4	....	0.75	0.70	....	....	....	....	....	High-speed	1928	Niederhoff	285
......	1.6	19	....	3.5	0.75	0.70	....	....	....	....	....	High-speed	1928	Niederhoff	285
......	1.6	19	4.5	10	0.75	0.85	....	....	....	....	....	High-speed	1928	Niederhoff	285
......	1.0	24.72	5.20	2.29	1.97	0.65	....	....	....	....	....	High-speed	1928	Rapatz	237
......	2.2	19.53	4.31	....	2.37	0.62	....	....	....	....	....	High-speed	1928	Rapatz	237
......	0.83	19.85	4.74	....	1.38	0.61	....	....	....	....	....	High-speed	1928	Rapatz	237
		16 to 18	....	4 to 5.5	0.25 to 1.5	....	....	....	....	....	....	High-speed	1929	Cazaud	252
......	0.5 to 2	....	2.75 to 3.75	....	5 to 10	0.5 to 0.8	0.1 to 0.3	....	....	....	....	High-speed	1929	Cazaud	252
......	1.12	18.25	3.90	....	0.08	0.66	0.26	0.09	0.027	0.012	....	High-speed	1929	French and Digges	260
......	1.53	18.32	4.23	7.8	0.96	0.69	0.017?	0.34	....	....	....	High-speed	1929	French and Digges	260
......	1.47	21.5	4.57	11.7	0.61	0.79	0.42	0.15	0.030	0.005	....	High-speed	1929	French and Digges	260
......	0.81	15.44	3.34	....	0.74	0.61	0.18	0.04	0.027	0.009	....	High-speed	1929	French and Digges	260
......	1.06	17.56	3.66	....	0.85	0.67	0.23	0.06	0.021	0.010	....	High-speed	1929	French and Digges	260
......	1.04	11.95	3.40	....	3.41	0.53	0.31	0.27	0.017	0.023	....	High-speed	1929	French and Digges	260
......	0.54	....	4.74	....	7.07	0.71	0.33	0.44	0.013	0.019	....	High-speed	1929	French and Digges	260
......	0.3	16 to 18	App. 0.5	....	0.5	0.65 to 0.80	....	....	....	....	....	High-speed	1929	Goerens	447
......	1.0	18 to 20	App. 0.5	....	0.5	0.65 to 0.80	....	....	....	....	....	High-speed	1929	Goerens	447
......	2.0	13 to 15	App. 0.5	....	App. 1.0	0.80	....	....	....	....	....	High-speed	1929	Goerens	447
......	1 to 2	20 to 28	App. 0.5	....	1 to 2	0.70 to 0.85	....	....	....	....	....	High-speed	1929	Goerens	447
......	0.75 to 2	17 to 22	4 to 5.50	....	....	0.65 to 0.80	0.25	0.20	....	....	....	Modern high-speed	1931	Parmiter	486
......	1 to 2.50	17 to 22	4.5 to 6.0	8 to 15	0.75 to 1.50	0.75 to 0.90	0.25	0.20	....	....	....	Super high-speed	1931	Parmiter	486

* This does not necessarily signify that the steel was used or invented by the author noted.

tained 3.5 per cent molybdenum. In many partial replacements of tungsten the molybdenum was in the neighborhood of 1 per cent or under. Thus it is evident that it is difficult to classify molybdenum-bearing high-speed steels according to their molybdenum content.

Certain manufacturers may have their own classifications but it is doubtful whether these would hold for steels of different manufacture. In general, it may be said that molybdenum is used in relatively smaller percentages than other alloying elements and is usually met with in percentages even below 2 per cent.

TABLE 105.—MOLYBDENUM SUBSTITUTED FOR TUNGSTEN*

Composition, per cent						Medium steel forging, standard speed†		Remarks
Mo	W	Cr	C	Mn	Si	Old style not treated T–W process	Treated T–W process	
0.56	....	....	1.05	0.20	0.120	16 ft. 10 in.		
0.84	....	2.01	1.02	0.53	.....	27 ft.	35 ft.	
0.94	....	....	1.07	0.20	0.15	21 ft. 10 in.		
1.77	....	1.64	0.89	0.50	.....	45 ft.‡	58 ft.	
2.03	4.53	2.03	2.02	1.69	0.282	31 ft. 36 ft.	58 ft. 4 in. 58 ft. 4 in.	Tendency to fire-crack
2.25	4.74	2.80	2.07	1.66	0.120	36 ft.	58 ft. 4 in.	Tendency to fire-crack
2.45	....	3.19	1.22	0.66	0.240	30 ft.	50 ft.	
3.67	....	3.86	1.84	0.30	0.230	27 ft. 6 in.	60 ft.	Irregular
4.20	....	3.95	1.18	0.08	.....	....	60 ft.	Irregular
4.58	....	3.43	1.61	1.65	0.285	....	59 ft.	Brittle in body; fire-cracks easily
4.59	....	3.46	1.51	1.62	0.245	45 ft. 3 in.	....	Brittle in body; fire-cracks easily
4.60	....	3.75	1.84	1.79	0.156	45 ft.	....	Brittle in body; fire-cracks easily

* Taylor.(35)

† Cutting speed (feet per minute) to ruin tool in 20 min.

‡ Run on another forging or casting, and cutting speeds given judged by qualities of two forgings or castings and speeds of other tools run at same time.

Another table (Table 105), though published in 1907, is of interest in throwing some light on the question of the useful percentages of molybdenum in tool steels. This is taken from the classical paper of Taylor,(35) On the Art of Cutting Metals, which appeared in the *Transactions* of the American Society of Mechanical Engineers. Here the molybdenum contents range from 0.56 to 4.60 per cent.

Also of interest are Taylor's statements concerning these steels:

> Molybdenum tools having high cutting speeds were experimented with during the development of the Taylor-White process, and from 4 per cent to 4½ per cent of molybdenum appeared to be a sufficient quantity to make a high-speed tool; whereas about 8 per cent of tungsten was required for this purpose. However, by noting our remarks made after most of these tools, it will be seen that they were brittle, had a tendency to fire-crack, were weak in the body of the tool, or else they were irregular in their cutting speeds.

Taylor's suggested explanation for the observed irregularity in cutting performance, which foreshadows the later more scientific one, was that the tools deteriorate. We now attribute such variations to loss in molybdenum as molybdic oxide or to surface decarburization in various stages of the manufacturing process involving the use of heat. The same thing could occur in hardening the tools made from this type of steel if no precautions were taken to guard against it. It should be borne in mind, however, that Taylor's steels covered but a limited portion of the alloy field. It is noteworthy, notwithstanding, that an increase in molybdenum content beyond a certain range was deleterious. With up to 2 per cent no difficulty was encountered. With 2 to 2.5 per cent the tendency to "fire-crack" was noted. With 2.5 to 4 per cent the tools were found to be "irregular" in their cutting ability. Above this they were brittle in body and subject to fire-cracking.

Two tables from a paper by Mathews[82] may be of interest in considering the composition of molybdenum tool steels. They were given to illustrate the transition from the use of self-hardening steels to high-speed steels in the years 1901–1902. This change followed the announcement of the Taylor-White process. Chemically it consisted of a radical lowering of the carbon and a great increase in the tungsten or molybdenum content. The increase in molybdenum will be noted from the tables; the 1901 analyses are more nearly comparable with Taylor's analyses in this regard. The tables in question are 106 and 107.

Chromium in the new steels was not materially altered as compared with self-hardening steels. Manganese, originally high in the Mushet steel, is not now important in high-speed steel; chromium takes its place.

TABLE 106.—TYPICAL ANALYSES OF SELF-HARDENING STEELS (1901)*

Number	Composition, per cent				
	C	Mn	Cr	W	Mo
1	2.19	1.32	0.50	5.63	
2	1.69	0.45	3.73	7.63	
3	1.14	0.33	2.09	7.98	
4	1.79	0.50	3.96	....	4.54
5	1.55	0.24	3.22	7.80	
6	1.55	0.21	3.67	9.42	1.10
7	1.78	1.18	....	7.22	
8	1.40	1.65	3.69	....	4.59
9	1.75	3.92	....	6.61	

* Mathews.[82]

TABLE 107.—TYPICAL ANALYSES OF HIGH-SPEED STEELS (1902)*

Number	Composition, per cent				
	C	Mn	Cr	W	Mo
21	0.63	....	4.00	.....	6.00
22	0.42	....	4.95	10.75	
23	0.57	0.43	3.30	11.58	
24	0.75	....	....	19.50	
25	0.37	....	5.10	13.83	
26	0.62	....	6.50	21.06	
27	0.84	0.07	2.76	11.25	
28	0.56	....	2.95	9.74	
29	0.60	0.30	....	.....	9.25

* Mathews.[82]

In their recent book, Oertel and Grützner[485] stated that, owing to the shortage of tungsten, a high-speed steel of the following analysis was developed in Germany in 1916: 0.5 to 0.8 per cent carbon, 6.0 to 10.0 per cent molybdenum, 3.0 to 6.0 per cent chromium, 0.75 to 2.0 per cent vanadium, and 1.5 to 3.5 per cent cobalt. The cutting life of this type of steel was, however, not so long as that of the best tungsten high-speed steel, and its use has now been discontinued. Furthermore, difficulties in the production of this type of steel resulted from the formation of molybdic oxide (MoO_3) during hot working and from the ease with which the steel could be overheated. Molybdenum additions of 1 or 2 per cent are now made to the tungsten high-speed steels. Such additions result in an increased cutting life and hardness and promote the solubility of the carbides.

159. Critical Ranges.—The first important published work on the critical ranges of molybdenum-bearing high-speed steels was that of Carpenter.[29] The steels included in his series which bear on the present discussion were chromium-molybdenum steels. Their compositions are given in Table 108, arranged according to molybdenum content. These were studied in conjunction with tungsten and chromium-tungsten steels.

TABLE 108.—COMPOSITION OF CHROMIUM-MOLYBDENUM HIGH-SPEED TOOL STEELS*

Composition, per cent			
C	Si	Cr	Mo
0.28	Low	Absent	0.95
1.31	0.64	3.40	3.90
0.47	0.15	2.99	4.29
1.00	0.06	3.00	6.00
0.57	Low	Absent	9.25
0.63	0.47	1.80	10.87

* Carpenter.[29]

Carpenter pointed out that the rationale of the presence of tungsten and molybdenum in high-speed steels is fairly evident from results of his experiments. The action of either of these elements consists in hindering, under certain conditions, and in altogether preventing, under suitably chosen ones, changes in iron-carbon alloys which would soften the material. These elements also impart to the alloys a high resistance to tempering. The author's heating curves showed no evidence of tempering below 500°C. (930°F.) or 600°C. (1110°F.).

Each of the steels examined, provided it was not heated above 850°C. (1560°F.) or 900°C. (1650°F.), underwent on air cooling a critical change in the neighborhood of 700°C. (1290°F.) as a result of which the steel was softened. The only exception to this was the 6Mo–3Cr–1C alloy, but when cooled from 900°C. (1650°F.) the alloy was quite soft.

With slow cooling, as the initial temperature was raised, the softening still took place on cooling but not within such a narrow range of temperature. The transformation was usually split into two or more parts or spread over a wide range of temperature, namely, from about 700°C. (1290°F.) to 300°C. (570°F.) or 400°C. (750°F.), and even as low as 100°C. (210°F.) in the case of the 6Mo–3Cr–1C alloy previously mentioned. Depending upon the composition of the alloy, this split occurred when the initial temperature was anything between 900°C. (1650°F.) and 1200°C. (2190°F.). Molybdenum was more active than tungsten in promoting this split.

In the case of the 3.40Cr–3.90Mo–1.31C alloy, cooled in the furnace from 1200°C. (2190°F.), a martensitic structure was obtained. The 2.99Cr–4.29Mo–0.47C alloy showed an austenitic structure under the same conditions.

With reference to a suitable heat treatment for tool steels, Carpenter stated that to produce an austenitic structure, which will render the alloy both hard and tough, all that it is necessary to do is to cool the nose of the tool in air. Judged from this point of view the 10.87Mo–1.80Cr–0.63C was the best. No advantage would appear to be gained by treating tools above 1000°C. (1830°F.), for no further lowering or suppression of the change is brought about under ordinary cooling conditions by taking them to a higher temperature. Each steel, it was pointed out, however, has to be judged from at least two points of view: ease of hardening, and ease of tempering.

Briefly, the hardening of high-speed tool steels appeared to Carpenter to involve two factors:

1. The widening, splitting, or lowering of the critical ranges by the special alloying element.
2. The complete, or practically complete, suppression of the widened, split, or lowered range by a mild quenching such as an air blast.

Maurer and Schilling[158] investigated the properties and reaction to heat treatment of high-speed steels by microscopic examination, hardness determinations, magnetic and electric measurements, thermal analysis, and thermal expansion. The two molybdenum steels investigated were of the following composition:

Designation	Composition, per cent	
	C	Mo
No. 5	0.74	4.25
No. 8	0.66	7.50

The steels showed secondary hardness after quenching from 1100°C. (2010°F.) or 1280°C. (2335°F.) when tempered at 600°C. (1110°F.).

The magnetic and electric properties, when plotted against the tempering temperature, indicated changes at about 300°C. (570°F.) and 600°C. (1110°F.), being intermediate between carbon and ordinary high-speed steels. The former show changes at 200 to 300°C. (390 to 570°F.) and the latter at 500 to 600°C. (930 to 1110°F.). Electric-resistance measurements indicated that little of the molybdenum was retained in solution.

Differential heating curves on the quenched samples indicated points at 350°C. (660°F.) and 650°C. (1200°F.) for both steels. Secondary breaks in the curves in the neighborhood of 150°C. (300°F.) for the steel of lower molybdenum content were noted.

B. MECHANICAL PROPERTIES

The mechanical properties of high-speed steels at room temperature are of considerably less interest than those at elevated temperatures, since it is the properties of the tool at a dull-red heat which are of primary importance. Even here, as will be seen from the following discussion, a correlation between the ordinary mechanical properties and cutting performance is difficult to obtain.

160. Mechanical Properties at Normal Temperatures.—Giesen[39] stated, in 1909, that molybdenum steels with 0 to 4 per cent molybdenum and 0.3 per cent carbon, or 0 to 2 per cent molybdenum and 0.95 per cent carbon, gave results approximating those furnished by tungsten steel for tensile strength, yield strength, elongation, hardness, and brittleness, when the ratio of added molybdenum to tungsten was 1 to 2.225. It will be necessary, then, to refer to his statements regarding tungsten steels of that period:

In the case of tungsten steels of pearlitic structure, and containing 0 to 15 per cent of tungsten and 0.3 per cent carbon, or 0 to 8 per cent of tungsten and 0.95 per cent carbon, the tensile strength, yield strength, and breaking load increase with the percentage of tungsten, whereas the ductility diminishes. The hardness is generally a little greater than that of ordinary carbon steels with a corresponding carbon content. The brittleness remains entirely unchanged, even when the percentage of tungsten exceeds 15 and 18 per cent in presence of 0.3 and 0.95 per cent of carbon respectively. With this high proportion of tungsten the only properties that vary are the yield strength, ductility, and breaking load, the two first named increasing very slightly, whilst the breaking load rises with the content of carbon and tungsten. Tungsten steels of pearlitic structure, and containing 0.25 per cent carbon and over 9 per cent tungsten, or 0.85 per cent carbon and over 4 per cent tungsten, increase in hardness as the tungsten content rises. Tungsten steels with double carbide attain sufficient hardness only when the carbon content is high, though their high fragility remains the same.

In 1921, d'Arcambal[96] reported the results of some hardness tests on typical high-speed steels, among which was a cobalt-chromium steel containing molybdenum. The composition of the steel was as follows:

Composition, per cent							
C	Mn	P	S	Si	Cr	Co	Mo
0.70	0.18	0.026	0.024	0.41	4.43	5.25	4.90

The Brinell hardness of this steel was 255 as compared with 217 to 286 for tungsten-chromium-vanadium steels in the annealed condition.

From his data on hardness, microstructure, cutting tests, and physical-property determinations, d'Arcambal drew some general conclusions of which the following are of interest in the present case.

[1] The greatest degrees of secondary hardness and the highest actual red-hardness are obtained in specimens given the highest quenching temperature, 1260°C. (2300°F.). The micrographs of the quenched samples show that partial austenization has taken place in the steel

given this high quenching temperature, with almost complete solution of the carbides and tungstides not in massive or envelope formation . . .

[2] High-speed steel, quenched from a high temperature, 1260°C. (2300°F.), and drawn to 595 to 620°C. (1100 to 1150°F.), shows as great scleroscope hardness as in the undrawn condition, sometimes greater. Micrographs show that the small amount of austenite present in the undrawn material has changed to martensite.

Toughness and cutting efficiency were increased from 100 to 200 per cent by the 595°C. (1100°F.) tempering. Cutters quenched from a high temperature, and tempered at 425°C. (800°F.) failed more quickly when tempered at 230°C. (445°F.).

[3.] High-speed steel quenched into a bath whose temperature is about 595°C. (1100°F.), then cooled from that temperature to room temperature and not drawn, does not possess the same good properties as when drawn back to 595°C. (1100°F.) after quenching. In other words, high-speed steel cannot be quenched and drawn in one operation. Taylor, in his experiments conducted twenty years ago at the Bethlehem Steel Co., found that it was necessary to draw his tools to 595° to 620°C. (1100 to 1150°F.) after they had been quenched in a bath at about the same temperature.

D'Arcambal also found that high-speed steel, in the larger-size rounds, as received from the manufacturer is seldom free from segregations of massive carbide. These masses will not go into solution upon hardening but require forging. Tools made of material of this nature are of inferior quality due to brittleness and deficient red hardness caused by the large amount of undissolved carbides.

The scleroscope, Brinell, and file hardness of a high-speed steel tool give no indication of its cutting qualities. The cobalt-molybdenum steels show considerably lower hardness at 315 to 480°C. (600 to 895°F.) than the tungsten steels.

In two recent papers, Emmons[(439A, 509A)] presented results of torsional tests on hardened tool steels. By means of this test, he was able to determine both the strength and plasticity of hardened tool steel and to investigate the effects of heat treatment on these properties. In the more recent paper, Emmons[(509A)] described the effect of various heat treatments on the properties of a high-speed steel containing 18 per cent tungsten, 4 per cent chromium, and 1 per cent vanadium (the standard 18–4–1 steel). He found that there was apparently no direct relationship between Rockwell hardness and torsional strength, and that the plasticity varied between wide limits with variation in hardening and tempering temperatures.

Emmons has also determined the torsional properties of some molybdenum high-speed steels and expects to present his findings before the 1932 fall meeting of the American Society for Steel Treating. Through the courtesy of Mr. Emmons and officers of the Cleveland Twist Drill Co., however, some of these data on molybdenum high-speed steels can be included here.

The analyses of some molybdenum high-speed steels tested in torsion are listed in Table 109. Figure 122 shows the properties

TABLE 109.—CHEMICAL COMPOSITION OF SOME MOLYBDENUM HIGH-SPEED STEELS*

Number	Composition, per cent							
	C	Mn	Si	Cr	W	Mo	V	Co
1	0.57	....	....	3.48	.....	7.39	0.87	Trace
2	0.66	0.24	0.28	4.26	0.10	10.19	1.14	
3	0.67	0.05	0.24	4.32	0.04	10.29	1.19	9.11
4	0.73	0.10	0.30	3.73	13.87	4.18	1.68	

* Emmons.

of these steels after having been tempered at various temperatures, and Fig. 123 shows the properties of these steels quenched from various temperatures and tempered at 560°C. (1040°F.). The specimens on which the torsional tests were made had a reduced cylindrical section with a diameter of 3⁄16 in. and a length of 3 in. The torque in the figures is given in inch-pounds, and the plastic deformation in degrees. The latter value was obtained from the stress-strain curve.

The Rockwell hardness of the molybdenum steels after quenching and tempering was not essentially different from that observed for 18–4–1 steel. The torsional strength was definitely lower except in the case of steel 3, containing high cobalt. The plasticity was also lower except in the case of steel 1, which had a carbon content of 0.57 per cent. Drilling tests proved that steels 1, 2, and 3 were decidedly inferior to 18–4–1 steel, but that steel 4 was as efficient as the standard high-speed steels. These drilling tests will be discussed in a later section. A difference noted in the microstructure was that for similar carbon contents, the quenched and tempered molybdenum high-speed steels showed fewer carbides present than 18–4–1 steels. The high-cobalt steel 3 was an exception, showing a normal quantity of carbides.

The properties of a steel containing 0.69 per cent carbon, 3.66 per cent chromium, 14.46 per cent molybdenum, and 1.01

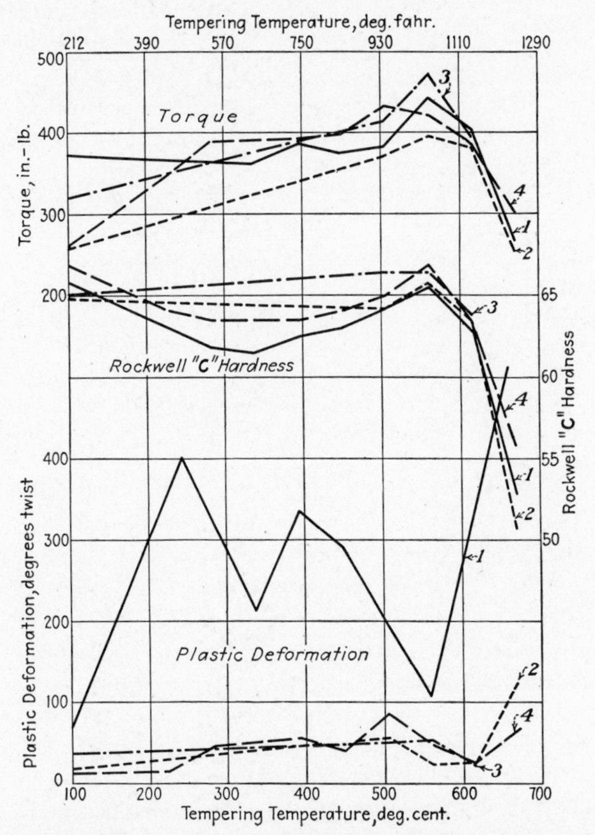

FIG. 122.—Torsional properties and hardness of some molybdenum high-speed steels. Nos. 1, 2, and 3 were quenched from 1225°C. (2235°F.); No. 4 was quenched from 1285°C. (2345°F.). (*Emmons.*)

per cent vanadium were also determined by Emmons, who found that its hardness and strength after heat treatment were quite definitely lower than the same properties of a standard 18–4–1 steel. The highest hardness observed was Rockwell *C* 55, while the highest torque was 268 in-lb.

161. Properties at Elevated Temperatures.—As pointed out later in the discussion of the requirements for good cutting properties of a high-speed tool steel, the properties at elevated temperatures are of prime importance. In this connection may be mentioned some material from the work of Oertel and Pölzguter.[140] These authors studied the mechanical properties of several high-speed steels in relation to their cutting performance. Figure 124 gives the results of their high-temperature tests on hardness.

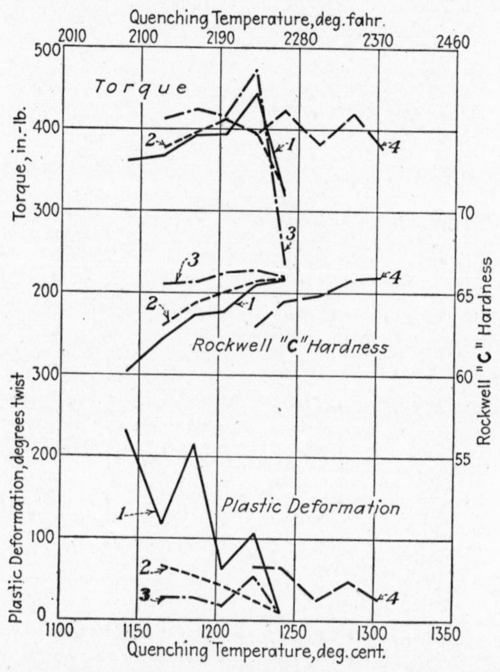

FIG. 123.—Torsional properties and hardness of some molybdenum high-speed steels quenched from various temperatures and tempered at 560°C. (1040°F.). (*Emmons.*)

The method of testing was that of Wüst and Bardenheuer,[93] in which a mounted ball of known weight is allowed to fall from a given height on to the test piece; in this method the diameter of the impression is measured and the Brinell hardness calculated. The weight used was 1 kg. (2.2 lb.) and the falling distance 400 mm. (15.7 in.).

The high-temperature hardness of steel 7Mo–7Co–1.3V was a little lower than that of steel 6Mo but the latter showed poorer

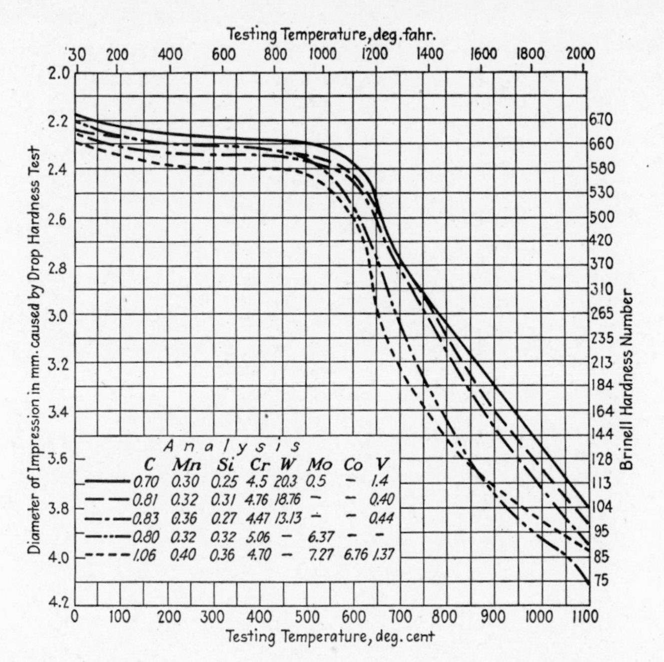

Fig. 124.—Hardness vs. temperature of several high-speed steels. (*Oertel and Pölzguter.*(140))

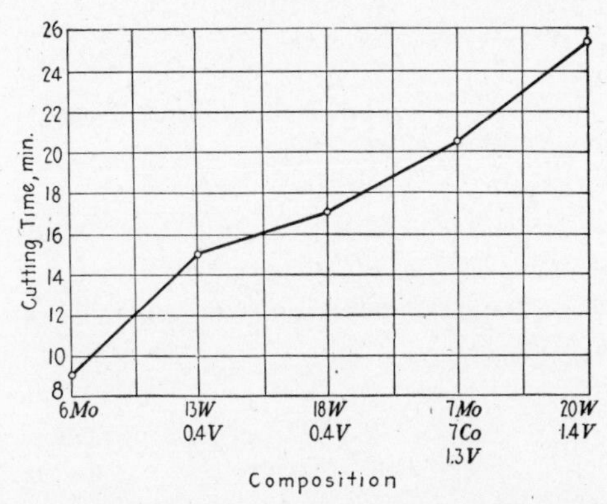

Fig. 125.—Cutting test on high-speed steel. Strength of arbor 75 kg./sq. mm., cutting speed 17 m./min., depth of cut 4 mm., feed 1.4 mm. (*Oertel and Pölzguter.*(140))

cutting ability. The softening point for the molybdenum steels was at about 620°C. (1150°F.). Although the molybdenum steels lost their hardness at lower temperatures than the tungsten steels, the steel 7Mo–7Co–1.3V showed better cutting ability than the steels 13W–0.4V and 18W–0.4V. The high-temperature hardness tests, then, do not give an indication of the cutting ability. This will be seen by comparison of Fig. 124 with Fig. 125.

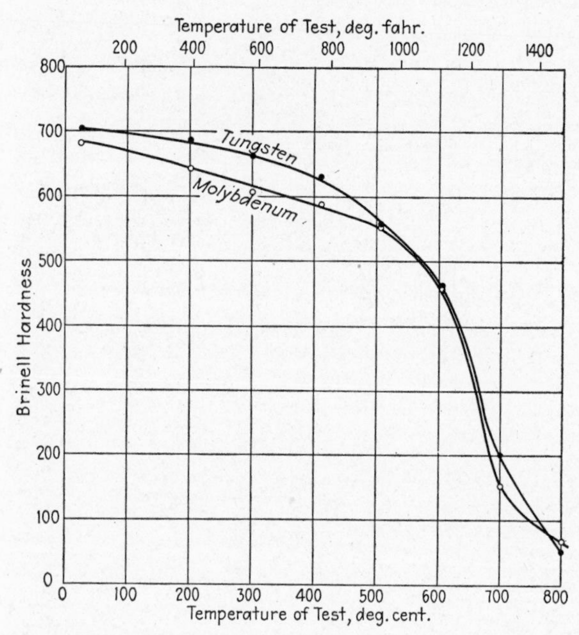

Fig. 126.—Brinell hardness of high-speed steels at elevated temperature obtained by mutual indentation test. (*Battelle Memorial Institute.*)

Mutual indentation-hardness values at temperatures as high as 800°C. (1470°F.) obtained at the Battelle Memorial Institute by Grove with a quenched and tempered molybdenum high-speed steel are shown in Fig. 126. Values obtained from several tungsten high-speed steels of the 18–4–1 type are also shown for comparison. The analysis of the molybdenum steel was:

	Per Cent
Carbon	0.70
Chromium	3.50
Molybdenum	9.50
Vanadium	1.20

This steel was quenched in oil from 1175°C. (2150°F.) and tempered at 500°C. (930°F.). The tungsten steels were quenched in oil from 1260 or 1285°C. (2300 or 2350°F.) and tempered at 565, 580, or 595°C. (1050, 1075, or 1100°F.).

The hardness values were obtained by the method described by Cowdrey[328A] in which two cylinders of the dimensions 0.39 × 0.39 in. (1 × 1 cm.) are forced together under a known load and the Brinell hardness is calculated from the width of the flat section formed on the surface of the cylindrical samples. In making the test, the axes of the two cylindrical test pieces are parallel and the applied force is perpendicular to the axes of the samples. With this method, materials may be tested at any desired temperature. A series of tests by Cowdrey and by Grove indicated that the hardness numbers obtained by the mutual-indentation method correspond to those obtained with the usual ball test.

According to the results of the tests made by Grove, the molybdenum high-speed steel is softer than the tungsten steel at temperatures below 500°C. (930°F.), but above this temperature there is little or no difference in hardness between the two steels. The Rockwell *C* hardness of the molybdenum steel was 64.6 after quenching and 63.3 after tempering.

162. Requirements for Modern Tool Steels.—Before discussing the cutting ability of molybdenum-bearing tool steels, it may be of interest to review briefly along the lines suggested by Grossmann and Bain[450] the requirements of a cutting tool. These and other special requirements are becoming of more and more importance in modern mass production and in the machining of modern alloy steels.

In a general way the tool which retains its cutting hardness at the temperatures met with in high-speed lathe work will be the "fastest" tool.

This follows from the fact that the limit of cutting speed is that rate of cutting whose attendant heat evolution transmitted to the tool can just be dissipated by the tool without such temperature rise as to cause material loss in cutting hardness. Regardless of whether the subsequent *room temperature* hardness is impaired or not by the heat of cutting—the tool must be hard *at the temperature* developed by the desired cutting rate if the tool is to meet a specified demand. It, therefore, becomes evident what the term red hardness as applied to hardened high-speed steel signifies. A cutting tool possesses red hardness if at the visibly red heat developed in service it still maintains substantially its cutting hardness.

Concerning the effect of molybdenum on high-speed steels, these authors pointed out that molybdenum is one of the elements retaining considerable hardness in itself at elevated temperatures. It imparts to some extent this characteristic to the material with which it is alloyed.

C. CUTTING PERFORMANCE

Studies of the cutting performance of high-speed steels may be made by a number of methods among which are lathe breakdown tests under controlled conditions and actual shop tests of various types of tools in production service. In the lathe breakdown test the tool is run to destruction, and various methods have been used to determine this point, but the most successful one is that of Taylor mentioned in this section; the life of the tool is judged on the basis of "Taylor speed."

163. Cutting Performance of Molybdenum High-speed Steels. In a paper dealing with tempering and cutting tests of high-speed steels, Carpenter[31] sought to determine whether the temperature at which high-speed steels soften could be raised above 700°C. (1290°F.). The chromium-molybdenum steels investigated in comparison with chromium-tungsten steels were of the composition given in Table 110.

TABLE 110.—COMPOSITIONS OF CHROMIUM-MOLYBDENUM STEELS*

Composition, per cent			
C	Si	Cr	Mo
0.47	0.15	2.99	4.29
1.31	0.64	3.40	3.90
1.00	0.06	3.00	6.00
0.63	0.47	1.80	10.87

* Carpenter.[31]

These were included among the steels previously used by Carpenter[29] in his work on the structure and transformation points of high-speed steels. The specimens were quenched from 1200°C. (2190°F.) in an air blast and tempered for 1 hr. at various lower temperatures. After air-quenching, the alloys possessed the "white polyhedral structure" characteristic of such hardened steels. The 4.29Mo–2.99Cr–0.47C alloy was unique in that it revealed this structure after being cooled from 1200°C. (2190°F.) in the furnace to room temperature over a period of 3 hr. The progress of tempering was followed by etching tests and by cutting tests on a high-speed lathe.

The 4.29Mo–2.99Cr–0.47C steel, which was not a recognized type of high-speed steel, was the only one with which any success was had in raising the softening temperature above 700°C. (1290°F.); this alloy appeared to resist softening by thermal influences at 800°C. (1470°F.). However, mechanical stress at high temperatures must be taken into consideration in judging any tool.

French and Strauss(108) made lathe breakdown tests on twenty-five commercial brands of high-speed steels produced by various manufacturers during the period 1919–1922. Results of chemical analyses of forty brands were also reported. As a result of their breakdown tests with roughing tools on 3 per cent nickel steel forgings, they concluded that "the performance of commercial low-tungsten, high-vanadium and cobalt steels was superior to that of the high-tungsten, low-vanadium type and special steels containing about 0.25 per cent uranium and 0.75 per cent molybdenum." A tungstenless steel, on the other hand, of the following composition:

Composition, per cent								
C	Si	Mn	Cr	V	Co	Mo	Ni	Cu
0.65	0.48	0.55	4.62	0.68	4.73	4.72	1.03	0.12

showed poorer cutting properties than all the Cr–W–V steels. Strauss,(127) however, in milling-cutter tests, showed this steel to be but little inferior to Cr–W–V high-speed steel in the forged condition, although the composition of the latter was not what is now regarded as the best.

Oertel and Pölzguter,(139) in an investigation of the influence of cobalt and vanadium on the properties of high-speed steel in 1924, studied molybdenum-bearing steels of the composition given in Tables 111 and 112.

TABLE 111.—CHEMICAL COMPOSITION OF THE WROUGHT TOOLS OF MOLYBDENUM HIGH-SPEED STEEL*

Number	Designation	Composition, per cent						
		C	Mn	Si	Cr	Mo	Co	V
1	6 Mo	0.80	0.32	0.32	5.06	6.37		
2	6 Mo Co3	0.76	0.53	0.12	5.00	6.75	3.19	
3	6 Mo Co6	0.79	0.56	0.25	4.42	6.34	5.65	
4	8 Mo Co9	0.71	0.33	0.33	4.00	7.90	8.86	
5	8 Mo V1	0.71	0.38	0.25	4.78	7.85	....	1.01
6	8 Mo Co6 V1	0.60	0.56	0.36	4.05	7.96	5.83	0.98
7	8 Mo Co6 V2	0.63	0.58	0.32	4.41	7.80	5.64	1.92
8	7 Mo Co7 V1.3	1.06	0.40	0.38	4.70	7.27	6.76	1.37
9	5 Mo	0.75	0.15	0.14	4.30	5.17		
10	5 Mo Co5 V1	0.79	0.56	0.45	4.73	5.10	5.01	1.10

* Oertel and Pölzguter.(139)

TABLE 112.—CHEMICAL COMPOSITION OF THE CAST TOOLS OF HIGH-SPEED STEEL CONTAINING MOLYBDENUM*

Number	Designation	Composition, per cent						
		C	Mn	Si	Cr	Mo	Co	V
1	5 Mo	0.80	0.38	0.28	5.15	5.40		
2	5 Mo Co3	0.80	0.38	0.28	5.09	5.10	2.65	
3	5 Mo Co6	0.80	0.38	0.28	4.97	5.40	6.10	
4	5 Mo Co9	0.80	0.38	0.28	4.91	5.01	9.76	
5	5 Mo Co9 V0.8	0.90	0.38	0.28	5.14	5.45	9.76	0.84
6	5 Mo Co9 V1	0.90	0.38	0.28	5.17	5.41	9.76	1.08
7	5 Mo Co9 V2	0.90	0.38	0.28	5.25	5.40	9.76	2.02
8	5 Mo Co9 V2.6	0.90	0.38	0.28	5.02	5.04	9.76	2.6

* Oertel and Pölzguter.(139)

In Figs. 127, 128, 129, and 130 are given, respectively, the relation between: Brinell hardness and hardening temperature; cutting life in minutes and the type of forged steel; cutting life and type of steel in the cast condition and the hardened condition; and Brinell hardness and the annealing temperature.

In Fig. 127 is shown the relationship between hardening temperature and Brinell hardness of several high-speed steels. The straight molybdenum steel attained its highest degree of hardness at 1000°C. (1830°F.). When the hardening temperature was increased above 1150°C. (2100°F.), the hardness values fell off.

The hardness results for the steels containing vanadium are rather surprising. The higher the vanadium content, the lower were the hardness values for the lower hardening temperature. After hardening from temperatures of the order of 1200°C. (2190°F.), however the results approached those of the vana-

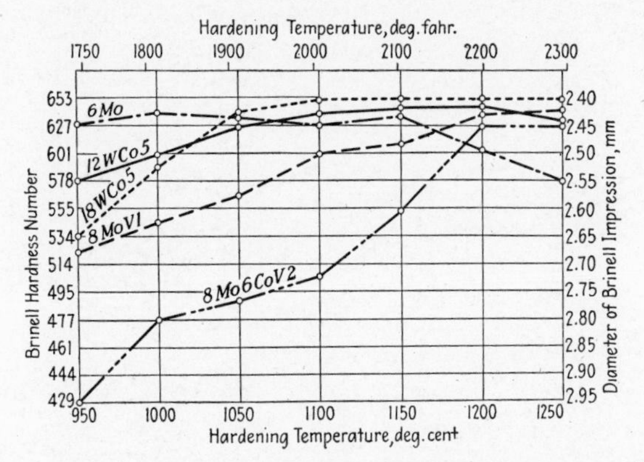

FIG. 127.—Effect of hardening temperature on Brinell hardness of high-speed steel. (*Oertel and Pölzguter.*[139])

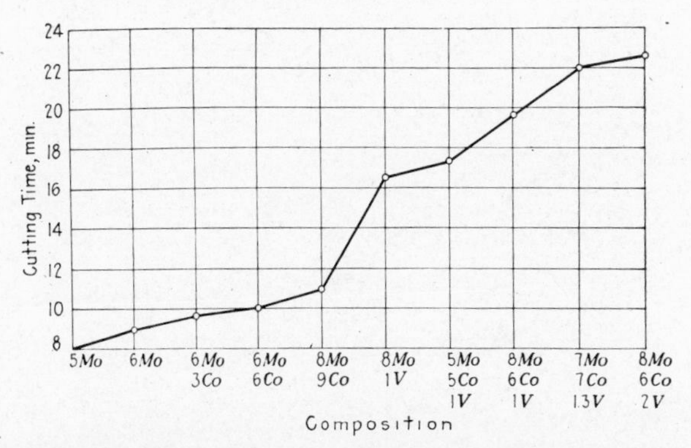

FIG. 128.—Cutting tests with forged high-speed steel tools. Cross-section 20 × 20 mm., strength of material cut 75 kg./sq. mm., cutting speed 17 m./min., depth of cut 4 mm., feed 1.4 mm. (*Oertel and Pölzguter.*[139])

dium-free steels. An explanation for this phenomenon is to be sought in the higher carbon content of the vanadium secondary cementite and the high solution temperature (at the A_{cm} point) of this cementite. No improvement at the high hardening temperature was effected by increasing the vanadium content above 2 per cent.

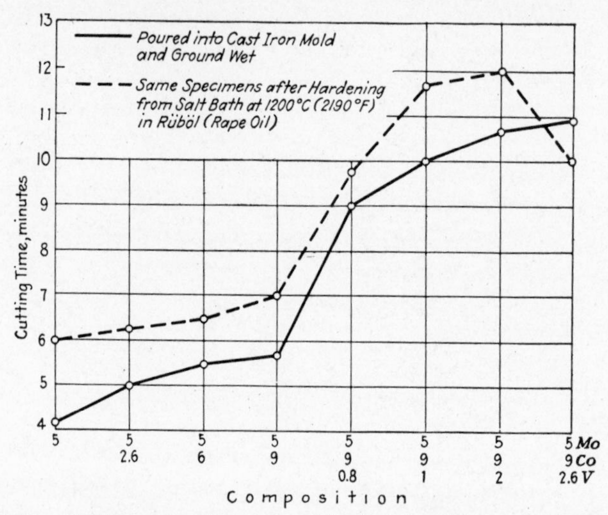

FIG. 129.—Cutting tests with cast and hardened tools of molybdenum high-speed steel. Conditions of test same as given in Fig. 128. (*Oertel and Pölzguter.*[139])

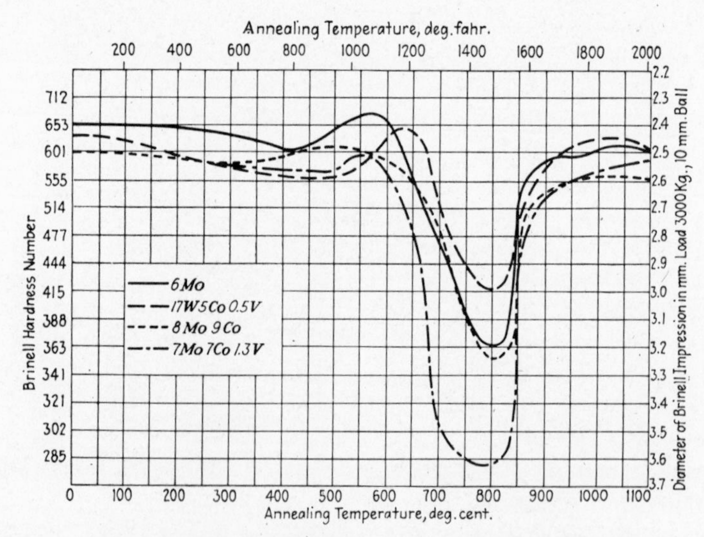

FIG. 130.—Effect of tempering on Brinell hardness of high-speed steel. (*Oertel and Pölzguter.*[139])

In Fig. 128 are summarized some results of the study of the cutting performance of the steels. The principal point to be noted is that the cutting properties may be improved by the addition of cobalt and vanadium. For example, the addition of 9 per cent cobalt to a molybdenum steel increased the cutting performance about 37 per cent; the addition of 1 per cent vanadium to a molybdenum steel increased the cutting ability 100 per cent. The benefit of a cobalt addition in the presence of vanadium, however, was not great. The greatest improvement in performance seemed to be obtained with about 1.5 per cent vanadium.

In lathe tests of cast tools the addition of cobalt to a molybdenum steel was also shown to be an advantage, about 30 per cent improvement being noted. With the addition of 1 per cent vanadium, a still greater improvement (90 per cent) was noted. These points are brought out in Fig. 129.

Figure 130 is of interest in showing the behavior of the different steels with respect to tempering temperature. Up to 450°C. (840°F.) the hardness of all steels decreased. A maximum hardness was reached between 550 and 625°C. (1020 and 1155°F.). Above 625°C. (1155°F.) the hardness fell off suddenly to a minimum; it increased again at 850°C. (1560°F.). At 950 to 1000°C. (1740 to 1830°F.) it was high again owing to the air-hardening properties of the steels. For molybdenum steels, the highest hardness values were at approximately 575°C. (1065°F.).

The cutting performance of molybdenum-bearing steels in comparison with other high-speed steels was studied by French and Digges.[149] The two steels containing molybdenum were of the chromium-vanadium and tungsten-chromium-vanadium types, respectively. In one case molybdenum was substituted wholly, and in the other case partially, for tungsten. The steels with which they were compared were tungsten-chromium-vanadium steels, with or without nickel or tantalum additions. The criterion of the tool life in each case was the "Taylor speed" (the cutting speed in feet per minute to ruin the tool in 20 min.). Results, together with the compositions, and heat treatments are summarized in Fig. 131.

Concerning the results of the tests, French and Digges stated that with the steel in which 3.4 per cent molybdenum replaced 6 per cent tungsten slightly better tool performance was obtained than with the customary high-tungsten, low-vanadium steel.

e authors called attention to difficulties encountered in ng the molybdenum steels. They also found that the steel hich 18 per cent tungsten was replaced by about 7 per cent molybdenum need not be quenched from so high a temperature as tungsten steels.

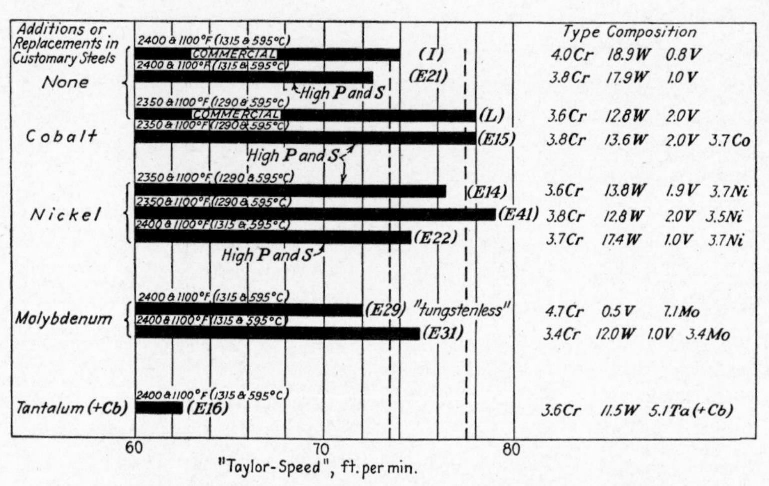

FIG. 131.—Comparison of "Taylor-speed" of high-speed steels. Hardening and tempering temperatures are shown at left. (*French and Digges.*[149])

French and Digges[260] also included a discussion of some steels containing molybdenum in a paper dealing with lathe turning with shallow cuts. The four molybdenum steels fell

TABLE 113.—STEELS USED BY FRENCH AND DIGGES[260]

Composition, per cent								
C	Mn	P	S	Si	Cr	W	V	Mo
0.61	0.18	0.027	0.009	0.04	3.34	15.44	0.81	0.74
0.67	0.23	0.021	0.010	0.06	3.66	17.56	1.06	0.85
0.53	0.31	0.017	0.023	0.27	3.40	11.95	1.04	3.41
0.71	0.33	0.013	0.019	0.44	4.74	.....	0.54	7.07

into two classes: those in which molybdenum was introduced as an impurity in the ferrotungsten addition (ferrotungsten made from California Scheelite ores) and those in which molybdenum was added intentionally. The compositions were as given in Table 113.

The steels were oil-quenched from 1320°C. (2400°F.) and tempered at 595°C. (1105°F.).

From their results it appeared that molybdenum could be substituted in part or in entirety for tungsten without radically changing the lathe tool performance under shallow cuts and fine feeds or under heavy duty. If the results show any definite trend, they state, it is that molybdenum is somewhat disadvantageous from the standpoint of shallow cuts but may improve the steels for heavy duty.

Emmons, at the Cleveland Twist Drill Co., investigated the cutting properties of a number of molybdenum high-speed steels used as drills and found the cutting properties of the molybdenum steels studied inferior to those of the standard 18–4–1 tungsten high-speed steel. His tests were made by determining the number of holes drilled without resharpening the drills and comparing this value with that obtained by drills of a stock 18–4–1 steel drilling the same materials. In testing each tool steel, several materials of different hardnesses were drilled.

Drills from a steel made at Watertown Arsenal containing 0.67 per cent carbon, 3.62 per cent chromium, 8.56 per cent molybdenum, and 1.17 per cent vanadium were tested by drilling chromium-nickel steel armor plate of a Brinell hardness of 351, S.A.E. 1020 steel of a Brinell hardness of 126, and cast iron of a Brinell hardness of 143. The drills were heat-treated in accordance with recommendations from the Arsenal. In soft steel, the performance of the molybdenum high-speed drills was excellent, but their cutting life in drilling cast iron and armor plate was much shorter than that of the stock drills. Drills of another size made from steel furnished by Watertown Arsenal and of practically the same composition and heat treatment were tested by drilling armor plate having a Brinell hardness of 388, S.A.E. 1040 steel with a Brinell hardness of 170, and cast iron with a Brinell hardness of 143. The molybdenum steel drills were excellent for drilling the S.A.E. 1040 steel but were definitely inferior to the stock drills for cutting the other materials.

The average performance of drills made from the steels listed in Table 109 (page 330) expressed in percentages of the number of holes drilled by stock drills was found to be:

Steel Number	Per Cent
1	43
2	60
3	68
4	100

These values were obtained from tests made on different ferrous materials of several hardnesses.

D. POSSIBLE LIMITATIONS AND ADVANTAGES IN THE USE OF MOLYBDENUM

While it is not intended to reiterate by pointing out all the characteristics of molybdenum-bearing high-speed steels, it is felt that one or two points under the heading of possible limitations and advantages, which may have been suggested in the text, bear a little further discussion.

164. Limitations.—As has already been noted, one of the comments that was made in regard to molybdenum-bearing tool steels was that they were brittle and had a tendency to "fire-crack." Such statements appeared in the literature of 1907–1908.[35, 36] This tendency seemed to be noted in tools containing from 2 to 2.5 per cent and above 4 per cent molybdenum. As previously noted, Taylor[35] and his coworkers found molybdenum-bearing tools to be irregular in their cutting performance, and Taylor suggested that the tools deteriorated.

In 1915, Hibbard[70] made the statement that the use of molybdenum in tool steels was being discontinued, or that it was being used in smaller amounts as an auxiliary rather than a major constituent. The reasons given for this were that the tools had a tendency to crack in quenching; the steel was apt to be seamy and to contain other physical imperfections; the tools deteriorated on repeated heating for dressing and treatment. These effects were probably due to surface decarburization.

In an article published in 1920, Arnold[87] stated that the use of vanadium stabilizes the variable properties of molybdenum steel and prevents cracking during water-hardening. The steel was said to be of notable hardness and remarkable thermal stability.

A number of other authors have referred to the loss of molybdenum during the manufacturing process. French and Digges[149] referred to the "sweating out" of this element and noted that cobalt had been suggested to overcome this difficulty. The sweating out was noted by the presence of thick bluish fumes arising from the steel, but they were observed only during forging Difficulty was also experienced in the cracking of the ingots during forging. Their experience confirms that of previous investigators who believed that molybdenum should not be substituted *in toto*, or in large proportions, for tungsten.

In 1931, Grossmann and Bain[450] stated, apropos of the foregoing, that working against the beneficial effects of molybdenum is the fact that the oxide MoO_3 has a high volatility, and that during processes of fabrication which involve heat the molybdenum near the surface is readily oxidized and lost as a white vapor. This fact, coupled with the high rate of diffusibility of molybdenum, results in considerable loss of this element. When molybdenum is used as a supplementary element in high-speed steel, to the extent of 1 or 2 per cent, this loss is not serious.

TABLE 114.—RELATIVE COSTS OF RAW MATERIALS FOR HIGH-SPEED STEELS*

Name	Mushet self-hardening	Taylor-White		Present average	Super high-speed	Molybdenum high-speed
Date	1868	1900	Later	1930	1930	1930
Present cost per 100 lb. raw material	$11.44	$14.78	$28.43	$32.25	$58.30	$18.80
Composition, per cent						
Tungsten	5.50	8.00	17.0 to 18.0	18.0	18.0 to 22.0	
Chromium	0.30	3.80	5.5 to 6.0	4.0	4.0	3.50
Carbon	1.50	1.85	0.65 to 0.70	0.70	0.70 to 0.75	0.68
Vanadium	......	......	.....	1.00	1.50	1.25
Manganese	1.75	0.30	0.30	0.20	0.20	0.25
Silicon	1.00	0.15	0.15	0.25	0.20	0.25
Phosphorus	......	0.025	0.025	0.025	.....	0.025
Sulphur	......	0.030	0.030	0.030	.....	0.025
Molybdenum	......	......	......	......	0.50	9.50
Cobalt	......	......	......	......	7.0 to 10.0	

* Ritchie.[395]

The formation of a soft or "white" layer on the surface of molybdenum steels was attributed by Ritchie,[395] as discussed in a later section, to be due principally to the loss of carbon rather than molybdenum. In a verbal discussion, Emmons stated that he had also observed that the so-called "demolybdenized" layer was actually a decarburized area and that, while molybdenum steels decarburize somewhat more readily than tungsten steels, the same precautions now observed to prevent decarburization in tungsten high-speed steels will generally prevent the formation of a soft surface on molybdenum steel.

165. Advantages.—The advantages in the use of molybdenum in high-speed steels have largely been dealt with, particularly in the discussion of the use of molybdenum as a replacing element for tungsten. Two other arguments for its use in the further development of high-speed steels are apparent from a consideration of its relative cost at the present day as compared with tungsten, and its "strategic" importance to the United States. It was pointed out by Ritchie[395] that, since 28 per cent of the total world supply of tungsten comes from China where labor is cheap and huge deposits of ore permit of surface mining, the development of a substitute element in case this supply were cut off would be highly desirable. The relative cost of the raw materials for molybdenum steels compared with other high-speed steels is given in Table 114.

E. DEVELOPMENT WORK AT WATERTOWN ARSENAL

A study of molybdenum high-speed steels was recently completed at Watertown Arsenal, and, because of the scope of the work and the care with which it was carried out, it can best be reviewed in a separate division. This review is made possible by the article by Ritchie[395] and the courtesy of Colonel Dickson, Commanding Officer at Watertown Arsenal, who permitted the use of unpublished data obtained at the Arsenal.

166. Steels Studied.—High-speed steels in which tungsten had been only partly replaced by molybdenum were first studied, and it was reported that in such steels there was "no apparent loss of cutting efficiency as the molybdenum replaced the tungsten, and results obtained were such as to justify proceeding with the complete substitution."

In order to study the properties of high-speed steels, containing no tungsten, alloys of the compositions listed in Table 115 were made. These steels were worked into tools of various kinds, including lathe and planer tools as large as 1¾ × 2½ in. and drills, reamers, end millers, and milling cutters. Steels 29 to 96 inclusive were made from 75-lb. ingots. Other steels were cast into ingots weighing as much as 375 lb.

It was pointed out that all the chromium and vanadium contents of this series of steels were practically constant, and that better steels might possibly result from a variation in one or both of these elements.

TABLE 115.—MOLYBDENUM HIGH-SPEED STEELS TESTED*

Number	Composition, per cent								
	C	Mn	Si	S	P	Cr	V	W	Mo
29	0.60	0.22	0.78	0.016	0.015	4.00	1.02	0	9.42
04	0.55	0.10	0.317	.....	.....	3.68	1.20	0	7.52
1,104	0.65	0.14	0.475	.....	.....	3.77	1.14	0	8.00
70	0.91	0.35	0.725	0.026	0.009	3.40	1.15	0	11.19
71	0.75	0.36	0.66	0.026	0.010	3.54	1.23	0	9.50
72	0.46	0.35	0.73	0.025	0.009	3.64	1.23	0	9.05
76	0.49	0.27	0.250	0.017	0.009	3.44	1.20	0	9.36
77	0.69	0.24	0.200	0.015	0.011	3.42	1.14	0	9.67
86	0.625	0.30	0.255	0.020	0.011	3.41	1.14	0	9.33
87	0.575	0.26	0.215	0.024	0.009	3.65	1.29	0	11.30
88	0.55	0.30	0.210	0.016	0.008	3.73	1.23	0	10.80
89	0.63	0.30	0.245	0.016	0.013	3.69	1.20	0	9.10
90	0.655	0.31	0.215	0.017	0.013	3.53	1.28	0	9.80
91	0.62	0.31	0.160	0.016	0.013	3.59	0.97	0	9.58
92	0.68	0.27	0.230	0.017	0.008	3.53	1.22	0	9.39
93	0.80	0.29	0.260	0.017	0.009	3.59	1.26	0	9.67
94	0.755	0.28	0.250	0.018	0.008	3.63	1.26	0	8.84
95	0.58	0.32	0.290	0.019	0.010	3.64	1.17	0	7.76
96	0.84	0.32	0.270	0.016	0.010	3.74	1.15	0	9.36
*H*14	0.64	0.27	0.260	0.010	0.010	3.51	1.33	0	9.47
*H*17	0.615	0.30	0.305	0.012	0.010	3.47	1.35	0	9.58
*H*18	0.645	0.30	0.350	0.010	0.010	3.50	1.32	0	9.60
*H*31	0.60	0.26	0.560	0.011	0.010	3.46	1.32	0	9.31
*H*54	0.60	0.27	0.300	0.012	0.010	3.50	1.29	0	9.08

* Watertown Arsenal.

167. Working and Heat-treating Molybdenum Steels.—During the early part of the investigation many of the steels cracked during forging and hardening, but it was found that this trouble was due to heating or cooling too rapidly or to an improper forging technique rather than to any inherent defects in the molybdenum steel. "Once the working and hardening temperatures were established and with the care ordinarily taken in fabricating high-speed steel no further difficulty was experienced." It was found that these molybdenum high-speed steels

FIG. 132.—Variations in structure and "white layer" in fractures of high-speed steel. (*Watertown Arsenal.*)

should not in general be heated above about 1150°C. (2100°F.) and should not be forged at temperatures below 950°C. (1740°F.).

In certain cases a soft "white layer" was formed on the surface of the molybdenum steel. This soft layer has been considered by most investigators to be due to loss in molybdenum from the surface of the steel, but work at the Arsenal proved that decarburization rather than demolybdenization was the chief factor in forming the layer, as is indicated by the analyses given in Table

116. This layer cannot be hardened by any treatment, but its formation can be easily prevented by coating the steel with a thin layer of borax, which melts and forms a glassy protecting film that adheres to the steel even during forging. Some tools having a heavy white layer are shown in Fig. 132. The variations in the appearance of the fracture that can be produced by heat treatment are also shown in this figure.

After studying the effect of various heat treatments, it was found that both the quenching and tempering temperatures for molybdenum high-speed steels should be somewhat lower than for tungsten high-speed steels. The optimum hardening temperature was found to be between 1175 and 1200°C. (2145 and 2190°F.), and the optimum tempering temperature between 500 and 525°C. (930 and 975°F.). Microstructures of tools of composition 29 after quenching from 1100, 1175, 1200, and 1250°C. (2010, 2145, 2190, and 2280°F.) are shown in Figs. 133 to 136. These micrographs show quite plainly that a quenching temperature of 1100°C. (2010°F.) is too low and that the steel was "burned" by heating to 1250°C. (2280°F.). After having been quenched from 1200°C. (2190°F.) and tempered at 500°C. (930°F.) steel 29 had a Rockwell *C* hardness of 70. In general it was found that the behavior of the molybdenum steels on tempering was similar to that of the tungsten steels.

TABLE 116.—SURFACE AND CORE OF MOLYBDENUM HIGH-SPEED STEELS*
(No protection during forging or heat treatment)

Location of sample	Composition, per cent					
	C	Mn	Si	Cr	V	Mo
Center of tool 1	0.645	0.30	0.350	3.50	1.32	9.60
Surface of tool 1	0.10	0.23	0.340	3.22	1.19	9.17
Center of tool 2	0.91	0.35	0.725	3.40	1.15	11.19
Surface of tool 2	0.31	0.35	0.645	3.40	1.46	9.97

* Watertown Arsenal.

168. Cutting Tests.—It was considered that no one method of testing could cover all conditions of service, and that the best method for the evaluation of molybdenum high-speed steels was to put them in service "side by side with the regular shop tools on forgings and castings, steel, cast iron and non-ferrous, hard and soft, heavy duty and light duty." Consequently many types of molybdenum high-speed steel tools were made and their life

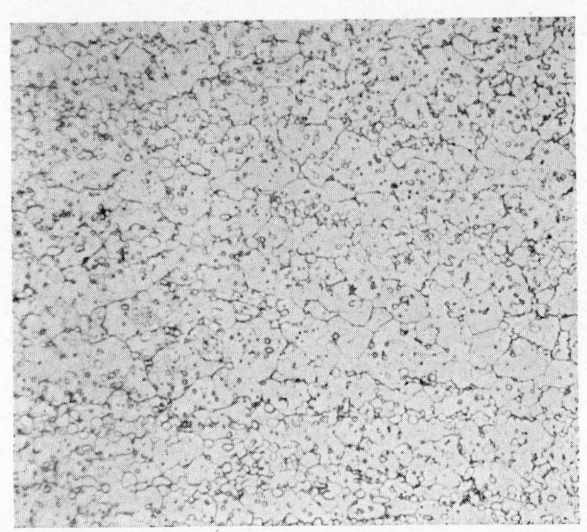

Fig. 133.—High-speed steel containing 0.60 per cent carbon, 9.42 per cent molybdenum, 4.00 per cent chromium and 1.02 per cent vanadium. Quenched from 1100°C. (2010°F.). Etched with alcoholic nitric acid. 500×. (*Watertown Arsenal.*)

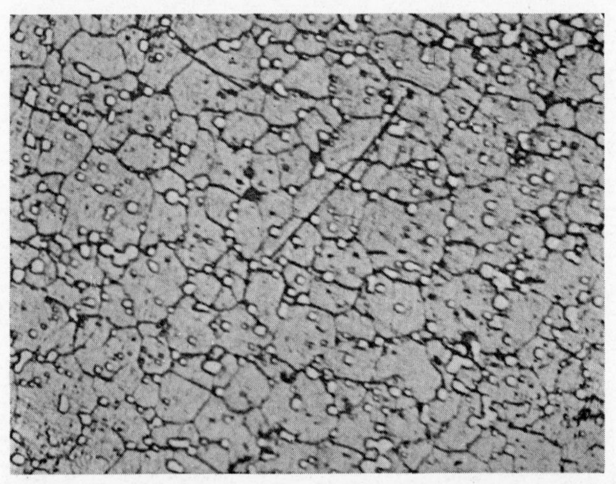

Fig. 134.—Same steel as shown in Fig. 133. Quenched from 1175°C. (2145°F.). Etched with alcoholic nitric acid. 1000×. (*Watertown Arsenal.*)

was compared with the life of tungsten high-speed steel tools. One of the standard tungsten steels contained 0.68 per cent

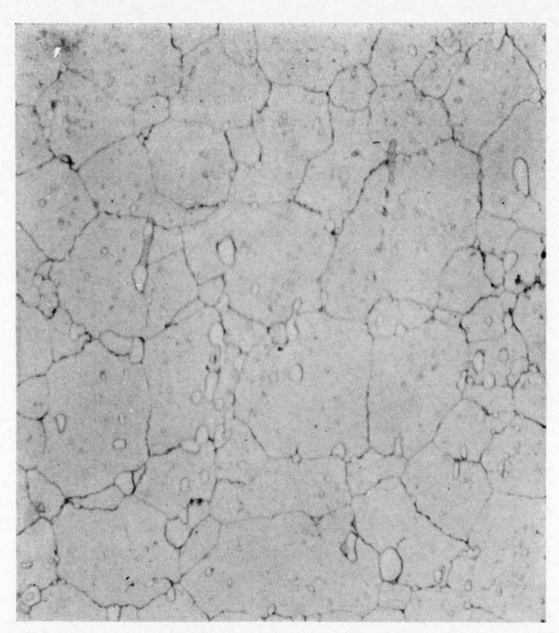

FIG. 135.—Same steel as shown in Fig. 133. Quenched from 1200°C. (2190°F.). Etched with alcoholic nitric acid. 500×. (*Watertown Arsenal.*)

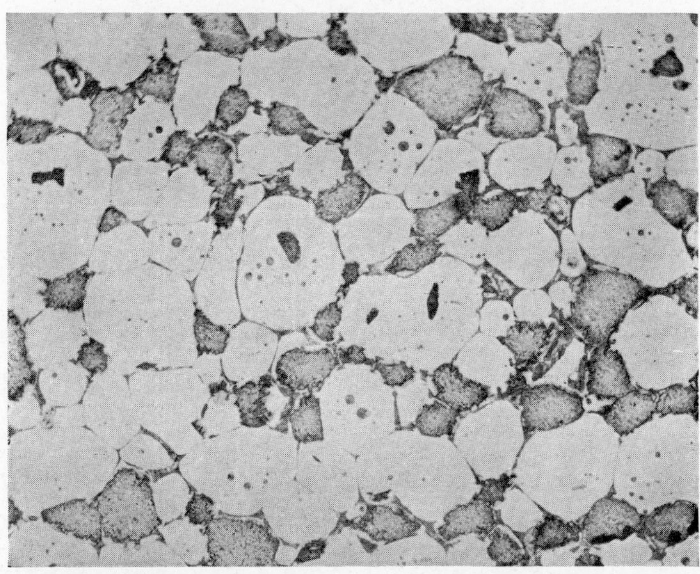

FIG. 136.—Same steel as shown in Fig. 133. Quenched from 1250°C. (2280°F.). Etched with alcoholic nitric acid. 100×. (*Watertown Arsenal.*)

carbon, 17.69 per cent tungsten, 3.60 per cent chromium, and 0.74 per cent vanadium. The other tungsten steels were of similar composition.

From the analyses of the data on tool life it was considered that the best all-purpose molybdenum high-speed steel composition was as follows:

	Per Cent
Carbon	0.68
Manganese	0.25
Silicon	0.25
Chromium	3.50
Molybdenum	9.50
Vanadium	1.25

It is estimated that for heavy planer tools and very heavy lathe tools, the molybdenum steel is about 90 per cent as efficient as the standard tungsten steel. For small and medium lathe and planer tools and form cutters the molybdenum tools are practically as efficient as the regular tungsten tools.

Some molybdenum steel tools made at Watertown Arsenal were sent to other plants to be used in comparison with tungsten steels and, in the majority of the tests made, the molybdenum steels were found to be superior to the tungsten steels. An exception was met in a short series of tests in drilling hard steel (350 to 390 Brinell) or cast iron. In turning, also, the molybdenum steels were characterized as "perhaps somewhat inferior to tungsten steels" for cutting stock of over 300 Brinell.

169. Directions for Handling Molybdenum High-speed Steel. The directions for forming and heat-treating the steel containing from 0.65 to 0.75 per cent carbon and from 9.0 to 10.0 per cent molybdenum, as formulated at Watertown Arsenal, are:

Rolling

Practice should be patterned on best practice in handling tungsten high-speed steel. Slow cooling of the ingot, followed by slow heating for rolling is recommended. Temperature for rolling should be not over 1150°C. (2100°F.), preferably around 1100°C. (2010°F.). Rolling should stop at 950°C. (1740°F.).

Forging

Before any forging is done, the stock should be thoroughly annealed as follows:

Heat slowly to 850 to 875°C. (1560 to 1605°F.), hold 1 hr. for each inch of thickness, or until uniformly soaked, and cool very slowly in ashes or lime, or in the furnace. The range of temperatures for forging is from 1100 to 1150°C. (2010 to 2100°F.) down to 950°C. (1740°F.). Cool slowly after forging. The steel forges as easily as tungsten high-speed and, except as noted below, requires no greater precautions.

Heat Treatment

Before hardening, all forged tools should be annealed as described above under Forging.

To harden, handle essentially the same way as tungsten high-speed steel.

Preheat to 850°C. (1560°F.).
Sweat at 1175°C. (2145°F.).
Quench in oil or salt bath at not over 565°C. (1050°F.).
Cool in air.
Temper at 500°C. (930°F.).
Cool in air.

Note that the sweating and tempering temperatures are lower than for tungsten high-speed steel.

Protection under Heat

The following is of the utmost importance, especially in final forging operations and hardening small tools and form cutters. Whenever this material is in contact with air or in an oxidizing atmosphere at 400°C. (750°F.) or hotter, a volatile oxide of molybdenum is formed. This oxide escapes and leaves a soft, partially decarburized and demolybdenumized skin which will not harden. This skin has been observed as deep as 1/8 in., a condition brought about by unusually long holding at high temperatures. To avoid the formation of this layer, a very simple method may be employed. Whenever the metal is to be heated to 400°C. (750°F.) or over, powdered borax is sprinkled over the piece much as salt is sprinkled on food. The borax melts and forms a greasy-looking film that adheres to the metal even during forging operations under the hammer. This film excludes air and furnace gases perfectly. When possible to do so, a salt bath furnace should be used for hardening and tempering operations. The bath will exclude the air and prevent the formation of the soft layer in much the same manner as the borax.

Cleaning

Ordinary pickling in a 10 per cent solution of sulphuric acid is recommended for cleaning borax and scale from the finished product.

170. Large-scale Manufacture of Molybdenum High-speed Steel.—The Ludlum Steel Co. recently made a 2,100-lb. lot of molybdenum high-speed steel of the following composition:

	Per Cent
Carbon	0.65 to 0.75
Manganese	0.15 to 0.30
Silicon	0.15 to 0.30
Chromium	3.25 to 3.75
Molybdenum	9.25 to 9.75
Vanadium	1.15 to 1.35

The following excerpt from a private communication from F. B. Lounsberry, Ludlum Steel Co., describes the production of the 2,100-lb. lot of steel:

> From the melting standpoint we experienced absolutely no difficulty using our regular basic electric furnace and ordinary materials. The molybdenum addition was made with low-carbon ferromolybdenum. It was comparatively easy to hit the analysis and we experienced no casting difficulties whatsoever. Larger sizes of ingots were charged hot into our reheating furnaces for hammer cogging. Smaller-sized ingots were allowed to cool in the soaking pit, after which they were annealed. They were then charged cold into reheating furnaces for hammer cogging.
>
> We were advised by the Watertown Arsenal regarding the decarburization or demolybdenumization which took place on the surface of this type of steel during the heating operation. Consequently precautions had to be taken during all heating operations in order to prevent or keep this action at a minimum. For this reason, all ingots and billets in heating furnaces were kept covered with borax. This was sprinkled on and of course as it fused formed a complete covering over the surface of the steel, preventing further decarburization or demolybdenumization during the process of forging. This at first was somewhat cumbersome and messy, but we soon became accustomed to it and it caused no serious difficulty. We did find the ingots and billets somewhat slippery on the hammer dies when covered with this borax coating. During the process of working either on the hammer or in the mill, as soon as the metal became bare, or as soon as we noticed a rather bluish white smoke coming over the metal, we immediately sprinkled it with borax.
>
> It was interesting to note that on all rolled bars from this molybdenum high-speed steel which were kept covered as above outlined during the heating and rolling operations, we found no greater decarburization than on our regular products of high-speed steel. On the hammer-finished sizes, however, due to the increased difficulty of keeping them covered, we did experience somewhat greater decarburization.
>
> The bars after finishing either by rolling or hammering were annealed in the usual manner without difficulty. In all cases a very refined fracture was obtained and a comparatively low Brinell hardness of around 196 to 212.
>
> We found this steel to be structurally sound and from a recovery standpoint equally as good, if not better, than regular 18–4–1 type high-speed. It hardened very satisfactorily, giving a very refined silky fracture, and on hardened pieces a Rockwell *C* hardness as high as 62 to 64 was obtained.

F. AUTHOR'S SUMMARY

1. Although the rôle of molybdenum in hign-speed steels is frequently considered to be that of a partial or complete replacing element for tungsten, there are certain dissimilarities between common tungsten high-speed steel and tungsten-free molybdenum high-speed steel. For some uses, the molybdenum high-speed steel appears to be as satisfactory as the tungsten high-speed steel, while for other uses it is decidedly inferior. It should, of course, be realized that any high-speed steel is a complex alloy in which the function of each element is not entirely understood, and that future work may lead to the development of molybdenum steels that are superior to any of the present commercial high-speed steels.

2. The effect of molybdenum is in the same direction but of greater magnitude than that of tungsten. The ratio of the amount of molybdenum to the amount of tungsten required to produce corresponding effects varies according to the properties of the finished tools on which the comparison is based. Thus, ratios from 1 to 1.3 up to 1 to 4 are included in the estimates of various writers. The mean would lie in the neighborhood of 1 to 2+. This corresponds to the approximate ratio of the atomic weights.

3. During the first quarter of the twentieth century, molybdenum contents as low as 0.25 per cent and as high as 15 per cent were encountered in the many types of experimental and commercial steels reported.

Taylor's experiments, during the early history of high-speed steel, indicated that 2 per cent was the highest molybdenum percentage practicable in chromium-molybdenum and chromium-tungsten-molybdenum "high"-carbon steels. Above this amount, difficulty was experienced with fire-cracking, irregularity in cutting performance, or brittleness.

In 1901 and 1902, following the announcement of the Taylor-White process, there occurred a transition from the use of self-hardening to high-speed steels. Chemically, the change consisted of a radical lowering of the carbon content (from about 1.7 per cent to 0.6 per cent on the average) and a considerable increase in the tungsten and molybdenum contents. The distinguishing feature of the process, however, was the quench from a high temperature.

Successful high-speed steels have recently been made containing 9.5 per cent molybdenum (no tungsten) and 0.68 per cent carbon.

4. Constitutionally, the rôle of molybdenum, like tungsten, chromium, and vanadium, is that of a modifier of the temperature range of the gamma phase. This is due to the greater solubility of molybdenum in alpha than in gamma iron. It is manifested in the widening, splitting, lowering, or the complete suppression, of the transformation point by the special alloying element.

5. Few numerical data on the mechanical properties of high-speed steels at normal temperatures are available in the literature. This is due chiefly to difficulties encountered in testing such relatively hard and brittle materials, and partly to the fact that the cutting properties at elevated temperatures (dull red heat) rather than those at normal temperatures are frequently those in which one is interested. It is perhaps sufficient to state that the few data available indicate that the strength, ductility, and hardness of molybdenum high-speed steels are not widely different from those of tungsten high-speed steels when molybdenum replaces tungsten in the approximate ratio of 1 to 2.

6. More data on these steels at elevated temperatures are available owing to the fact that attempts have been made to correlate the mechanical properties with the cutting performance at the temperatures met with in heavy-duty service. As shown by work of Oertel and Pölzguter, hardness tests comparable with the Brinell tests do not give an indication of the tools' cutting ability at corresponding temperatures. A like conclusion was also reached by d'Arcambal.

7. The contents of this chapter, but preferably the original papers, should be consulted for numerical data concerning the cutting life of various high-speed steels. In general, it may be stated that molybdenum-bearing steels compare favorably with other high-speed steels under certain conditions of test, composition, and treatment.

8. Among the objections offered to the use of molybdenum high-speed steels during the period of these developments were fire-cracking and irregularity in cutting performance. Less is heard on this score today, probably owing to increased knowledge regarding both the preparation of the steels and the heat treatment of the tools. The production of a "white" or soft layer at the surface of molybdenum steels was found by workers at the

Watertown Arsenal to be due to decarburization and a slight loss of molybdenum. This was prevented by the use of a borax film in the fabricating processes involving heat. Molybdenum tool steels can be made with little if any more decarburized surface than is found on other tool steels, if any of the well-recognized methods of protecting the steel from oxidizing influences while above the critical range are used.

9. The heat treatment of molybdenum-bearing as well as other high-speed steels usually involves quenching the steel from the highest temperature practicable—for example, 1175°C. (2145°F.)—and tempering at 500°C. (930°F.) depending upon the composition. Molybdenum steels require a slightly lower hardening temperature than tungsten steels to fulfill the condition that they shall be quenched from as close to the solidus line as possible.

10. The cost of the raw materials for a high-speed steel at the present time may be decreased by replacing the tungsten by molybdenum. In the United States, in particular, the substitution of molybdenum for tungsten in high-speed steels is of strategic importance because of the relative quantities of these two elements that can be produced in this country.

CHAPTER X

MOLYBDENUM IN NITRIDING STEELS

Nitriding Steels—Effects of Molybdenum in Nitriding Steels—Properties of Nitriding Steels before and after Nitriding—Uses of Nitrided Steels—Author's Summary

During the past few years the use of molybdenum in steels that are to be surface-hardened by nitriding has become quite general. As should be evident from the discussion in this chapter, the function of molybdenum is to decrease or eliminate surface-brittleness of the nitrided case and to prevent temper-brittleness in the core.

A. NITRIDING STEELS

Satisfactory carburized cases can be produced on carbon and many low-alloy steels. To date, however, useful nitrided cases have been produced on only a limited number of alloy steels. The alloying element most effective in favoring production of a useful hard surface is aluminum, and this element is found in almost all commercial nitriding steels. Many of these steels also contain chromium, and recently most of them have contained from 0.20 to 1.0 per cent or more of molybdenum.

171. Development of Nitriding Steels.—The steels which were first commercialized for nitriding in this country were alloyed with 0.80 to 1.3 per cent aluminum and 1.5 to 1.7 per cent chromium. Some of them also contained 1.5 per cent nickel (Adolf Fry, U. S. Patent 1,649,398, Nov. 15, 1927). This type of nitriding steel has now been modified by the addition of molybdenum, usually about 0.20 per cent.

C. H. Wills proposed nitriding steels containing molybdenum or chromium and molybdenum but substantially free from aluminum. These steels do not seem to have had extensive commercial application and about the only information on them is in the Wills patent (U. S. Patent 1,647,847, Nov. 1, 1927).

A third type of nitriding steel contains from about 0.1 to 4.0 per cent molybdenum as a characterizing element, and 0.1 to

4.0 per cent aluminum (W. H. Phillips, U. S. Patent 1,697,083, Jan. 1, 1929). A typical analysis is given as 2.0 to 3.0 per cent aluminum, 0.25 to 0.35 per cent carbon, and 0.75 to 1.0 per cent molybdenum. The use of this steel is claimed by the inventor to decrease the nitriding time from one-half to one-fifth of that usually required. Compositions of commercial steels of this type are illustrated by Nos. 1 and 2 in Table 117.

A fourth type of nitriding steel containing molybdenum, which has had some use, particularly as exhaust valves in internal-combustion engines, contains 0.45 to 0.60 per cent carbon, 1 to 2 per cent silicon, 7 to 9 per cent chromium, and 0.40 to 1.00 per cent molybdenum.

Steels of the chromium-vanadium type containing about 0.50 per cent vanadium, 1.5 per cent chromium, and 0.25 per cent carbon have also been used for nitriding purposes. A recently developed nitriding steel is of the high-carbon, high-chromium type and contains 1 per cent each of molybdenum and vanadium.

172. Compositions of Nitriding Steels.—Table 117 lists twenty-seven steels containing molybdenum, which are being used or have been used for nitriding. It will be observed from this table that these steels fall into certain groups. Thus, the aluminum-chromium steels most frequently contain about 0.20 per cent molybdenum, although some contain as much as 0.50 per cent. In the aluminum-molybdenum steels, the molybdenum content is usually about 1.0 per cent, but there is one with only 0.15 to 0.25 per cent. In the chromium-molybdenum steels the molybdenum varies from 0.40 to 2.4 per cent, while the chromium varies from 0.80 to 3.0 per cent.

The development of a free-machining nitriding steel of a composition similar to Nos. 22 to 25 except that the sulphur is increased from about 0.03 to 0.15 per cent was reported by Sergeson.[401] This steel is claimed to be superior in machining properties and to have the other desirable properties of the usual nitriding steels.

Compositions of nitriding steels which do not contain molybdenum were reported by various investigators as was indicated by Harder.[453, 454]

173. The Nitriding Operation.—In hardening steel by nitriding, the parts to be hardened are heated to 455 to 650°C. (850 to 1200°F.) in ammonia gas for 2 to 90 hr., depending upon the

TABLE 117.—NITRIDING STEELS CONTAINING MOLYBDENUM

Number	Composition, per cent							Reference
	C	Mn	Si	Al	Cr	Mo	Ni	
1	0.25 to 0.40	0.70 to 0.90	....	1.00	....	1.00	....	Merten[233]
2	0.33	0.67	0.47	0.87	....	0.77	....	McQuaid and Ketcham[232]
3*	0.26 to 0.31	0.50 to 0.60	0.20 to 0.35	1.0 to 1.2	....	0.15 to 0.25	....	Herbert[348]
4	0.15	0.40	0.25	....	0.85	0.41	....	Hengstenberg and Mailänder[346]
5	0.12	....	....	....	0.80	1.2	....	Satoh[292]
6	0.12	....	....	....	1.00	2.4	....	Satoh[292]
7	0.22	....	....	....	1.5	0.4	(0.35-V)	Fry[261]
8	0.18	....	....	....	3.0	0.4	....	Fry[261]
9	0.36	0.51	0.27	1.23	1.49	0.18	0.48	Homerberg and Walsted[273]
10	0.23	0.51	0.20	1.24	1.58	0.20	0.57	Homerberg and Walsted[273]
11	0.16	0.55	0.46	0.88	1.70	0.21	0.53	Homerberg and Walsted[273]
12	0.40 to 0.45	0.40 to 0.50	0.20 to 0.35	0.35 to 0.45	1.1 to 1.3	0.25 to 0.35	....	Steel made by Aubert & Duval, Frères
13	0.26 to 0.31	0.40 to 0.50	0.20 to 0.35	0.35 to 0.45	1.1 to 1.3	0.25 to 0.35	....	Same as No. 12
14	0.50 to 0.55	0.50 to 0.60	0.20 to 0.35	1.0 to 1.2	1.6 to 1.8	0.40 to 0.50	....	Same as No. 12
15	0.50 to 0.55	0.50 to 0.60	0.20 to 0.35	1.0 to 1.2	1.5 to 1.7	0.15 to 0.25	....	Same as No. 12
16	0.40 to 0.45	0.50 to 0.60	0.20 to 0.35	0.90 to 1.1	1.6 to 1.8	0.15 to 0.25	....	Same as No. 12
17	0.26 to 0.31	0.50 to 0.60	0.20 to 0.35	0.90 to 1.1	1.5 to 1.7	0.15 to 0.25	....	Same as No. 12
18	0.23 to 0.26	0.40 to 0.50	0.15 to 0.30	0.90 to 1.1	1.4 to 1.6	0.15 to 0.25	....	Same as No. 12
19	0.16 to 0.20	0.30 to 0.40	0.10 to 0.30	0.80 to 1.0	1.1 to 1.3	0.10 to 0.20	....	Same as No. 12
20	0.52	0.72	0.22	0.93	1.24	0.34	....	Hengstenberg and Mailänder[346]
21	0.20 to 0.40	....	....	1.0 to 2.0	2.0	0.30 to 0.50	0.50 to 1.0	Daubois[329]
22	0.10 to 0.20	0.40 to 0.70	....	0.60 to 1.2	0.80 to 1.3	0.15 to 0.25	....	Sergeson and Clark[402]
23	0.20 to 0.30	0.40 to 0.70	....	0.60 to 1.2	0.80 to 1.3	0.15 to 0.25	....	Sergeson and Clark[402]
24	0.30 to 0.40	0.40 to 0.70	....	0.60 to 1.2	0.80 to 1.3	0.15 to 0.25	....	Sergeson and Clark[402]
25	0.55 to 0.65	0.40 to 0.70	....	0.60 to 1.2	0.80 to 1.3	0.15 to 0.25	....	Sergeson and Clark[402]
26	0.45 to 0.60	....	1.0 to 2.0	0.25 to 1.0	7.0 to 9.0	0.40 to 1.0	....	Colwell[326]
27	1.5	....	....	....	12.0 to 14.0	1.0	(1.0-V)	Firth-Sterling Steel Co.[442]

* A private communication reports that this steel contains chromium and is similar to No. 23.

depth and character of the case desired. Duplex nitriding cycles in which the steel is nitrided first at a low temperature and then at a high temperature and vice versa are also in use. The nitrided work is then cooled to 100 to 150°C. (210 to 300°F.) in the ammonia gas. No further heat treatment is required.

Some use has been made of molten cyanide baths as a means of nitriding. The cyanide baths are used to produce a thin, but hard, wear-resistant case which can be obtained in shorter time than by nitriding in ammonia gas.[227, 277, 361, 437]

Because of the relatively long time required for the usual nitriding treatment, numerous attempts have been made to accelerate nitriding. Kinzel and Egan[361] reported that packing the material to be nitrided in finely divided magnesia, copper gauze, chips or filings, or prenitrided steel chips increases the depth of case in a given time of nitriding in ammonia.

Egan has patented (U. S. Patent 1,793,309, Feb. 17, 1931) a means for accelerating the nitriding process, in which he uses nitric oxide with the ammonia, a mixture of 40 per cent ammonia and 60 per cent nitric oxide by weight being mentioned as an example.

The use of high-frequency oscillations was applied to the nitriding process by Mahoux,[474] who subjected two steels to high-frequency oscillations for periods of 9 hr. at 500°C. (930°F.) in an atmosphere of ammonia gas. The steels had the following compositions:

Steel number	Chemical composition, per cent						
	C	Cr	Mo	Ni	Si	Mn	W
1	0.35	3.0	1.0	3.0	0.25	0.25	
2	0.31	19.8	0.23	8.0	2.50	0.35	4.0

After the above treatment steel 1 showed a Vickers hardness value of 1033 and a penetration of 0.35 mm. (0.014 in.), whereas without the high-frequency oscillations this steel showed no measurable increase in hardness and a penetration of only 0.10 mm. (0.004 in.). Steel 2 after this treatment showed a Vickers hardness value of 1035, while in the absence of the high-frequency oscillations there was no increase in the hardness.

British Patent 345,659, Apr. 9, 1931, provides for coating alloy steel with copper,[1] silver, platinum, arsenic, cobalt, or molybdenum, or any other suitable metal or metalloid as a means of nitriding steels which are not satisfactorily hardened by the usual process. Specific mention is made of the following alloy steels:

Number	Composition, per cent					
	C	Cr	Ni	W	Mn	Mo
1	0.36	14.0	14.0	2.0		
2	0.12	20.0	8.0			
3	0.50	3.5	12.0	...	5.0	
4	0.3	1.0	....	...	0.4	0.2
5	0.14	17.0	8.0			
6	0.25	13.0	0.3			
7	1.0	....	....	...	13.0	

According to the patent claims, these steels by the "improved" process can be made as hard as the now generally used nitriding steels.

From the above it is evident that researchers are studying methods of accelerating the nitriding reaction both as a means of shortening the time required and as a means of producing hard surfaces on steels which are not satisfactorily hardened by the usual nitriding treatment.

Parts or surfaces which are to be kept soft are protected by coating with some material such as nickel or tin not readily penetrated by the gas.

Manufacturers of nitriding steel are now insisting that all steels to be hardened by nitriding be previously heat-treated, as by quenching and tempering, and that all decarburized surfaces be removed. Otherwise, dense adherent cases may not be obtained.

B. EFFECTS OF MOLYBDENUM IN NITRIDING STEELS

Inasmuch as this monograph is primarily concerned with the behavior of molybdenum in iron alloys, it is desirable to discuss the effects of molybdenum in nitriding steels before continuing

[1] Copper coating or plating is extensively used to prevent the entrance of carbon into the steel in the case carburizing process.

with a detailed account of the properties of such steels. As previously mentioned, the outstanding effect of molybdenum is in decreasing brittleness in both case and core, but it is also desirable to know whether or not it has other effects which may or may not be advantageous.

TABLE 118.—EFFECT OF COMPOSITION ON SUSCEPTIBILITY TO TEMPER-BRITTLENESS IN NITRIDING*

(All samples were quenched in oil and tempered at 700°C. (1290°F.). Half of them were nitrided 90 hr. at 500°C. (930°F.), the case removed, and then tested in impact, using notched 10 × 10 × 50 mm. (0.39 × 0.39 × 1.97 in.) specimens.)

Sample number	Composition, per cent					Brinell hardness		Charpy impact, m-kg.	
	C	Al	Cr	Mo	Ni	Original	Nitrided	Original	Nitrided
1	0.41	0.94	1.40	....	....	241	241	17.2	9.2
2	0.41	0.90	1.49	....	....	262	262	15.4	5.0
3	0.28	0.82	1.23	....	....	228	228	20.5	11.2
4	0.26	0.80	1.30	....	....	217	217	19.0	10.2
						Average.........		18.0	8.9
5	0.26	1.11	1.73	....	1.82	228	228	18.0	2.8
6	0.23	0.93	1.98	....	1.82	212	212	25.0	4.7
7	0.13	1.04	1.95	....	1.71	241	241	19.0	3.0
						Average.........		20.7	3.5
8	0.41	1.23	2.00	0.35	0.62	311	311	13.0	12.7
9	0.30	1.75	2.10	0.34	0.58	277	277	16.0	15.5
10	0.33	1.33	1.99	0.32	0.50	302	302	13.4	13.3
						Average.........		14.1	13.8

* Guillet.[194]

174. Effect of Molybdenum on Temper-brittleness.—The fact that the nitriding treatment requires prolonged heating at about 540°C. (1000°F.), followed by relatively slow cooling, imposes a condition which is known to cause temper-brittleness in certain steels. Guillet[194] investigated the effect of nitriding 90 hr. at 500°C. (930°F.) on the Charpy impact properties of the core of nitrided specimens. He studied aluminum-chromium, aluminum-chromium-nickel, and aluminum-chromium-molybdenum steels. His data are shown in Table 118. For the

0.26 to 0.41 per cent carbon, 0.80 to 0.94 per cent aluminum, and 1.23 to 1.49 per cent chromium steels the Charpy impact value was decreased from 18.0 to 8.9 m-kg. For the 0.13 to 0.26 per cent carbon, 0.93 to 1.11 per cent aluminum, 1.73 to 1.98 per cent chromium, and 1.71 to 1.82 per cent nickel steels the Charpy impact was decreased from 20.7 to 3.5 m-kg., or about 83 per cent. On the other hand, steels containing 0.30 to 0.41 per cent carbon, 1.23 to 1.75 per cent aluminum, 1.99 to 2.10 per cent chromium, and 0.32 to 0.35 per cent molybdenum, with only 0.50 to 0.62 per cent nickel showed practically no loss in impact strength.

Likewise, Homerberg and Walsted(273) found that holding at the nitriding temperature reduced the impact resistance of chromium-aluminum and especially chromium-aluminum-nickel steels but had no effect on a chromium-aluminum-molybdenum steel. Nitriding standard-size Charpy test bars reduced the impact resistance, owing to the formation of the hard case.

Daubois(329) found that aluminum-chromium-nickel nitriding steels might have their impact resistance reduced from 18 to 3 kg.[1] by heating from 40 to 90 hr. at 500°C. (930°F.), while with an addition of 0.3 per cent molybdenum the impact was reduced only from 18 to 12 kg.

Others who reported on the beneficial effect of molybdenum additions to nitriding steels in increasing core and case toughness include Freeland,(334) McQuaid,(279) and McQuaid and Ketcham.(232)

175. Effect of Molybdenum on Toughness of Nitrided Cases.—Regarding the effect of molybdenum on the toughness of nitrided cases, McQuaid and Ketcham(232) concluded as follows: "The Vickers tests indicate by cracking of the impression that steels containing high chromium and aluminum but no molybdenum are quite brittle in their outside layers." As pointed out by Sergeson,(293) the toughness of the nitrided case is greatly influenced by the nitriding temperature, and even brittle cases may be made tough by heating to 620 to 650°C. (1150 to 1200°F.).

176. Effect of Molybdenum on Depth of Case.—Investigators are not entirely in agreement with regard to the effect of molybdenum on the rate of penetration in the nitriding treatment. Freeland(334) concluded that the addition of molybdenum to aluminum-chromium-nickel nitriding steels possibly improved

[1] The unit reported by Daubois is kg. Probably this should be m-kg.

the depth of penetration. McQuaid[279] experimented with aluminum-molybdenum and aluminum-chromium nitriding steels and found that the former seemed to require a higher nitriding temperature. On the other hand, curves by McQuaid and Ketcham[232] seem to show a slightly greater penetration for the aluminum-molybdenum as compared with the aluminum-chromium steels. Guillet[173] reported that molybdenum diminished the diffusion of the nitrogen into the case. Thus, the data available seem to indicate that, for concentrations in which molybdenum has been studied in nitriding steels, its effect on the depth of case is not important.

177. Effect of Molybdenum on Hardness of Case.—Eilender and Meyer[438] nitrided iron-molybdenum alloys containing 0.25, 0.54, 1.55, 2.15, 3.50, and 8.16 per cent molybdenum and 0.05 to 0.08 per cent carbon at 550°C. (1020°F.) for 24 and 36 hr. Alloys containing more than 2.15 per cent molybdenum did not show nitride needles. Surface hardness as determined by means of the Rockwell instrument (*A* scale) and by the Herbert pendulum tester (time hardness) increased with molybdenum content to a maximum in the 3.5 per cent alloy. Specimens nitrided 36 hr. showed higher hardness than those nitrided only 24 hr. These authors made comparisons between the iron-molybdenum and iron-vanadium alloys and found that for given quantities of alloy additions the vanadium alloys gave harder nitrided cases, but the nitrided molybdenum alloy cases were tougher. Depth-hardness curves for these nitrided iron-molybdenum alloys are shown in Fig. 137.

McQuaid and Ketcham[232] concluded that under the same nitriding conditions a 0.45 per cent carbon, 1.68 per cent aluminum, 1.59 per cent chromium steel gave greater case hardness than a 0.33 per cent carbon, 0.87 per cent aluminum, 0.77 per cent molybdenum steel, but that the former was too brittle for many uses. Guillet[173] reported that molybdenum increases the hardness of the case by diminishing the rate of diffusion of the nitrogen into the steel.

Satoh[292] nitrided chromium-molybdenum steels (Nos. 5 and 6 in Table 117) 4½ hr. at 580°C. (1075°F.) and then determined the Brinell hardness, using a 1-mm. ball and 30-kg. load. Steel 5 increased in hardness from 206 to 400, while steel 6 increased from 310 to 600, thus indicating that increasing the molybdenum content increases the hardening by nitriding.

Fry's[261] depth-hardness curve shows over 1100 Vickers-Brinell number for a 0.18 per cent carbon, 3.0 per cent chromium, 0.40 per cent molybdenum steel (No. 8 in Table 117).

The data available seem to indicate that an addition of 0.20 per cent molybdenum probably has little effect on the hardness of the nitrided case, but that larger additions increase the hardness.

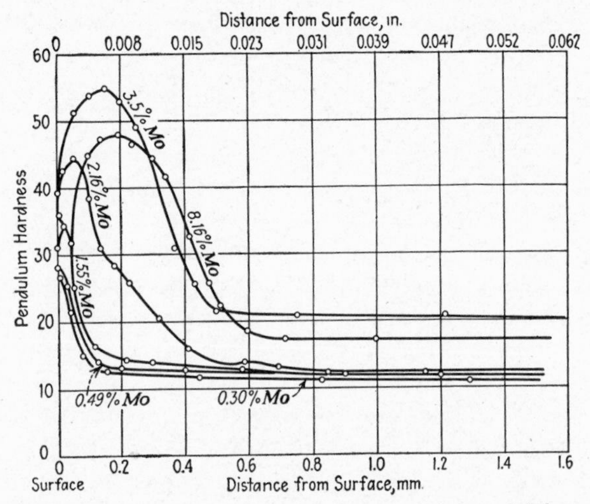

FIG. 137.—Pendulum hardness of nitrided case of iron-molybdenum alloys. (*Eilender and Meyer*.[438])

178. Other Effects of Molybdenum.—Data are not available to show the effect of molybdenum on machinability, forgeability, cleanness, and corrosion resistance of the various nitriding steels. Merten,[480] however, suggested that in the production of large ingots (5 tons) better results were obtained with aluminum-molybdenum steel than with aluminum-chromium-molybdenum steel. He reported less shrinkage and less segregation of alloying elements. Available data are also insufficient to show the effect of molybdenum on the stability and properties of nitrided cases at elevated temperatures.

C. PROPERTIES OF NITRIDING STEELS BEFORE AND AFTER NITRIDING

Extensive studies on nitriding have yielded much information regarding the mechanical properties of nitriding steels. The properties which were determined are tensile strength, hardness, wear resistance, endurance limits, creep resistance, etc. In some cases these properties were determined both at room temperature and at elevated temperatures. The effects of heating to elevated temperature on the properties of nitrided steels after cooling to room temperature received considerable attention. Some work was also reported on corrosion, on fatigue resistance, and on corrosion-fatigue resistance.

179. General Consideration of Mechanical Properties.—It is now general practice to heat-treat all steels prior to nitriding. The heat treatment usually consists in heating to 925 to 950°C. (1700 to 1750°F.), quenching in water or oil, and then tempering at about 650°C. (1200°F.). This heat treatment produces a machinable product of high strength and toughness, relieves strains, practically prevents warpage, and finally gives a better case in the nitriding treatment. Where warpage is to be kept to a minimum, a low-temperature anneal is introduced between rough machining and finishing. Since the case is quite thin, 0.005 to 0.030 in., it adds little to the tensile strength but does appear to add materially to the endurance properties in repeated bending, as will be shown later. The core properties of the heat-treated steels are, therefore, the important ones for consideration in presenting the properties of nitriding steels, both before and after nitriding, as well as at ordinary and elevated temperatures. The mechanical properties, in so far as data are available, of the steels listed in Table 117 are given in Table 119 for specimens quenched and tempered at 540 to 650°C. (1000 to 1200°F.).

180. Properties of Nitriding Steels at Elevated Temperatures. The Colonial Steel Company[413] recently published results of tensile tests at elevated temperatures on a nitriding steel of the type represented by No. 2 in Table 117 (0.25 per cent carbon, 0.80 per cent molybdenum, 1.20 per cent aluminum). The steel was quenched in oil from 940°C. (1725°F.), tempered at 650°C. (1200°F.), and tested at the temperatures shown below.

Temperature		Tensile strength, lb./sq. in.	Yield strength,* lb./sq. in.	Elongation in 2 in., per cent	Reduction of area, per cent
°C.	°F.				
480	900	111,000	79,000	24.5	68.0
565	1050	95,000	71,000	23.5	84.0
650	1200	73,000	61,000	26.0	87.0

* Reported as yield point.

TABLE 119.—PHYSICAL PROPERTIES OF NITRIDING STEELS CONTAINING MOLYBDENUM
(Quenched and then tempered as indicated)

Steel	Tempered		Tensile strength, lb./sq. in.	Yield strength,* lb./sq. in.	Elongation in 2 in., per cent	Reduction of area, per cent	Brinell hardness	Impact, ft-lb.		Reference
	°C.	°F.						Charpy	Izod	
2	540	1000	161,000	137,000	18	60	340	29	...	McQuaid and Ketcham[232]
3	500	930	157,000	134,000	15	..	410	(34)		Herbert[348]
3	750	1380	108,000	92,000	30	..	260	(62)		Herbert[348]
4	600	1110	130,000	106,000	15	55	...	..	...	Hengstenberg and Mailänder[346]
10	650	1200	112,000	75,000	26	54	...	..	...	Private Communication
20	650	1200	111,000	97,000	21	72	...	..	...	Hengstenberg and Mailänder[346]
22	540	1000	111,000	96,000	20	68	241	..	86	Sergeson and Clark[402]
22	650	1200	95,000	75,000	24	73	202	..	110	Sergeson and Clark[402]
23	540	1000	146,000	131,000	14	53	330	20	40	Sergeson and Clark[402]
23	650	1200	122,000	105,000	18	65	255	25	75	Sergeson and Clark[402]
24	540	1000	182,000	165,000	12	44	351	17	34	Sergeson and Clark[402]
24	650	1200	139,000	121,000	20	58	270	30	70	Sergeson and Clark[402]
25	540	1000	206,000	183,000	11	36	450	..	18	Sergeson and Clark[402]
25	650	1200	159,000	137,000	16	49	330	..	40	Sergeson and Clark[402]

* Reported as yield point.

180a. Hardness of Nitrided Steels.—Fry[261] reported depth-hardness in a series of curves for steels of 0.22 per cent carbon, 1.5 per cent chromium, 0.4 per cent molybdenum, 0.35 per cent vanadium; and 0.18 per cent carbon, 3.0 per cent chromium, 0.4 per cent molybdenum. Similar results for aluminum-chromium-molybdenum steels were reported by Sergeson,[293] McQuaid and Ketcham,[232, 280] Cowan,[328] Hengstenberg and Mailänder,[346] and others. Similar curves for aluminum-molybdenum steels were published by Hengstenberg and Mai-

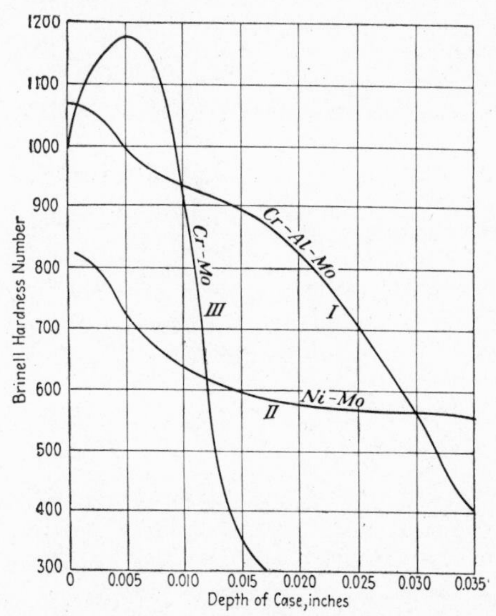

FIG. 138.—Depth-hardness curves for nitrided and carburized cases. I and III, nitrided; II, carburized. (*Fry*[261] *and Sergeson.*[293])

länder[346] and by McQuaid and Ketcham.[232] Only a few typical hardness-depth curves will be reproduced and discussed here.

Since nitriding is used in competition with case carburizing in the production of hard surfaces on steels, the properties of cases produced by these two methods may be compared.

Curves I and II in Fig. 138 from Sergeson's researches[293] are the hardness-depth curves for an aluminum-chromium-molybdenum nitriding steel (No. 24, Table 117), nitrided 90 hr. at 525°C. (975°F.), and a nickel-molybdenum carburizing steel (S.A.E. 4615), which was carburized 8 hr. at 900°C. (1650°F.), hardened by a double quench, and tempered at 150°C. (300°F.), respectively. It will be noted that the nitrided case has a surface hardness of about 1100 Brinell, while the carburized, hardened, and tempered steel has a maximum hardness of about 850. It will also be noted that at a depth of 0.015 in., at which the hardness of the carburized case is only 600, the nitrided case has a hardness of about 900. Thus the nitrided case has a higher order of hardness at the surface and maintains this advantage to a sufficient depth to present a hard, wear-resistant case, even after some wear.

Sergeson[293] determined the effect of heating to different temperatures on the room-temperature hardness of these two cases. He found that the nitrided case retained full hardness up to 540°C. (1000°F.), at which temperature the hardness of the carburized case had fallen to about 400. Thus, the nitrided case is shown to be far superior to the carburized case in retaining its hardness after heating to elevated temperatures.

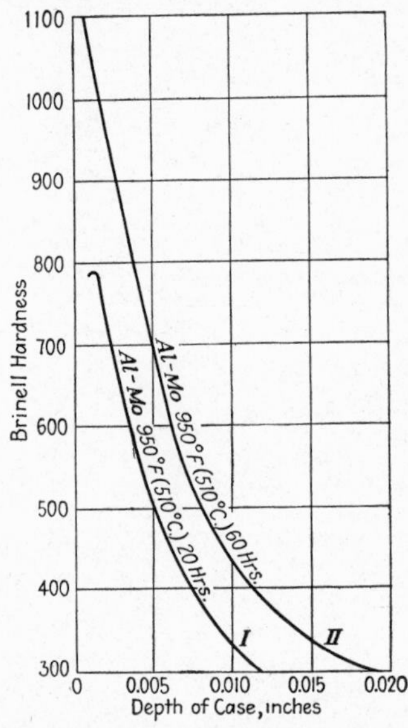

FIG. 139.—Depth-hardness curves for nitrided aluminum-molybdenum steel. (*McQuaid and Ketcham.*[232])

In Fig. 138, Curve III shows the hardness-depth curve for steel 8 in Table 117, as reported by Fry.[261] It will be noted that this steel contains 3.0 per cent chromium and 0.4 per cent molybdenum; these percentages are higher than usual for nitriding steels. The same author reported a maximum hardness of only 850 Brinell for a nitrided 0.22 per cent carbon, 1.5 per cent chromium, 0.40 per cent molybdenum, 0.35 per cent vanadium steel.

The depth-hardness curves for an aluminum-molybdenum steel (No. 2 in Table 117), nitrided at 510°C. (950°F.) for different times, are shown in Fig. 139.[232] Curve I represents 20 hr., and Curve II represents 60 hr. nitriding time. In this instance the longer time resulted in a greater hardness and a greater depth of case.

Malcolm[282] reported on the scratch hardness of nitrided steel and rates it much higher than that of high-speed steel.

He also found the abrasion resistance high. Under a pressure of 200 lb. a stainless steel (18Cr–9Ni) was badly abraded by 1,000 revolutions in a certain type of test, while a nitrided steel in the same test under the same pressure stood 100,000 revolutions with comparatively little wear.

181. Hot-hardness of Nitrided Cases.—Herbert[348] determined the hardness of a nitrided case at elevated temperatures. His curves are reproduced in Fig. 140. Curve I is for a 1.25

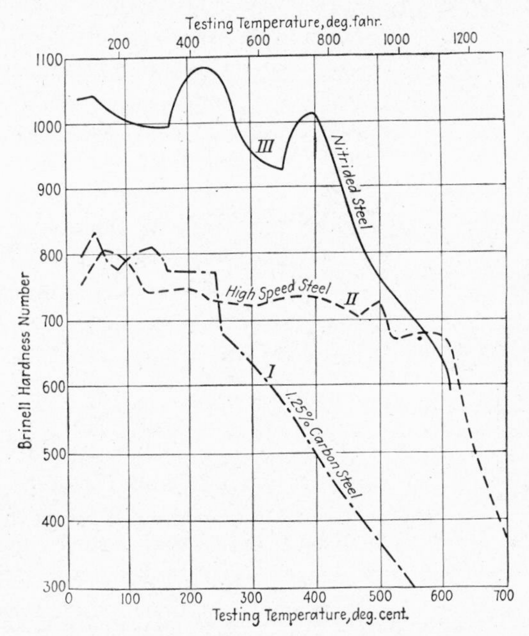

Fig. 140.—Hardness of a nitrided case at elevated temperatures. (*Herbert.*[348])

per cent carbon steel; Curve II is for a high-speed steel; and Curve III is for the nitrided case of steel 3 in Table 117. The hardness curve of the nitrided case shows two maxima—one at about 225°C. (435°F.) and another at about 400°C. (750°F.).

The hot-hardness of the nitrided case fell off rather rapidly above 400°C. (750°F.) but was still higher than that of the high-speed steel at 500°C. (930°F.). The hardness at about 610°C. (1130°F.) was 600 Brinell, but after cooling to room temperature the hardness was about 900.

These data indicate that nitrided cases may be expected to retain their full hardness up to 400°C. (750°F.).

182. Effect of Elevated Temperatures on Room Temperature Hardness of Nitrided Cases.—Numerous tests were made in which nitrided samples were reheated to various elevated temperatures and then tested for hardness at ordinary temperatures. A private communication is available which shows that nitrided samples of steel 24 (Table 117) were heated 200 hr. at 450°C. (840°F.) without any loss in hardness. Table 120 shows the effect on the hardness of reheating samples of nitrided steels (type 24). It is of interest to note that the sample of lowest initial hardness showed the lowest per cent decrease in hardness from heating at all temperatures between 595 and 870°C. (1100 and 1600°F.). The low original hardness and greater stability on heating suggest that this sample was nitrided at a higher temperature.

TABLE 120.—EFFECT OF REHEATING ON HARDNESS OF NITRIDED CASES

Reheating temperature		Hardness in per cent of hardness as nitrided			
°C.	°F.	Sample 1	Sample 2	Sample 3	Average
595	1100	.....	89	93	91
650	1200	81	82	85	83
705	1300	71	63	77	70
760	1400	57	54	70	60
815	1500	51	45	62	53
870	1600	34	?	54	44
Hardness as nitrided*......		1100	990	880	
Reheating time, hr........		1	1	5	

* Vickers-Brinell.

183. Tensile Properties of Nitrided Steels.—The effect of nitriding on the tensile properties of steel 24 in Table 117 was reported by Homerberg and Walsted.[(273)] Hengstenberg and Mailänder[(346)] made a similar study of a series of five steels.

Some of Homerberg and Walsted's results are shown in Table 121.

These data show that, with the low tempering temperature before nitriding, there may be a loss in both tensile strength and yield strength as a result of the nitriding treatment. When the specimens were tempered at 595 to 650°C. (1100 to 1200°F.), there was little or no change in strength. The "toughness" properties, elongation, reduction of area, and impact, were markedly lowered in all cases by the nitriding treatment.

TABLE 121.—EFFECT OF NITRIDING ON TENSILE PROPERTIES*
(Tensile test specimens nitrided 90 hr. at 480°C. (900°F.), slowly cooled. Tempered before nitriding, as indicated. Tested at room temperature)

Tempered		Condition tested	Tensile strength, lb./sq. in.	Yield strength,† lb./sq. in.	Elongation in 2 in., per cent	Reduction of area, per cent	Charpy impact, ft-lb.
°C.	°F.						
540	1000	Tempered	182,000	159,000	15	50	22
540	1000	Nitrided	171,000	139,000	6	13	14
595	1100	Tempered	156,000	138,000	16	57	35
595	1100	Nitrided	159,000	129,000	5	16	18
650	1200	Tempered	138,000	120,000	20	60	44
650	1200	Nitrided	138,000	110,000	4	17	21
705	1300	Tempered	121,000	103,000	23	62	55
705	1300	Nitrided	123,000	98,000	8	20	24

* Homerberg and Walsted.(273)
† Reported as yield point.

TABLE 122.—EFFECT OF TEMPERATURE ON STRENGTH OF NITRIDED SPECIMENS*

Testing temperature		Tensile strength, lb./sq. in.	Elongation in 2 in., per cent	Reduction of area, per cent
°C.	°F.			
425	800	134,000	6.5	30.5
480	900	124,000	9.5	31.0
540	1000	98,000	15.5	44.5
595	1100	42,000	†	†
650	1200	39,000	†	†
705	1300	28,000	†	†
760	1400	20,000	†	†

* Homerberg and Walsted.(273)
† Accurate values not obtainable.

Homerberg and Walsted(273) tested nitrided specimens of steel 24 at temperatures from 425 to 760°C. (800 to 1400°F.). These specimens were oil-quenched from 900°C. (1650°F.), tempered at 540°C. (1000°F.), and then nitrided 90 hr. at 480°C.

TABLE 123.—TENSILE PROPERTIES OF NITRIDED STEEL 24 AT ELEVATED TEMPERATURES*

Test piece	Temperature		Proportional limit, lb./sq. in.	Johnson limit, lb./sq. in.	Yield strength		Tensile strength, lb./sq. in.	Modulus of elasticity, million lb./sq. in.	Elongation in 3 in., per cent	Elongation in 2 in., per cent	Reduction of area, per cent
	°C.	°F.			0.2 per cent plastic, lb./sq. in.	0.5 per cent total, lb./sq. in.					
7	25	77	75,000	97,500	126,000	117,000	147,250	29.3	1.6	....	8.0
2	25	77	85,000	96,000	122,000	108,000	142,500	22.9	4.6	5.0	8.0
4	120	250	75,000	89,000	118,000	110,000	139,000	28.9	4.3	6.0	8.5
11	260	500	60,000	76,500	105,000	98,500	122,000	26.8	4.3	5.5	0.0
1	260	500	47,500	82,500	112,000	105,000	131,700	28.1	4.3	5.0	6.0
3	400	750	50,000	75,000	102,500	97,000	122,000	26.6	7.0	9.5	19.5
9	400	750	57,500	70,000	103,500	93,000	119,500	25.6	7.3	10.0	16.0
12	455	850	40,000	61,000	86,000	81,600	101,500	22.9	9.3	13.0	29.5
8	455	850	32,500	59,500	88,500	88,000	108,000	29.1	10.6	15.0	36.5
5	510	950	28,000	65,000	92,500	82,500	104,500	21.6	11.3	16.5	40 approx.
10	565	1050	22,500	36,000	63,700	63,500	76,000	21.0	15.0	22.0	

* Courtesy N. L. Mochel.

(900°F.). Their results are given in Table 122. These data show that the strength of this 0.30 to 0.40 per cent carbon aluminum-chromium-molybdenum steel falls off rapidly at temperatures above 540°C. (1000°F.). It showed better toughness at 540°C. (1000°F.) than at 425°C. (800°F.), but at 595°C. (1100°F.) and higher the values were not determinable with accuracy on account of the character of the failure.

Further data regarding tensile properties at elevated temperatures of a fully nitrided steel of type No. 24 in Table 117 are given in Table 123. The relation of proportional limit to Johnson limit and yield strength for 0.2 per cent plastic and 0.5 per cent total yield are particularly interesting. Elongation and reduction of area increase at temperatures above 260°C. (500°F.).

The steels studied by Hengstenberg and Mailänder[346] are listed with their heat treatments in Table 124. Some steels which do not contain molybdenum were included for comparison. Their steels FK 345 and FPK 13 are steels 4 and 20, respectively, in Table 117.

Results of tensile tests are given in Table 125. The values given are the average of two tests.

TABLE 124.—COMPOSITIONS AND HEAT TREATMENT OF SPECIMENS*

Specimen mark	Composition, per cent							Heat treatment				
								Quenched			Tempered in air	
	C	Si	Mn	Cr	Al	Ni	Mo	°C.	°F.	Medium	°C.	°F.
FP15	0.30	0.43	0.41	1.43	1.12	....	....	920	1690	Oil	650	1200
FP13	0.52	0.14	0.27	1.74	1.28	....	....	900	1650	Oil	650	1200
FP13A	0.52	0.14	0.27	1.74	1.28	....	....	880	1615	Oil	670	1240
FPK13	0.32	0.22	0.72	1.24	0.93	....	0.34	840	1545	Water	600	1110
FPE23	0.42	0.19	0.38	1.68	1.33	2.65	....	870	1600	Oil	660	1220
FK345	0.15	0.25	0.40	0.85	....	....	0.41	930	1705	Oil	650	1200

* Hengstenberg and Mailänder.[346]

These steels were tested in tension in three conditions:

A. Heat-treated (see Table 124).

B. Heat-treated, then heated 48 hr. at 500°C. (930°F.).

C. Heat-treated, then nitrided 48 hr. at 500°C. (930°F.).

TABLE 125.—RESULTS OF TENSILE TESTS*

Specimen mark	Heat treatment	Tensile strength, lb./sq. in.	Yield strength, lb./sq. in.	Elongation ($L = 5D$), per cent	Reduction of area, per cent
FP 15	*A*	115,000	92,400	22.2	68
	B	114,000	88,900	22.5	66
	C	118,000	95,300	†	25
FP13	*A*	136,200	114,500	13.0	52
	B	146,700	121,500	14.4	47
	C	154,400	†	†	7.5
FP 13A	*A*	131,000	105,000	20.7	60
	B	131,000	104,000	19.2	60
	C	132,600	108,000	†	14.5
FPK 13	*A*	130,000	106,000	15.4	55
	B	131,000	104,500	17.3	56
	C	144,000	113,000	7.2	14
FPE 23	*A*	157,000	136,000	17.4	54
	B	176,000	158,000	16.6	44
	C	169,000	†	0	1
FK 345	*A*	111,400	98,900	20.6	72
	B	110,500	95,300	20.9	72
	C	107,000	†	0	0

* Hengstenberg and Mailänder.[346]
† Not determinable.

It will be noted from the data in Table 125 that nitriding these steels caused a marked decrease in toughness as measured by elongation and reduction of area; however, they were not rendered brittle by heating at the nitriding temperature, as shown by the *B* specimens. Here again the changes in the strength due to nitriding were of minor importance. The steels listed in Table 124 were also tested for their endurance limits, the results of which will be discussed later.

184. Fatigue Resistance.—Fuller[339, 443] using a rotating-beam testing machine determined endurance properties of three nitriding steels at steam pressures up to 220 lb. per sq. in. and temperatures up to 370°C. (700°F.). His nitriding steels *F* and *G* correspond to Nos. 24 and 22, respectively, in Table 117 while the composition of his third steel (*H*) is not given.

Previous to machining these steels were heat-treated as indicated below:

Steel	Quenched in oil		Tempered	
	°C.	°F.	°C.	°F.
F	930	1705	650	1200
G-1	950	1740	650	1200
G-2	960	1760	625	1155
H	(not given)			

After machining, the specimens were nitrided 24 hr. at 500°C. (930°F.) in ammonia gas. The properties of these steels before and after nitriding are given in Table 126.

Endurance limits were determined in some instances on the basis of ten, and in others of fifty million cycles. Results are shown in Table 127.

It will be noted from Table 127 that steel *F*, before nitriding, showed endurance values ranging from 74,000 lb. per sq. in. in

TABLE 126.—PROPERTIES OF STEELS TESTED*

Steel	Condition	Tensile strength, lb./sq. in.	Yield point, lb./sq. in.	Yield strength,† lb./sq. in.	Elongation in 2 in., per cent	Reduction of area, per cent	Brinell hardness	Charpy impact (keyhole notch), ft-lb.
F	Before nitriding	123,000	99,000	84,000	21	62	...	45
F	After nitriding	125,000	100,000	......	13	34	...	23
G-1	Before nitriding	126,000	....	68,000	20	60	262	40
G-2	Before nitriding	129,000	....	83,000	19	61	263	40
H	Before nitriding	127,000	....	62,000	22	52	...	15

* Fuller.(339, 443)

† Reported as elastic limit.

air at room temperature to 50,000 lb. per sq. in. in 220 lb. steam at 370°C. (700°F.). Under similar conditions the nitrided specimens of this steel gave values ranging from 91,000 to 58,000 lb. per sq. in.

The endurance value of 73,000 lb. per sq. in. for nitrided steel *F* in a steam jet in atmosphere is high when compared with values of 24,000 lb. per sq. in. for a 3.5 per cent nickel, 0.35 per cent carbon steel of 119,000 lb. per sq. in. tensile strength, and of

33,000 lb. per sq. in. for a 12.5 per cent chromium, 0.10 per cent carbon iron of 102,000 lb. per sq. in. tensile strength. Fuller concluded:

The ratio of the air-room temperature endurance limit to ultimate strength was higher in the case of nitrided nitriding steels than in that of any of the others[1] tested . . .

A marked tendency of the endurance values of the nitrided nitriding steels to drop off with increasing temperature was observed . . .

The ratio of the steam-jet atmosphere to air-room temperature endurance values was higher in the case of the nitrided nitriding steels than in that of the other steels tested . . .

TABLE 127.—ENDURANCE PROPERTIES OF NITRIDING STEELS*

Steel	Treatment	Condition of test	Endurance limit, lb./sq. in.
F	Before nitriding	Air, room temperature	74,000
F	Before nitriding	Steam, 60 lb., 150°C. (300°F.)	64,000
F	Before nitriding	Steam, 220 lb., 370°C. (700°F.)	50,000
F	Nitrided	Air, room temperature	91,000
F	Nitrided	Steam jet in atmosphere	73,000
F	Nitrided	Steam, 60 lb., 150°C. (300°F.)	69,000
F	Nitrided	Steam, 220 lb., 370°C. (700°F.)	58,000
G-1	Nitrided	Air, room temperature	65,000
G-1	Nitrided	Steam jet in atmosphere	62,000
G-1	Nitrided	Steam, 60 lb., 150°C. (300°F.)	69,000
G-1	Nitrided	Steam, 220 lb., 370°C. (700°F.)	54,000
G-2	Nitrided	Air, room temperature	74,000
G-2	Nitrided	Steam jet in atmosphere	71,000
G-2	Nitrided	Steam, 60 lb., 150°C. (300°F.)	69,000
G-2	Nitrided	Steam, 220 lb., 370°C. (700°F.)	53,000
H	Nitrided	Air, room temperature	92,000

* Fuller.(443)

The 60-lb. 149°C. (300°F.) steam-endurance value of notched[2] nitrided specimens ranged from 74 to 83 per cent of that shown by corresponding unnotched specimens.

[1] The others were a nickel steel with 3.5 per cent nickel and 0.35 per cent carbon, a chromium iron with 12.5 per cent chromium and 0.10 per cent carbon, and three austenitic steels of the 18 per cent chromium, 8 per cent nickel type with carbon contents of 0.065, 0.085, and 0.15 per cent. They were subjected to various heat treatments before being tested.

[2] The notch used was 45-deg., 0.035 in. deep, with a 0.010-in. radius. The stress was calculated on the diameter at the base of the notch.

Mochel[380] used steel (No. 24, Table 117, page 360) which he heat-treated by quenching in oil from 955°C. (1750°F.), followed by reheating 1 hr. at 595°C. (1100°F.). One set of samples was nitrided 90 hr. at 510°C. (950°F.) and another set 48 hr. at 540°C. (1000°F.). Whether only heat-treated or heat-treated and nitrided, these specimens showed tensile-strength values of about 160,000 lb. per sq. in. The nitrided specimens showed Vickers-Brinell hardness numbers of 975 to 1065. He determined the endurance limit of nitrided samples as 84,000 lb. per sq. in., as compared with 76,000 lb. per sq. in. for the unnitrided specimens.

Endurance properties of the steels listed in Table 124 (page 375) were determined by Hengstenberg and Mailänder.[346] Their endurance tests were made on the Schenck four-point loading rotating-beam testing machine, and they made direct comparisons of the endurance limits of the steels in the three conditions of heat treatment given in connection with Table 124. The results of their tests are given in Table 128.

It will be observed that the ratio of endurance limit to tensile strength has a normal value for the steels in the quenched and tempered condition, and for those that were subjected to heating at the nitriding temperature for 48 hr. On the other hand, this ratio varies from 0.57 to 0.90 for the different nitrided steels but is always higher than for the unnitrided specimens. It was observed in the fatigue fractures that initial failure started at a point below the surface approximately representing the junction of case and core, which naturally would be at a lower stress than the maximum fiber stress of the surface.

It, therefore, appears that the higher strength of the case is responsible for the increased endurance limit of nitrided specimens. Hengstenberg and Mailänder[346] also showed that a slight imperfection or surface damage on nitrided specimens was not particularly harmful and did not lower the endurance limit as in the case of ordinary heat-treated steel specimens.

Specimen FK 345 (a chromium-molybdenum steel) showed a particularly marked increase in endurance limit due to nitriding, the endurance limit being raised approximately 50 per cent. In this specimen the maximum hardness of the case was only about 700 Brinell, but the case showed a greater depth than the other steels of this series. The increased depth of case apparently was responsible for the higher endurance limit. Since a tapered specimen was used in these tests and the failure was not always at the minimum diameter, the last column of Table 128 shows the calculated stress at the point at which failure started.

TABLE 128.—RESULTS OF ENDURANCE TESTS*

Specimen mark	Heat treatment	Endurance limit,† 1,000 lb./sq. in.	Ratio, endurance limit to tensile strength	Stress at point of beginning of fracture, 1,000 lb./sq. in.
	A	59.8	0.52	
FP 15..........	*B*	56.9 to 58.3	0.51	
	C	78.2	0.66	62.6
	A	71.2 to 72.6	0.53	
FP 13..........	*B*	74.0	0.5	
	C	95.3	0.62	75.4
FP 13A........	*A*	65.4 to 66.8	0.5	
	C	83.9	0.63	68.3
FPK 13.........	*A*	68.3 to 69.8	0.53	
	C	88.2 to 89.6	0.62	69.7
FPE 23.........	*A*	78.2	0.5	
	C	96.7	0.57	82.5
	A	61.2	0.55	
FK 345.........	*B*	65.4 to 66.8	0.59	
	C	95.3 to 96.7	0.9	66.9
Average for unnitrided specimens.........	..	....	0.53	

* Hengstenberg and Mailänder.(346)

† The endurance limit was taken as the maximum stress to withstand five million cycles of stress.

Sergeson and Clark,(402) working with steel 24 in Table 117, also reported that nitriding raises the endurance limit.

McAdam(471) included a nitriding steel (0.36 per cent carbon, 2.03 per cent aluminum, and 1.62 per cent chromium) in his studies of the influence of stress on corrosion. This steel was tested in the heat-treated and in the nitrided condition. The samples tested had the following properties:

Property	Unnitrided	Nitrided
Tensile strength, lb./sq. in.	148,500	146,800
Yield strength,* lb./sq. in.	102,500	81,400
Elongation in 2 in., per cent	17.8	7.3
Reduction of area, per cent	54.1	13.8

* Reported as proportional limit.

The other materials investigated were S.A.E. steels 3140 and 5135; stainless iron; nickel; aluminum-bronze; a 96 per cent copper, 3.2 per cent nickel, 0.8 per cent silicon alloy; and Muntz metal. McAdam found that under the conditions of his experiments the nitrided steel was superior in corrosion fatigue to stainless iron. The nitrided steel, in resistance to corrosion fatigue in carbonate or salt water, was found superior to any other alloy investigated.

The results presented above show that nitriding, while decreasing elongation and reduction of area in the tensile tests, materially raises the endurance limit. The only endurance tests at elevated temperatures are those by Fuller,[339, 443] in which he found nitrided steels superior to the others which he tested in steam at temperatures up to 370°C. (700°F.).

A word of caution should be added regarding the probable endurance in axial loading, in which the higher strength of the case may not be as beneficial as in rotary bending.

It should also be remembered that in practical service, where repeated stress may be accompanied by repeated impact, the results of the usual laboratory endurance test cannot always be taken as a sufficient criterion for service life. Since notched-bar impact strength is reduced by nitriding and actual life in rough service is usually a sort of balance between laboratory endurance limit and notched-bar impact strength, it might be a bit optimistic to quote the high figures without a word of caution.

185. Creep Tests on Nitrided Steel.—Malcolm[282] reported results of a long-duration test on a nitrided chromium-aluminum steel which was tested at 540°C. (1000°F.) under a load of 10,180 lb. per sq. in. The extension in the first 4,000 hr. amounted to 0.002 in. per in., and there was no further extension during an additional 5,000 hr.

186. Stability of Nitrided Cases.—In the previous discussion (page 372) it has been shown that nitrided cases have been found to withstand long periods of heating (200 hr.) at a temperature of 450°C. (840°F.) with no loss in hardness. Also that such cases will withstand heating, at least for short periods of time, to 540 to 595°C. (1000 to 1100°F.) with little or no loss in hardness. Cowan[328] studied the effect of heating a nitrided steel (No. 13, Table 117) for 36 hr. at 620°C. (1150°F.) in an atmosphere of hydrogen. Figure 141 shows the hardness-depth curve for this steel as nitrided in Curve I, and after heating in hydrogen in Curve II. There was a loss in hardness, but the loss is of the

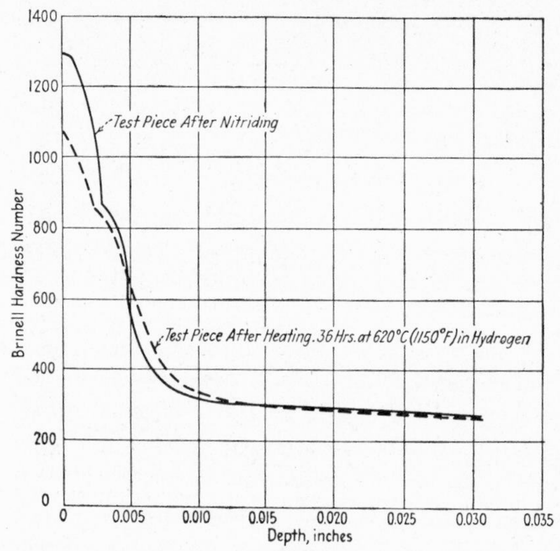

FIG. 141.—Depth-hardness curves for nitrided steel before and after heating in hydrogen. (*Cowan.*[328])

order shown in Table 120 (page 372), and Cowan concludes that molecular hydrogen has no action on the nitrided case.

187. Corrosion Resistance of Nitrided Steels.—Malcolm[282] reported that nitrided steel resists oxidation and corrosion under the action of superheated steam. Sergeson and Deal[403] studied the corrosion resistance of a nitrided steel (No. 24, Table 117), using samples which had been nitrided 90 hr. at 525°C. (975°F.). From their studies of the effects of various corroding media on nitrided steels Sergeson and Deal concluded that:

1. Nitrided steel is not adapted for use in acids, such as sulphuric and hydrochloric.
2. It is extremely resistant to alkali, atmosphere, crude oil, ethyl gasoline, natural gas combustion products, tap water, and still salt water.

3. It is slightly attacked in aerated soft water and by alternately wetting in salt water and drying.

4. There seems to be no action between it and brass in contact, either still or moving, immersed in hard water.

Homerberg and Walsted[273] reported that specimens nitrided 90 hr. withstood the action of salt spray over 100 hr.

It seems to be a general opinion that the original nitrided surface offers better resistance to corrosion than ground or even polished surfaces.

The nitriding treatment is being applied to plain carbon steel in certain uses as a means of preventing corrosion.

188. Welding Nitriding Steels.—Fry,[261] at the Nitriding Symposium in 1929, mentioned among the unsolved problems: "Obtaining welds in which the weld junction will be perfectly hard after nitriding." Apparently this problem has now been solved in the development of large cylinder bushings for locomotives which are made by forming the bushing from plates and then welding in the atomic hydrogen arc.

189. Expansion during Nitriding.—Hobrock,[221] using a steel of the type of No. 9 in Table 117, determined the expansion during nitriding and concluded that the expansion could be represented by

$$Kn = \frac{\text{change in linear dimension}}{\text{depth of case}}$$

in which Kn is defined as the coefficient of expansion. With cylinders in which the expansion of two faces is involved, the coefficient is expressed by

$$Kn = \frac{\text{total change in linear dimension}}{2(\text{depth of case})}$$

Hobrock took as the depth of case that depth at which the hardness was approximately of the same order as that of the specimen before nitriding.

The average value of Kn was found to decrease with increase of nitriding time; it varied from 0.040 for 10 hr. to 0.025 for 90 hr. With long nitriding times the material did not continue to grow. A calculated value for a specimen nitrided 24 hr. gave an expansion of 0.00114 in. as compared with an experimental value of 0.0011 in.

McQuaid and Ketcham[232] observed a growth in diameter of 0.001 in. on specimens nitrided 15 to 20 hr. They experimented with S.A.E. 1020, 4615, chromium-aluminum, and molybdenum-aluminum steels.

Homerberg and Walsted[273] experimented with steels of the types represented by Nos. 9, 10, and 11 in Table 117 (page 360) and reported that increasing the nitriding temperature increased the amount of growth during nitriding. Steel 9 after nitriding 48 hr. at 480, 540, 595, and 650°C. (900, 1000, 1100, and 1200°F.) showed increases in diameter of 0.0003, 0.0009, 0.0018, and 0.0018 in., respectively.

Sergeson[401] observed an increase of 0.001 to 0.003 in. in diameter, depending upon the time of nitriding.

After practical experience in nitriding parts up to 12 in. in diameter, Higgins[350] drew the following conclusion regarding growth: "Growth appears to be progressive in forgings ranging in size from 3 to 12 in. in diameter and is approximately 0.00025 in. for the smaller size to 0.002 in. for the large size."

The information available indicates that, for a given steel and a given nitriding treatment, the expansion during nitriding can be determined and allowed for in the final machining before nitriding.

The expansion at sharp corners is more pronounced, and such corners should be avoided in work to be nitrided. Some warpage may, of course, occur if thin plates are nitrided on one side only, as was clearly shown by Cunningham and Ashbury,[433] who nitrided strips (3 × ½ × 1/16 in.) of a nitriding steel 30, 50, and 80 hr. and observed warpages of 0.095, 0.113, and 0.142 in., respectively.

D. USES OF NITRIDED STEELS

The use of nitrided materials in general and at elevated temperatures in particular is dependent upon a high degree of hardness and resistance to wear, abrasion, erosion; to some extent upon resistance to corrosion; and possibly upon a high endurance limit when subjected to repeated bending stresses under the previously mentioned service condition.

Many uses of nitrided parts were noted by Alden,[302] Freeland,[334] Homerberg,[223] and Sergeson and Clark,[402] and in trade publications. More specialized uses were reported by French and Herschman,[192] Helquist,[271] Malcolm,[282] and Roshong.[1]

[1] Private communication.

The following are some of the automobile parts which have been made of nitrided steels: cam followers, cams, cam shafts, crank shafts, piston pins, pump shafts, push rods, seats for valves, steering worms, taper gears, tappets, timing gears, valves, valve push-rod rollers, and valve-stem guides. According to Freeland,[334] nitrided cylinder liners are used in the Hispano-Suiza car, which show unusually low wear in service, and nitrided bevel and transmission gears are used in some of the best cars in France and Germany.

Of the above uses the exhaust valve presents the severest high-temperature requirement. It is now generally agreed that the usual nitrided steels are attacked when used as valves with gasoline containing lead tetraethyl.

A most interesting report of the performance of nitrided valves in an airplane engine was given by Colwell:[326] steel 24 in Table 117 (page 360) was used for intake valves and steel 26 for exhaust valves. These steels were nitrided 90 hr. to produce a case of 90 to 100 scleroscope hardness and of 0.010 to 0.020 in. depth. The tips were tempered to a hardness of 75 to 85 to prevent chipping from tappet action. These valves were used in an endurance flight of 647 hr. at an average speed of 1,400 r.p.m., using "straight run aviation gas." After the run the valves were described as follows: " . . . the external appearance was splendid. Stems were bright with a beautiful glaze and showed no evidence of scratches or other wear. The seats were also bright and clean, without signs of pitting." It was estimated that during the run the valves opened and closed more than twenty-seven million times, the exhaust valve temperature ranging well over 540°C. (1000°F.).

Thus, in the absence of lead tetraethyl and its combustion products, it seems that nitrided steel gives satisfactory valve performance. For extremely high temperatures special nitriding steels should be used in order to provide greater high-temperature strength.

Mochel[380] reported the absence of seizing in the use of nitrided steels for valve-guide and valve-bonnet bushings, which have to operate under high-temperature conditions without lubrication. His tests were made at 400°C. (750°F.). He found that nitrided steel operated well against itself and against nickel bronze, chromium plating, monel metal, and stainless iron.

Alden(302) reported endurance tests on standard and nitrided crank shafts, in which the center bearing was 0.040 in. out of line with the end bearings. The standard shafts failed after 75 hr.—the nitrided shafts in about 1,500 hr. These tests indicate the durability of nitrided crank shafts for severe service. Likewise, the success of the nitrided cam shaft and mesh gear seems to be established; there is a question about nitrided clash gears, although some are in use.

In airplane motors the uses are similar to those in the automobile. Reduction gears nitrided 80 hr. at 540°C. (1000°F.) to give a case hardness of 950 to 1000 Vickers-Brinell and a case depth of about 0.030 in. are reported[1] to be giving satisfactory service against carburized steel at about 150°C. (300°F.). Piston pins and cam followers nitrided 25 hr. at 540°C. (1000°F.) are reported to be giving good service.

Alden(302) discussed the use of nitrided alloy steel in Diesel engines and listed the following parts: fuel-valve tappets and guides, pump plungers and cylinders, fuel-pump regulators, by-pass valves and guides, valve stems, valves and seats, piston pins,[2] piston rods, gears, fuel injection nozzles, crank shafts, cylinder liners, fuel-nozzle spray tips, fuel-nozzle check valves, and cams. The same author described a nitrided Diesel engine piston rod 14 ft. long, 6¼ in. in diameter, weighing about 1,400 lb., which warped only 0.020 in. in nitriding.

The use of nitrided steels for the trim on valves subjected to high-temperature and high steam-pressure service was reported by Malcolm(282) and others.[3] Malcolm found that a nitrided steel possessed properties of extreme hardness, wear and abrasion resistance, chemical stability under superheated steam, combined with a tough core having high impact value and tensile strength, together with a coefficient of expansion similar to ordinary steels. His long-time loading tests and abrasion tests were mentioned. By practical tests he found nitrided valve trim superior to either monel metal or stainless steel. As an illustration, an overload valve in a large steam station was trimmed with hardened stainless steel, which failed in ten days and was replaced by nitrided steel, which after a year was functioning satisfactorily.

[1] Private communication.

[2] Reports were received that nitrided automobile piston pins are attacked by the products of combustion of lead tetraethyl.

[3] Private communication.

Nitrided gate valves were used on 1400-lb. per sq. in. steam pressure stations. Valve installations of nitrided steel were found satisfactory at operating temperatures of 500 to 540°C. (930 to 1000°F.).

Sergeson,(401) in discussing recent developments in nitriding, mentioned a number of successful uses for nitrided parts, such as valves for injecting tar into open-hearth furnaces, link pins and bushings, by-pass pump cams, reamers for hard rubber, die inserts for forging connecting rods, and rivet sets for hot riveting.

Malcolm(282) also reported the use of nitrided steel for the seats and disks in valves in the oil-refining industry, which had been in service for a year without failure, whereas other materials had failed in about two weeks.

A manufacturer[1] reported that nitrided seat rings and disk rings in a line of cast-steel valves for 400, 600, 900, and 1350 lb. per sq. in. working pressure are proving quite satisfactory. A pressure of 1350 lb. per sq. in. corresponds to a temperature of about 310°C. (585°F.).

Nitrided plungers for pumps in the petroleum industry are reported[1] to be working satisfactorily with "sweet" oil at 400°C. (750°F.) and 900 lb. per sq. in. pressure. The nitrided plunger is said to resist the scoring and abrasive action of the packing better than any material tried so far. The nitrided plunger is not satisfactory in contact with "sour" oil.

French and Herschman(192) included a nitrided steel (0.43 per cent carbon, 1.85 per cent chromium, 1.29 per cent molybdenum) in their study of wear of plug gages. Chromium-plated gages showed the best resistance in the metal-to-metal wear test. The nitrided steel was second and was superior to such materials as high-speed steel, stellite, and high-carbon, high-chromium steel.

Roshong(291) found that a core which had been nitrided 50 hr. and used in a die-casting machine in which an aluminum-silicon alloy at 620°C. (1150°F.) was shot into the die was "file hard" after about two years and after producing over 125,000 castings. Helquist(271) also reported that nitrided-steel dies are useful in the production of aluminum die castings.

According to Davis,(434) several automobile manufacturers are using nitrided water-pump shafts treated to give a case 0.020 to 0.030 in. thick.

[1] Private communication.

E. AUTHOR'S SUMMARY

190. Present Status of Nitriding.—During the past few years, a large amount of research has been done in the field of nitriding. The quality of the steel has been improved, and the cost reduced. Improvements have been made in the design and operation of nitriding equipment, resulting in some decrease in the time required and improvement in the uniformity of the quality of the nitrided product.

The use of nitrided products has been extended. While there have been some failures of nitrided parts in service for which they were not well suited, or due to improper processing, the general field of uses of nitrided parts has been greatly increased. The use of nitrided parts at elevated temperatures, up to 540 to 650°C. (1000 to 1200°F.), seems quite promising, and further extension of the use of nitrided parts up to these somewhat elevated temperatures seems very likely. The corrosion resistance of nitrided surfaces at these temperatures also makes them more promising for this type of service.

191. Needed Information.—Data regarding the physical properties of nitrided steels, both at ordinary temperatures and at elevated temperatures, are incomplete. This is particularly true with reference to creep-test data and only to a slightly lesser degree to the endurance properties.

While quite a large variety of steels have been studied with reference to their suitability for nitriding, there are undoubtedly other compositions which deserve consideration.

The uses which have been made of nitrided steels indicate the types of services for which these steels will be satisfactory and offer numerous possibilities for further developments, especially if the attempts being made to accelerate the nitriding operation, on which some favorable results have been reported(361) (U. S. Patent 1,793,309, Feb. 17, 1931), are successful.

Considerable information, though not all of it is consistent, is available on the iron-nitrogen diagram, but little or no work has been done on the influence of a third element, such as molybdenum, on this diagram.

192. The Effect of Molybdenum.—Inasmuch as molybdenum is present in all but a very few nitriding steels—most of the steels in use containing aluminum, chromium, and molybdenum—and as those in which molybdenum is not used are of quite different basic composition, little information with respect to the exact effect conferred by molybdenum upon the properties of the unnitrided or nitrided steels is available. Hengstenberg and Mailänder's data[346] come the nearest to showing the effect of molybdenum, but the compositions and heat treatments recorded differ in the unnitrided condition. Their FP15 and FPK13 steels (page 375) would indicate a higher core strength in the presence of molybdenum, as well as a higher endurance limit. The importance of the freedom from temper-brittleness conferred by molybdenum is so great that this element appears to be essential in the usual aluminum-chromium type of nitriding steel. The toughness of the case is improved by molybdenum. It has not been definitely established that molybdenum appreciably affects the rate of nitriding or the depth of case.

As is the case with most other steels containing molybdenum, the molybdenum content of the nitriding steels has been materially reduced from the original higher percentages in early steels, present nitriding steels of the chromium-aluminum type seldom containing much over 0.2 per cent molybdenum, which seems sufficient to avoid temper-brittleness.

Nitrided steels have many useful applications for wear resistance, have some value for corrosion resistance, but will not resist mineral acids.

CHAPTER XI

OTHER IRON-MOLYBDENUM ALLOYS

Manganese-molybdenum Steels—Miscellaneous Structural Steels Containing Molybdenum—Corrosion- and Heat-resistant Alloys—Miscellaneous Alloys—Author's Summary

Perhaps the preface to this chapter should start with a comment on the difficulty of developing an outline in which all the iron-molybdenum alloys would readily find a place. The alloys discussed here consist of low-alloy or structural steels that do not have so wide a use as the steels previously discussed, of the complex alloys such as alloys resistant to hydrochloric and sulphuric acids, alloys used for valves in internal-combustion engines, other heat-resistant alloys, tool and die steels containing small amounts of molybdenum, cobalt magnet steels, age-hardenable austenitic alloys, and, finally, iron containing small amounts of copper and molybdenum, made in the open hearth, and sold under the trade name of "Toncan iron."

A. MANGANESE-MOLYBDENUM STEELS

The class of alloys designated as carbon steels generally contains less than 1 per cent manganese. Steels containing over 1 per cent manganese are usually termed manganese steels, and justifiably so, for a manganese content increased over that required for soundness of a carbon steel is equivalent to the addition of a true alloying element. The commercial manganese steels may be divided into two classes: (1) those containing between 1 and 3 per cent manganese, usually referred to as pearlitic, and (2) those containing about 13 per cent manganese, which are austenitic. It has been found that the addition of molybdenum to steels of the first group improves the mechanical properties, and the following discussion is confined to such steels.

193. Wrought Steels.—Although Sargent,[92] in 1920, mentioned manganese-molybdenum structural steels, the properties of such steels were first fully described by Gillett and Mack.[151] The properties of the heat-treated steels listed in Table 129

TABLE 129.—MECHANICAL PROPERTIES OF MANGANESE-MOLYBDENUM STEELS*

Number	Composition, per cent			Oil-quenched		Tempered		Tensile strength, lb./sq. in.	Yield strength,† lb./sq. in.	Elongation in 2 in., per cent	Reduction of area, per cent	Brinell hardness	Izod impact, ft-lb.	Endurance limit, lb./sq. in.
	C	Mn	Mo	°C.	°F.	°C.	°F.							
6	0.44	1.05	....	875	1605	350	660	209,000	160,000	7.0	17.0	395	10.5	
				875	1605	400	750	187,000	150,000	8.5	24.0	380	15	89,000
				875	1605	450	840	168,750	135,000	11.0	34.0	330	27	85,000
8	0.44	1.29	0.34	875	1605	375	700	220,250	185,000	11.0	37.2	430	9	
				875	1605	450	840	194,750	170,000	11.5	37.2	400	15	98,000
				875	1605	525	975	170,000	145,000	15.0	40.3	340	36.5	
7	0.43	1.24	0.73	875	1605	400	750	221,500	180,000	13.0	49.1	430	16	
				875	1605	475	880	193,250	160,000	14.5	51.9	395	20.5	96,000
				875	1605	550	1020	181,750	157,000	17.0	49.1	370	32	85,000

* Gillett and Mack.[151]

† Reported as yield point.

prove that steels containing slightly over 1 per cent manganese and less than 1 per cent molybdenum have properties closely approaching those of the better known chromium-molybdenum and nickel-molybdenum steels.

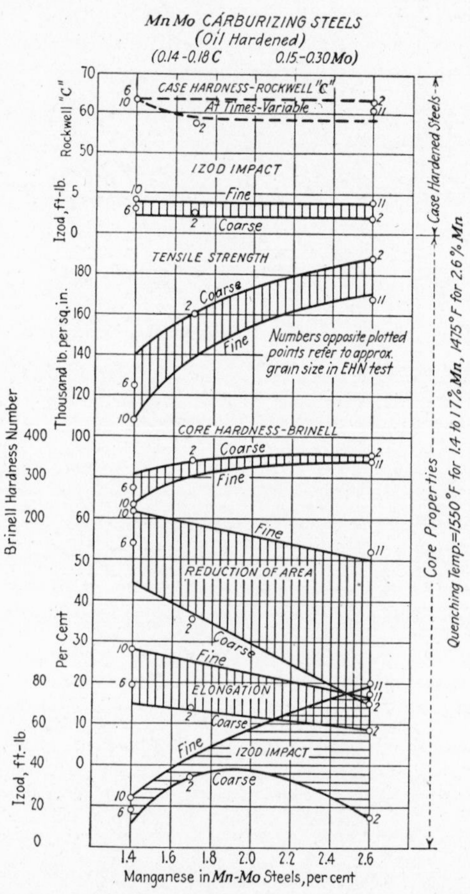

Fig. 142.—Effect of grain size and manganese content on the properties of manganese-molybdenum steels. (*French.*[337])

The suitability of the McQuaid-Ehn[112] carburizing test for detecting differences in properties of steels having the same chemical composition was discussed by Hardy,[218] who gave some data on manganese-molybdenum steels. The McQuaid-Ehn test consists in determining the effect of carburizing on the structure of both case and core of the specimens after slow cooling from the carburizing temperature. The structure of the core was the characteristic discussed by Hardy. If steels give a coarse-grained core, they are more readily hardened than steels giving a fine-grained core, but in the heat-treated condition the impact resistance and reduction of area are less. The statement that steels yielding a fine-grained core structure on the McQuaid-Ehn test have a higher impact resistance is substantiated by the data given in Table 130 for steels treated in the form of 1-in. diameter rods. This table also gives the tensile properties of two types of manganese-molybdenum steels.

Figure 142, given by French,[337] shows the grain size brought out by the McQuaid-Ehn test as well as the effect of manganese content on the properties of manganese-molybdenum carburizing steels.

To illustrate the effects of molybdenum in manganese electric-furnace steels, Thum[411] gave the data listed in Table 131 (size of section not given).

In the introduction to his recent paper describing a study of manganese-molybdenum structural steels, Burns[428] called attention to the extensive use in America of steels containing from 0.30 to 0.35 per cent carbon and from 1 to 1.5 per cent manganese. Burns claims, however, that these steels have the disadvantage of not hardening deeply and of being susceptible to temper-brittleness. In order to determine what improvement could be effected by the addition of molybdenum, two series of steels were prepared by crucible melting. Both series contained approximately 0.30 per cent carbon and a variable molybdenum content, while the two series contained, respectively, 1.3 and 2.3 per cent manganese. Critical ranges in the series containing 1.3 per cent manganese were obtained by means of the Rosenhain plotting chronograph, and the resulting curves are shown in Fig. 143. As Burns pointed out, the addition of molybdenum to steels of this type raises the Ac_1 point but has little effect on the end of the Ac_3 point, while on cooling Ar_3 is depressed slightly and Ar_1 is lowered, particularly by the addition of 0.3 per cent molybdenum.

The steels under discussion were rolled to bars ¾ × 1¾ in. in section, given various heat treatments at this size, and their tensile, hardness, and impact values determined. In the tensile test the yield strength was taken as that stress which gave a permanent extension of 0.2 per cent as determined by a Ewing

TABLE 130.—MECHANICAL PROPERTIES OF MANGANESE-MOLYBDENUM STEELS*
(Grain size after McQuaid-Ehn test)

Number	Composition, per cent			Grain size	Water-quenched		Tempered		Tensile strength, lb./sq. in.	Yield strength,† lb./sq. in.	Elongation in 2 in., per cent	Reduction of area, per cent	Brinell hardness	Izod impact, ft-lb.
	C	Mn	Mo		°C.	°F.	°C.	°F.						
26C	0.25	1.47	0.24	Coarse	830	1525	595	1100	128,800	115,300	20.5	63.2	269	74
26F	0.28	1.59	0.27	Fine	830	1525	595	1100	129,000	116,000	21.0	66.7	269	91
40C	0.39	1.74	0.26	Coarse	815	1500	555	1025	159,300	144,100	18.0	56.6	321	55
40F	0.39	1.77	0.24	Fine	815	1500	555	1025	159,500	145,000	18.0	57.1	321	64

* Hardy.[218]
† Reported as yield point.

extensometer. Notched-bar tests were made on a 120-lb. Izod machine using the standard B.E.S.A. test piece (45-deg. *V*-notch, 2 mm. deep, root radius 0.25 mm.). The properties obtained on normalized and quenched and tempered steels of the series containing 1.3 per cent manganese are listed in Table 132. The properties of steels of the 2.3 per cent manganese series, after similar treatment, are listed in Table 133. The properties, including torsional and Sankey bend tests, of the three steels containing 1.3 per cent manganese after having been heat-treated to produce a Brinell hardness of 250 are given in Table 134. The properties of a nickel-chromium-molybdenum steel are included for purposes of comparison.

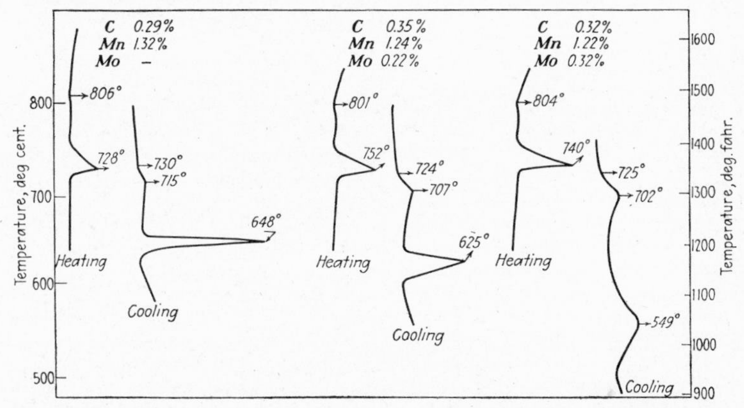

FIG. 143.—Heating and cooling curves of manganese-molybdenum steels. (*Burns*.[428])

Burns also investigated the susceptibility to temper-brittleness of some manganese-molybdenum steels. As Table 135 indicates, even the 1.3 per cent manganese steel containing no molybdenum is apparently free from temper-brittleness. The values for the steels containing approximately 2.3 per cent manganese are from the work of Greaves and Jones.[152] Table 136 gives some results of tests on a manganese-molybdenum steel made by the open-hearth process. The last column of this table gives approximate values of impact resistance for a steel containing no molybdenum, given the same heat treatment.

The tensile and impact values for a heat-treated manganese-molybdenum steel given in Table 137 indicate little difference between the properties of the steel heat-treated in a $1^{11}/_{16}$-in.

round and a 3½-in. gothic section. From his work Burns concluded:

In the steels containing 1.3 per cent of manganese, as normalized, the addition of molybdenum up to 0.3 per cent produces little improvement in the mechanical properties that could not be obtained equally well by an increase of the manganese, or manganese and carbon content. It has, however, a marked beneficial effect on the steel in the hardened and tempered condition . . .

The addition of 0.15 to 0.25 per cent of molybdenum reduces the tendency to temper-brittleness, and causes more uniform hardening throughout the thickness of a section . . .

TABLE 131.—EFFECT OF MOLYBDENUM ON MANGANESE ELECTRIC-FURNACE STEEL*

Tests made	With Mo	Without Mo
Chemical analysis:		
Carbon, per cent	0.28	0.26
Manganese, per cent	1.59	1.46
Molybdenum, per cent	0.27	
Phosphorus, per cent	0.02	0.02
Sulphur, per cent	0.02	0.02
Water-quenched	830°C. (1525°F.)	830°C. (1525°F.)
Brinell hardness, surface	534	517
Brinell hardness, center	534	477
Tempered	595°C. (1100°F.)	425°C. (800°F.)
Brinell hardness, surface	269	311
Brinell hardness, center	269	269
Tensile strength, lb./sq. in	129,000	129,000
Yield strength, lb./sq. in	116,000	107,000
Elongation in 2 in., per cent	21.0	21.0
Reduction of area, per cent	66.7	65.1
Izod impact, ft-lb	91	78

* Thum.[411]

TABLE 132.—MECHANICAL PROPERTIES OF MANGANESE-MOLYBDENUM STEELS CONTAINING 0.3 PER CENT CARBON AND 1.3 PER CENT MANGANESE*

Number	Composition, per cent			Tempered or normalized		Tensile strength, lb./sq. in.	Elastic limit, lb./sq. in.	Yield strength,† lb./sq. in.	Elongation in 2 in., per cent	Reduction of area, per cent	Izod impact, ft-lb.	Brinell hardness
	C	Mn	Mo	°C.	°F.							
Normalized												
KEH	0.29	1.32	Nil	890	1635	85,100	35,800	51,500	34	66	60	170
				860	1580	85,300	35,800	52,400	34	66	60	170
				830	1525	84,900	40,300	51,500	34	66	61	169
				800	1475	84,700	38,100	51,500	34	67	71	169
				770	1420	84,700	33,600	50,200	33	66	57	165
KEJ	0.35	1.24	0.22	890	1635	97,200	51,500	62,300	26	58	39	202
				860	1580	97,000	51,500	62,700	28	61	47	200
				830	1525	97,200	47,000	63,600	27	58	44	202
				800	1475	97,700	49,300	62,700	28	58	37	198
KEK	0.32	1.22	0.32	890	1635	99,500	40,300	69,000	23	59	28	215
				860	1580	99,900	42,600	68,100	24	58	24	217
				830	1525	99,500	44,800	69,000	24	58	30	215
				800	1475	99,200	47,000	68,100	24	58	32	219
				770	1420	98,800	47,000	64,500	25	59	30	209
GBH	0.38	1.39	Nil	800	1475	99,500	53,500	62,500	28	58	31	197
Oil-quenched from 820°C. (1510°F.)												
KEH	0.29	1.32	Nil	550	1025	95,600	58,200	63,600	25	64	67	194
				600	1110	91,300	44,800	60,500	31	67	73	187
				650	1200	85,100	49,300	56,000	32	69	82	172

TABLE 132.—(*Continued*)

Number	Composition, per cent			Tempered or normalized		Tensile strength, lb./sq. in.	Elastic limit, lb./sq. in.	Yield strength,† lb./sq. in.	Elongation in 2 in., per cent	Reduction of area, per cent	Izod impact, ft-lb.	Brinell hardness
	C	Mn	Mo	°C.	°F.							
Oil-quenched from 820°C. (1510°F.).—(*Continued*)												
KEJ...........	0.35	1.24	0.22	550	1025	107,500	69,400	80,200	25	64	70	234
				600	1110	103,900	73,900	78,400	28	66	77	219
				650	1200	94,500	60,500	72,600	30	68	90	196
KEK...........	0.32	1.22	0.32	550	1025	120,300	76,200	94,100	21	61	73	261
				600	1110	109,000	67,200	80,600	24	65	86	233
				650	1200	98,700	58,200	71,700	26	67	94	210
Water-quenched from 850°C. (1560°F.)												
KEH...........	0.29	1.32	Nil	550	1025	112,200	73,900	89,600	22	62	60	254
				600	1110	103,300	67,200	79,700	24	67	69	229
				650	1200	94,100	60,500	71,200	28	69	80	204
KEJ...........	0.35	1.24	0.22	550	1025	137,500	82,900	119,200	20	62	57	308
				600	1110	115,800	76,200	96,800	24	67	75	255
				650	1200	106,400	71,700	87,800	26	69	78	234
KEK...........	0.32	1.22	0.32	550	1025	143,100	107,500	126,100	20	61	61	313
				600	1110	130,600	98,600	113,800	21	62	73	286
				650	1200	106,800	71,700	88,300	25	64	91	238

* Burns.[428]

† Reported as yield point.

TABLE 133.—MECHANICAL PROPERTIES OF MANGANESE-MOLYBDENUM STEELS CONTAINING 0.3 PER CENT CARBON AND 2.3 PER CENT MANGANESE*

Number	Composition, per cent			Tempered		Tensile strength, lb./sq. in.	Elastic limit, lb./sq. in.	Yield strength,† lb./sq. in.	Elongation in 2 in., per cent	Reduction of area, per cent	Izod impact, ft-lb.	Brinell hardness
	C	Mn	Mo	°C.	°F.							
Oil-quenched from 900°C. (1650°F.)												
CDO...........	0.36	2.24	Nil	600	1110	116,700	82,900	96,800	25	61	21	249
				670	1240	110,000	29,100	60,500	23	51	41	224
DWW..........	0.30	2.30	0.52	525	975	171,800	125,200	156,800	17	53	26	370
				600	1110	152,300	116,500	138,000	17	55	41	330
				650	1200	145,200	112,000	131,300	18	55	47	314
				675	1250	130,300	100,800	115,600	19	61	53	287
				700	1290	116,500	91,800	100,800	22	63	69	250
Water-quenched from 900°C. (1650°F.)												
DWW..........	0.30	2.30	0.52	550	1025	168,400	123,200	150,100	17	51	32	356
				600	1110	149,900	116,500	135,700	17	57	43	329
				650	1200	147,200	116,500	134,000	17	56	45	320
Air-cooled from 900°C. (1650°F.)												
DWW..........	0.30	2.30	0.52	None	....	141,300	31,400	92,700	17	47	6	291
				550	1025	128,800	80,600	102,100	20	57	25	270

* Burns.(428)

† Reported as yield point.

In the steels containing 2.3 per cent of manganese, the addition of 0.5 per cent of molybdenum almost eliminates the susceptibility to temper-brittleness and gives mechanical properties approximating to those of nickel-chromium-molybdenum steels in the oil-hardened and tempered condition.

TABLE 134.—MECHANICAL PROPERTIES OF STEELS TREATED TO GIVE A BRINELL HARDNESS OF 250*

Tests made	KEH	KEJ	KEK	DKH
Composition, per cent	C, 0.29 Mn, 1.32 Mo, Nil	C, 0.35 Mn, 1.24 Mo, 0.22	C, 0.32 Mn, 1.22 Mo, 0.32	C, 0.33 Ni, 2.70 Cr, 0.58 Mo, 0.57
Treatment:				
Hardening temperature	850°C. (1560°F.)	850°C. (1560°F.)	850°C. (1560°F.)	900°C. (1650°F.)
Hardening medium	Water	Water	Water	Oil
Tempering temperature	550°C. (1025°F.)	610°C. (1130°F.)	620°C. (1150°F.)	670°C. (1240°F.)
Hours tempered	2	2	2	3
Tensile tests:				
Elastic limit, lb./sq. in.	67,200	76,200	91,800	98,600
Yield strength,† lb./sq. in.	83,300	96,800	100,400	105,100
Tensile strength, lb./sq. in.	107,700	115,800	116,500	121,200
Elongation, per cent	24	24	24	23
Reduction of area, per cent	67	67	67	64
Torsion test (0.4 in. diameter; parallel 5 in.):				
Elastic limit, lb./sq. in.	47,000	47,000	56,000	62,700
Maximum shear, lb./sq. in.	101,900	103,900	101,900	108,900
Degrees of twist per in. length	400	310	355	400
Brinell hardness	249	252	256	254
Izod impact, ft-lb	62	75	82	61
Sankey bend test:				
Ft-lb	2,962	3,516	2,733	3,560
Number of bends	26	31	24	27

* Burns.(428)

† Reported as yield point.

A manganese-molybdenum steel rail, tested by Freeman and France,(335) containing 0.45 per cent carbon, 1.70 per cent

TABLE 135.—SUSCEPTIBILITY TO TEMPER-BRITTLENESS OF MANGANESE AND MANGANESE-MOLYBDENUM STEELS*
(Sections 5 × ¾ × ¾ in., Izod impact values in ft-lb.)

Number	Composition, per cent			Hardened and tempered 625°C. (1155°F.) for 2 hr.		Susceptibility
	C	Mn	Mo	Cooled in water	Cooled at 0.3°C. (0.5°F.) per min.	
KEH†	0.29	1.32	Nil	97	89	1.09
KEJ†	0.35	1.24	0.22	87	81	1.07
KEK†	0.32	1.22	0.32	86	82	1.05
CDO‡	0.36	2.24	Nil	74	4	18.5
DWW‡	0.30	2.30	0.52	59	50	1.2

* Burns.(428)
† Quenched in water from 850°C. (1560°F.), others quenched in oil from 900°C. (1650°F.).
‡ From Greaves and Jones.(152)

TABLE 136.—MECHANICAL PROPERTIES OF AN OPEN-HEARTH STEEL CONTAINING 0.35 PER CENT CARBON, 1.30 PER CENT MANGANESE, AND 0.16 PER CENT MOLYBDENUM*
(Quenched in water from 860°C. (1580°F.), tempered at 580°C. (1075°F.), and cooled as indicated. To show effects of molybdenum on temper-brittleness.)

Cooled from tempering temperature	Tensile strength, lb./sq. in.	Yield strength,† lb./sq. in.	Elongation in 2 in., per cent	Reduction of area, per cent	Izod impact, ft-lb.	Izod of Mo-free steel
In water	141,600	121,000	19	56	53	35
In air	143,800	125,400	19	56	50	15 to 20
In furnace	139,800	118,700	18	57	53	15

* Burns.(428)
† Reported as yield point.

manganese, and 0.38 per cent molybdenum, had the following properties:

Brinell hardness of head	268.3
Brinell hardness of web and base	271.6
Tensile strength, lb./sq. in.	128,500
Elongation in 2 in., per cent	18.0
Reduction of area, per cent	44.0
Endurance limit, lb./sq. in.	62,600

The tensile properties of this steel for temperatures up to 700°C. (1290°F.), as reported by Freeman and Quick,[336] are shown in Fig. 144.

TABLE 137.—MASS EFFECT IN STEEL CONTAINING 0.32 PER CENT CARBON, 1.34 PER CENT MANGANESE, AND 0.21 PER CENT MOLYBDENUM*
(Quenched in water from 850°C. (1560°F.) and tempered at 555°C. (1030°F.))

Section	Tensile strength, lb./sq. in.	Yield strength,† lb./sq. in.	Elongation in 2 in., per cent	Reduction of area, per cent	Izod impact, ft-lb.
3½ in. gothic..........	136,600	112,000	17	42	36
1^{11}⁄$_{16}$ in. round........	139,800	118,700	19	57	53

* Burns.[428]
† Reported as yield point.

According to a private communication, the Delaware and Hudson Railroad in cooperation with the Molybdenum Corpora-

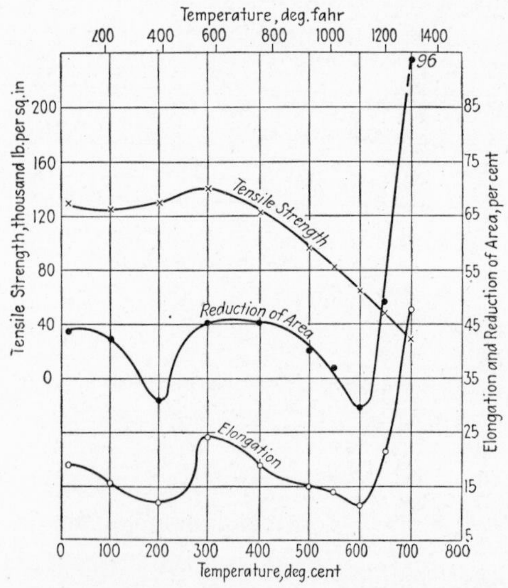

FIG. 144.—Results of tensile tests at elevated temperature of manganese-molybdenum rail steel, heat E1. (*Freeman and Quick.*[336])

tion of America tested a small quantity of manganese-molybdenum rail steel. In 1927, some 90-lb. rails of the following composition were produced and installed:

	Per Cent
Carbon	0.65 to 0.75
Manganese	1.45 to 1.75
Silicon	0.15 to 0.25
Molybdenum	0.35 to 0.45
Phosphorus	0.04 maximum

"The 90-lb. manganese-molybdenum rail put in service in 1927 is still in service (October, 1931), and we expect a little over four years' life for this rail as compared against one and one-half year's life for open-hearth rail laid in same section of track." The open-hearth rail steel with which the comparison was made contained from 0.62 to 0.77 per cent carbon and from 0.60 to 0.99 per cent manganese. The life of 130-lb. manganese-molybdenum steel rails is also being observed, but they have not been in service long enough to give an indication of their probable life.

The properties of a manganese-molybdenum steel reported by Bremmer(320) are given in Table 138. The tensile specimens were cut from the wall of tubing having a wall thickness of 0.35 in. The steel pierced and rolled satisfactorily. The impact specimens were obtained by upsetting a portion of the tubing in order to obtain a standard Izod specimen.

In 1930, Thum(412) spoke of the recent development of a manganese-molybdenum steel for case carburizing. Molybdenum has the function of reducing the mass effect. It is well established that 0.25 per cent molybdenum will improve the Izod impact value of medium-manganese steel at least 10 per cent. Molybdenum also appears to improve the uniformity of response to heat treatment.

Medium-manganese steels with molybdenum carburize about 75 per cent deeper in a given time than the nickel-molybdenum steels (S.A.E. 4615). Flexural strength of hardened bars is about the same, but the impact strength of the case-hardened and heat-treated Izod bars is much inferior. Vickers hardness of the steel, oil-quenched from the pot, is 715, and this hardness is maintained to a depth of 0.035 in.

It was reported that a manganese-molybdenum carburizing steel is used by a large manufacturing company in the manufacture of roller bearings.

The properties of a manganese-molybdenum steel were exhaustively studied by Linke.(370) A 6-ton ingot was made containing 0.27 per cent carbon, 0.20 per cent silicon, 0.042 per cent sulphur, 0.017 per cent phosphorus, 2.67 per cent manganese, 0.24 per cent nickel, 0.44 per cent molybdenum, and 0.08 per cent copper. The critical points were obtained by means of a Brown transformation-point recorder. The *Ac* point was determined at 735°C. (1350°F.) and the *Ar* point at 460°C. (860°F.).

The ingot was forged into 1-in., 2-in., 4-in., and 6-in. square bars which were then normalized at 900°C. (1650°F.) and given various heat treatments consisting of water, oil, and air quenching from temperatures from 760 to 980°C. (1400 to 1800°F.), followed by tempering at 425 to 705°C. (800 to 1300°F.). In all normalizing, quenching, and tempering operations the 1-in. bars were held for 1 hr. at the temperature, the 2-in. bars for 2 hr., the 4-in. bars for 4 hr., and the 6-in. bars for 6 hr. Tensile, bend, and torsion tests were made, and the impact resistance and hardness determined. Table 139 gives some of the results of the mechanical tests on bars of different cross-sections which had been given identical heat treatments. As may be seen from the table, practically the same results were obtained by water, oil, and air quenching; however, the mass effect was considerable, the 2-in. bar being markedly superior to the other sizes. Linke found that quenching from 785 to 870°C. (1450 to 1600°F.), followed by tempering at 620 to 675°C. (1150 to 1250°F.) for 1- and 2-in. bars, and at 620°C. (1150°F.) for 4- and 6-in. bars produced good physical properties. Quenching from 980°C. (1800°F.) caused cracking of the steel. The steel, after normalizing and also after quenching and tempering at 425 to 650°C. (800 to 1200°F.), had a fine sorbitic structure; on tempering at 705°C. (1300°F.) it showed grain growth and as a consequence a reduced ductility. Quenched and tempered steels showed banded structure, which, according to Linke, is due to dendritic segregation in the original ingot.

As may be seen from Table 140, the steel when properly heat-treated is very resistant to shearing action in the torsion test and withstands bending without breaking. In the bend test the specimens were first bent around a 1-in. mandrel; those which withstood bending through 180 deg. were then bent flat on themselves; the specimens marked with a dagger did not break in this latter test.

Linke also investigated the carburizing properties of the steel. He found that the steel can be easily carburized, and the core can be refined by a proper heat treatment. The machinability of the steel was found to be good.

TABLE 138.—MECHANICAL PROPERTIES OF A MANGANESE-MOLYBDENUM STEEL* CONTAINING 0.27 PER CENT CARBON, 1.71 PER CENT MANGANESE, 0.25 PER CENT MOLYBDENUM

Condition	Tensile strength, lb./sq. in.	Yield strength,† lb./sq. in.	Elongation in 2 in., per cent	Reduction of area, per cent	Brinell hardness	Izod impact, ft-lb.
As rolled	120,100	78,000	18.9	37.2	225 to 255	
Normalized 870°C. (1600°F.)	127,100	88,000	20.5	32.5	262 to 269	27.5
Water-quenched 840°C. (1550°F.), tempered 480°C. (900°F.)	160,500	142,400	16.4	39.0	332 to 340	
Water-quenched 840°C. (1550°F.), tempered 540°C. (1000°F.)	149,200	132,100	18.0	38.4	311 to 321	47
Water-quenched 840°C. (1550°F.), tempered 595°C. (1100°F.)	136,000	119,300	20.5	42.8	286 to 293	52.5
Water-quenched 840°C. (1550°F.), tempered 650°C. (1200°F.)	118,800	106,300	24.6	47.8	248 to 255	63.5

* Bremmer.[320]
† Reported as yield point.

194. Cast Steels.—An anonymous article in *Zeitschrift für die gesamte Giessereipraxis*(210) states that from 0.2 to 0.4 per cent molybdenum was sometimes used in cast steel containing from 1 to 1.5 per cent manganese.

TABLE 139.—MECHANICAL TESTS OF MANGANESE-MOLYBDENUM STEEL*
(0.27 per cent carbon, 0.20 per cent silicon, 0.042 per cent sulphur, 0.017 per cent phosphorus, 2.67 per cent manganese, 0.24 per cent nickel, 0.44 per cent molybdenum, 0.08 per cent copper; quenched in water from 870°C. (1600°F.) and tempered at 650°C. (1200°F.).)

Size, in.	Quenching medium	Tensile strength, lb./sq. in.	Yield strength,† lb./sq. in.	Reduction of area, per cent	Elongation in 2 in., per cent	Fracture	Hardness		Izod impact, ft-lb.	
							Rockwell *C*	Vickers	*A*	*B*
1	Water	123,750	113,200	62.5	22.5	Fibrous	23	268	85	75
2	Water	126,750	118,500	61.3	21.0	Fibrous	24	274	92	97
4	Water	116,500	104,000	61.9	22.3	Fibrous	21.5	265	62	63
6	Water	107,500	90,000	59.4	22.5	Silky	17	...	38	39
1	Oil	114,950	102,050	65.9	23.7	Fibrous	22	265	75	75
2	Oil	131,500	125,000	61.3	21.5	Fibrous	26	292	78	81
4	Oil	117,500	102,000	59.4	21.0	Fibrous	21	256	52	53
6	Oil	108,750	87,500	55.2	21.0	Silky	20	...	46	45
1	Air	113,100	94,250	64.6	23.0	Fibrous	19.7	255	91	82
2	Air	119,750	100,000	61.1	21.5	Star	20	258	70	66
4	Air	111,750	91,000	59.3	21.5	Fibrous	18.5	253	48	49

* Linke.(370)
† Reported as yield point.

The Bonney-Floyd Co., according to trade circulars and private discussion with members of this company, uses a manganese-molybdenum steel for castings. This steel usually contains 0.25 to 0.35 per cent carbon, 0.90 to 1.25 per cent manganese, and 0.15 to 0.45 per cent molybdenum. The properties of this steel after casting in the form of 1-in. squares, water quenching, tempering, and machining to test-piece size are shown in Fig. 145. The endurance or fatigue strength of this steel after quenching from 870°C. (1600°F.) in water and tempering at 675°C. (1250°F.) was found to be 53,500 lb. per sq. in. The tensile properties coexisting with this endurance limit were 100,000 and 75,000 lb. per sq. in. for tensile strength and yield strength, respectively, 26 per cent elongation in 2 in., and 60.5 per cent reduction of area. Manganese-molybdenum steel is made both in the electric furnace and in the open hearth.

According to a private communication from D. Zuege, the Sivyer Steel Casting Co. has been making molybdenum alloy steels for a number of years. Three types of molybdenum steels for castings made by this company are: (1) a manganese-molybdenum steel, the properties of which are shown in Table 141; (2) a manganese-chromium-molybdenum steel, the properties of which are shown in Table 142; and (3) a manganese-chromium-nickel-molybdenum steel, the properties of which are shown in

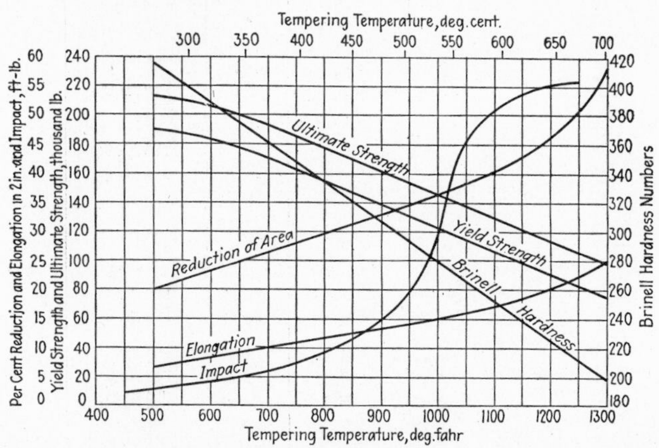

Fig. 145.—Properties of a cast manganese-molybdenum steel, water-quenched from 870°C. (1600°F.) and tempered at indicated temperatures. Izod specimens quenched from 840°C. (1550°F.). (*Bonney-Floyd Co.*)

Tables 143 and 144. The last-mentioned type of steel is marketed under the name of "Miraculoy." It was found that this steel will develop hardness values by air-cooling that can be obtained in more common steels only by a liquid quench, and that it is, therefore, particularly well adapted for intricate shapes that cannot be quenched in a liquid. It was also found that after a liquid quench and a low-temperature temper this steel has good ductility values as well as a high hardness. In the normalized and tempered condition no difficulty is encountered in producing the following minimum values: 113,650 lb. per sq. in. tensile strength, 87,600 lb. per sq. in. yield strength, 22.5 per cent elongation in 2 in., and 55 per cent reduction of area.

The manganese-chromium-nickel-molybdenum steel (Miraculoy) is rather difficult to handle in the foundry, especially with

TABLE 140.—BEND AND TORSION TESTS OF MANGANESE-MOLYBDENUM STEEL, CONTAINING 0.27 PER CENT CARBON, 0.44 PER CENT MOLYBDENUM, 2.67 PER CENT MANGANESE*

Quenched		Tempered		Quenching medium	Bend test, deg.	Torsion test	
°C.	°F.	°C.	°F.			Shearing stress of outer fiber	Degrees twist per in.
980	1800	595	1100	Water	75		
980	1800	650	1200	Water	180	120,200	161.1
980	1800	705	1300	Water	180		
925	1700	595	1100	Water	75		
925	1700	650	1200	Water	180†		
925	1700	675	1250	Water	180†		
925	1700	705	1300	Water	180†	118,100	117.0
870	1600	595	1100	Water	180		
870	1600	650	1200	Water	180	120,000‡	185.0‡
870	1600	675	1250	Water	180†		
870	1600	705	1300	Water	180†		
840	1550	620	1150	Water	180†		
815	1500	595	1100	Water	180	133,400	185.8
815	1500	650	1200	Water	180†	112,950	106.0
815	1500	705	1300	Water	180†	120,000	126.1
760	1400	595	1100	Water	180		
760	1400	650	1200	Water	180†	119,000	146.8
760	1400	705	1300	Water	180†	126,900	124.4
980	1800	595	1100	Oil	78		
980	1800	650	1200	Oil	180	120,300‡	256.0‡
980	1800	705	1300	Oil	180	113,500‡	272.5‡
925	1700	595	1100	Oil	180		
925	1700	650	1200	Oil	180	118,500‡	171.5‡
925	1700	705	1300	Oil	180†	116,100‡	256.0‡
870	1600	595	1100	Oil	75		
870	1600	650	1200	Oil	180	108,000‡	257.5
870	1600	675	1250	Oil	180†		
870	1600	705	1300	Oil	180†	114,400‡	136.8‡
840	1550	620	1150	Oil	180†		
815	1500	595	1100	Oil	180		
815	1500	650	1200	Oil	180†	127,500‡	246.0‡
815	1500	705	1300	Oil	180†	119,500‡	140.0‡
760	1400	595	1100	Oil	180		
760	1400	650	1200	Oil	180†	119,200	122.8
760	1400	595	1100	Oil	180†	123,800	128.1

* Linke.(370)

† Flat on itself.

‡ 0.375-in. diameter; other torsion-test specimens 0.750-in. diameter.

TABLE 141.—PROPERTIES OF HEAT-TREATED CAST STEEL CONTAINING APPROXIMATELY 1.60 PER CENT MANGANESE AND 0.35 PER CENT MOLYBDENUM*

C, per cent	Tensile strength, lb./sq. in.	Yield strength,† lb./sq. in.	Elongation in 2 in., per cent	Reduction of area, per cent	Brinell hardness	Charpy impact, ft-lb.
Air-quenched, 900°C. (1650°F.), tempered, 370°C. (700°F.)						
0.30	145,750	100,500	13.5	37.6	321	1.3
0.30	144,900	101,750	13.5	40.0	321	
0.35	136,000	103,950	16.0	45.4	293	2.2
0.35	135,150	101,500	14.0	44.3	293	
0.28	117,600	97,750	16.5	51.7	269	2.9
0.28	117,700	100,050	18.5	52.1	269	
0.39	128,350	101,700	16.5	46.0	286	2.6
0.39	143,700	102,700	13.5	35.1	286	
Avg. 0.33	133,640	101,240	15.25	44.0	292	2.25
Air-quenched, 900°C. (1650°F.), tempered, 540°C. (1000°F.)						
0.30	111,400	96,100	16.5	38.7	302	7.1
0.30	111,250	96,250	Flaw	Flaw	302	
0.35	126,350	76,500	19.0	46.6	277	7.3
0.35	124,550	88,850	19.0	48.9	277	
0.28	113,900	91,450	19.5	48.6	255	11.7
0.28	114,550	92,300	21.0	50.3	255	
0.39	134,000	100,500	12.0	37.9	286	8.8
0.39	126,650	99,800	19.0	47.2	286	
Avg. 0.33	120,330	92,720	18.0	45.4	280	8.7
Air-quenched, 900°C. (1650°F.), tempered, 675°C. (1250°F.)						
0.30	101,600	67,350	25.5	57.3	228	23.2
0.30	102,050	68,600	22.5	53.3	228	
0.35	98,400	70,500	26.5	56.8	217	20.5
0.35	98,200	69,450	25.5	54.7	217	
0.28	91,150	66,650	28.5	60.7	196	25.3
0.28	89,550	66,500	27.5	62.1	196	
0.39	95,350	67,650	24.0	58.3	202	23.2
0.39	94,800	67,230	23.0	57.3	202	
Avg. 0.33	96,400	67,990	25.5	57.5	210	23.0
Oil-quenched, 855°C. (1575°F.), tempered, 540°C. (1000°F.)						
0.30	174,100	161,000	15.5	41.3	375	11.4
0.30	173,650	159,500	15.5	41.6	375	
0.35	178,850	168,850	15.5	40.7	364	12.6
0.35	176,100	164,200	15.5	43.1	364	
0.28	135,500	116,250	16.5	46.9	340	13.9
0.28	134,200	112,600	16.5	47.2	340	
0.39	185,500	165,450	14.0	39.1	418	11.4
0.39	183,550	164,950	14.0	41.0	418	
Avg. 0.33	167,700	151,600	15.3	42.6	374	12.3
Oil-quenched, 855°C. (1575°F.), tempered, 675°C. (1250°F.)						
0.30	104,750	63,300	19.0	52.5	228	25.8
0.30	103,500	64,150	26.5	53.6	228	
0.35	107,200	86,950	23.5	59.4	228	28.8
0.35	106,950	87,650	25.5	57.3	228	
0.28	93,650	70,450	27.5	61.6	228	32.0
0.28	99,950	77,350	26.0	61.8	228	
0.39	101,050	80,250	29.0	59.6	228	29.5
0.39	101,500	81,000	29.5	58.8	228	
Avg. 0.33	102,300	76,400	25.8	58.0	228	29.0

* Zuege.
† Reported as yield point.

TABLE 142.—PROPERTIES OF HEAT-TREATED CAST STEEL CONTAINING APPROXIMATELY 1.50 PER CENT MANGANESE, 0.65 PER CENT CHROMIUM, 0.35 PER CENT MOLYBDENUM*

C, per cent	Tensile strength, lb./sq. in.	Yield strength,† lb./sq. in.	Elongation in 2 in., per cent	Reduction of area, per cent	Brinell hardness	Charpy impact, ft-lb.
Air-quenched, 900°C. (1650°F.), tempered, 370°C. (700°F.)						
0.31	159,600	125,950	11.5	31.2	351	2.2
0.31	159,050	111,250	11.5	33.9	351	
0.35	175,350	143,650	12.5	38.7	387	2.6
0.35	176,250	137,350	12.5	36.0	387	
0.28	152,700	129,000	13.0	39.7	340	3.7
0.28	154,000	131,100	13.0	41.0	340	
0.42	173,400	138,350	9.5	23.4	364	2.8
0.42	177,300	138,500	12.0	34.7	364	
Avg. 0.34	165,950	131,900	12.0	34.8	360	2.8
Air-quenched, 900°C. (1650°F.), tempered, 540°C. (1000°F.)						
0.31	153,550	114,500	15.0	36.0	340	6.6
0.31	153,400	110,000	15.5	36.0	340	
0.35	159,550	104,650	14.5	35.4	351	7.1
0.35	159,750	106,100	16.0	36.9	351	
0.28	144,150	102,500	16.0	38.7	332	7.1
0.28	144,050	107,900	15.5	38.5	332	
0.42	157,950	116,600	16.0	41.3	351	7.9
0.42	155,800	118,450	15.0	38.8	351	
Avg. 0.34	153,500	110,100	15.4	37.7	343	7.1
Air-quenched, 900°C. (1650°F.), tempered, 675°C. (1250°F.)						
0.31	109,850	83,500	23.0	57.3	241	18.7
0.31	111,250	80,000	23.0	56.0	241	
0.35	114,300	84,100	23.0	56.8	248	19.0
0.35	115,550	85,400	23.0	57.0	248	
0.28	104,250	74,200	26.0	57.5	223	21.7
0.28	103,800	76,600	24.0	55.2	223	
0.42	112,650	82,650	21.0	50.0	241	
0.42	111,350	81,250	21.5	56.8	241	
Avg. 0.34	110,400	81,000	23.0	55.8	238	19.8
Oil-quenched, 855°C. (1575°F.), tempered, 540°C. (1000°F.)						
0.31	180,450	165,300	13.0	32.1	402	10.3
0.31	179,050	170,960	13.0	32.8	402	
0.35	190,100	177,400	12.5	33.1	418	10.3
0.35	189,650	179,300	12.5	34.7	418	
0.28	175,000	158,950	16.0	46.9	387	13.3
0.28	176,300	162,100	16.5	46.9	387	
0.42	195,900	179,650	12.5	36.0	418	9.2
0.42	195,550	176,250	10.5	28.2	418	
Avg. 0.34	185,250	171,250	13.3	36.3	406	10.7
Oil-quenched, 855°C. (1575°F.), tempered, 675°C. (1250°F.)						
0.31	110,000	88,800	24.0	53.8	255	24.5
0.31	110,050	86,700	23.5	54.7	255	
0.35	118,500	98,200	21.0	54.4	262	23.2
0.35	113,700	99,800	23.5	57.0	262	
0.28	111,100	90,300	24.0	60.1	241	29.5
0.28	112,400	94,500	23.0	58.8	241	
0.42	119,650	98,550	21.0	55.5	269	27.4
0.42	112,950	91,500	24.5	54.7	269	
Avg. 0.34	113,550	93,550	23.0	56.1	256	26.1

* Zuege.
† Reported as yield point.

TABLE 143.—PROPERTIES OF HEAT-TREATED CAST STEEL CONTAINING APPROXIMATELY 1.35 PER CENT MANGANESE, 1.15 PER CENT NICKEL, 0.60 PER CENT CHROMIUM, 0.35 PER CENT MOLYBDENUM*

C, per cent	Tensile strength, lb./sq. in.	Yield strength,† lb./sq. in.	Elongation in 2 in., per cent	Reduction of area, per cent	Brinell hardness	Charpy impact, ft-lb.
Air-quenched, 900°C. (1650°F.), tempered, 370°C. (700°F.)						
0.28	174,350	145,850	11.5	30.9	364	2.6
0.28	175,950	151,550	11.5	34.7	364	2.6
0.34	238,200	174,750	10.0	30.5	477	3.1
0.34	242,000	176,000	8.5	28.9	477	3.1
0.28	159,250	112,300	13.0	41.0	340	2.3
0.28	161,050	114,200	13.5	40.0	340	10.3
0.42	206,200	160,300	10.0	31.5	430	3.1
0.42	204,350	173,150	6.0	11.5	430	2.8
Avg. 0.33	195,150	151,000	10.5	31.2	402	3.7
Air-quenched, 900°C. (1650°F.), tempered, 540°C. (1000°F.)						
0.28	164,050	112,300	13.5	32.8	364	8.1
0.28	163,350	125,000	13.5	29.5	364	5.8
0.34	177,000	145,750	13.5	35.0	387	9.2
0.34	174,650	139,000	13.5	38.1	387	9.6
0.28	153,300	116,700	15.5	35.4	340	8.1
0.28	153,750	116,000	15.5	36.3	340	7.9
0.42	179,150	148,750	15.5	37.0	402	7.3
0.42	176,000	143,300	13.5	35.4	402	7.3
Avg. 0.33	167,650	130,850	14.2	34.9	373	7.9
Air-quenched, 900°C. (1650°F.), tempered, 675°C. (1250°F.)						
0.28	119,300	90,400	22.5	53.3	255	23.3
0.28	118,100	86,750	23.0	51.9	255	22.2
0.34	123,450	90,900	23.0	51.7	269	20.1
0.34	123,650	93,250	22.5	50.6	269	21.7
0.28	111,750	81,700	22.0	51.1	241	19.0
0.28	111,400	80,600	23.0	51.7	241	17.7
0.42	119,200	91,100	19.5	40.1	269	23.8
0.42	119,700	90,550	19.5	45.4	269	23.2
Avg. 0.33	118,300	88,150	21.8	49.4	258	22.8
Oil-quenched, 855°C. (1575°F.), tempered, 540°C. (1000°F.)						
0.28	181,450	167,000	13.0	36.6	402	11.4
0.28	182,700	176,700	12.5	32.1	402	10.3
0.34	197,100	171,750	11.0	25.4	418	8.1
0.34	194,600	171,850	11.0	22.7	418	7.6
0.28	181,150	173,750	15.5	44.0	418	11.4
0.28	183,350	169,500	15.5	45.2	418	12.1
0.42	193,000	171,000	11.0	27.2	418	7.1
0.42	192,400	168,600	10.5	23.4	418	8.1
Avg. 0.33	188,200	171,250	12.5	32.0	414	9.5
Oil-quenched, 855°C. (1575°F.), tempered, 675°C. (1250°F.)						
0.28	120,200	93,900	22.5	43.4	255	22.5
0.28	117,700	91,000	21.5	48.1	255	19.0
0.34	126,500	92,350	21.5	42.8	269	23.2
0.34	125,000	103,500	17.5	48.6	269	19.0
0.28	114,050	81,100	25.0	53.8	255	25.8
0.28	114,300	75,850	24.0	53.3	255	24.5
0.42	121,950	93,000	21.5	39.1	269	20.5
0.42	127,650	94,500	17.0	23.7	269	21.7
Avg. 0.33	120,900	90,850	21.3	44.1	262	22.0

* Zuege.
† Reported as yield point.

respect to cracks. "The tendency to crack is particularly noticeable in those sections of castings which because of their location may be slightly less dense than the rest of the casting." In spite of the excellent physical properties of this steel in the heat-treated condition, micrographs have shown that a well-refined structure is not produced.

The creep properties of several cast steels as determined by J. A. Capp of the General Electric Company, and reported by Bull,[427] are as follows:

Steel	Composition, per cent							Stress, lb./sq. in.	
	C	Ni	Cr	Mo	V	Mn	Si	450°C. (840°F.)	500°C. (930°F.)
Nickel-chromium	0.44	1.19	0.54	....	....	0.64	0.16	10,300	
Manganese-vanadium	0.33	....	....	....	0.26	0.97	0.29	5,900	2,500
Manganese-molybdenum	0.33	....	....	0.30	....	0.99	0.31	15,000	12,600

The "stress" represents the stress which will just fail to produce an elongation of 1 per cent in 100,000 hr. The heat treatment

TABLE 144.—PROPERTIES OF HEAT-TREATED CAST STEEL CONTAINING 0.40 PER CENT CARBON, 1.56 PER CENT MANGANESE, 0.55 PER CENT SILICON, 1.26 PER CENT NICKEL, 0.65 PER CENT CHROMIUM, AND 0.40 PER CENT MOLYBDENUM*

(All bars tempered at 565°C. (1050°F.))

Bar number	Cooled from†		Hours at temperature	Tensile strength, lb./sq. in.	Yield strength,§ lb./sq. in.	Elongation in 2 in., per cent	Reduction of area, per cent	Brinell hardness
	°C.	°F.						
1	900	1650	3	146,200	130,400	18.0	42.5	302
2	950	1750	3	158,300	109,400	15.5	36.6	321
3	1010	1850	3	164,900	132,850	14.0	32.5	302
4	950	1750	5	162,150	127,450	14.5	36.0	331
5	950	1750	5	163,250	115,400	14.5	37.9	321
6	1010‡	1850	5	165,550	119,550	14.5	36.9	321

* Zuege.

† With the exception of No. 4 bars were cooled in still air. No. 4 cooled with fan.

‡ After this treatment air-cooled from 900°C. (1650°F.).

§ Reported as yield point.

was not reported. The methods of creep testing used were reported by Coffin and Swisher.[432]

B. MISCELLANEOUS STRUCTURAL STEELS CONTAINING MOLYBDENUM

Structural steels containing molybdenum, other than those previously mentioned, have not been extensively used, but there are some data on such steels which are included here.

195. Molybdenum-vanadium Steels.—Swinden[61] determined the properties of a molybdenum-vanadium steel, and his results are listed in Table 145.

The properties of a steel containing 0.45 per cent carbon, 0.60 per cent manganese, 0.30 per cent molybdenum, and 0.15 per cent vanadium after quenching in water from 855°C. (1575°F.) and tempering at 455°C. (850°F.) were given by Petinot[392] as:

Tensile strength, lb. per sq. in.	130,000
Yield strength, lb. per sq. in.	97,000
Elongation in 2 in., per cent	20
Reduction of area, per cent	63

TABLE 145.—MECHANICAL PROPERTIES OF A MOLYBDENUM-VANADIUM STEEL CONTAINING 0.30 PER CENT CARBON, 0.52 PER CENT MOLYBDENUM, 0.215 PER CENT VANADIUM*

Quenched		Quenching medium	Tempered		Tensile strength, lb./sq. in.	Yield strength,† lb./sq. in.	Elongation in 2 in., per cent	Reduction of area, per cent	Brinell hardness
°C.	°F.		°C.	°F.					
		As rolled	...	....	135,000	101,900	18.5	45.8	282
900	1650	Air	...	....	89,300	66,000	26.5	54.8	176
900	1650	Oil	500	930	110,400	90,700	21.0	63.6	238
900	1650	Oil	550	1020	114,300	92,000	20.5	63.6	241
900	1650	Oil	600	1110	109,300	88,400	22.0	63.0	241
850	1560	Water	500	930	139,800	116,000	17.0	59.2	302
850	1560	Water	550	1020	147,900	112,900	19.0	61.6	297
850	1560	Water	600	1110	140,900	112,700	19.0	59.5	320
850	1560	Water	650	1200	104,600	79,500	23.0	64.8	216

* Swinden.[61]
† Reported as elastic limit.

A process for casting guns centrifugally was developed under the direction of Colonel Dickson, of Watertown Arsenal, and a molybdenum-vanadium steel was selected as the steel most suitable for this purpose. The centrifugal casting process was described by Colonel Dickson,[330, 331] and the data given here were made available through his courtesy. In the centrifugal process metal is slowly poured into a rotating mold of such a size as to produce a casting the outside diameter of which is slightly larger than the diameter of the finished gun. Sufficient metal is poured into the rotating mold to form a casting, the bore of which is from ½ to 1½ in. smaller than the bore of the finished gun. The casting is heat-treated, machined, and expanded hydraulically in accordance with the practice for forged guns. Guns produced by such a process are said to be equal or superior to forged guns, and the production costs and time are, of course, lessened.

Centrifugally cast guns have been made from both molybdenum and molybdenum-vanadium steel. The analysis of the steel finally adopted for centrifugally cast guns is:

	Per Cent
Carbon	0.35 to 0.45
Manganese	0.50 to 0.80
Silicon	0.15 to 0.35
Molybdenum	0.25 to 0.35
Vanadium	0.10

In this connection it was also found that forged steel of this composition has better properties than some of the more common alloy steels containing greater quantities of alloying elements, and that it is particularly well suited for axles. The properties of some forged molybdenum-vanadium steels are shown in Table 146. In this table and in other tables giving data obtained at Watertown Arsenal the "Charpy round" value refers to a specially designed tensile-impact test specimen used on a Charpy machine. The reduced section of the round specimen, however, is short enough so that impact values rather than tensile values are measured. The energy absorbed by this type of specimen is somewhat greater than that absorbed by a standard Charpy specimen; in one specification a requirement of 24 ft-lb. on the round Charpy test was substituted for a requirement of 14 ft-lb. on a standard Charpy specimen.

A typical heat treatment for a centrifugally cast gun consists in normalizing at 950°C. (1740°F.) for 4 hr., annealing at 850°C. (1560°F.) for 6 hr., quenching in water after holding at a temperature of 860°C. (1580°F.) for 5 hr., and tempering at about 700°C. (1290°F.) for 6 hr. The properties of samples taken from

TABLE 146.—PROPERTIES OF FORGED MOLYBDENUM-VANADIUM STEELS NORMALIZED AT 925°C. (1700°F.)*
(Quenched in water from 850 or 860°C. (1560 or 1580°F.), and tempered for 4½ or 5 hr. at indicated temperature. Sections treated 3 × 4 in.)

Steel number	Composition, per cent					Tempered		Tensile strength, lb./sq. in.	Yield strength,† lb./sq. in.	Elongation in 2 in., per cent	Reduction of area, per cent	Charpy round impact, ft-lb.	Brinell hardness
	C	Mn	Si	Mo	V	°C.	°F.						
1	0.46	0.58	0.285	0.28	0.15	460	860	131,000	97,000	20.0	64.7	43	285
2	0.46	0.58	0.305	0.28	0.15	460	860	134,500	100,000	17.0	62.3	43.5	
2	0.46	0.58	0.305	0.28	0.15	450	840	142,000	105,000	19.0	62.3	40.0	255
3	0.46	0.52	0.275	0.28	0.15	450	840	126,200	94,500	21.2	62.4	43.2	255
4	0.46	0.52	0.240	0.25	0.15	450	840	127,700	96,500	21.5	61.0	42.3	255
5	0.43	0.65	0.25	0.32	0.14	450	840	132,200	100,000	19.7	61.0	49.0	255
6	0.43	0.65	0.33	0.32	0.14	460	860	128,500	99,000	19.7	57.2	46.8	
7	0.41	0.58	0.225	0.28	0.10	460	860	126,300	93,300	20.2	62.9	47.7	
8	0.45	0.61	0.280	0.33	0.10	460	860	126,800	97,000	19.2	63.1	45.7	
9	0.45	0.64	0.24	0.31	0.10	460	860	136,200	102,700	19.5	60.8	42.5	

* Watertown Arsenal.
† Reported as proportional limit.

TABLE 147.—TENSILE AND IMPACT PROPERTIES OF CENTRIFUGALLY CAST 75-mm. MORTARS*
(Molybdenum and molybdenum-vanadium steels)

Gun number	Composition, per cent		Tempered		Tensile strength, lb./sq. in.	Yield strength,† lb./sq. in.	Elongation in 2 in., per cent	Reduction of area, per cent	Charpy round impact, ft-lb.
	C	Mo	°C.	°F.					
Castings containing from 0.40 to 0.52 per cent molybdenum and no vanadium; from breech, 1¾-in. wall									
1	0.32	0.48	690	1275	87,000	63,000	26.5	68.1	45
2	0.36	0.52	690	1275	94,500	73,000	24.5	53.1	41
3	0.40	0.51	690	1275	97,750	68,000	22.25	51.7	42
4	0.35	0.51	690	1275	91,500	69,000	27.25	64.7	43
5	0.36	0.40	690	1275	103,250	81,000	25.0	54.5	40
Avg	0.36	0.48	...	....	94,800	70,800	25.1	58.4	42
Same as above except from muzzle, 1½-in. wall									
1	0.32	0.48	690	1275	86,750	60,000	26.5	54.0	42
2	0.36	0.52	690	1275	94,500	69,000	21.75	43.25	37
3	0.40	0.51	690	1275	95,750	67,000	24.75	60.8	44
4	0.35	0.51	690	1275	93,500	69,000	27.5	65.7	42
5	0.36	0.40	690	1275	98,000	72,500	25.0	58.0	41
Avg	0.36	0.48	...	....	93,700	67,500	25.1	56.35	41
Castings containing from 0.26 to 0.32 per cent molybdenum and no vanadium; from breech, 1¾-in. wall									
6	0.34	0.31	675	1250	94,750	73,000	25.75	64.7	46
7	0.38	0.27	675	1250	87,000	50,000	28.2	57.5	46
8	0.34	0.30	675	1250	96,500	60,000	22.5	57.5	42
9‡	0.38	0.27	675	1250	97,000	62,000	28.0	58.4	40
10	0.36	0.32	650	1200	97,000	61,000	24.6	59.2	46
11	0.36	0.26	650	1200	93,500	60,000	23.2	60.6	44
Avg	0.36	0.29	...	....	94,300	61,000	25.4	59.65	44
Same as above except from muzzle, 1½-in. wall									
6	0.34	0.31	675	1250	93,750	72,000	26.5	67.0	45
7	0.38	0.27	675	1250	87,000	52,000	22.5	64.9	49
8	0.34	0.30	675	1250	91,000	60,000	26.0	70.0	51
9	0.38	0.27	675	1250	91,000	60,000	26.0	64.5	50
10	0.36	0.32	650	1200	91,000	60,000	27.0	65.4	47
11	0.36	0.26	650	1200	97,000	64,000	25.0	61.0	44
Avg	0.36	0.29	...	....	91,800	61,300	25.5	65.5	48

some 75-mm. mortars made from molybdenum and molybdenum-vanadium steels of varying composition are shown in Table 147.

TABLE 147.—(*Continued*)

Gun number	Composition, per cent		Tempered		Tensile strength, lb./sq. in.	Yield strength,† lb./sq. in.	Elongation in 2 in., per cent	Reduction of area, per cent	Charpy round impact, ft-lb.
	C	Mo	°C.	°F.					
Castings containing from 0.27 to 0.30 per cent molybdenum and 0.05 per cent vanadium; from breech, 1¾-in. wall									
12	0.40	0.27	700	1290	96,000	72,000	27.1	60.3	42
13	0.43	0.27	700	1290	102,000	76,000	25.6	60.0	38
14	0.40	0.27	700	1290	100,500	76,000	24.3	59.4	41
15	0.42	0.30	700	1290	98,000	71,000	26.9	57.9	44
16	0.42	0.27	700	1290	101,000	73,000	25.0	57.5	40
17	0.43	0.27	700	1290	97,500	72,000	24.1	50.5	37
Avg	0.42	0.275	...	....	99,200	73,300	25.5	57.6	40
Same as above except from muzzle, 1½-in. wall									
12	0.40	0.27	700	1290	99,000	72,000	27.0	60.8	42
13	0.43	0.27	700	1290	100,000	68,000	26.5	61.7	39
14	0.40	0.27	700	1290	99,000	72,000	29.0	63.1	41
15	0.42	0.30	700	1290	90,000	60,000	30.0	60.2	41
16	0.42	0.27	700	1290	91,500	61,000	28.1	58.4	42
17	0.43	0.27	700	1290	89,000	62,000	32.8	60.2	43
Avg	0.42	0.275	...	....	94,750	65,800	28.9	60.7	41
Castings containing over 0.45 per cent carbon and 0.05 per cent vanadium; from breech, 1¾-in. wall									
18	0.51	0.32	715	1320	101,000	75,000	26.0	58.8	40
19	0.51	0.29	715	1320	97,000	74,000	29.4	60.3	41
20	0.52	0.33	715	1320	99,500	77,000	24.7	55.9	40
Avg	0.51	0.31	...	....	99,200	75,300	26.7	58.3	40
Same as above except from muzzle, 1½-in. wall									
18	0.51	0.32	715	1320	102,000	72,000	20.5	58.1	43
19	0.51	0.29	715	1320	99,000	72,000	28.5	59.6	44
20	0.52	0.33	715	1320	101,000	76,000	27.5	56.0	43
Avg	0.51	0.31	...	....	100,700	73,300	25.5	57.9	43

* Watertown Arsenal.
† Reported as proportional limit.
‡ No. 9 is No. 7 reheat-treated.

All of these guns had been heat-treated in the manner outlined above. Table 148 lists the average, maximum, and minimum values obtained on thirty-five heat-treated guns of various caliber.

TABLE 148.—TENSILE AND IMPACT PROPERTIES OF THIRTY-FIVE MOLYBDENUM-VANADIUM CENTRIFUGAL CASTINGS AFTER HEAT TREATMENT*

Size and number tested†	Tensile strength, lb./sq. in.	Yield strength,‡ lb./sq. in.	Elongation in 2 in., per cent	Reduction of area, per cent	Charpy round impact, ft-lb.
75-mm. P.H. small machine (10):					
Breech Avg	101,400	72,300	21.2	52.7	33.9
Breech Max	114,000	82,000	27.0	64.8	40.2
Breech Min	92,000	64,000	12.0	34.0	23.6
Muzzle Avg	97,000	70,200	24.9	57.4	36.9
Muzzle Max	100,000	74,000	29.0	62.8	44.7
Muzzle Min	88,000	62,000	18.0	43.4	28.0
75-mm. P.H. medium machine (4):					
Muzzle Avg	98,800	74,800	24.9	57.0	34.1
Muzzle Max	102,000	78,000	27.0	62.4	39.4
Muzzle Min	90,000	68,000	21.0	50.4	28.5
75-mm. field gun (2):					
Breech Avg	92,500	67,000	19.8	37.4	28.4
Breech Max	95,000	68,000	22.1	42.8	30.1
Breech Min	90,000	66,000	17.1	29.3	25.6
Muzzle Avg	94,800	73,000	23.3	48.8	36.0
Muzzle Max	96,000	74,000	25.7	57.4	39.9
Muzzle Min	94,000	72,000	20.0	37.1	31.7
105-mm. howitzer (90-mm. gun) (3):					
Breech Avg	101,900	73,000	21.2	40.8	33.5
Breech Max	109,000	78,000	26.0	59.8	35.8
Breech Min	88,000	63,000	17.0	27.0	27.3
Muzzle Avg	100,200	75,000	22.4	49.7	34.3
Muzzle Max	105,000	78,000	27.0	57.0	38.6
Muzzle Min	95,000	70,000	19.0	36.3	31.1
3-in. A.A. liners M3 (16) (Including 3-in. AA M1917 tubes and 75-mm. P.H. made from castings of this size)					
Breech Avg	96,700	72,300	22.4	49.9	35.7
Breech Max	106,500	85,000	28.0	60.8	40.4
Breech Min	90,000	64,000	18.5	30.7	23.6
Muzzle Avg	98,700	73,300	22.3	47.6	37.8
Muzzle Max	108,000	88,000	29.5	58.4	42.7
Muzzle Min	90,000	64,000	18.0	37.2	26.7

* Watertown Arsenal.

† Number of specimens tested is shown in parentheses.

‡ Reported as proportional limit.

Watertown Arsenal investigators also studied the properties of manganese-free molybdenum-vanadium steel and found that satisfactory steel can be produced by "deoxidizing" with zirconium instead of manganese. The properties of the heat-treated zirconium steels for both forged and centrifugally cast alloys were approximately the same as for the manganese-containing alloys.

196. Chromium-molybdenum-vanadium Steels.—The expected properties of a 0.40 per cent carbon chromium-molybdenum-vanadium steel were given by Barton.[118]

Creep tests by "accelerated" methods on a steel analyzing 0 20 per cent carbon, 0.87 per cent chromium, 0.22 per cent vanadium, and 0.29 per cent molybdenum were reported by Eckardt.[257] Below are listed the tensile properties of this steel at room temperature and the creep limit (load for a calculated elongation of 2 per cent in 11.4 years) at 460°C. (860°F.). Sample V1 was quenched in oil from 950°C. (1740°F.) and tempered at 600 to 620°C. (1110 to 1150°F.), while V2 was quenched in oil from 860°C. (1580°F.) and tempered as V1.

Properties	V1	V2
Tensile strength, lb./sq. in.	131,000	116,700
Yield strength (0.2 %), lb./sq. in.	113,800	99,500
Elongation ($L = 5D$), per cent	17	20
Creep limit at 460°C. (860°F.), lb./sq. in.	44,000	35,600

Of the steels tested this one had the highest creep limit at 460°C. (860°F.).

In determining the high-temperature properties of a number of alloys, French, Kahlbaum, and Peterson[338] tested a steel containing 0.75 per cent carbon, 1.45 per cent chromium, 0.54 per cent molybdenum, and 0.27 per cent vanadium. After quenching in oil from 840°C. (1550°F.) and tempering at 595°C. (1100°F.), the steel had the following properties at room temperature as determined on a section $5/8 \times 0.1565$ in.:

Tensile strength, lb. per sq. in.	174,000
Elongation, per cent	7.5
Reduction of area, per cent	16.7

The high-temperature properties can be intelligibly discussed only when the properties of the other alloys studied are considered.

197. Nickel-chromium-molybdenum-vanadium Steels.—According to Hatfield,[270] a steel containing 0.21 per cent carbon, 0.54 per cent manganese, 3.07 per cent nickel, 1.5 per cent chromium, 0.56 per cent molybdenum, and 0.18 per cent vanadium after quenching in oil from 850°C. (1560°F.) and tempering at 640°C. (1180°F.) had a tensile strength of 172,000 lb. per sq. in. and a proof stress (0.1 per cent extension) of 146,000 lb. per sq. in.

In another paper Hatfield[345] listed the properties given below for a steel containing 0.25 per cent carbon, 0.63 per cent manganese, 3.10 per cent nickel, 1.35 per cent chromium, 0.55 per cent molybdenum, and 0.22 per cent vanadium. This steel was quenched in oil from 850°C. (1560°F.) and tempered at 650°C. (1200°F.).

Tensile strength at 15°C. (60°F.), lb. per sq. in.	134,400
Yield point, lb. per sq. in.	122,000
Yield strength,* lb. per sq. in.	92,300
Elongation in 2 in. at 15°C. (60°F.), per cent	22.5
Reduction of area at 15°C. (60°F.), per cent	70.4
Time-yield at 400°C. (750°F.), lb. per sq. in.	40,300
Time-yield at 500°C. (930°F.), lb. per sq. in.	16,800
Time-yield at 550°C. (1025°F.), lb. per sq. in.	6,500

* Reported as limit of proportionality.

The "time-yield" values represent the stress within which, at a given temperature, apparent stability of dimensions is attained within a period of 24 hr. for a further period of 48 hr. with an extension not exceeding the elastic deformation of 0.5 per cent on the gage length. Hatfield stated that at 500°C. (930°F.) the steel described above "showed outstanding merit."

At a recent Open-hearth Conference, Grim[449] mentioned the manufacture of a 0.30 per cent carbon nickel-chromium-vanadium-molybdenum steel (percentages not stated) for piston rods. Rods up to 7 in. are oil-quenched and tempered while larger rods are normalized. The requirements are as follows:

Size	Tensile strength, lb./sq. in.	Yield strength,* lb./sq. in.	Elongation in 2 in., per cent	Reduction of area, per cent	Izod impact, ft-lb.	Scleroscope hardness
Up to 4 in.	140,000	125,000	20	60	55	45 to 49
4 to 7 in.	138,000	120,000	19	58	50	39 to 45
7 to 10 in.	120,000	100,000	18	55	45	36 to 42
10 to 15 in.	115,000	95,000	18	52	40	36 to 42

* Reported as elastic limit.

TABLE 149.—MECHANICAL PROPERTIES OF NICKEL-SILICON STEELS WITH AND WITHOUT MOLYBDENUM*
(Plates quenched in oil from 860°C. (1575°F.))

Direction†	Composition, per cent					Tempered		Tensile strength, lb./sq. in.	Yield strength,‡ lb./sq. in.	Elongation in 2 in., per cent	Reduction of area, per cent	Computed Izod impact, ft-lb.	Brinell hardness	Endurance limit, lb./sq. in.
	C	Si	Mn	Ni	Mo	°C.	°F.							
L	0.41	2.47	0.70	3.00	....	415	775	254,000	211,500	8	31.5	21.5	505	115,000 ±
T	....	....	....	....	....	415	775	246,000	224,500	1	4.5	19	...	95,000 ±
L	....	....	....	....	....	510	950	192,500	170,000	11	26	6	410	90,000
T	....	....	....	....	....	510	950	192,000	169,500	10	20	7	...	94,000
L	....	....	....	....	....	595	1100	169,500	145,500	14	26.5	12	360	85,000
T	....	....	....	....	....	595	1100	173,000	152,000	14.5	29	7.5	...	82,000
L	....	....	....	....	....	595	1100	164,500	148,000	14	28	17	345	88,000
T	....	....	....	....	....	595	1100	158,000	147,500	5	7	17	...	82,000
L	0.37	2.50	0.52	2.95	0.70	400	750	275,000	227,000	7	34	21	515	
T	....	....	....	....	....	400	750	272,500	228,500	6	22	15	...	100,000 ±
L	...	....	....	....	....	595	1100	185,500	163,500	7	29	17.5	385	92,000
T	....	....	....	....	....	595	1100	191,000	166,000	6	8.5	12.5		
L	....	....	....	....	....	620	1150	176,000	145,500	12	28	8.5	340	92,000
T	....	....	....	....	..	620	1150	167,000	140,000	11.5	22.5	15.5		
L	....	....	....	....	....	620	1150	171,000	146,500	15	37	26	340	92,000
T	....	....	....	....	....	620	1150	160,000	138,500	15	29	19		

* Gillett and Mack.[151]
† *L* = longitudinal; *T* = transverse.
‡ Reported as proportional limit.

198. Nickel-silicon-molybdenum Steels.—The values given in Table 149 from Gillett and Mack[151] indicate the effects of molybdenum in nickel-silicon steel. These two steels were rolled into ¼-in. plate, and flat tensile specimens were used. Izod tests were made on small specimens and the values for standard-sized specimens calculated from these tests.

199. Other Steels.—In a discussion of steels suitable for use at high temperatures, Christmann[324] mentioned a steel sold under the name of "Sicromal" which contains 0.05 per cent carbon, 5.5 per cent chromium, 0.8 per cent aluminum, 0.4 per cent silicon, 0.3 per cent manganese, 0.4 per cent molybdenum, and 0.05 per cent vanadium; he gave curves to show that this steel is much stronger than carbon steel at elevated temperatures. It could not be welded satisfactorily with a welding rod containing the same amount of aluminum, but it could be welded with a nickel-chromium steel rod.

C. CORROSION- AND HEAT-RESISTANT ALLOYS

Many of the iron-chromium and iron-nickel-chromium alloys have a high resistance to attack by nitric acid and many other corrosive agents, but their resistance to sulphuric and hydrochloric acids is usually poor. It has been found that some nickel-base alloys containing molybdenum are resistant to these two acids, and such materials are mentioned below even though they contain no iron. Molybdenum is added to many complex steels that are to be used at high temperatures. In such materials the chief requirements are high strength and absence of scaling at the service temperature. Exhaust valves for gasoline engines require a heat-resistant steel, and several types of steel in these valves contain some molybdenum, although data regarding the effects of molybdenum in these complex alloys do not appear to be available. Molybdenum has also been added to nickel-chromium heat-resisting alloys, but there is considerable question whether or not it is really beneficial in this material.

200. Acid-resistant Alloys.—The resistance of various molybdenum alloys to attack by the more common chemicals was studied by Guertler and Liepus.[153] These alloys included iron-molybdenum, nickel-molybdenum, cobalt-molybdenum, nickel-silicon-molybdenum, nickel-chromium-molybdenum, and other combinations. Small sections of each alloy were polished and immersed in the solutions. The alloys were examined at the end of 8, 24, and 48 hr. by means of a microscope, and the attack was judged by the time required to etch each specimen. In all, about ninety different alloys were tested in forty different solutions. A free translation of the authors' conclusions follows:

From this work it is evident that it is difficult to find acid-resistant alloys. The only alloys resistant to nitric acid solutions were nickel-chromium-cobalt and nickel-chromium-molybdenum combinations (60 per cent nickel, 20 per cent chromium, 20 per cent molybdenum, 0.62 per cent carbon; 30.4 per cent nickel, 30.4 per cent chromium, 30.4 per cent cobalt, 8.8 per cent molybdenum; 26.9 per cent nickel, 26.9 per cent chromium, 26.9 per cent cobalt, 19.3 per cent molybdenum). Alloys resistant to hydrochloric acid solutions contained 90 per cent nickel, 3 per cent silicon, 7 per cent molybdenum; 10 per cent nickel, 34 per cent cobalt, 56 per cent molybdenum; 40 per cent cobalt, 50 per cent manganese, 10 per cent molybdenum. Alloys resistant to sea water were found in great number, but the effects of air and sea water together require careful study. The only alloys resistant to mercuric chloride were the nickel-base alloys containing molybdenum with or without aluminum or chromium.

An attempt was made by Siedschlag[164] to determine the main features of the ternary diagram chromium-nickel-molybdenum. The results of 1-hr. loss in weight tests in various acids indicated that the alloy containing approximately 70 per cent nickel, 15 per cent chromium, and 15 per cent molybdenum had a notably small loss of weight in hot hydrochloric acid. The samples were in the form of cubes, but their dimensions and weights were not given.

A series of vacuum-melted alloys resistant to corrosion was studied by Rohn.[178, 239] The alloys were cold-rolled and tested both in the cold-rolled condition and after annealing. The materials studied included iron-chromium, iron-nickel-chromium, and iron-nickel-chromium-molybdenum alloys and were tested by determining the loss of weight in nitric, sulphuric, hydrochloric, acetic, and phosphoric acids. The nickel-iron-chromium-molybdenum alloys had the best resistance to sulphuric and hydrochloric acids. These alloys were almost as resistant as fine gold to 10 per cent aqua regia. The best alloys with respect to resistance to acids contained 60 per cent nickel, 15 per cent chromium, from 2.5 to 7 per cent molybdenum, and about 2 per cent manganese. Photographs of water bath rings that had been used in a chemical laboratory showed that an alloy containing 15 per cent iron, 61 per cent nickel, 15 per cent chromium, 2 per cent manganese, and 7 per cent molybdenum was corroded much less than the best iron-nickel-chromium or iron-chromium alloys. Photographs of specimens of the various alloys after having been exposed to acid solutions also showed the superiority of the molybdenum-containing alloy.

An alloy resistant to hydrochloric and sulphuric acids, discussed by Field,[(259)] contained 20 per cent iron, 20 per cent molybdenum, and the balance nickel.[1] This alloy was selected with a view to corrosion resistance, cost, and workability. It can be rolled into sheets and welds readily. The physical properties of the alloy are:

Specific gravity, forged	8.8
Melting point, °C	1300
Coefficient of expansion, in./°C	10.7×10^{-6}
Thermal conductivity, cal./sq. cm./cm./°C./sec	0.04
Electric resistance, microhms/cu. cm. at 24°C	126.7
Shrinkage, sand castings, in./ft	¼
Forgings: yield strength, lb./sq. in	51,700 to 69,100
Tensile strength, lb./sq. in	112,600 to 117,300
Elongation in 2 in., per cent	33.5 to 24.1
Reduction of area, per cent	37.9 to 31.2
Brinell hardness, average	207
Rockwell *B* hardness, average	97

An alloy resistant to sulphuric and hydrochloric acids, as described by Czepl in Swiss Patent 146,613, July 1, 1931, contains 0.05 per cent carbon, 28 per cent nickel, 5 per cent molybdenum, 3 per cent copper, and the balance iron.

Among the corrosion- and heat-resistant alloys in a list presented by the American Society for Testing Materials,[(304)] several molybdenum-containing alloys were included. The composition of "Durimet," manufactured by the Duriron Co., is 25 per cent nickel, 5 per cent silicon, 1 per cent copper, and not more than 1 per cent molybdenum. Of the molybdenum-containing alloys manufactured by the Haynes Stellite Co., "Hastelloy A" contains 58 per cent nickel, 20 per cent molybdenum, 2 per cent manganese, and 20 per cent iron, while "Hastelloy C" contains 58 per cent nickel, 17 per cent molybdenum, 5 per cent tungsten, 14 per cent chromium, and 6 per cent iron.

[1] Clement, U. S. Patent 1,375,083, 1921; and F. M. Becket, U. S. Patent 1,710,445, 1929.

A corrosion-resistant alloy containing molybdenum among its many constituents was developed by Parr[68] for use in calorimeter work. The alloy was named "Illium," and a typical analysis is:

	Per Cent
Copper	6.42
Manganese	0.98
Silicon	1.04
Tungsten	2.13
Nickel	60.65
Aluminum	1.09
Iron	0.76
Chromium	21.07
Molybdenum	4.67
Total	98.81

Carbon and boron were not determined.

201. Valve Steels.—According to Hurst and Moore,[80] wear of exhaust valves for gasoline engines is due to the combined effect of mechanical action and the action of the elevated temperature. A molybdenum-containing valve steel was successfully used during the World War. The composition and properties of this type of steel are given in Table 150. The preferred heat treatment was to cool in still air from 950°C. (1740°F.), reheat to 800°C. (1470°F.), and again cool in still air.

Some tests on cobalt-chromium valve steels containing approximately 1 per cent molybdenum were reported by Johnson and Christiansen,[138] but they were not such as to show whether or not the molybdenum had any effect. The analyses of the molybdenum-containing steels were:

Composition, per cent							
C	Mn	Si	Cr	Ni	Mo	Co	W
0.49	....	2.81	7.80	....	0.78		
1.12	....	1.03	12.17	....	0.81	2.47	
1.52	0.34	0.39	13.16	0.63	1.05	1.25	
0.47	0.53	3.21	7.89	....	0.90	....	3.15

All of these steels began to scale at 870°C. (1600°F.).

The requirements for steels used in valves and a study of some valve steels were discussed by Mahoux.[157] One of the steels tested contained 9.04 per cent chromium, 2.67 per cent silicon, and 0.17 per cent molybdenum. It was stated that the molybdenum content in this type of steel did not exceed 0.5 per cent.

TABLE 150.—COMPOSITION AND PROPERTIES OF A VALVE STEEL*

Composition and properties	Sample 1	Sample 2
Carbon, per cent	0.08	0.09
Silicon, per cent	0.21	0.24
Manganese, per cent	trace	trace
Sulphur, per cent	0.010	0.012
Phosphorus, per cent	0.007	0.009
Tungsten, per cent	16.40	16.40
Molybdenum, per cent	0.73	0.70
Vanadium, per cent	0.97	1.01
Chromium, per cent	3.08	3.10
Tensile strength, lb./sq. in.	111,000	114,300
Yield strength,† lb./sq. in.	63,800	53,200
Elongation in 2 in., per cent	15	17
Reduction of area, per cent	26	32
Brinell hardness	223	217

* Hurst and Moore.(80)
† Reported as yield point.

Grard(172) reported that a steel containing 0.5 per cent carbon, 10 per cent chromium, 2.6 per cent silicon, and 1 per cent molybdenum had a satisfactory life in airplane exhaust valves. However, a similar steel containing no molybdenum was also satisfactory.

The results of tests on the following two valve steels were described by Ostroga.(204)

Number	Composition, per cent						
	C	Si	Cr	Co	Mo	Mn	Ni
1	1.21	0.31	13.16	4.88	0.64	0.12	0.59
2	1.78	0.40	13.06	2.40	1.14	0.20	0.11

Boegehold and Johnson(424) also mentioned the use of this type of steel in valves. A steel used for both inlet and exhaust valves in airplane engines, according to French,(216) contains 1.3 per cent carbon, 13.0 per cent chromium, 0.75 per cent molybdenum, and 3.0 per cent cobalt. Strauss(409) stated that a steel containing 1.30 per cent carbon, 12 per cent chromium, 3.5 per cent cobalt, and 0.75 per cent molybdenum was used for these valves. It is heat-treated by cooling slowly from 900°C. (1650°F.) to 700°C. (1290°F.) and then cooling in air. The use of this steel in valves was also mentioned by Johnson.(353)

The properties of a number of steels containing chromium were investigated by Page and Partridge(388) in order to determine their suitability for exhaust valves in gasoline engines. One steel contained 1.41 per cent carbon, 11.70 per cent chromium, 2.94 per cent cobalt, and 0.38 per cent molybdenum. The results on this steel were disappointing because of the high carbon content.

202. Other Heat-resistant Alloys.—Rohn(207) tested the stability at elevated temperatures of wires of the following compositions:

Number	Composition, per cent			
	Ni	Cr	Fe	Mo
3	80	20		
4	63	15	22	
8	63	15	15	7

In tests for resistance to oxidation at temperatures up to 1250°C. (2280°F.) it was found that No. 8 would be the best at temperatures below 1100°C. (2010°F.). In resistance to oxidation below 1000°C. (1830°F.) it is much better than No. 4 and nearly equal to No. 3. At temperatures above 1100°C. (2010°F.), however, alloy 8 had poor resistance to oxidation.

The life of heating elements of nickel-chromium alloys, some of which contained molybdenum, was studied by Smithells, Williams, and Avery.(244) The alloys were in the form of spirals and were maintained at a temperature of 1100°C. (2010°F.) by the passage of an electric current. The alloys containing molybdenum contained from 70 to 85 per cent nickel, 10 to 20 per cent chromium, and 5 to 20 per cent molybdenum. It was found that the life of the molybdenum alloys was shorter than that of binary alloys in which the molybdenum had been replaced by additional chromium.

Investigations of the high-temperature strength of nickel-chromium-iron alloys by Rosenhain and his coworkers(396) indicated that the presence of 4 per cent molybdenum in such alloys did not increase the strength at high temperatures.

According to Hatfield,[(269)] a steel containing 0.58 per cent carbon, 0.12 per cent manganese, 3.9 per cent chromium, 7.91 per cent molybdenum, 0.99 per cent vanadium, 5.41 per cent cobalt, and 0.36 per cent tungsten had the following properties:

Properties	15°C. (60°F.)	800°C. (1470°F.)
Tensile strength, lb./sq. in.	128,000	19,700
Yield strength, lb./sq. in.	109,400	
Elongation in 2 in., per cent	15.2	48
Reduction of area, per cent	23.4	83

A steel containing 0.34 per cent carbon, 0.33 per cent manganese, 1.18 per cent silicon, 13.80 per cent chromium, 8.44 per cent nickel, 1.44 per cent molybdenum, and 1.06 per cent aluminum, after air cooling from 1000°C. (1830°F.), had the following properties:

Properties	15°C. (60°F.)	800°C. (1470°F.)
Tensile strength, lb./sq. in.	125,500	32,100
Yield strength, lb./sq. in.	48,200	
Elongation in 2 in., per cent	21	68

And, finally, a steel containing 0.59 per cent carbon, 0.27 per cent manganese, 1.08 per cent silicon, 19.10 per cent chromium, 7.73 per cent nickel, and 9.73 per cent molybdenum, air-cooled from 700°C. (1290°F.), had the following properties:

Properties	15°C. (60°F.)	800°C. (1470°F.)
Tensile strength, lb./sq. in.	134,400	47,000
Yield strength, lb./sq. in.	107,000	
Elongation in 2 in., per cent	4.5	36.0
Reduction of area, per cent	4.0	49.6

Recently, Gruber[(451)] determined the resistance of a number of alloys to attack by hydrogen sulphide at temperatures from 700 to 1000°C. (1290 to 1830°F.). One alloy contained 15 per cent iron, 61 per cent nickel, 15 per cent chromium, 2 per cent manganese, and 7 per cent molybdenum; and several were binary alloys of nickel and molybdenum. None of the molybdenum alloys was particularly resistant to the hydrogen sulphide.

A recent patent by Hadfield (British Patent 344,500, Dec. 5, 1929) describes a steel possessing considerable resistance to corrosion, oxidation, and creep at high temperatures. An example of the steels covered is one containing 0.09 per cent carbon, 0.43 per cent chromium, 0.38 per cent copper, 0.92 per cent molybdenum, 0.05 per cent silicon, and 0.15 per cent manganese. The tensile properties of this steel at room temperatures were: 67,200 lb. per sq. in. tensile strength, 17,900 lb. per sq. in. elastic limit, 31,400 lb. per sq. in. yield strength, 38 per cent elongation in 2 in., and 65 per cent reduction of area. The "limiting creep stress," on the basis of 0.001 per cent extension per hour, was 31,400 lb. per sq. in. at 500°C. (930°F.), 22,400 lb. per sq. in. at 550°C. (1020°F.), and 10,000 lb. per sq. in. at 600°C. (1110°F.). This type of steel was also found to have high resistance to dilute sulphuric acid and to scaling in an oxidizing atmosphere at elevated temperature.

An alloy containing 61 per cent nickel, 15 per cent chromium, 15 per cent iron, 7 per cent molybdenum, and 2 per cent manganese, according to Honegger,[(274)] had the following tensile strength at the indicated loads when the loading time was 25 hr.:

71,100 lb. per sq. in. at 600°C. (1110°F.)
49,800 lb. per sq. in. at 700°C. (1290°F.)
17,000 lb. per sq. in. at 800°C. (1470°F.)

This alloy was claimed to be the strongest at high temperatures of any known alloy.

French Patent 699,142, July 19, 1930,[(367)] granted to Fried. Krupp, A.-G., covers a steel of high resistance to heat, containing molybdenum or vanadium separately or in mixtures dissolved in the ferrite. Titanium is added to prevent the combination of the molybdenum or vanadium with carbon.

Recent work by Schmidt and Jungwirth[(514)] indicated that 1 per cent of molybdenum did not improve the resistance to deterioration at elevated temperatures of a steel containing 0.3 per cent carbon and 20 per cent chromium. In their studies, the steels used were maintained at a temperature of 900°C. (1650°F.)

for various periods of time and the resistance of the steels estimated from the angle through which they could be bent when cooled to room temperature.

D. MISCELLANEOUS ALLOYS

Molybdenum is used in many complex alloy steels, and in such alloys it is usually difficult to determine just what effect it produces. For die steels and other complex alloys it is only possible to list the compositions of the steels used and, occasionally, give the properties of the alloys described. The low-alloy copper-molybdenum steels or irons are discussed in this section simply because they did not appear to belong in any definite class of materials previously discussed.

203. Tool and Die Steels.—A molybdenum tool steel has been used by the Cleveland Twist Drill Co. in producing tools whose cutting properties are superior in some respects to those made from carbon and some other low-alloy steels. The torsional properties and hardness of an example of this steel after quenching in oil from 1015°C. (1860°F.) and tempering at various temperatures are shown in Fig. 146. The properties of a well-known type of tungsten steel quenched in oil from 980°C. (1800°F.) are included for comparison. The analyses of the two steels are:

Composition of steels	Mo	W
Carbon, per cent	1.02	1.45
Silicon, per cent	1.24	0.10
Molybdenum, per cent	1.35	
Tungsten, per cent	0.22	3.87
Chromium, per cent	0.98	0.98
Vanadium, per cent	0.25	0.05

The analysis of one of several die steels used by Spitzner[182] in studying the life of dies for hot-pressing bolts was 0.43 per cent carbon, 0.48 per cent silicon, 2.05 per cent chromium, 0.15 per cent molybdenum, and 2.82 per cent tungsten.

Of the high-chromium tool steels discussed by Parmiter,[389] one contained 1.4 per cent carbon, 0.50 per cent silicon, 0.25 per cent manganese, 12.50 per cent chromium, 0.50 per cent nickel, 3.50 per cent cobalt, and 0.80 per cent molybdenum. Parmiter claimed that a chromium-molybdenum-vanadium die steel had the following advantages: (1) high hardness without brittleness, (2) same hardness whether oil- or air-quenched, (3) good resistance to abrasion, (4) comparative ease of machining for a high-alloy steel, (5) small change of dimension on hardening, and (6) deep-hardening properties.

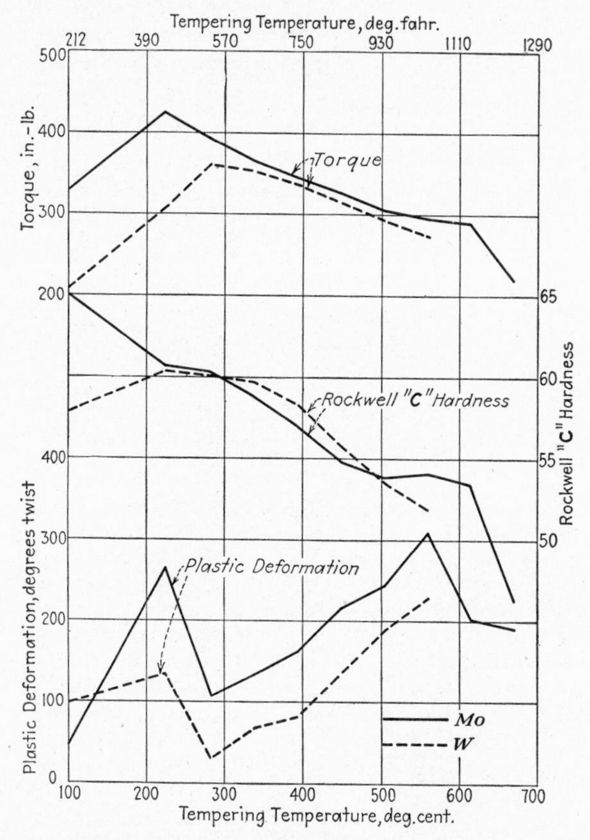

FIG. 146.—Hardness and torsional properties of quenched tool steels. Composition given in table, page 430. (*Emmons.*)

Mention of a tool steel suitable for chisels was made by Saklatwalla, Strauss, Chandler, and Norris.[399] It contained 1.4 to 1.7 per cent carbon, 0.30 per cent manganese, 12 to 14 per cent chromium, 1.0 per cent vanadium, and 0.50 to 1.0 per cent molybdenum. This steel was also listed in a table presented by Petinot,[392] and it was stated that it is used for drawing and cold-heading dies and shear blades.

The following note is from *Steel:*(307)

Alvin L. Davis, research engineer, Scovill Mfg. Co., Waterbury, Conn., gave the composition of an alloy which his company has developed for extrusion rams working at 675°C. (1250°F.), and at pressures up to 150,000 lb. per sq. in. He said that hundreds of different materials had been introduced before a satisfactory alloy was developed. His alloy for this work was as follows: carbon 0.60 to 0.70, manganese 0.60 to 0.70, chromium 1.25 to 1.50, molybdenum 0.4 to 0.7, vanadium 0.25 per cent.

The composition of a steel for battering tools (chisels, punches, etc.), according to the *Vancoram Review*,(421) is 0.50 per cent carbon, 0.90 per cent manganese, 1.85 per cent silicon, 1.30 per cent molybdenum, and 0.35 per cent vanadium. For applications not involving severe duty the molybdenum content can be greatly lowered. Low-alloy die steels for extremely severe hot-forging operations contain approximately 0.55 per cent carbon, 1.25 per cent nickel, 0.65 per cent chromium, 0.20 per cent molybdenum, and 0.20 per cent vanadium. High-carbon, high-chromium steels used extensively for cutting dies and other parts demanding a high resistance to abrasion can be greatly benefited by reducing the carbon to 1.5 per cent, with a chromium content of 12 per cent, and adding 1.0 per cent vanadium together with molybdenum or cobalt.

A typical analysis of a high-chromium tool steel was given by Comstock in U. S. Patent 1,815,613, July 21, 1931, as 1.50 per cent carbon, 11.50 per cent chromium, 1.00 per cent molybdenum, and 1.00 per cent vanadium.

Tool steels containing nickel, listed by Waehlert,(503) included the following:

Composition, per cent					Treatment, °C.*	Use
C	Ni	Cr	W	Mo		
0.40 to 0.50	2.5 to 3.0	1.0 to 1.2	0.8 to 1.0	0.2 to 0.3	820 to 850 (oil or air)	Shears and dies
0.40 to 0.50	1.5 to 2.0	0.6 to 0.7	......	0.1 to 0.2	800 to 830 (oil) 820 to 850 (air)	Hot working dies
0.20 to 0.30	4.0 to 4.5	0.7 to 0.9	4.0 to 4.5	0.6 to 0.8	820 to 850 (oil)	Punch for pilger mill
0.25 to 0.35	4.8 to 5.2	0.3 to 0.5	......	1.3 to 1.7	820 to 850 (oil)	Punch for pilger mill

* 820 to 850°C. = 1510 to 1560°F.; 800 to 830°C. = 1470 to 1525°F.

The use of complex molybdenum steel in rolls was mentioned by Kayser[226] and Hruska.[460]

204. Cobalt Magnet Steels.—The complex alloy steel developed by Honda, containing as much as 40 per cent cobalt, frequently contains molybdenum, as well as chromium and tungsten.

A typical cobalt-chromium steel, according to Watson,[144] contains 1.0 per cent carbon, 9.0 per cent chromium, 1.5 per cent molybdenum, and 15.0 per cent cobalt. Such a steel with appropriate heat treatment would have a coercive force of 210 oersteds and a residual induction of 8,500 gausses. A steel of practically the same composition was mentioned by Schulz, Jenge, and Bauerfeld[180] and by Kershaw.[360]

A steel containing 1.09 per cent carbon, 9.97 per cent chromium, 16.0 per cent cobalt, and 1.67 per cent molybdenum was studied by Gould[448] who attributed the air-hardening properties of the steel to the molybdenum content. Furthermore, " . . . during the normal production of magnets from this steel occasions have arisen when the air-hardening property has been completely lacking, due to the reduction of the molybdenum below 1 per cent although reasonably good results could still be obtained by oil-quenching."

205. Armor Plate.—According to Persoz[234] a steel used for armor plate contains 0.35 to 0.40 per cent carbon, 0.20 to 0.40 per cent chromium, 4 to 5 per cent nickel, 2 to 4 per cent tungsten, and 0 to 0.5 per cent molybdenum.

206. Age-hardening Austenite.—Two types of age-hardenable austenitic steels were described by Hensel.[457] One type was a nickel-manganese-iron-molybdenum alloy made by adding molybdenum powder to an iron-base alloy containing 10 per cent manganese, 15 per cent nickel, and "practically no carbon." Alloys containing 13 per cent or more molybdenum could be hardened by quenching from 1200°C. (2190°F.) and reheating to temperatures in the neighborhood of 800°C. (1470°F.). Although a marked increase in hardness was produced in these alloys by quenching and aging, the increase in tensile strength was not great and the alloys became very brittle. The effects of aging on the Vickers-Brinell hardness of four of the molybdenum alloys are shown in Fig. 147. The composition of the alloys is as follows:

Alloy number	Composition, per cent		
	Ni	Mn	Mo
29	13.07	8.87	13.50
30	12.56	8.32	16.71
31	12.06	7.82	20.68
32	11.70	7.36	23.40

207. Copper-molybdenum-iron Alloys.—A proposed tentative A.S.T.M. specification[305] for open-hearth iron includes an alloy with a minimum copper content of 0.40 per cent and a minimum

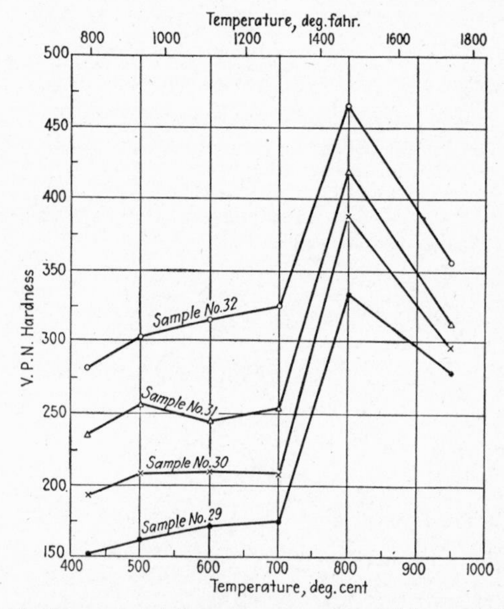

FIG. 147.—Hardness of nickel-manganese-iron-molybdenum alloys, quenched from 1200°C. (2190°F.) and aged 1½ hr. at indicated temperatures. Composition given in table above. (*Hensel.*[457])

molybdenum content of 0.05 per cent. This specification was obviously proposed in order to cover the alloy sold under the name of "Toncan." Romer and Eaton,[241] in a discussion of this material, claimed that copper increases the corrosion resistance of the iron, while molybdenum not only increases corrosion resistance but adds strength and toughness. Excellent results, according to these authors, have been obtained with boiler tubes of this material in railway practice.

There are practically no data on this alloy obtained by investigators other than those connected with the firm producing it, so its properties can only be judged from the claims of the makers as given in trade-promotion literature. A large quantity of this material is produced, which may be taken as evidence that the molybdenum benefits either the fabricating properties or the properties of a finished alloy, or both. It is claimed that the corrosion resistance of the alloy is superior to other irons, and that its mechanical properties are better, owing to the finer grain resulting from the addition of molybdenum. It is also asserted that it is particularly resistant to corrosion fatigue. It seems well established that the alloy, like copper-bearing steels in general, is rather resistant to chemical solution in hydrochloric acid. This, of course, has no direct bearing on the behavior of such alloys under atmospheric or other corrosion.

Christmann[324] mentioned the use of a low-carbon copper-molybdenum iron in boiler construction in Germany. This type of steel was stated to have the following yield strength values at the indicated temperatures:

Composition, per cent			Properties					
C	Mo	Cu	20°C. (70°F.)	100°C. (210°F.)	200°C. (390°F.)	300°C. (575°F.)	400°C. (750°F.)	500°C. (930°F.)
0.08 to 0.12	0.25 to 0.30	0.15 to 0.25	38,000	38,000	38,000	28,000	26,000	21,000
0.12 to 0.16	0.25 to 0.30	0.15 to 0.25	40,000	40,000	40,000	33,000	30.000	26,000

Baumann[318] mentioned the production of this type of steel by a British firm and claimed that its creep limit at 400°C. (750°F.) was twice that of a mild-carbon steel, while at 500°C. (930°F.) its creep limit was three times that of the latter steel.

In a discussion of structural steels of the type used in bridges in Germany, Petersen[488] mentioned the use of a steel containing about 0.15 per cent carbon, 0.50 per cent silicon, 1.1 to 1.5 per cent manganese, and 0.3 to 0.6 per cent copper. This analysis has been modified by the addition of a small amount of molybdenum (0.1 to 0.2 per cent), and with the molybdenum addition the silicon content can be lowered to 0.3 per cent without an essential change in the mechanical properties. The principal effect of the molybdenum is to increase the yield strength.

E. AUTHOR'S SUMMARY

1. Manganese-molybdenum steels have properties approaching but not equal to the properties of nickel-molybdenum steels, for with a given strength or hardness the ductility of the former is not so great as the ductility of nickel-molybdenum steels.

2. The properties of manganese-molybdenum steels are such that they can be successfully used in many carburized parts.

3. The properties of cast manganese-molybdenum steels apparently warrant their commercial production.

4. Data have been given for a few structural steels such as molybdenum-vanadium, chromium-molybdenum-vanadium, nickel-chromium-molybdenum-vanadium, nickel-silicon-molybdenum, and other steels, but the information available is insufficient to permit their evaluation. From the data presented for other molybdenum steels it would be expected that molybdenum would at least not be harmful in any of these less-understood alloys.

5. Some nickel-iron-molybdenum alloys have a high resistance to hydrochloric and sulphuric acids. The nickel-iron-chromium-molybdenum-manganese alloy described by Rohn appears to have a corrosion resistance approaching that of precious metals.

6. A number of valve steels contain molybdenum together with several other alloying elements, but the function of molybdenum in such alloys is not evident.

7. Molybdenum has been added to heat-resistant alloys of the "Nichrome" type, but the replacement of some chromium by molybdenum is apparently not beneficial to heat resistance.

8. Like the valve steels, numerous tool and die steels contain some molybdenum, but the effect of the molybdenum has not been made clear. Molybdenum in such steels would be expected to increase the ease of hardening and to permit relieving of strains by the use of a higher tempering temperature than would be possible if the molybdenum were absent. In general it appears that very frequently, when a tool is to be subjected to extreme abuse, it is made from a steel containing some molybdenum.

9. An age-hardenable austenitic steel containing molybdenum was recently described by Hensel, but it probably is only of

academic interest, because another alloy, in which the ability to age-harden was produced by the addition of titanium, appears to have better mechanical properties.

10. An ingot iron containing small quantities of copper and molybdenum has an extensive use, but its properties have not been reported by enough observers to allow an accurate appraisal of the effect of the molybdenum.

APPENDIX I[1]

THE IRON-CARBON-MOLYBDENUM SYSTEM

The first attempt at complete determination of the iron-carbon-molybdenum system was made recently by Takesi Takei.[2] This report represents a vast amount of experimental work. It is worthy of special note that this is probably the first time that the initial diagram of a ferrous ternary system is constructed in accordance with phase-rule requirements. It is probable, then, that future contributions to this system will chiefly bring adjustments rather than effect radical changes.

The experimental work consisted of thermal, dilatometric, magnetic, and microscopic studies of 156 alloys in groups of approximately constant-molybdenum contents. From these data various sections of the ternary diagram were constructed, and finally the ternary diagram was constructed, in accordance with the following observations:

1. The ternary phase ω (double carbide) is formed by the peritectic reaction:

$$\text{Melt} + Mo_2C \rightleftharpoons \omega$$

This phase forms eutectics with the binary phases.

2. γ(Fe)-phase is decomposed by the peritecto-eutectoid reaction:

$$\gamma + \omega \rightleftharpoons Fe_3C + \alpha(\text{Fe})$$

3. γ-phase never coexists with ϵ-phase (Fe_3Mo_2).

4. η-phase (FeMo) is decomposed by a eutectoid reaction as in the binary system.

5. ξ-phase, another ternary, has been observed in high-molybdenum, high-carbon alloys.

The complete diagram, although of considerable theoretical interest, would demand much more space for adequate presentation than is available at this late hour. Furthermore, it is most probable that the original report will be published in English

[1] Prepared by J. S. Marsh, associate editor, *Alloys of Iron Research.*

[2] On the Equilibrium Diagram of the Fe-Mo-C System, *Kinzoku no Kenkyu,* v. 9, 1932, pp. 97–124, 142–173.

at an early date, possibly even before the publication of this book. It seems sufficient, then, to present at this time the portion of the diagram of practical interest and value.

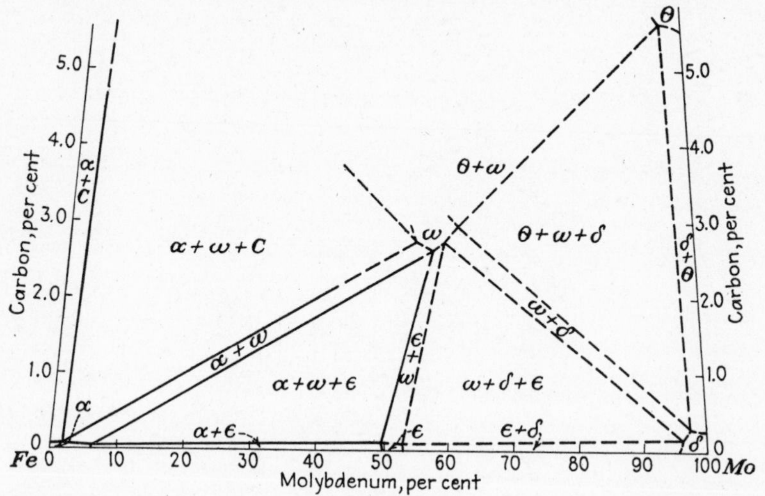

FIG. 148.—Ordinary-temperature section of the iron-carbon-molybdenum diagram.

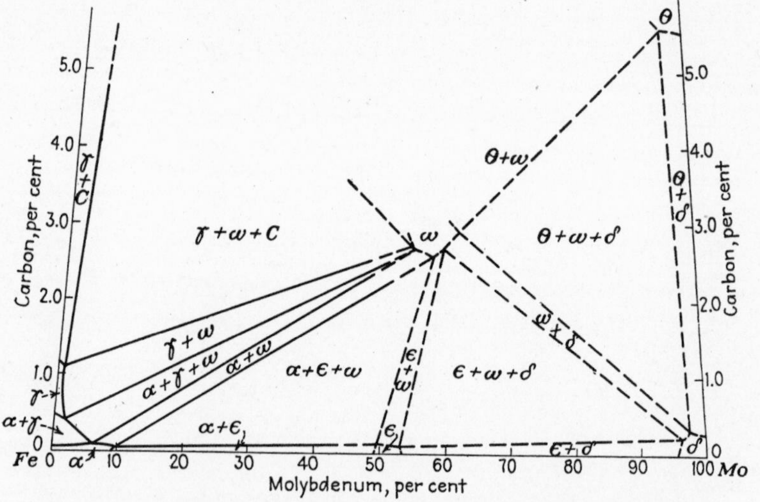

FIG. 149.—Section at 800°C. of the iron-carbon-molybdenum diagram.

Perhaps the easiest way to grasp the nature of iron-carbon-molybdenum alloys is by way of isothermal sections of the ternary diagram. Three such sections are shown in Figs. 148 to

150—at ordinary temperatures, 800, and 1200°C., respectively.[1] Figure 148 shows that the constitution of iron-carbon-molybdenum alloys, in substantial equilibrium at ordinary tem-

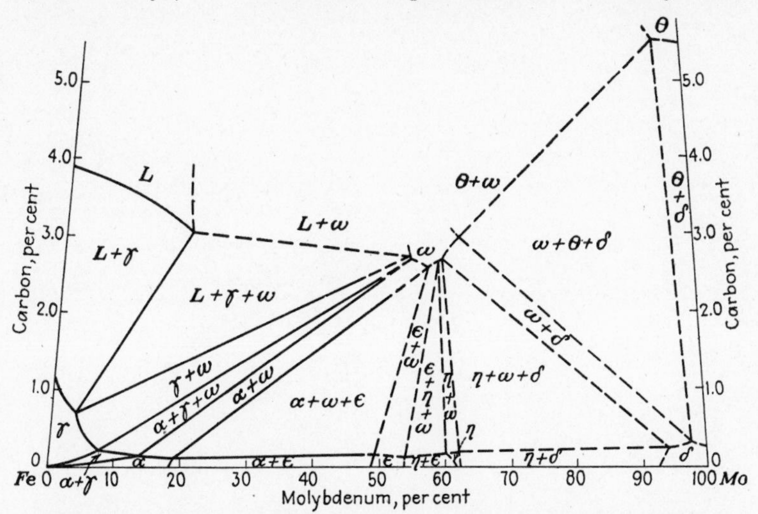

FIG. 150.—Section at 1200°C. of the iron-carbon-molybdenum diagram.

peratures, is fairly simple. The 800°C. level (Fig. 149) differs chiefly by virtue of the presence of γ-phase, and the 1200°C. level (Fig. 150) by virtue of the presence of liquid phase.

The phases shown are identified below:

IRON-CARBON-MOLYBDENUM SYSTEM PHASES

Phase	Explanation
α	Solution of Mo and C in Fe
γ	Solution of Mo and C in Fe
C	Fe_3C (capable of dissolving Mo, C, and Fe)*
ω	Double carbide of Fe and Mo
ε	Fe_3Mo_2 containing Fe and C in solution
η	FeMo containing Fe and C in solution
θ	Mo_2C (capable of dissolving Fe and Mo)
δ	Solution of Fe and C in Mo
L	The melt

* TAKEI, TAKESI, On the Ferromagnetic Carbides in Molybdenum Steels, *Sci. Rep.*, Sendai, Ser. 1, v. 21, 1932, pp. 127–148.

[1] The regions adjacent to the molybdenum axis are not drawn to scale. This has the advantage of showing clearly the shapes of these regions, but perhaps with the disadvantage of giving an erroneous impression of magnitudes. A good "yardstick" may be found in remembering that the origin of the alpha-phase boundary in the 0 per cent molybdenum plane at ordinary temperatures is in the vicinity of 0.008 per cent carbon.

The complete diagram becomes speculative at high molybdenum and carbon concentrations. The portion which has been established with reasonable certainty—*i.e.*, for low-molybdenum contents—is also the portion of greatest practical importance.

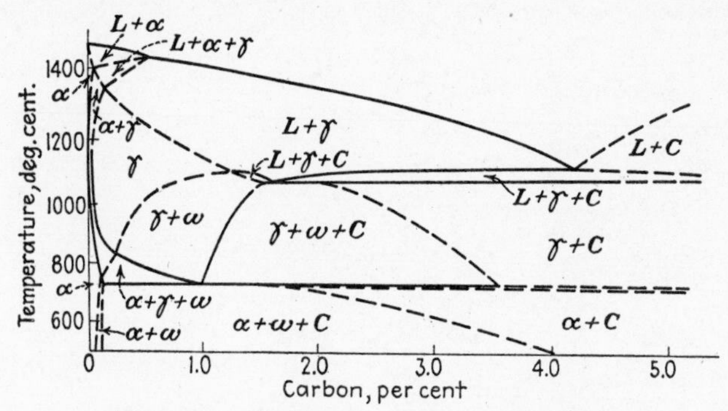

FIG. 151.—Section at 2 per cent molybdenum.

The isothermal sections alone, of course, tell nothing of what happens to the alloys as they are heated or cooled, although the trends of the various boundaries may be inferred from inspection of the three sections. This information is given most lucidly by vertical sections of the ternary diagram, and for ordinary use sections parallel to the carbon side, at constant

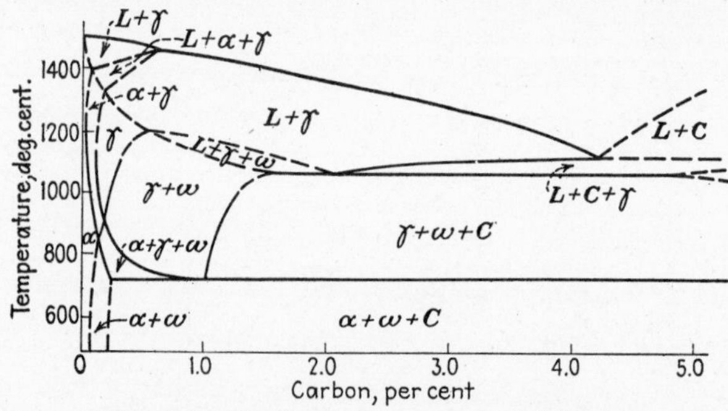

FIG. 152.—Section at 4 per cent molybdenum.

molybdenum concentrations, will be sufficient. Further, sections at molybdenum concentrations less than 20 per cent will be more than ample to cover present-day molybdenum steels.

Figures 151 to 154 are the sections at 2, 4, 10, and 20 per cent molybdenum. The outstanding characteristic of these sections is that they are more complex than are corresponding sections of more familiar ternary diagrams, such as of the iron-carbon-silicon system. This complication is caused principally by the appearance of ω-phase (the double carbide). The reason why this should be true is evident from phase-rule considerations. In this brief presentation of Takei's findings it is out of place to discuss the sections with any degree of completeness, although

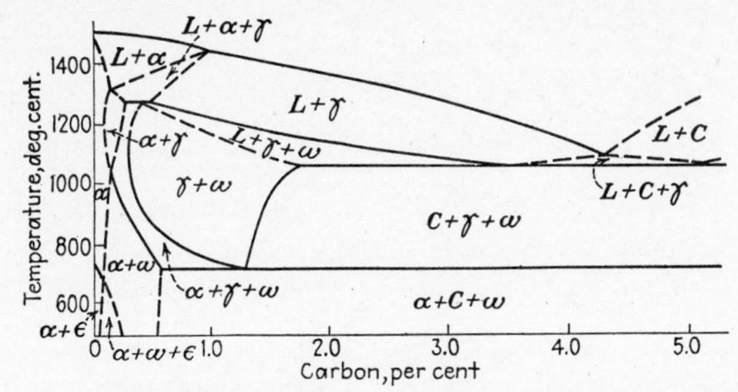

FIG. 153.—Section at 10 per cent molybdenum.

one point is worthy of special mention. In sections of the system iron-carbon-silicon the areas associated with the eutectoid are monovariant—*i.e.*, the eutectoid line of the iron-carbon diagram is expanded to three-phase intervals ($\alpha + \gamma + \mathrm{C}$). Examining Figs. 151 to 154, the 2 to 20 per cent molybdenum

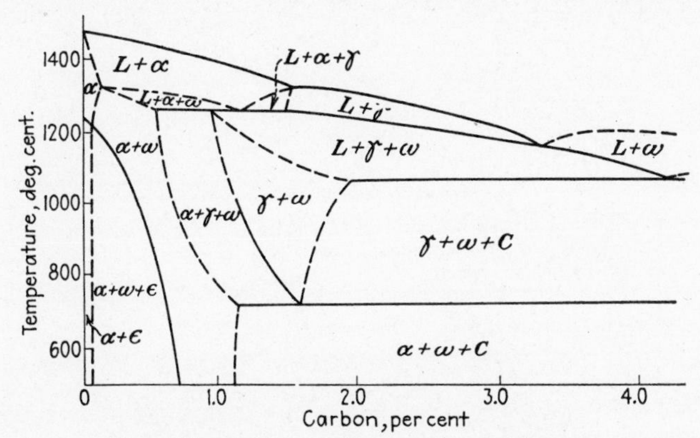

FIG. 154.—Section at 20 per cent molybdenum.

sections, it is seen that the line which resembles the eutectoid horizontal of the iron-carbon diagram is in reality four-phase equilibrium ($\alpha + \gamma + \mathrm{C} + \omega$). Four-phase equilibrium in a system of three components *must be non-variant.* For this reason the familiar "pearlite interval," in its usual form, is absent.

Other details of the sections follow directly from the alloying of a "loop-forming" element with iron and carbon, and because of the appearance of the double-carbide phase. The diminution and final disappearance of homogeneous γ-phase, and the merging of α and δ regions, with increasing molybdenum concentrations, as shown by Figs. 151 to 154, are phenomena characteristic of loop-forming elements. Were it not for the occurrence of ω-phase, the phase fields would be reduced to the same number as is found in non-double-carbide systems.

The chief thing to remember in using these sections is that they, in general, cannot be used to estimate relative proportions and compositions of phases present; they do show, however, the number and nature of phases present at any temperature and composition.

BIBLIOGRAPHY

1. Anon.: Molybdän und Kupfer im Meteoreisen (Molybdenum and Copper in Meteorites), *Ann. d. Phys. u. Chem.*, Poggendorff, Ser. 2, v. 24, 1832, pp. 651–652.
2. Stromeyer, H.: Chemische Untersuchung der unlängst bei Magdeburg entdeckten und für Meteoreisen gehaltenen Eisenmasse (Chemical Investigation of Some Meteorites Recently Discovered Near Magdeburg), *Ann. d. Phys. u. Chem.*, Poggendorff, Ser. 2, v. 28, 1833, pp. 551–566.
3. Debray, H.: Recherches sur le molybdène (Research on Molybdenum), *C. R. Acad. Sci.*, Paris, v. 46, 1858, pp. 1098–1102.
4. Debray, H.: Sur la formule de l'acide molybdique et l'équivalent du molybdène (On the Formula for Molybdic Acid and the Equivalent of Molybdenum), *C. R. Acad. Sci.*, Paris, v. 66, 1868, pp. 732–735.
5. Moissan, H.: Préparation au four électrique de quelques métaux réfractaires: tungstène, molybdène, vanadium (Preparation in the Electric Furnace of Some Refractory Metals: Tungsten, Molybdenum, Vanadium), *C. R. Acad. Sci.*, Paris, v. 116, 1893, pp. 1225–1227.
6. Moissan, H.: Préparation au four électrique de quelques métaux réfractaires: tungstène, molybdène et vanadium (Preparation of Some Refractory Metals in the Electric Furnace: Tungsten, Molybdenum and Vanadium), *Bull. Soc. Chim.*, Paris, Ser. 3, v. 11, 1894, pp. 857–859.
7. Moissan, H.: Legierungen (Alloys), *Z. f. Elektrochemie*, v. 2, 1895, p. 265. Original: German Patent 82,624, Nov. 9, 1894.
8. Moissan, H.: Préparation et propriétés du molybdène pur fondu (Preparation and Properties of Pure Cast Molybdenum), *Bull. Soc. Chim.*, Paris, Ser. 3, v. 13, 1895, pp. 966–972. Also: *Bull. Soc. d'Encouragement pour l'Ind. Nat.*, Ser. 4, v. 10, 1895, pp. 743–747.
9. Moissan, H.: Préparation et propriétés du molybdène pur fondu (Preparation and Properties of Pure Cast Molybdenum), *C. R. Acad. Sci.*, Paris, v. 120, 1895, pp. 1320–1326.
10. Anon.: Darstellungen, Eigenschaften und Anwendung des Molybdäns (Manufacture, Properties, and Use of Molybdenum), *Stahl u. Eisen*, v. 16, 1896, pp. 693–694.
11. Anon.: Legierung des Stahls mit Molybdän und Chrom (Alloys of Iron with Molybdenum and Chromium), *Österr. Z. f. Berg- u. Hüttenwesen*, v. 44, 1896, p. 590. Original: *La Métallurgie*, Mar. 4, 1896.
12. Carnot, A., and E. Goutal: Recherches sur l'état où se trouvent, dans les fontes et aciers, les éléments autres que le carbone (Research on the State in Which Elements Other than Carbon Are Found in Cast Irons and Steels), *C. R. Acad. Sci.*, Paris, v. 125, 1897, pp. 213–216.

13. Lipin, W. v.: Einige Eigenschaften des Molybdänstahls (Some Properties of Molybdenum Steel), *Stahl u. Eisen*, v. 17, 1897, pp. 571–572.
14. Curie, Mme. M.: Propriétés magnétiques des aciers trempés (Magnetic Properties of Hardened Steels), *Bull. Soc. d'Encouragement pour l'Ind. Nat.*, Ser. 5, v. 3, 1898, pp. 36–76. Condensed: *L'Éclairage Électrique*, v. 15, 1898, pp. 471–477, 501–508; v. 16, 1898, pp. 117–126, 151–155.
15. Helmhacker, R.: Relative Resistance of Tungsten and Molybdenum Steel, *Eng. Min. J.*, v. 66, 1898, p. 430.
16. Le Chatelier, H.: Sur la résistance électrique des aciers (On the Electric Resistance of Steels), *C. R. Acad. Sci.*, Paris, v. 126, 1898, pp. 1709–1711. Also: *Bull. Soc. d'Encouragement pour l'Ind. Nat.*, Ser. 5, v. 3, 1898, pp. 743–744.

17. Thallner, O.: Der Stahl der Bethlehem Steel Co. und der Taylor-White-Process (The Steel of the Bethlehem Steel Co. and the Taylor-White Process), *Stahl u. Eisen*, v. 21, 1901, pp. 169–176, 215–220.
18. Kern, S.: Hard Tool-steel, *Chem. N.*, v. 85, 1902, p. 282.
19. Mathews, J. A.: A Comparative Study of Some Low Carbon Steel Alloys, *J. Iron Steel Inst.*, v. 61, 1902, pp. 182–219; discussion, *ibid.*, v. 61, 1902, pp. 220–236.
20. Ohly, J.: Alloys Used for Steel Making, *Mines and Minerals*, v. 24, 1903, pp. 109–110, 211–212; v. 25, pp. 44–45.
21. Ohly, J.: Molybdenite and the Commercial Products Derived Therefrom, Part II, *Mining Reporter*, v. 48, July, 1903, pp. 71–72.
22. Rossi, A. J.: A Brief Study of the Ferro Metals and Their Electrical Manufacture, *Iron Age*, v. 72, Nov. 12, 1903, pp. 10–15.
23. Gledhill, J. M.: The Development and Use of High-speed Tool Steel, *J. Iron Steel Inst.*, v. 66, 1904, pp. 127–167; discussion, *ibid.*, v. 66, 1904, pp. 168–182. Also: *Am. Mach.*, v. 27, 1904, pp. 1696–1700, 1730–1734; v. 28, 1904, pp. 46–51. Also: *Engineer*, v. 98, 1904, pp. 482–483; discussion, *ibid.*, v. 98, 1904, pp. 464–465. Abst.: *Iron Age*, v. 74, Nov. 10, 1904, pp. 12–15. Abst.: *Iron Tr. Rev.*, v. 37, no. 44, 1904, pp. 83–89.
24. Guillet, L.: Aciers au molybdène (Molybdenum Steels), *Rev. de Mét., Mém.*, v. 1, 1904, pp. 390–401. Also: *C. R. Acad. Sci.*, Paris, v. 139, 1904, pp. 540–542.
25. Guillet, L.: Recherches sur les aciers au molybdène (Researches on Molybdenum Steels), *Le Génie Civil*, v. 45, 1904, pp. 242–244.
26. Metcalf, W.: Alloy Steels, *Proc. Am. Soc. Test. Mat.*, v. 4, 1904, pp. 204–210; discussion, *ibid.*, v. 4, 1904, pp. 211–214. Condensed: *Iron Age*, v. 73, June 23, 1904, pp. 8–9. Condensed: *Iron Steel Mag.*, v. 8, 1904, pp. 107–113.
27. Moissan, H., and M. K. Hoffmann: Ueber ein neues Molybdäncarbid, MoC (On a New Molybdenum Carbide MoC), *Ber. Deutsch. Chem. Ges.*, v. 37, 1904, pp. 3324–3327.
28. Saladin, E.: New Autographic Method to Ascertain the Critical Points of Steel and Steel Alloys, *Iron Steel Mag.*, v. 7, 1904, pp. 237–252.

29. Carpenter, H. C. H.: The Types of Structure and the Critical Ranges on Heating and Cooling of High-speed Tool Steels under Varying Thermal Treatment, *J. Iron Steel Inst.*, v. 67, 1905, pp. 433–473.
30. Guillet, L.: Comparaison des propriétés et classification des aciers ternaires (Comparison of the Properties and Classification of the Ternary Steels), *Rev. de Mét., Mém.*, v. 2, 1905, pp. 350–367. Tr.: *Stahl u. Eisen*, v. 25, 1905, pp. 1439–1444.

31. Carpenter, H. C. H.: Tempering and Cutting Tests of High-speed Steels, *J. Iron Steel Inst.*, v. 71, 1906, pp. 377–396.
32. Guillet, L.: Quaternary Steels, *J. Iron Steel Inst.*, v. 70, 1906, pp. 1–141. Tr.: *Metallurgie*, v. 3, 1906, pp. 581–586, 622–627.
33. Vigouroux, E.: Sur les ferromolybdènes purs (On Pure Ferromolybdenum), *C. R. Acad. Sci.*, Paris, v. 142, 1906, pp. 889–891, 928–930.
34. Lautsch and G. Tammann: Über die Legierungen des Eisens mit Molybdän (On the Alloys of Iron with Molybdenum), *Z. f. anorg. Chem.*, v. 55, 1907, pp. 386–401.
35. Taylor, F. W.: On the Art of Cutting Metals, *Trans. Am. Soc. Mech. Eng.*, v. 28, 1907, pp. 31–279; discussion, *ibid.*, v. 28, 1907, pp. 281–350.
36. Baskerville, C.: Rare Metals. III: Molybdenum, *Eng. Min. J.*, v. 86, 1908, p. 1055.
37. Haenig, A.: Die seltenen Metalle, Kobalt, Vanadium, Molybdän, Titan, Uran, Wolfram und ihre Bedeutung für die Technik unter besonderer Berücksichtigung der Stahlindustrie (The Rare Metals, Cobalt, Vanadium, Molybdenum, Titanium, Uranium, Tungsten and Their Technical Importance with Special Reference to the Steel Industry), *Österr. Z. f. Berg- u. Hüttenwesen*, v. 56, 1908, pp. 177–180, 196–199, 208–211, 221–224 (208–209).
38. Burgess, C. F., and J. Aston: Some Physical Characteristics of Iron Alloys, *Electrochem. Met. Ind.*, v. 7, 1909, pp. 436–438.
39. Giesen, W.: The Special Steels in Theory and Practice, *Iron Steel Inst., Carn. Schol. Mem.*, v. 1, 1909, pp. 1–59.
40. Portevin, A. M.: Contribution to the Study of the Special Ternary Steels, *Iron Steel Inst., Carn. Schol. Mem.*, v. 1, 1909, pp. 230–364. Tr.: *Rev. de Mét., Mém.*, v. 6, 1909, pp. 1264–1362.
41. Robin, F.: La dureté des aciers aux basses températures (Hardness of Steels at Low Temperatures), *Rev. de Mét., Mém.*, v. 6, 1909, pp. 162–179.
42. Robin, F.: Note additionelle au mémoire sur la dureté à chaud des aciers (Additional Note on the Hardness of Steels at Elevated Temperatures), *Rev. de Mét., Mém.*, v. 6, 1909, pp. 180–184.
43. Burgess, C. F., and J. Aston: Some Alloys for Permanent Magnets, *Met. Chem. Eng.*, v. 8, 1910, pp. 673–676.
44. Fink, C. G.: Ductile Tungsten and Molybdenum, *Trans. Am. Electroch. Soc.*, v. 17, 1910, pp. 229–233; discussion, *ibid.*, v. 17, 1910, pp. 233–234. Condensed: *Am. Mach.*, v. 33, part 1, 1910, pp. 983–984.
45. Girod, P.: Studies in the Electrometallurgy of Ferroalloys and Steel, *Trans. Farad. Soc.*, v. 6, 1910, pp. 172–182; discussion, *ibid.*, v. 6, 1910, pp. 182–184.

46. SMITH, W. G.: High-speed Steel and Its Heat Treatment, *Mech. Engineer*, v. 25, 1910, pp. 537–540.

47. Anon.: Alloys for Permanent Magnets, *Iron Coal Tr. Rev.*, v. 83, 1911, p. 581.

48. DITTUS, E. J., and R. G. BOWMAN: The Direct Production of Molybdenum Steel in the Electric Furnace, *Trans. Am. Electroch. Soc.*, v. 20, 1911, pp. 355–372; discussion, *ibid.*, v. 20, 1911, pp. 372–373. Abst.: *Iron Coal Tr. Rev.*, v. 83, 1911, p. 614.

49. GUILLET, L.: L'état actuel de la théorie et de la pratique de la cémentation (Theory and Practice of Cementation), *Le Génie Civil*, v. 59, 1911, pp. 158–163, 183–187, 203–207, 226–229, 241–247, 266–269, 286–288.

50. MONNARTZ, P.: Beitrag zum Studium der Eisenchromlegierungen unter besonderer Berücksichtigung der Säurebeständigkeit (Note on the Study of Iron-chromium Alloys with Special Regard to Corrosion Resistance), *Metallurgie*, v. 8, 1911, pp. 161–176, 193–201.

51. PORTEVIN, A.: Les alliages pseudo-binaires (Pseudo-binary Alloys), *Rev. de Mét., Mém.*, v. 8, 1911, pp. 7–37.

52. SWINDEN, T.: Carbon Molybdenum Steels. *Iron Steel Inst., Carn. Schol. Mem.*, v. 3, 1911, pp. 66–124.

53. Anon.: Acid Resisting Alloys, *Engineer*, v. 114, 1912, p. 83.

54. BENNER, R. C.: Recent Advances in Industrial Chemistry, *Min. Sci. Press*, v. 105, 1912, pp. 629–630.

55. BORCHERS, W., and P. MONNARTZ: Eisenlegierung (Iron Alloy), *Metallurgie*, v. 9, 1912, p. 461. Original: German Patent 246,035.

56. HESS, F. L.: Cobalt, U. S. Geological Survey, *Min. Res.*, part 1, 1912, pp. 963–968.

57. LAKE, E. F.: The Carbonizing of Steel by the Use of Gas, *Iron Age*, v. 89, 1912, pp. 81–83.

58. DUISBERG, C.: Fortschritte und Probleme der chemischen Industrie (Progress and Problems of the Chemical Industry), *Z. f. angew. Chem.*, Aufsatzteil, v. 26, 1913, pp. 1–10.

59. DUPUY, E. L., and A. PORTEVIN: Influence de divers métaux sur les propriétés thermo-électriques des alliages fer-carbone (Influence of Various Metals on Thermoelectric Properties of Iron-carbon Alloys), *C. R. Acad. Sci.*, Paris, v. 157, 1913, pp. 776–779.

60. HANEMANN, H., and R. KÜHNEL: Das Verhalten gehärteter und angelassener untereutektoider Stähle (The Behavior of Hardened and Tempered Hypoeutectoid Steels), *Stahl u. Eisen*, v. 33, 1913, pp. 1686–1689.

61. SWINDEN, T.: A Study of the Constitution of Carbon-molybdenum Steels with an Appendix on the Mechanical Properties of Some Low Molybdenum Alloy Steels, *Iron Steel Inst., Carn. Schol. Mem.*, v. 5, 1913, pp. 100–168.

62. FRIEND, J. N., and C. W. MARSHALL: The Influence of Molybdenum upon the Corrodibility of Steel, *J. Iron Steel Inst.*, v. 89, 1914, pp. 503–507. Also: *Engineering*, v. 98, 1914, p. 139. Abst.: *Iron Age*,

v. 93, 1914, p. 1458. Abst.: *Iron Coal Tr. Rev.*, v. 88, 1914, p. 678. Abst.: *Iron Tr. Rev.*, v. 54, 1914, pp. 834, 849.

63. LANTSBERRY, F.: High-speed Steels, *J. West Scotland Iron Steel Inst.*, v. 22, 1914–1915, pp. 101–124.
64. AITCHISON, L.: Experiments on the Corrosion of Molybdenum Steel, *J. Chem. Soc.*, v. 107, 1915, pp. 1531–1538.
65. ARNOLD, J. O., and A. A. READ: The Chemical and Mechanical Relations of Iron, Molybdenum and Carbon, *Proc. Inst. Mech. Eng.*, 1915, pp. 629–651. Also: *Engineering*, v. 100, 1915, pp. 555–557. Abst.: *Iron Age*, v. 96, 1915, p. 1426. Abst.: *Mech. Engineer*, v. 36, 1915, pp. 453–454.
66. DUPUY, E. L., and A. PORTEVIN: The Thermo-electric Properties of Special Steels, *J. Iron Steel Inst.*, v. 91, 1915, pp. 306–335. Tr.: *Rev. de Mét., Mém.*, v. 12, 1915, pp. 657–679.
67. HADFIELD, R. A.: Addendum on Alloys of Iron and Molybdenum, *Proc. Inst. Mech. Eng.*, 1915, pp. 701–713.
68. PARR, S. W.: The Development of an Acid-resisting Alloy, *Trans. Am. Inst. Metals*, v. 9, 1915, pp. 211–217.

69. FLECK, H.: A Treatise on Molybdenum, *Colorado School of Mines Quart.*, v. 11, no. 3, 1916, pp. 22–32. Condensed: *Iron Age*, v. 98, 1916, p. 1117.
70. HIBBARD, H. D.: Manufacture and Uses of Alloy Steels, U. S. Bur. Mines, *Bull.* 100, 1916, 77 pp. Abst.: *Mech. Engineer*, v. 38, 1916, pp. 4–6, 31–32.
71. HORTON, F. W.: Molybdenum; Its Ores and Their Concentration with a Discussion of Markets, Prices, and Uses, U. S. Bur. Mines, *Bull.* 111, 1916, 132 pp.
72. PORTEVIN, A.: Influence du temps de chauffage avant la trempe sur les résultats de cette opération (Influence of Time of Heating before Quenching on the Results of This Operation), *Rev. de Mét., Mém.*, v. 13, 1916, pp. 9–78.
73. CAMPION, A.: Influence of Some Special Constituents on Cast Iron, *Foundry Tr. J.*, v. 20, 1918, pp. 467–470.
74. ESCARD, J.: Sur la préparation au four électrique de quelques métaux susceptibles d'utilisation industrielle (Preparation in the Electric Furnace of Some Metals of Industrial Application), *Rev. Gén. d'Électricité*, v. 4, 1918, pp. 375–386.
75. OKOCHI, M., M. MAJIMA, and N. SATO: Molybdenum Steel vs. Gun Erosion, Tokyo Imp. Univ., *J. Coll. Eng.*, v. 9, no. 5, 1918, pp. 153–195, 239–265.
76. ARNOLD, J. O., and F. IBBOTSON: The Molecular Constitutions of High-speed Tool Steels and Their Correlations with Lathe Efficiencies, *J. Iron Steel Inst.*, v. 99, 1919, pp. 407–428; discussion, *ibid.*, v. 99, 1919, pp. 429–435.
77. BONARDI, J. P.: Notes on the Metallurgy of Wulfenite, *Chem. Met. Eng.*, v. 21, 1919, pp. 364–369. Abst.: *J. Franklin Inst.*, v. 188, 1919, pp. 411–412.

78. Campion, A.: Influence of Constituents of Cast Iron, *Foundry Tr. J.*, v. 21, 1919, pp. 164–165.
79. Cohade, J. J.: On the Woody Structures of Fractures of Transverse Test-pieces Taken from Certain Special Steels, *J. Iron Steel Inst.*, v. 100, 1919, pp. 187–201; discussion, *ibid.*, v. 100, 1919, pp. 211–229. Condensed: *Chem. Met. Eng.*, v. 22, 1919, pp. 259–264. Condensed: *Engineering*, v. 108, 1919, pp. 421–423.
80. Hurst, J. E., and H. Moore: Materials for the Exhaust Valves of Internal-combustion Engines, *Engineering*, v. 108, 1919, pp. 672–674.
81. Liebig, J. O.: A Brief Record of Results of the Annealing of a Chromium-molybdenum and a Chromium Steel, *J. Am. Steel Treaters Soc.*, v. 2, 1919, pp. 168–171.
82. Mathews, J. A.: Modern High-speed Steel, *Proc. Am. Soc. Test. Mat.*, v. 19, part 2, 1919, pp. 142–156; discussion, *ibid.*, v. 19, part 2, 1919, pp. 157–181.
83. Poliakoff, R.: Durability of High-speed Steels, *Iron Age*, v. 103, 1919, pp. 295–296.
84. Anderson, R. J.: Recent Developments in the Ferro-alloy Industry, *Trans. Am. Electroch. Soc.*, v. 37, 1920, pp. 265–294; discussion, *ibid.*, v. 37, 1920, pp. 294–297.
85. Anon.: Industrial Excursions of the Chicago Meeting of the American Chemical Society, *Chem. Met. Eng.*, v. 23, 1920, pp. 835–840.
86. Anon.: Qualities of the Molybdenum Steels, *Automotive Ind.*, v. 42, 1920, pp. 358–361.
87. Arnold, J. O.: The Properties of Water-quenched Vanadium-molybdenum High-speed Steel, *Engineer*, v. 129, 1920, p. 480.
88. British Engineering Standards Association: Report of the Steel Research Committee Founded by the Institution of Automotive Engineers and the Society of Motor Manufacturers and Traders on an Investigation Conducted to Establish the Mechanical Properties of British Standard Wrought Automobile Steels and Factors Governing Testing Procedure in Connection Therewith, *Rep.* 75, October, 1920.
89. Hultgren, A.: "A Metallographic Study of Tungsten Steels," John Wiley & Sons, Inc., New York, 1920.
90. Keeney, R. M.: Manufacture of Ferro-alloys in the Electric Furnace, *Trans. Am. Inst. Min. Met. Eng.*, v. 62, 1920, pp. 28–79; discussion, *ibid.*, v. 62, 1920, pp. 79–82. Tr.: *Rev. de Mét., Mém.*, v. 16, 1919, pp. 269–310.
91. Kissock, A.: Calcium Molybdate as an Addition Agent in Steel Making, *Chem. Met. Eng.*, v. 22, 1920, pp. 1018–1020.
92. Sargent, G. W.: Molybdenum as an Alloying Element in Structural Steels, *Proc. Am. Soc. Test. Mat.*, v. 20, part 2, 1920, pp. 5–28; discussion, *ibid.*, v. 20, part 2, 1920, pp. 28–30. Condensed: *Iron Age*, v. 106, 1920, pp. 579–581. Abst.: *Chem. Met. Eng.*, v. 22, 1920, pp. 1190–1191. Abst.: *Engineering and Contracting*, v. 54, 1920, pp. 419–420.
93. Wüst, F., and P. Bardenheuer: Härteprüfung durch die Kugelfallprobe (Hardness Testing by Means of the Loaded Drop Ball Method), *Mitt. K. W. Inst. Eisenforschung*, v. 1, 1920, pp. 1–30.

94. Anon.: Heat-treated Steel Castings of Chrome-molybdenum Steel, *Iron Age*, v. 107, 1921, p. 1052. Also: *Trans. Am. Soc. Steel Treat.*, v. 1. 1921, p. 588.

95. Anon.: Molybdenum Steel in the Motor Car, *Scientific American*, v. 125, 1921, pp. 62–63.

96. d'Arcambal, A. H.: Hardness of High-speed Steel, *Chem. Met. Eng.*, v. 25, 1921, pp. 1168–1173.

97. Burgess, G. K., and R. W. Woodward: Manufacture and Properties of Steel Plates Containing Zirconium and Other Elements, U. S. Bur. Stand., *Tech. Paper* 207, v. 16, 1921–1922, pp. 123–171.

98. Guertler, W.: Die Verwendbarkeit des Molybdäns als Legierungszusatz (Utility of Molybdenum as an Addition to Alloys), *Z. f. Metallkunde*, v. 13, 1921, pp. 243–244. Abst.: *J. Inst. Metals*, v. 34, 1925, pp. 437–438.

99. Hunter, A. H.: Molybdenum, *Year Book Am. Iron Steel Inst.*, v. 11, 1921, pp. 127–146; discussion, *ibid.*, v. 11, 1921, pp. 147–151. Also: *Blast Fur. Steel Plant*, v. 9, 1921, pp. 356–358, 426–429. Condensed: *Chem. Met. Eng.*, v. 25, 1921, pp. 21–22. Condensed: *Iron Tr. Rev.*, v. 68, 1921, pp. 1523–1525, 1531. Abst.: *Iron Age*, v. 107, 1921, pp. 1469, 1511–1512.

100. MacPherran, R. S.: Comparative Tests of Steels at High Temperatures, *Proc. Am. Soc. Test. Mat.*, v. 21, 1921, pp. 852–860; discussion, *ibid.*, v. 21, 1921, pp. 861–875.

101. McKnight, C.: A Discussion of Molybdenum Steels, *Trans. Am. Soc. Steel Treat.*, v. 1, 1921, pp. 288–296.

102. Sargent, G. W.: The Value of Molybdenum Alloy Steels, *Trans. Am. Soc. Steel Treat.*, v. 1, 1921, pp. 589–596; discussion, *ibid.*, v. 1, 1921, pp. 596–597.

103. Schmid, M. H.: Molybdenum Steel and Its Application, *Trans. Am. Soc. Steel Treat.*, v. 1, 1921, pp. 500–505. Also: *Chem. Met. Eng.*, v. 24, 1921, pp. 927–929. Abst.: *Iron Age*, v. 107, 1921, pp. 1444–1445,

104. Cutter, J. D.: Use of Molybdenum Steel in the Automotive Industry, *J. Soc. Automotive Eng.*, v. 10, 1922, pp. 340–342; discussion, *ibid.*, v. 10, 1922, pp. 342–344, 347.

105. Dana, E. S. (revised and enlarged by W. E. Ford): "A Text-book of Mineralogy with an Extended Treatise on Crystallography and Physical Mineralogy," Ed. 3, John Wiley & Sons, Inc., New York, 1922.

106. Dawe, C. N.: Chromium-molybdenum-steel Applications from the Consumer's Viewpoint, *J. Soc. Automotive Eng.*, v. 10, 1922, pp. 47–50, 62. Condensed: *Iron Age*, v. 109, 1922, pp. 725–728; discussion, *ibid.*, v. 109, 1922, pp. 384–387. Abst.: *Chem. Met. Eng.*, v. 26, 1922, pp. 369–370.

107. French, H. J.: Effect of Heat Treatment on Mechanical Properties of a Carbon-molybdenum and a Chromium-molybdenum Steel, *Trans. Am. Soc. Steel Treat.*, v. 2, 1922, pp. 769–797; discussion, *ibid.*, v. 2, 1922, pp. 797–799. Abst.: *Chem. Met. Eng.*, v. 25, 1921, pp. 713–714. Abst.: *Engineering and Contracting*, v. 56, 1921, p. 318.

108. French, H. J., and J. Strauss: Lathe Breakdown Tests of Some Modern High-speed Tool Steels, *Trans. Am. Soc. Steel Treat.*, v. 2, 1922, pp. 1125–1154. Also: U. S. Bur. Stand., *Tech. Paper* 228, v. 17, 1922, pp. 183–225.

109. Janitzky, E. J.: Influence of Mass in Heat Treatment, *Iron Age*, v. 110, 1922, pp. 788–790.

110. Jones, J. A.: The Properties of Some Nickel-chromium Steels, Res. Dept., Woolwich, *R. D. Rep.* 55, 1922, 51 pp.

111. Mathews, J. A.: Molybdenum Steels, *Trans. Am. Inst. Min. Met. Eng.*, v. 67, 1922, pp. 137–141; discussion, *ibid.*, v. 67, 1922, pp. 141–144. Condensed: *Chem. Met. Eng.*, v. 24, 1921, pp. 395–396. Condensed: *Iron Age*, v. 107, 1921, pp. 505–506. Abst.: *Iron Coal Tr. Rev.*, v. 102, 1921, p. 568. Abst.: *Iron Tr. Rev.*, v. 68, 1921, pp. 547–548.

112. McQuaid, H. W., and E. W. Ehn: Effect of Quality of Steel on Case-carburizing Results, *Trans. Am. Inst. Min. Met. Eng.*, v. 67, 1922, pp. 341–362; discussion, *ibid.*, v. 67, 1922, pp. 362–391.

113. Nelson, T. H.: Comparison of American and English Methods of Producing High Grade Crucible Steel, *Trans. Am. Soc. Steel Treat.*, v. 3, 1922, pp. 279–298.

114. Oertel, W.: Molybdän in Bau- und Werkzeugstählen (Molybdenum in Structural and Tool Steels), *Stahl u. Eisen*, v. 42, 1922, pp. 186–188.

115. Smalley, O.: The Effect of Special Elements on Cast Iron, *Foundry Tr. J.*, v. 26, 1922, pp. 519–522.

116. Spalding, S. C.: A Comparison of the Rate of Penetration of Carbon into Various Commercial Steels in Use for Case Carburizing, *Trans. Am. Soc. Steel Treat.*, v. 2, 1922, pp. 950–976.

117. Tammann, G.: Über die Diffusion des Kohlenstoffs in Metalle und die Mischkristalle des Eisens (Diffusion of Carbon in Metals and the Mixed Crystals of Iron), *Stahl u. Eisen*, v. 42, 1922, pp. 654–659.

118. Barton, L. J.: Heat Treatment of Electric Carbon and Alloy Forging Steels, *Forging and Heat Treating*, v. 9, 1923, pp. 102–105.

119. Bratton, W. N.: Molybdenum in Cast Steel and Iron Rolls, *Iron Age*, v. 112, 1923, pp. 1509–1510.

120. French, H. J., and W. A. Tucker: Strength of Steels at High Temperatures, *Iron Age*, v. 112, 1923, pp. 193–195, 275–278.

121. Hibbard, H. D.: Calorific Value of Steel-making Elements, *Iron Age*, v. 111, 1923, pp. 143–144, 211–213, 347–349.

122. McAdam, D. J., Jr.: Endurance Properties of Steel: Their Relation to Other Physical Properties and to Chemical Composition, *Proc. Am. Soc. Test. Mat.*, v. 23, part 2, 1923, pp. 56–105; discussion, *ibid.*, v. 23, part 2, 1923, pp. 122–129.

123. Moore, R. R., and E. V. Schaal: The Heat Treatment of Alloy Steels, *Forging and Heat Treating*, v. 9, 1923, pp. 113–121.

124. Nischk, K.: Studien über Umsetzungen zwischen Metallen oder Metalloxyden und Kohlenstoff (Studies on the Reaction between Metals or Metal Oxides and Carbon), *Z. f. Elektrochemie*, v. 29, 1923, pp. 373–390.

125. PULSIFER, H. B., and O. V. GREENE: Structure of Chromium-nickel Steel, *Chem. Met. Eng.*, v. 28, 1923, pp. 354–356.
126. SMALLEY, O.: Special Cast Iron, *Met. Ind.*, London, v. 22, 1923, Iron Foundry Sect., pp. 35–38, 59–61, 82–85. (Paper read before the Institute of British Foundrymen.)
127. STRAUSS, J.: Performance of High-speed Cutting Tools, *Iron Age*, v. 111, 1923, pp. 1103, 1150–1151.
128. TAMMANN, G., and E. SOTTER: Über das elektrochemische Verhalten der Legierungen des Eisens mit Chrom, des Eisens mit Molybdän und des Eisens mit Aluminium (On the Electrochemical Behavior of Alloys of Iron with Chromium, Iron with Molybdenum, and Iron with Aluminum), *Z. f. anorg. Chem.*, v. 127, 1923, pp. 257–272.
129. WOODWARD, W. E.: The Effects of Time and Temperature on Certain Special Steels, *J. West Scotland Iron Steel Inst.*, v. 31, 1923–1924, pp. 32–34; discussion, *ibid.*, v. 31, 1923–1924, pp. 35–39.

130. ANDREW, J. H.: Special Steels, *Proc. Cleveland Inst. Eng.*, Session 1924–1925, pp. 223–233; discussion, *ibid.*, Session 1924–1925, pp. 234–251. Also: *Iron Coal Tr. Rev.*, v. 110, 1925, pp. 427–428; discussion, *ibid.*, v. 110, 1925, p. 428.
131. ANDREW, J. H., and H. HYMAN: High-temperature Growth of Special Cast Irons, *J. Iron Steel Inst.*, v. 109, 1924, pp. 451–460; discussion, *ibid.*, v. 109, 1924, pp. 461–463.
132. ARMSTRONG, P. A. E.: Corrosion-resistant Alloys—Past, Present and Future—with Suggestions as to Future Trend, *Proc. Am. Soc. Test. Mat.*, v. 24, part 2, 1924, pp. 193–207; symposium discussion, *ibid.*, v. 24, part 2, 1924, pp. 422–453. (Part of symposium on corrosion-resistant, heat-resistant and electrical-resistance alloys.)
133. DOWDELL, R. L.: Investigation of the Treatment of Steel for Permanent Magnets, *Trans. Am. Soc. Steel Treat.*, v. 5, 1924, pp. 27–65; discussion, *ibid.*, v. 5, 1924, pp. 65–66.
134. DREIBHOLZ and GUERTLER: Untersuchungsergebnisse molybdänhaltiger Cr-Ni-Stähle (Results of Investigation on Chromium-nickel Steels Containing Molybdenum), *Giesserei Z.*, v. 21, 1924, pp. 349–351.
135. GROSSMANN, M. A.: Brittle Range in Low-alloy Steels, *Iron Age*, v. 114, 1924, pp. 149–151.
136. GROTTS, F.: Broadening the Field for Steel Castings through the Use of Alloys and Heat Treatment, *Trans. Am. Foundrymen's Assoc.*, v. 32, part 1, 1924, pp. 730–743; discussion, *ibid.*, v. 32, part 1, 1924, pp. 744–745.
137. HESS, F. L.: Molybdenum Deposits, a Short Review, U. S. Geological Survey, *Bull.* 761, 1924, 34 pp.
138. JOHNSON, J. B., and S. A. CHRISTIANSEN: Characteristics of Materials for Valves Operating at High Temperatures, *Proc. Am. Soc. Test. Mat.*, v. 24, part 2, 1924, pp. 383–400; symposium discussion, *ibid.*, v. 24, part 2, 1924, pp. 422–453. (Part of symposium on corrosion-resistant, heat-resistant and electrical-resistance alloys.)

139. Oertel, W., and F. Pölzguter: Beitrag zur Kenntnis des Einflusses von Kobalt und Vanadin auf die Eigenschaften von Schnellarbeitsstahl (Influence of Cobalt and Vanadium on the Properties of High-speed Steel), *Stahl u. Eisen*, v. 44, 1924, pp. 1165–1169.
140. Oertel, W., and F. Pölzguter: Mechanische Eigenschaften einiger Schnellstähle im Vergleich zu ihrer Schnittleistung (Mechanical Properties of Some High-speed Steels in Comparison with Their Cutting Efficiency), *Stahl u. Eisen*, v. 44, 1924, pp. 1708–1713.
141. Pierce, E. W.: Molybdenum Steel—Some Production Data, *Trans. Am. Soc. Steel Treat.*, v. 5, 1924, pp. 571–576.
142. Speller, F. N.: Discussion to Symposium on Effect of Temperature on the Properties of Metals, *Proc. Am. Soc. Test. Mat.*, v. 24, part 2, 1924, pp. 162–164.
143. Sykes, W. P.: Tensile Properties of Some Steel Wires at Liquid Air Temperatures, *Trans. Am. Soc. Steel Treat.*, v. 6, 1924, pp. 138–144.
144. Watson, E. A.: Cobalt Magnet Steels, *Engineering*, v. 118, 1924, pp. 274–276, 302–304. (Paper read before Section G of the British Assoc. for the Advancement of Science, Aug. 13, 1924.)

145. Anon.: Williams' Chrome-molybdenum Wrenches, *Am. Mach.*, v. 63, 1925, p. 871.
146. Camp, J. M., and C. B. Francis: "The Making, Shaping and Treating of Steel," Carnegie Steel Co., Pittsburgh, Ed. 4, 1925.
147. Clapp, E. C., and F. C. Devereaux: Tests with Molybdenum Steel Balls at Matahambre, Cuba, *Eng. Min. J.*, v. 120, 1925, p. 891.
148. Eardley-Wilmot, V. L.: Molybdenum; Metallurgy and Uses and the Occurrence, Mining and Concentration of Its Ores, Canada Dept. Mines, *Mines Branch Rep.* 592, 1925, 292 pp.
149. French, H. J., and T. G. Digges: Experiments with Nickel, Tantalum, Cobalt and Molybdenum in High-speed Steels, *Trans. Am. Soc. Steel Treat.*, v. 8, 1925, pp. 681–699; discussion, *ibid.*, v. 8, 1925, pp. 699–702; v. 9, 1926, p. 143.
150. Friederich, E., and L. Sittig: Herstellung und Eigenschaften von Carbiden (Manufacture and Properties of Carbides), *Z. f. anorg. Chem.*, v. 144, 1925, pp. 169–189.
151. Gillett, H. W., and E. L. Mack: "Molybdenum, Cerium and Related Alloy Steels," Chemical Catalog Co., New York, 1925.
152. Greaves, R. H., and J. A. Jones: Temper-brittleness of Steel; Susceptibility to Temper-brittleness in Relation to Chemical Composition, *J. Iron Steel Inst.*, v. 111, 1925, pp. 231–255; discussion, *ibid.*, v. 111, 1925, pp. 261–264.
153. Guertler, W., and T. Liepus: Chemische Beständigkeit einer Anzahl Metalle und Legierungen besonders mit Molybdängehalten (Chemical Resistance of a Number of Metals and Alloys Especially Those Containing Molybdenum), *Z. f. Metallkunde*, v. 17, 1925, pp. 310–315.
154. Guillet, L.: Les aciers à outils à coupe rapide renfermant du cobalt (High-speed Tool Steels Containing Cobalt), *Rev. de Mét., Mém.*, v. 22, 1925, pp. 88–91.

155. HOHAGE, R., and A. GRÜTZNER: Schneidversuche mit Schnellarbeitsstählen (Cutting Tests with High-speed Steels), *Stahl u. Eisen*, v. 45, 1925, pp. 1126–1130.
156. KURTZ, C. M., and R. J. ZAUMEYER: The Corrosion of Iron Alloys by Copper Sulphate Solution, *Trans. Am. Electroch. Soc.*, v. 46, 1924, pp. 319–328; discussion, *ibid.*, v. 46, 1924, pp. 328–330. Abst. tr.: *Korrosion u. Metallschutz*, v. 1, 1925, pp. 39–40.
157. MAHOUX: Note sur les soupapes (Note on Valves), *Rev. de Mét.*, *Mém.*, v. 22, 1925, pp. 39–51.
158. MAURER, E., and G. SCHILLING: Das Wesen der Schnellarbeitsstähle (High-speed Steels), *Stahl u. Eisen*, v. 45, 1925, pp. 1152–1169.
159. MEYER, H., and W. WESSELING: Die Änderung der Festigkeitseigenschaften überwiegend perlitischer Stähle durch Wärmebehandlung (Changes in the Tensile Properties of Predominantly Pearlitic Steels by Heat Treatment), *Stahl u. Eisen*, v. 45, 1925, pp. 1169–1173.
160. OBERHOFFER, P.: "Das Technische Eisen: Konstitution und Eigenschaften," Julius Springer, Berlin, Ed. 2, 1925.
161. PIWOWARSKY, E.: Die Gusseisenveredelung durch Legierungszusätze (Improvement of Cast Iron by Alloy Additions), *Stahl u. Eisen*, v. 45, 1925, pp. 289–297.
162. SASAGAWA, K.: Recherche sur les aciers à coupe rapide avec et sans cobalt (High-speed Tool Steels with and without Cobalt), *Rev. de Mét.*, *Mém.*, v. 22, 1925, pp. 92–106.
163. SHEPHERD, B. F.: Carburizing and Heat Treatment of Carburized Objects, *Trans. Am. Soc. Steel Treat.*, v. 7, 1925, pp. 774–789.
164. SIEDSCHLAG, E.: Das Dreistoffsystem Chrom-Nickel-Molybdän (The Ternary System, Chromium-nickel-molybdenum), *Z. f. Metallkunde*, v. 17, 1925, pp. 53–56.
165. SISCO, F. T., and H. W. BOULTON: Welding Steel Tubing and Sheet with Chromium-molybdenum Welding Wire, *Trans. Am. Soc. Steel Treat.*, v. 8, 1925, pp. 589–619; discussion, *ibid.*, v. 8, 1925, pp. 619–620, 665–668.
166. TUPHOLME, C. H. S.: Some Alloy Steels for Automobile Construction, *Metallurgist*, v. 1, 1925, pp. 98–101.

167. Anon.: Standard Molybdenum Steels Used, *J. Soc. Automotive Eng.*, v. 18, 1926, p. 426.
168. DANIELS, S.: The Fusion-joining of Metallic Materials in Aircraft Construction, *Mech. Eng.*, v. 48, 1926, pp. 1240–1246.
169. FRENCH, H. J.: Metals to Resist Corrosion or High Temperatures, *Trans. Am. Electroch. Soc.* v. 50, 1926, pp. 47–81; discussion, *ibid.*, v. 50, 1926, pp. 81–89. Abst.: *Chem. Met. Eng.*, v. 33, 1926, pp. 591–593.
170. FRENCH, H. J., and T. G. DIGGES: Rough Turning with Particular Reference to the Steel Cut, *Trans. Am. Soc. Mech. Eng.*, v. 48, 1926, pp. 533–599; discussion, *ibid.*, v. 48, 1926, pp. 599–607. Also: *Mech. Eng.*, v. 49, 1927, pp. 339–352; discussion, *ibid.*, v. 49, 1927, pp. 352–354.

171. Gill, J. P., and M. A. Frost: The Chemical Composition of Tool Steels, *Trans. Am. Soc. Steel Treat.*, v. 9, 1926, pp. 75–88; discussion, *ibid.*, v. 9, 1926, pp. 88–98.

172. Grard M.: Influence de la zone thermique de travail sur la sélection des métaux pour moteurs d'aviation (Application of Range of Working Temperatures on the Selection of Steels for Airplane Motor Valves), *Rev. de Mét., Mém.*, v. 23, 1926, pp. 317–330.

173. Guillet, L.: Sur la nitruration des aciers ordinaires et spéciaux (On the Nitriding of Ordinary and Special Steels), *C. R. Acad. Sci.*, Paris, v. 182, 1926, pp. 903–907.

174. Guillet, L., and M. Ballay: La fragilité de revenu des aciers (Temper-brittleness of Steels), *Rev. de Mét., Mém.*, v. 23, 1926, pp. 507–520.

175. Johnson, J. B.: Relationship of Metallurgy to the Development of Aircraft, *Trans. Am. Soc. Steel Treat.*, v. 9, 1926, pp. 517–538.

176. Jones, J. A.: The Influence of Molybdenum on Medium Carbon Steels Containing Nickel and Chromium, Res. Dept., Woolwich, *R. D. Rep.* 67, 1926, 59 pp. Abst.: *Chem. Age*, Monthly Met. Sect., v. 16, 1927, pp. 17–19. Abst.: *Foundry Tr. J.*, v. 35, 1927, p. 177. Abst.: *Iron Coal Tr. Rev.*, v. 114, 1927, p. 279. Abst.: *Mech. Eng.*, v. 49, 1927, p. 686.

177. Monypenny, J. H. G.: "Stainless Iron and Steel," John Wiley & Sons, Inc., New York, 1926.

178. Rohn, W.: Säurefeste Legierungen mit Nickel als Basis (Acid-resisting Nickel-base Alloys), *Z. f. Metallkunde*, v. 18, 1926, pp. 387–396. Condensed tr.: *Chem. Met. Eng.* v. 34, 1927, pp. 417–420.

179. Sawamura, H.: Influence of the Various Elements on the Graphitization in Cast Iron, *Mem. Kyoto Imp. Univ.*, Coll. Eng., v. 4, 1926, pp. 159–260.

180. Schulz, E. H., W. Jenge, and F. Bauerfeld: Neue Fortschritte auf dem Gebiet der Hochleistungslegierungen (Latest Progress in the Sphere of High-duty Alloys), *Z. f. Metallkunde*, v. 18, 1926, pp. 155–158.

181. Schwartz, H. A., and G. M. Guiler: Chemical Elements Inhibiting Graphitization, *Trans. Am. Foundrymen's Assoc.*, v. 33, 1926, pp. 639–645.

182. Spitzner, W.: Gesenkverschleiss und Stahlfrage in der Warmpresserei (Wear of Dies and the Problem of Die Material in Hot Forming), *Maschinenbau*, v. 5, 1926, pp. 880–887.

183. Sykes, W. P.: The Iron-molybdenum System, *Trans. Am. Soc. Steel Treat.*, v. 10, 1926, pp. 839–869; discussion, *ibid.*, v. 10, 1926, pp. 870–871, 1035. Abst.: *Metallurgist*, v. 3, 1927, p. 67.

184. Thompson, J. G.: Resistance of Metals to Nitric Acid, *Chem. Met. Eng.*, v. 33, 1926, pp. 614–616.

185. Westgren, A., and G. Phragmén: Röntgenanalyse der Systeme Wolfram-Kohlenstoff und Molybdän-Kohlenstoff (Röntgen Analysis of the Tungsten-carbon and Molybdenum-carbon Systems), *Z. f. anorg. Chem.*, v. 156, 1926, pp. 27–36.

186. Andrew, J. H., M. S. Fisher, and J. M. Robertson: The Properties of Some Nickel-chromium-molybdenum Steels, *J. Iron Steel Inst.*,

v. 115, 1927, pp. 685–712; discussion, *ibid.*, v. 115, 1927, pp. 713–715. Condensed: *Iron Coal Tr. Rev.*, v. 114, 1927, pp. 892–893.

187. Anon.: Fafnir Molybdenum Steel Ball Bearings, *Machinery, N. Y.*, v. 33, 1927, p. 792.
188. Becker, K., and R. Hölbling: Einige Eigenschaften des Wolframcarbides W_2C (Some Properties of Tungsten Carbide W_2C), *Z. f. angew. Chem.*, v. 40, 1927, pp. 512–513.
189. Bullens, D. K.: "Steel and Its Heat Treatment," John Wiley & Sons, Inc., New York, Ed. 3, 1927.
190. French, H. J.: Comparison of the Alloying Elements Chromium, Nickel, Molybdenum and Vanadium in Structural Steels, *Trans. Am. Soc. Steel Treat.*, v. 11, 1927, pp. 845–884, 1000.
191. French, H. J., chairman: Preliminary Report on Comparative High-temperature Tension Tests on a Carbon Steel and on a Chromium-molybdenum Steel at Different Laboratories, *Proc. Am. Soc. Test. Mat.*, v. 27, part 1, 1927, pp. 143–152. Also: *Mech. Eng.*, v. 49, 1927, pp. 1111–1114.
192. French, H. J., and H. K. Herschman: Recent Experiments Relating to the Wear of Plug Gages, *Trans. Am. Soc. Steel Treat.*, v. 12, 1927, pp. 921–945; discussion, *ibid.*, v. 12, 1927, pp. 945–953.
193. French, H. J., H. C. Cross, and A. A. Peterson: Creep in Five Steels at Different Temperatures, U. S. Bur. Stand., *Tech. Paper* 362, v. 22, 1927, pp. 235–267.
194. Guillet, L.: Sur la nitruration des aciers spéciaux (On the Nitriding of Special Steels), *C. R. Acad. Sci.*, Paris, v. 185, 1927, pp. 818–821.
195. Herschman, H. K., Air-hardening Rivet Steels, U. S. Bur. Stand., *Tech. Paper* 358, v. 22, 1927, pp. 141–169.
196. Honda, K., and K. Takahasi: On the Quantitative Measurement of the Cutting Power of Cutlery, *J. Iron Steel Inst.*, v. 116, 1927, pp. 357–375; discussion, *ibid.*, v. 116, 1927, pp. 376–384.
197. Johnson, J. B.: Welding the Aircraft Structure, *J. Am. Weld. Soc.*, v. 6, no. 9, 1927, pp. 102–119. Abst.: *Iron Age*, v. 120, 1927, pp. 939–940.
198. Kjerrman, B.: Heat Treatment of Two Ball Bearing Steels, *Trans. Am. Soc. Steel Treat.*, v. 12, 1927, pp. 759–777. Condensed: *Forging Stamping Heat Treating*, v. 13, 1927, pp. 412–416.
199. Laissus, J.: Contribution à l'étude des cémentations métalliques. Cémentation des alliages ferreux par le molybdène et par le tantale (Metallic Cementations. Cementation of Ferrous Alloys by Means of Molybdenum and Tantalum), *Rev. de Mét., Mém.*, v. 24, 1927, pp. 377–395.
200. Lantsberry, F. C. A. H.: High-speed Steels, *Trans. Am. Soc. Steel Treat.*, v. 11, 1927, pp. 711–725; discussion, *ibid.*, v. 11, 1927, pp. 725–729, 803.
201. Müller, A.: Über das System Eisen-Molybdän (On the Iron-molybdenum System), *Stahl u. Eisen*, v. 47, 1927, pp. 1341–1342.
202. Oertel, O., and K. Würth: Über den Einfluss des Molybdäns und Siliziums auf die Eigenschaften eines nichtrostenden Chromstahls (Influence of Molybdenum and Silicon on the Properties of Stainless Chromium Steel), *Stahl u. Eisen*, v. 47, 1927, pp. 742–753.

203. Okochi, M., and M. Okoshi: New Method for Measuring the Cutting Force of Tools and Some Experimental Results, *Sci. Papers*, Inst. Phys. Chem. Res., Tokyo, v. 5, 1927, pp. 261–301.

204. Ostroga, F. M.: Note sur les aciers au chrome et au cobalt (Note on Cobalt-chromium Steels), *Rev. de Mét., Mém.*, v. 24, 1927, pp. 135–145. Also: *C. R. Acad. Sci.*, Paris, v. 183, 1926, pp. 882–885.

205. Pokorny, E.: "Molybdän," W. Knapp, Halle (Saale), 1927.

206. Robinson, T. L.: Comparative Tests on Ball Bearing Steels, *Trans. Am. Soc. Steel Treat.*, v. 11, 1927, pp. 607–618.

207. Rohn, W.: Vergleichende Untersuchungen über die Oxydation von Chromnickellegierungen bei hohen Temperaturen (Comparative Investigations on the Oxidation of Chromium-nickel Alloys at High Temperatures), *Elektrotechnische Z.*, v. 48, 1927, pp. 227–230, 317–320.

208. Wedekind, E., and O. Jochem: Darstellung von kompaktem und kolloidem Molybdänmetall (Preparation of Compact and Colloidal Metallic Molybdenum), *Z. f. angew. Chem.*, v. 40, 1927, pp. 434–438.

209. Anon.: Second Report on the Heterogeneity of Steel Ingots, *J. Iron Steel Inst.*, v. 117, 1928, pp. 401–548; discussion, *ibid.*, v. 117, 1928, pp. 548–571. Abst.: *Engineering*, v. 125, 1928, pp. 583–584; discussion, *ibid.*, v. 125, 1928, pp. 600–601.

210. Anon.: Stahlguss-Legierungen (Cast-steel Alloys), *Z. f. d. gesamte Giessereipraxis, Eisen-Zeitung*, v. 49, 1928, pp. 367–369.

211. Arnfelt, H.: On the Constitution of the Iron-tungsten and the Iron-molybdenum Alloys, *Iron Steel Inst., Carn. Schol. Mem.*, v. 17, 1928, pp. 1–21.

212. Becker, K.: Die Konstitution der Wolframkarbide (The Constitution of Tungsten Carbides), *Z. f. Elektrochemie*, v. 34, 1928, pp. 640–642.

213. Endo, H.: The Corrosion of Steel by Acid Solutions, *Sci. Rep.*, Sendai, Ser. 1, v. 17, 1928, pp. 1245–1263.

214. Engle, E. W.: The Gaseous Reduction of Tungsten and Molybdenum Oxides, *Trans. Am. Electrochem. Soc.*, v. 51, 1928, pp. 397–401.

215. Frank, J. W.: General Characteristics of Alloy Steel Castings, *Trans. Am. Foundrymen's Assoc.*, v. 36, 1928, pp. 119–128.

216. French, H. J.: Steel Requirements of the Aircraft Industry, *Year Book Am. Iron Steel Inst.*, v. 18, 1928, pp. 350–387; discussion, *ibid.*, v. 18, 1928, pp. 388–398.

217. Guillet, L.: "Le nickel dans les industries de l'automobile et de l'aviation" (Nickel in the Automobile and Aviation Industries), Centre d'Information du Nickel pour Toutes Applications Techniques et Industrielles, Paris, 1928, Ser. B, no. 1, 10 pp.

218. Hardy, T. W.: Grain Size Controls Toughness, *Iron Age*, v. 122, 1928, pp. 1557–1562.

219. Hatfield, W. H.: Heat-resisting Steels—Part II: Mechanical Properties, *J. Iron Steel Inst.*, v. 117, 1928, pp. 573–594; discussion, *ibid.*, v. 117, 1928, pp. 595–610. Condensed: *Engineering*, v. 125, 1928, pp. 589–590, 622; discussion, *ibid.*, v. 125, 1928, pp. 601–602, 632.

220. Hess, F. L.: Rare Metals, U. S. Geological Survey, *Min. Res.*, part 1, 1928, pp. 105–143.

221. Hobrock, R. H.: A Note on the Expansion Due to Nitration of a Special Alloy Steel, *Trans. Am. Soc. Steel Treat.*, v. 14, 1928, pp. 337–342.

222. Hohage, R., and R. Rollett: Über den Einfluss des Streckungs- und Stauchungsgrades auf die Leistungsfähigkeit von Schnellstahlfräsern (Influence of Drawing and Compression on the Efficiency of High-speed Cutters), *Stahl u. Eisen*, v. 48, 1928, pp. 1243–1247.

223. Homerberg, V. O.: Recent Developments in the Application of Nitrogen to the Surface Hardening of Steel, *Fuels and Furnaces*, v. 6, 1928, pp. 1153–1157.

224. Jenckes, E. K.: Pure Oxides and Salts of Tungsten and Molybdenum, *Trans. Am. Electroch. Soc.*, v. 51, 1928, pp. 387–396; discussion, *ibid.*, v. 51, 1928, p. 396.

225. Johnson, J. B.: Chrome-molybdenum Steel in Airplane Construction, *Iron Age*, v. 121, 1928, pp. 1076–1078.

226. Kayser, J. F.: High Chromium Cast Iron Rolls, *Foundry Tr. J.*, v. 38, 1928, p. 94.

227. Kinzel, A. B.: Steels for Case Nitrification, *Trans. Am. Soc. Steel Treat.*, v. 14, 1928, pp. 248–253; discussion, *ibid.*, v. 14, 1928, pp. 253–254.

228. Knerr, H. C.: Aircraft Metallurgy, *Trans. Am. Soc. Steel Treat.*, v. 13, 1928, pp. 723–753; discussion, *ibid.*, v. 13, 1928, pp. 753–758.

229. Knerr, H. C.: Inspection of Aircraft Tubing, *Iron Age*, v. 121, 1928, pp. 201–203.

230. Langenberg, F. C., and C. McKnight: Alloy Bearings Applied to Trains, *Iron Age*, v. 121, 1928, pp. 130–131.

231. MacKenzie, W. J.: Steels Used by the Automotive Industry, *Year Book Am. Iron Steel Inst.*, v. 18, 1928, pp. 469–486; discussion, *ibid.*, v. 18, 1928, pp. 486–492.

232. McQuaid, H. W., and W. J. Ketcham: Some Practical Aspects of the Nitriding Process, *Trans. Am. Soc. Steel Treat.*, v. 14, 1928, pp. 719–743.

233. Merten, W. J.: The Process of Surface Hardening of Steel by Nitriding, *Fuels and Furnaces*, v. 6, 1928, pp. 1371–1376.

234. Persoz, L: Les principaux aciers spéciaux et leurs usages (Principal Special Steels and Their Uses), *Aciers Spéciaux*, v. 3, 1928, pp. 53–61, 112–121.

235. Prömper, P., and E. Pohl: Kessel- und Behälterbaustoffe mit gesteigerter Widerstandsfähigkeit bei hohen Betriebstemperaturen (High Tensile Material for Boilers and Tanks at High Working Temperatures), *Arch. f. d. Eisenhüttenwesen*, v. 1, 1928, pp. 785–793.

236. Py, G.: Progrès de la métallurgie et leur influence sur l'aëronautique (Progress in Metallurgy and Its Influence on Aeronautics), *Mém. et C. R. Soc. Ing. Civils*, v. 81, 1928, pp. 113–170.

237. Rapatz, F.: Influence of the Structure "As Cast" upon Manufacturing and Qualities of Some Alloyed, Especially High Speed Steels, *Trans. Am. Soc. Steel Treat.*, v. 13, 1928, pp. 1009–1022.

238. RICHARDSON, E. A.: Steel for Aircraft Construction, *Trans. Am. Inst. Min. Met. Eng.*, Iron Steel Tech., v. 80, 1928, pp. 157–175; discussion, *ibid.*, v. 80, 1928, pp. 175–176. Abst.: *Engineering*, v. 125, 1928, p. 695.

239. ROHN, W.: Säurefeste Metalle und Legierungen (Acid-resisting Metals and Alloys), *Korrosion u. Metallschutz*, v. 4, 1928, pp. 49–53.

240. ROLF, R. L.: The Automobile Drive Shaft, *Trans. Am. Soc. Steel Treat.*, v. 14, 1928, pp. 72–80.

241. ROMER, J. B., and W. W. EATON: Alloy Materials for Boiler Shells and Tubes, *Power*, v. 68, 1928, pp. 195–197. (Paper presented before the meeting of the National Board of Boiler and Pressure Vessel Inspectors at Erie, Pa., June 19, 1928.)

242. ROWE, F. W.: Molybdenum Steels, *Iron and Steel Ind.*, v. 1, 1928, pp. 339–341.

243. SISCO, F. T., and D. M. WARNER: Effect of Heat Treatment on the Properties of Chromium-molybdenum Sheet Steel, *Trans. Am. Soc. Steel Treat.*, v. 14, 1928, pp. 177–192.

244. SMITHELLS, C. J., S. V. WILLIAMS, and J. W. AVERY: Laboratory Experiments on High-temperature Resistance Alloys, *J. Inst. Metals*, v. 40, 1928, pp. 269–290; discussion, *ibid.*, v. 40, 1928, pp. 290–296.

245. STAHL, E.: Molybdän in der Metallurgie des Eisens (Molybdenum in the Metallurgy of Iron), *Metallbörse*, v. 18, 1928, pp. 2499–2500.

246. TAKEI, T.: On the Equilibrium Diagram of the Molybdenum-carbon System, *Sci. Rep.*, Sendai, Ser. 1, v. 17, 1928, pp. 939–944.

247. WESTGREN, A., and G. PHRAGMÉN: On the Double Carbide of High Speed Steel, *Trans. Am. Soc. Steel Treat.*, v. 13, 1928, pp. 539–552; discussion, *ibid.*, v. 13, 1928, pp. 552–554.

248. ANDREW, J. H.: The Effects of Certain Elements upon the Segregation of Cementite, and Its Relation to the Modification Process, *Roy. Tech. Coll. Met. Club J.*, no. 7, 1929–1930, pp. 16–17.

249. ANDREW, J. H., and D. BINNIE: The Liquidus and Solidus Ranges of Some Commercial Steels, *J. Iron Steel Inst.*, v. 119, 1929, pp. 309–346. (Section II of the 3d Rep. on the Heterogeneity of Steel Ingots.)

250. Anon.: Motor-car Steels, *Mech. World and Eng. Rec.*, v. 85, 1929, pp. 107–108.

251. CARPENTER, H. C. H., chairman: Third Rep. of the Gas Cylinders Research Committee (Alloy Steel Light Cylinders), Dept. Sci. and Ind. Res., London, 1929, 74 pp. Abst.: *J. Iron Steel Inst.*, v. 119, 1929, p. 800.

252. CAZAUD, R.: Le molybdène (Molybdenum), *Aciers Spéciaux*, v. 4, 1929, pp. 413–416, 465–469, 518–524, 589–597.

253. CHRISTMANN, N.: Prüfung von Rohren aus Kruppschem Chrom-Molybdänstahl auf ihre Eignung als Kesselrohre (Testing of Krupp's Chromium-molybdenum Steel Tubes for Suitability for Boiler Tubes), *Veröffentlichungen des Zentral-Verbandes der Preussischen Dampfkessel-Überwachungs-Vereine*, v. 6, 1929, pp. 77–82.

254. Cone, E. F.: Ascendency of Alloy Iron Castings, *Iron Age*, v. 123, 1929, pp. 861–863, 924.

255. Coonan, F. L.: Molybdenum in Malleable Cast Iron, *Heat Treating and Forging*, v. 15, 1929, pp. 1561–1563.

256. Dickie, H. A.: The Strength of Steels at High Temperatures, *Roy. Tech. Coll. Met. Club J.*, no. 7, 1929–1930, pp. 32–37.

257. Eckardt: Dauerzugbeanspruchung von Stahl bei erhöhter Temperatur; ein Beitrag zur Dauerstandfestigkeitsfrage (Creep Testing of Steel at Elevated Temperatures; A Note on the Question of Creep Strength), *Veröffentlichungen des Zentral-Verbandes der Preussischen Dampfkessel-Überwachungs-Vereine*, v. 7, 1929, pp. 7–71.

258. Elmen, G. W.: Magnetic Alloys of Iron, Nickel, and Cobalt, *J. Franklin Inst.*, v. 207, 1929, pp. 583–617.

259. Field, B. E.: Some New Developments in Acid-resistant Alloys, *Trans. Am. Inst. Min. Met. Eng.*, Inst. Metals Div., v. 83, 1929, pp. 149–158; discussion, *ibid.*, v. 83, 1929, pp. 158–159. Abst.: *Iron Age*, v. 123, 1929, pp. 668–669.

260. French, H. J., and T. G. Digges: Turning with Shallow Cuts at High Speeds, *Bur. Stand. J. Res.*, v. 3, 1929, pp. 829–898. Abst.: *Am. Mach.*, v. 71, 1929, pp. 935–936. Abst.: *Iron Age*, v. 124, 1929, pp. 1663, 1704–1705.

261. Fry, A.: The Nitriding Process, *Trans. Am. Soc. Steel Treat.*, v. 16, no. 5, 1929, pp. 111–118.

262. Galibourg, J.: "Essais de traction à chaud sur aciers (450°C.)" (Tensile Strength of Steels at High Temperatures (450°C.)), Centre d'Information du Nickel pour Toutes Applications Techniques et Industrielles, Paris, 1929, 19 pp.

263. Greaves, R. H., H. H. Abram, and S. H. Rees: The Erosion of Guns, *J. Iron Steel Inst.*, v. 119, 1929, pp. 113–167; discussion, *ibid.*, v. 119, 1929, pp. 168–177. Condensed: *Engineering*, v. 127, 1929, pp. 653–655; discussion, *ibid.*, v. 127, 1929, p. 573. (See letter by T. H. Webster on pp. 723–724.)

264. Guillet, L., J. Galibourg, and M. Samsoen: Emploi de l'extensomètre à miroirs de Martens pour les essais de traction à chaud (Use of the Martens Mirror Extensometer for Hot-tensile-strength Tests), *Rev. de Mét., Mém.*, v. 26, 1929, pp. 427–434.

265. Hackett, W., Jr.: Stainless Steel and Iron, *J. Roy. Aeronautical Soc.*, v. 33, 1929, pp. 235–238.

266. Hackett, W. W.: Steel Tubes, Tube Manipulation, and Tubular Structures for Aircraft, *J. Roy. Aeronautical Soc.*, v. 33, 1929, pp. 226–234.

267. Hardecker, J. F.: Building of Aircraft Is Specialized, *Iron Tr. Rev.*, v. 85, 1929, pp. 839–842, 852.

268. Hatfield, W. H.: The Application of Science to the Steel Industry, Sects. IV and V, *Trans. Am. Soc. Steel Treat.*, v. 15, 1929, pp. 986–1026; v. 16, 1929, pp. 121–154.

269. Hatfield, W. H.: The Response of Steels at Elevated Temperatures, *J. West. Scotland Iron Steel Inst.*, v. 36, 1929, pp. 60–65; discussion, *ibid.*, v. 36, 1929, pp. 65–70. Abst.: *Iron Age*, v. 124, 1929, pp. 348–350.

270. Hatfield, W. H.: Steels for Automobiles and Aeroplanes, *Metallurgia*, v. 1, no. 2, 1929, pp. 51–52. (Abstract of paper read before a joint meeting of the Inst. of Automobile Engineers and the Iron and Steel Inst.)

271. Helquist, J. L.: The Nitriding Process and Its Advantages, *Machinery, N. Y.*, v. 35, 1929, p. 647.

272. Herrick, G. S.: Metals Used in Airplane Making, *Iron Age*, v. 124, 1929, pp. 211–214.

273. Homerberg, V. O., and J. P. Walsted: A Study of the Nitriding Process I, *Trans. Am. Soc. Steel Treat.*, v. 16, no. 5, 1929, pp. 67–103; discussion, *ibid.*, v. 16, no. 5, 1929, pp. 103–110. (See *Iron Age*, v. 126, 1930, pp. 990–992.)

274. Honegger, E.: Beiträge zu den Baustoffragen für Hochdruck und Hochüberhitzung (Notes on Structural Materials for High Pressure and High Temperatures), Reprint from the *Berichtsheft über die* 4. *Mitgliedversammlung, Vereinigung der Elektrizitätswerke, E. V.*, Feb. 22–23, 1929, Mannheim.

275. Johnson, W. A.: Alloy Steels for Locomotive Construction, *Proc. Inst. Mech. Eng.*, part 2, 1929, pp. 1087–1097. Abst.: *Vancoram Rev.*, v. 1, 1930, p. 159.

276. Kindelberger, J. H.: Chromium-molybdenum-steel Tubing Fuselage Construction, *J. Soc. Automotive Eng.*, v. 25, 1929, pp. 474–477.

277. Kinzel, A. B., and J. J. Egan: Short-time Nitriding of Steel in Molten Cyanide, *Trans. Am. Soc. Steel Treat.*, v. 16, no. 5, 1929, pp. 175–179; discussion, *ibid.*, v. 16, no. 5, 1929, pp. 179–182.

278. Knerr, H. C.: Heat Treating Aircraft Parts, *Iron Age*, v. 124, 1929, pp. 519–524.

279. McQuaid, H. W.: Working Rules for Nitrogen Hardening, *Iron Age*, v. 123, 1929, pp. 1272–1274. (Paper read before the Western Society of Engineers, Mar. 18, 1929.)

280. McQuaid, H. W., and W. J. Ketcham: A Few Practical Fundamentals of the Nitriding Process, *Trans. Am. Soc. Steel Treat.*, v. 16, no. 5, 1929, pp. 183–195; discussion, *ibid.*, v. 16, no. 5, 1929, pp. 195–203.

281. McQuaid, H. W., and O. W. McMullan: Selection of Case Hardening Steels for Highly Stressed Gears, *Trans. Am. Soc. Steel Treat.*, v. 16, 1929, pp. 860–883; discussion, *ibid.*, v. 16, 1929, pp. 883–892.

282. Malcolm, V. T.: Use of Nitrided Steel in High Temperature–High Pressure Steam Service, *Trans. Am. Soc. Steel Treat.*, v. 16, no. 5, 1929, pp. 205–216.

283. Messkin, W. S.: Der Einfluss des Kaltreckens auf die magnetischen Eigenschaften eines Kohlenstoffstahles (Influence of Cold Working on the Magnetic Properties of a Carbon Steel), *Arch. f. d. Eisenhüttenwesen*, v. 3, 1929, pp. 417–425.

284. Mock, R. M.: Welding in Aircraft Construction, *J. Am. Weld. Soc.*, v. 8, no. 4, 1929, pp. 32–40.

285. Niederhoff, O.: Über die Erfassung des spezifischen und absoluten Dampfverbrauches von Schmiedehämmern bei Reckschmiedung legierter Stähle (Calculation of the Specific and Absolute Steam Consumption of Hammers in the Forging of Alloy Steels), *Arch. f. d. Eisenhüttenwesen*, v. 2, 1929, pp. 545–556.

286. OBERHOFFER, P., H. HOCHSTEIN, and W. HESSENBRUCH: Sauerstoff in Eisen und Stahl. II. Der Einfluss des Sauerstoffs auf das Gefüge und einige Eigenschaften verschiedener Baustähle (Oxygen in Iron and Steel. Part II. Influence of Oxygen on the Structure and Some Properties of Different Structural Steels), *Arch. f. d. Eisenhüttenwesen*, v. 2, 1929, pp. 725–735. Abst.: *Stahl u. Eisen*, v. 49, 1929, pp. 799–800.

287. PHILLIPS, C. B.: Forging Dies Made by Improved Methods, *Iron Tr. Rev.*, v. 85, 1929, pp. 901–903. Also: *Fuels and Furnaces*, v. 7, 1929, pp. 1761–1763. Also: *Heat Treating and Forging*, v. 15, 1929, pp. 1481–1483.

288. PHILLIPS, C. B.: Heat-treating Alloy Steel Airplane Parts, *Machinery, N. Y.*, v. 35, 1929, pp. 943–945.

289. PHILLIPS, C. B.: Heat Treatment of Alloy Steels in Airplane Work, *Aviation*, v. 27, 1929, pp. 781–784.

290. ROHN, W.: Bimetall (Bimetal), *Z. f. Metallkunde*, v. 21, 1929, pp. 259–264. Also: *Metallurgia*, v. 3, 1930, pp. 17–19, 25, 59–61.

291. ROSHONG, R. G.: Nitride and Cyanide Hardening of Vacuum Cleaner Parts, *Fuels and Furnaces*, v. 7, 1929, pp. 1393–1396, 1408.

292. SATOH, S.: Influence of Nitrogen on Special Steels and Some Experiments on Case-hardening with Nitrogen, Am. Inst. Min. Met. Eng., *Tech. Pub.* 260, 1929, 19 pp. Tr.: *Rev. de Mét., Mém.*, v. 26, 1929, pp. 248–258. Abst.: *Fuels and Furnaces*, v. 8, 1930, pp. 523–526. Abst.: *Heat Treating and Forging*, v. 15, 1929, pp. 1583–1588.

293. SERGESON, R.: Investigations in Nitriding, *Trans. Am. Soc. Steel Treat.*, v. 16, no. 5, 1929, pp. 145–168; discussion, *ibid.*, v. 16, no. 5, 1929, pp. 168–174.

294. SMITH, E. K., and H. C. AUFDERHAAR: Molybdenum in Cast Iron, *Iron Age*, v. 124, 1929, pp. 1507–1509. Abst.: *Aciers Spéciaux*, v. 6, 1930, pp. 188–189. (See letter by William J. Grede in *Iron Age*, v. 125, 1930, p. 252.)

295. Society of Automotive Engineers: "Handbook," 1929 Ed., New York, 1929.

296. STOGOFF, A. F., and W. S. MESSKIN: Untersuchungen an Molybdänstählen zur Prüfung ihrer Verwendbarkeit als Dauermagnete (Molybdenum Steels and Their Use in Permanent Magnets), *Arch. f. d. Eisenhüttenwesen*, v. 2, 1929, pp. 595–600. Abst.: *Stahl u. Eisen*, v. 49, 1929, pp. 429–430. Abst.: *Iron Age*, v. 123, 1929, p. 1490.

297. TAKEI, T., and T. MURAKAMI: On the Equilibrium Diagram of the Iron-molybdenum System, *Trans. Am. Soc. Steel Treat.*, v. 16, 1929, pp. 339–358; discussion, *ibid.*, v. 16, 1929, pp. 358–371. Also: *Sci. Rep.*, Sendai, Ser. 1, v. 18, 1929, pp. 135–153.

298. TYLER, P. M., and A. V. PETAR: Rare Metals: Cobalt, Molybdenum, Tantalum, Radium, Uranium, and Vanadium in 1929, U. S. Geological Survey, *Min. Res.*, part 1, 1929, pp. 79–116.

299. URQUART, J. W.: English and American Die Tool Steels, *Heat Treating and Forging*, v. 15, 1929, pp. 177–182.

300. VANICK, J. S.: Low-cost Corrosion Resistance with Alloyed Cast Iron, *Chem. Met. Eng.*, v. 36, 1929, pp. 537–539.

301. AGTE, C., and A. ALTERTHUM: Untersuchungen über Systeme hochschmelzender Carbide nebst Beiträgen zum Problem der Kohlenstoffschmelzung (Contributions to the Problem of Carbon Fusion in Systems of High-melting Carbides), *Z. f. tech. Phys.*, v. 11, 1930, pp. 182–191.

302. ALDEN, C. R.: Nitride Hardening of Alloy Steel for Diesel-engine Use, *Trans. Am. Soc. Mech. Eng.*, v. 52, 1930, Sec. OGP-52-9, pp. 57–61; discussion, *ibid.*, v. 52, 1930, Sec. OGP-52-9, pp. 61–63.

303. ALLEN, H. B.: Improvement in Saw Steels Attributed to Alloys, *Steel*, v. 87, no. 19, 1930, p. 54. (From paper read before the Wood Industries Division of the Am. Soc. Mech. Eng., October, 1930.)

304. Am. Soc. Test. Mat.: Tables of Chemical Composition, Physical and Mechanical Properties and Corrosion-resistant Properties of Corrosion-resistant and Heat-resistant Alloys, *Proc. Am. Soc. Test. Mat.*, v. 30, part 1, 1930, plates V to XV.

305. Am. Soc. Test. Mat.: Tentative Specifications for Open-hearth Plates of Flange Quality, *Proc. Am. Soc. Test. Mat.*, v. 30, part 1, 1930, pp. 965–968.

306. ANGELL, W. R.: Mechanical Properties of Some Structural Steels Hardened Below the Ac_3 and Above the Ar_3 Point, *Trans. Am. Soc. Steel Treat.*, v. 17, 1930, pp. 262–272.

307. Anon.: Alloy Steels Expected to Withstand Temperatures above 1000 Degrees, *Steel*, v. 87, no. 24, 1930, p. 50. (Abstract of paper read by T. L. Clark and A. E. White before the Am. Soc. Mech. Eng., December, 1930.)

308. Anon.: Carburizing Steels, *Vancoram Rev.*, v. 1, 1930, pp. 145–148.

309. Anon.: Chrome-nickel Steel Symbols Standardized, *Am. Mach.*, v. 73, 1930, p. 1028b.

310. Anon.: Employs Salt Bath Annealing in Drawing Hollow Wire, *Steel*, v. 87, no. 1, 1930, pp. 62, 66.

311. Anon.: The Enterprise, a Metal Yacht, *Metal Progress*, v. 18, no. 4, 1930, pp. 75–80.

312. Anon.: Heat-treating Practice in Making Tractor Parts, *Iron Age*, v. 126, 1930, pp. 615–617.

313. Anon.: A Modern Motor Cycle, *Nickel Bull.*, v. 3, no. 3, 1930, pp. 75–80.

314. Anon.: Le molybdène dans les aciers spéciaux (Molybdenum in Special Steels), *Aciers Spéciaux*, v. 5, 1930, pp. 27–32. Abst.: *Iron Age*, v. 125, 1930, p. 1341. Abst.: *Nickel Bull.*, v. 3, 1930, p. 164.

315. Anon.: Notably Light Airplane Wings of Alloy Steel Heat-treated, *Iron Age*, v. 126, 1930, p. 485.

316. Anon.: Physics as an Aid to Metallurgy, *Iron Age*, v. 126, 1930, pp. 1066–1067, 1117–1119.

317. BANNISTER, L. C., and U. R. EVANS: The Passivity of Metals. Part V. The Potential-time Curves of Some Iron Alloys, *J. Chem. Soc.*, 1930, pp. 1361–1374.

318. BAUMANN, K.: Some Considerations Affecting Future Developments of the Steam Cycle, *Proc. Inst. Mech. Eng.*, 1930, pp. 1305–1354; discussion, *ibid.*, 1930, pp. 1355–1396. Also: *Engineering*, v. 130,

1930, pp. 597–599, 661–664, 723–727; discussion, *ibid.*, v. 130, 1930, pp. 626–627.

319. BOEGEHOLD, A. L.: Present Day Methods in Production and Utilization of Automotive Cast Iron, *Am. Soc. Test. Mat.*, Symposium on Developments in Automotive Materials, special reprint, 1930, pp. 1–17.

319*A*. BOSTON, O. W.: Machining Properties of Some Cold-drawn Steels, Am. Soc. Mech. Eng., advance paper 9, 1930, 12 pp. Also: *Trans. Am. Soc. Mech. Eng.*, v. 53, 1931, Sec. MSP-53-6, pp. 41–52; discussion *ibid.*, v. 53, 1931, Sec. MSP-53-6, pp. 52–55.

320. BREMMER, F. W.: Development of Casing for Deep Wells, *Trans. Am. Inst. Min. Met. Eng.*, Iron Steel Div., v. 90, 1930, pp. 293–306; discussion, *ibid.*, v. 90, 1930, pp. 306–310.

321. CARTY, F. J.: Discussion of paper by H. L. Miller on: Thermal Expansion of the Locomotive Boiler and Its Relation to Failures of Material, *Proc. New England Railroad Club*, Nov. 4, 1930, pp. 155–167); discussion, *ibid.*, pp. 167–184.

322. CHALLANSONNET, J.: Étude sur les fontes au nickel-vanadium et au nickel-molybdène (Study of Nickel-vanadium and Nickel-molybdenum Cast Irons), *Rev. de Mét.*, *Mém.*, v. 27, 1930, pp. 573–603, 654–671. Abst.: *Iron Age*, v. 127, 1931, p. 1901.

323. CHARTKOFF, E. P., and W. P. SYKES: X-ray Notes on the Iron-molybdenum and Iron-tungsten Systems, *Trans. Am. Inst. Min. Met. Eng.*, Inst. Metals Div., v. 89, 1930, pp. 566–573; discussion, *ibid.*, v. 89, 1930, p. 574.

324. CHRISTMANN, N.: Erfahrungen mit legierten und höher gekohlten Kesselbaustoffen (Experiences with Alloy and Higher Carbon Boiler Steels), *Arch. f. Wärmewirtschaft*, v. 11, 1930, pp. 353–358.

325. Climax Molybdenum Co.: "Calcium Molybdate," New York, 1930.

326. COLWELL, A. T.: An Endurance Record for Valves, *Aviation Engineering*, v. 3, no. 11, 1930, pp. 22–23.

327. CONE, E. F.: Alloy Steels of Yesterday, Today and Tomorrow, *Iron Age*, v. 126, 1930, pp. 1485–1487.

328. COWAN, R. J.: The Development of a Continuous Nitriding Furnace, *Fuels and Furnaces*, v. 8, 1930, pp. 1517–1520, 1552.

328*A*. COWDREY, I. H.: Hardness by Mutual Indentation, *Proc. Am. Soc. Test. Mat.*, v. 30, part 2, 1930, pp. 559–570; discussion, *ibid.*, v. 30, part 2, 1930, p. 571.

329. DAUBOIS: La nitruration des aciers au four électrique (Nitriding of Steels in the Electric Furnace), *J. du Four Électrique*, v. 39, 1930, pp. 133–134.

330. DICKSON, T. C.: Alloy Steel Guns Cast Centrifugally with Mounts of Welded Parts, *Iron Age*, v. 125, 1930, pp. 1521–1522. (From a paper read before the Cleveland Engineering Soc., May 13, 1930.)

331. DICKSON, T. C.: Centrifugal Castings Make Excellent Artillery, *Metal Progress*, v. 18, no. 3, 1930, pp. 38–39. (From paper read before the Nat. Metal Congress, Chicago.)

332. DOWNES, T. W.: Metal Joints in Aircraft Construction, *Proc. Am. Soc. Test. Mat.*, v. 30, part 2, 1930, pp. 137–139; discussion, *ibid.*, v. 30,

part 2, 1930, pp. 206–212. (Part of symposium on Aircraft Materials.)

333. Esser, H., and W. Eilender: Über die Stahlhärtung (On Steel Hardening), *Arch. f. d. Eisenhüttenwesen*, v. 4, 1930, pp. 113–144.

334. Freeland, H. G.: Nitralloy in the Automotive Industry, *S.A.E. Jour.*, v. 26, 1930, pp. 612–615; discussion, *ibid.*, v. 26, 1930, pp. 616–617.

335. Freeman, J. R., Jr., and R. D. France: Endurance Properties of Some Special Rail Steels, *Bur. Stand. J. Res.*, v. 4, 1930, pp. 851–874.

336. Freeman, J. R., Jr., and G. W. Quick: Tensile Properties of Rail and Some Other Steels at Elevated Temperatures, *Bur. Stand. J. Res.*, v. 4, 1930, pp. 549–591. *Trans. Am. Inst. Min. Met. Eng.*, Iron Steel Div., v. 90, 1930, pp. 225–270; discussion, *ibid.*, v. 90, 1930, pp. 270–279. Abst.: *Blast Fur. and Steel Plant*, v. 18, 1930, pp. 457–461.

337. French, H. J.: A Study of the Quenching of Steels, Part II, *Trans. Am. Soc. Steel Treat.*, v. 17, 1930, pp. 798–888.

338. French, H. J., W. Kahlbaum, and A. A. Peterson: Flow Characteristics of Special Fe–Ni–Cr Alloys and Some Steels at Elevated Temperatures, *Bur. Stand. J. Res.*, v. 5, 1930, pp. 125–183. Abst.: *Steel*, v. 87, no. 2, 1930, p. 62.

339. Fuller, T. S.: Endurance Properties of Steel in Steam, *Trans. Am. Inst. Min. Met. Eng.*, Iron Steel Div., v. 90, 1930, pp. 280–290; discussion, *ibid.*, v. 90, 1930, pp. 290–292.

340. Gabel, S. L., and H. C. Knerr: The Story of Aircraft Tubing, *Aviation*, v. 28, 1930, pp. 632–635, 763–766, 847–850.

341. Gebrüder Sulzer, A-G.: Hochwertige Gusseisen (High-duty Cast Iron), *First communications of the New Int. Assoc. for the Testing of Materials*, Group A, 1930, pp. 49–63.

342. Gill, J. P.: Rational Choice of Tool Steels, *Iron Age*, v. 125, 1930, pp. 782–785. (Paper read before the New York and New Jersey Chapters of the Am. Soc. Steel Treat.)

343. Grube, G., and F. Lieberwirth: Die Oberflächenveredlung der Metalle durch Diffusion. 4. Mitteilung. Die Diffusion von Molybdän und Eisen im festen Zustand (Surface Hardening of Metals by Diffusion—Part 4. Diffusion of Molybdenum and Iron in the Solid State), *Z. f. anorg. Chem.*, v. 188, 1930, pp. 274–289.

344. Hardy, T. W.: Calcium Molybdate, Iron and Steel Making, *Blast Fur. and Steel Plant*, v. 18, 1930, pp. 613–617, 784–788, 795. Also: *Heat Treating and Forging*, v. 16, 1930, pp. 471–474, 480, 608–613. Abst.: *Metallurgist*, v. 6, 1930, pp. 110–111.

345. Hatfield, W. H.: Permanence of Dimensions under Stress at Elevated Temperatures, *J. Iron Steel Inst.*, v. 122, 1930, pp. 215–232; discussion, *ibid.*, v. 122, 1930, pp. 233–247. Condensed: *Engineer*, v. 150, 1930, pp. 408–410; discussion, *ibid.*, v. 150, 1930, p. 345. Condensed: *Engineering*, v. 130, 1930, pp. 600–603; discussion, *ibid.*, v. 130, 1930, p. 404.

346. Hengstenberg, O., and R. Mailänder: Biegeschwingungsfestigkeit von nitrierten Stählen (Vibratory Strength of Nitrided Steels),

Kruppsche Monatshefte, v. 11, 1930, pp. 252–254. Abst.: *Iron Age*, v. 127, 1930, pp. 400–401.

347. Herb, C. O.: Airplane Welding Done in Jigs, *Machinery, N. Y.*, v. 36, 1930, pp. 372–375.

348. Herbert, E. G.: Nitrided Steel: Measuring the Hardness and Thickness of the Case, *Mech. Eng.*, v. 52, 1930, pp. 597–600.

349. Hiemenz, H.: The Thermal Expansion of Some Alloys of the System Nickel-iron and the Effect of Heat Treatment Thereon, *J. Inst. Metals*, v. 44, 1930, p. 510. Original: "Festschrift zum 70. Geburtstage von Wilhelm Heraeus."

350. Higgins, J. H.: Nitriding the Larger Forgings, *Trans. Am. Soc. Steel Treat.*, v. 18, 1930, pp. 523–530; discussion, *ibid.*, v. 18, 1930, pp. 530–532.

351. Hildorf, W. G., and C. H. McCollam: Metal Pellets, Produced by Spark Tests, Used to Identify Alloy Steels, *Iron Age*, v. 126, 1930, pp. 1–4.

352. Houdremont, E.: Die rostfreien Stähle, ihre Eigenschaften und Herstellung (Production and Properties of Stainless Steels), *Kruppsche Monatshefte*, v. 11, 1930, pp. 270–286. Also: *Stahl u. Eisen*, v. 50, 1930, pp. 1517–1528. Abst.: *Iron Age*, v. 127, 1931, pp. 466–469.

353. Johnson, C. M.: Corrosion- and Heat-resisting Steels as Applied to Automobile and Bus Use, Am. Soc. Test. Mat., Symposium on Developments in Automotive Materials, special reprint, 1930, pp. 28–53. Abst.: *Metals & Alloys*, v. 1, 1930, pp. 547–553.

354. Johnson, J. B.: Alloy Steel Sheets for Aircraft, *Iron Age*, v. 125, 1930, pp. 502–505.

355. Johnson, J. B.: Dependence of Aviation on Metallurgy, *Metals & Alloys*, v. 1, 1930, pp. 450–454.

356. Johnson, J. B.: Ferrous Metals Used in Airplane Construction, *Proc. Am. Soc. Test. Mat.*, v. 30, part 2, 1930, pp. 28–33; discussion, *ibid.*, v. 30, part 2, 1930, pp. 171–181. (Part of symposium on Aircraft Materials.)

357. Jungbluth, H.: Werkstoffe für den Dampfkesselbau (Steam Boiler Materials), *Kruppsche Monatshefte*, v. 11, 1930, pp. 177–184.

358. Kanter, J. J., and L. W. Spring: Some Long-time Tension Tests of Steels at Elevated Temperatures, *Proc. Am. Soc. Test. Mat.*, v. 30, part 1, 1930, pp. 110–132.

359. Keeney, R. M.: Industrial Heating for Heat Treatment, *Metals & Alloys*, v. 1, 1930, pp. 508–513.

360. Kershaw, H. E.: Cobalt Magnet Steels, *Edgar Allen N.*, v. 9, 1930, pp. 701–705. Also: *Foundry Tr. J.*, v. 43, 1930, p. 248. (From paper read before the Sheffield Metallurgical Soc.)

361. Kinzel, A. B., and J. J. Egan: Nitriding in Packing Materials and Ammonia, *Trans. Am. Soc. Steel Treat.*, v. 18, 1930, pp. 459–468; discussion, *ibid.*, v 18, 1930, pp. 468–473.

362. Knerr, H. C.: Heat Treatment of Aircraft Parts, *Proc. Am. Soc. Test. Mat.*, v. 30, part 2, 1930, pp. 154–170; discussion, ibid., v. 30, part 2, 1930, pp. 212–214. (Part of symposium on Aircraft Materials.)

363. KNERR, H. C.: Symposium on Aircraft Materials, *Proc. Am. Soc. Test. Mat.*, v. 30, part 2, 1930, pp. 26–27. (Introduction to symposium on Aircraft Materials.)

364. KOTHNY, E.: Legierter Guss (Alloy Castings), *Giesserei Z.*, v. 27, 1930, pp. 291–300, 323–327.

365. KREUTZBERG, E. C.: Nickel-chromium Steels More Widely Used, *Iron Tr. Rev.*, v. 86, no. 16, 1930, pp. 45–49; v. 86, no. 17, 1930, pp. 53–56.

366. KŘÍŽ, A.: The Heterogeneity of an Ingot Made by the Harmet Process, *J. Iron Steel Inst.*, v. 122, 1930, pp. 13–28; discussion, *ibid.*, v. 122, 1930, pp. 29–41. Condensed: *Foundry Tr. J.*, v. 43, 1930, pp. 217–218; discussion, *ibid.*, v. 43, 1930, p. 219.

367. KRUPP, FRIEDRICH, A.-G.: Alloys of Steel, *Vancoram Rev.*, v. 2, 1931, p. 153. (Abstract of French Patent 699,142, July 19, 1930.)

368. LAKE, E. F.: Constructing Fuselages for Airplanes, *Machinery, N. Y.*, v. 36, 1930, pp. 702–708.

369. LIESTMANN, W., and C. SALZMANN: Über die Warmfestigkeit von Stahlguss mit geringen Zusätzen von Nickel und Molybdän (Influence of Small Amounts of Nickel and Molybdenum on the Heat Resistance of Cast Steel), *Stahl u. Eisen*, v. 50, 1930, pp. 442–446. Abst.: *Iron Age*, v. 126, 1930, p. 484. Abst.: *Nickel Bull.*, v. 3, 1930, p. 164.

370. LINKE, LT. GERALD D., U. S. Navy: Private communication.

371. LORENZ, A. W.: Trends in Heat Treatment of Alloy Steel Castings, *Iron Age*, v. 126, 1930, pp. 693–695, 755–756.

372. LOSANA, L.: Corrosione degli acciai a temperatura elevata (Corrosion of Steels at Elevated Temperatures), *L'Industria Chimica*, v. 5, 1930, pp. 288–291, 565–571; v. 6, 1931, pp. 11–15.

373. LOWRY, E. J.: High Strength Cast Iron, *Trans. Am. Soc. Steel Treat.*, v. 17, 1930, pp. 538–557; discussion, *ibid.*, v. 17, 1930, pp. 558–562.

374. MACRAE, A. E.: "Overstrain in Metals and Its Application to the Autofrettage Process of Cylinder and Gun Construction," His Majesty's Stationery Office, London, 1930.

375. MCKNIGHT, C.: Nickel Alloy Steel Forgings, *Trans. Am. Soc. Steel Treat.*, v. 18, 1930, pp. 1–12; discussion, *ibid.*, v. 18, 1930, pp. 12–18. Abst.: *Iron Age*, v. 125, 1930, pp. 851–852, 902.

376. MCKNIGHT, C.: Recent Developments in Nickel Iron and Steel, *Year Book Am. Iron Steel Inst.*, 1930, pp. 195–212; discussion, *ibid.*, 1930, pp. 212–221. Abst.: *Iron Age*, v. 125, 1930, pp. 1525–1527; discussion, *ibid.*, v. 125, 1930, p. 1527.

377. MAITA, S.: The Corner Ghost in Steel Ingots, *J. Iron Steel Inst.*, v. 121, 1930, pp. 477–493. Condensed: *Blast Fur. and Steel Plant*, v. 18, 1930, pp. 1701–1703.

378. MALOWAN, S. L.: Molybdän und seine Verwendung in der Technik (Molybdenum and Its Technical Application), *Chemiker Z.*, v. 54, 1930, pp. 893–894.

379. MITCHELL, H. A.: Getting the Most out of Steel Castings, *Iron Age*, v. 126, 1930, pp. 914–917.

380. MOCHEL, N. L.: A Note on Fatigue Tests of Nitrided Steel, *Proc. Am. Soc. Test. Mat.*, v. 30, part 2, 1930, pp. 406–410. Abst.: *Engineering*, v. 130, 1930, p. 282.

381. Monypenny, J. H. G.: Corrosion-resisting Steels and Their Applications, *Iron and Steel Ind.*, v. 3, 1930, pp. 111–115, 149–154, 209–214.
382. Monypenny, J. H. G.: Some Metallurgical Problems Connected with the Possible Use of Very High Steam Temperatures, *Metallurgia*, v. 2, 1930, pp. 22–25, 46–48.
383. Moore, R. R.: Materials of Construction in Aircraft Engines, *Proc. Am. Soc. Test. Mat.*, v. 30, part 2, 1930, pp. 88–98; discussion, *ibid.*, v. 30, part 2, 1930, pp. 194–200. (Part of symposium on Aircraft Materials.)
384. Morton, H. T.: How to Select Thin Plate for Deep Drawing, *Metal Progress*, v. 18, no. 6, 1930, pp. 54–59.
385. Musatti, I., and G. Calbiani: Le ghise speciali con particolare reguardo à quelle al molibdeno (Special Cast Irons Particularly in Regard to That of Molybdenum), *Met. Italiana*, v. 8, 1930, pp. 649–669.
386. Mutchler, W. H., and R. W. Buzzard: Methods for the Identification of Aircraft Tubing of Plain Carbon Steel and Chromium-molybdenum Steel, Nat. Advisory Committee for Aeronautics, *Tech. Notes* 350, 1930, 27 pp.
387. Neath, F. K.: Recent Developments in Cast Iron and Foundry Practice, British Cast Iron Research Assoc., *Bull.* 30, 1930, pp. 310–311.
388. Page, A. R., and J. H. Partridge: The Properties of Some Steels Containing Chromium, *J. Iron Steel Inst.*, v. 121, 1930, pp. 393–415.
389. Parmiter, O. K.: New Tool and Die Steels Give High Production, *Iron Tr. Rev.*, v. 86, no. 16, 1930, pp. 52–54.
390. Pearce, J. G.: Cast Iron Testing in Great Britain, *First communications of the New Int. Assoc. for the Testing of Materials*, Group A, 1930, pp. 1–4.
391. Perkins, K.: Careful Design Is Necessary in Airplane Welding, *Iron Tr. Rev.*, v. 86, no. 6, 1930, pp. 77–78, 80. (From paper delivered before the Int. Acetylene Assoc., Chicago, November, 1929.)
392. Petinot, N.: Vanadium Additions Improve Properties of Steel. II, *Steel*, v. 87, no. 9, 1930, pp. 47–49.
393. Pohl, E., H. Scholz, and H. Juretzek: Ergebnisse von Dauerbelastungsversuchen mit verschiedenen Baustählen bei hohen Temperaturen (Results of Creep Tests on Different Structural Steels at High Temperatures), *Arch. f. d. Eisenhüttenwesen*, v. 4, 1930, pp. 105–110. Abst.: *Stahl u. Eisen*, v. 50, 1930, pp. 1330–1331. Abst.: *Iron Age*, v. 126, 1930, p. 1821.
394. Pomey, J., and P. Voulet: Contribution à l'étude des aciers inattaquables pour l'industrie chimique (Non-corrosive Steels in the Chemical Industry), *Rev. de Mét., Mém.*, v. 27, 1930, pp. 334–335. (From paper read before the Barcelona meeting of the Congress of Industrial Chemistry.)
395. Ritchie, S. B.: Molybdenum in High-speed Steel, *Army Ordnance*, v. 11, no. 61, 1930, pp. 12–19.
396. Rosenhain, W., *et al.*: Some Alloys for Use at High Temperatures; Nickel-chromium and Complex Iron-nickel-chromium Alloys, *J. Iron Steel Inst.*, v. 121, 1930, pp. 225–304; discussion, *ibid.*, v. 121,

1930, pp. 305–314. (Part I is by W. Rosenhain and C. H. M. Jenkins, and Part II is by C. H. M. Jenkins, H. J. Tapsell, C. R. Austin, and W. P. Rees.)

397. Rowe, F. W.: Modern Casehardening Practice, *J. West Scotland Iron Steel Inst.*, v. 38, 1930, pp. 27–42. Also: *Heat Treating and Forging*, v. 17, 1931, pp. 372–373, 475–479.

398. Rys, A.: Legierter Stahlformguss in Theorie und Praxis (Alloy Cast Steel in Theory and Practice), *Kruppsche Monatshefte*, v. 11, 1930, pp. 47–74. Also: *Stahl u. Eisen*, v. 50, 1930, pp. 423–438. Abst.: *Iron Age*, v. 125, 1930, pp. 1821–1822; v. 126, 1930, pp. 549, 598. Abst.: *Metallurgist*, v. 6, 1930, pp. 68–69.

399. Saklatwalla, E. B., J. Strauss, H. Chandler, and G. Norris: Mémoire sur l'emploi du vanadium dans l'industrie sidérurgique (Use of Vanadium in the Metallurgical Industry), *Aciers Spéciaux*, v. 5, 1930, pp. 390–406.

400. Sauvageot, M., and L. Lauprète: Attaque de divers types d'aciers inoxydables par les principaux acides usuels (Attack of Different Types of Stainless Steels by Common Acids), *Rev. de Mét., Mém.*, v. 27, 1930, pp. 362–367.

401. Sergeson, R.: Recent Developments in Nitriding, *Iron Age*, v. 126, 1930, pp. 680–682.

402. Sergeson, R. S., and M. M. Clark: Nitriding Analyses; Their Physical Properties and Adaptability, *Iron Age*, v. 126, 1930, p. 992. (From Paper read before the Fourth Nat. Machine Shop Practice Meeting of the Am. Soc. Mech. Eng., September, 1930.)

403. Sergeson, R., and H. J. Deal: Further Investigations in Nitriding, *Trans. Am. Soc. Steel Treat.*, v. 18, 1930, pp. 474–497; discussion, *ibid.*, v. 18, 1930, pp. 497–501.

404. Shaw, B.: Iron and Steel Foundry Practice. V, *Metallurgia*, v. 2, 1930, pp. 135–136, 155.

405. Sisco, F. T.: The Constitution of Steel and Cast Iron. Sec. II, Part XIV, *Trans. Am. Soc. Steel Treat.*, v. 17, 1930, pp. 111–129.

406. Smith, E. K., and H. C. Aufderhaar: Tests Show Effect of Using Alloy Scrap in Making Pig Iron, *Iron Age*, v. 126, 1930, pp. 156–158.

407. Smith, J. K.: Molybdenum Improves Gray Iron, *Foundry*, v. 58, no. 12, 1930, pp. 54–55.

408. Stäger, H.: Verhalten von metallischen Werkstoffen bei hohen Temperaturen (Behavior of Metals at High Temperatures), *First communications of the New Int. Assoc. for the Testing of Materials*, Group A, 1930, pp. 89–96.

409. Strauss, J.: The Highly Alloyed Steels in Aircraft Construction, *Proc. Am. Soc. Test. Mat.*, v. 30, part 2, 1930, pp. 41–47; discussion, *ibid.*, v. 30, part 2, 1930, pp. 171–181. Abst.: *Engineering*, v. 130, 1930, p. 282. (Part of symposium on Aircraft Materials.)

410. Thum, E. E.: Medium-manganese Steel for Seamless Tubing, *Iron Age*, v. 125, 1930, p. 1075.

411. Thum, E. E.: Molybdenum Steel Gaining Favor, *Iron Age*, v. 125, 1930, pp. 141–144, 201–202.

412. THUM, E. E.: The New Manganese Alloy Steels, *Proc. Am. Soc. Test. Mat.*, v. 30, part 2, 1930, pp. 215–236; discussion, *ibid.*, v. 30, part 2, 1930, pp. 237–240.
413. Vanadium Alloys Steel Co. and Colonial Steel Co.: "Nitralloy Steel and the Process of Nitride Hardening," 1930.
414. WHITTEMORE, H. L., and W. C. BRUEGGEMAN: Strength of Welded Joints in Tubular Members for Aircraft, Nat. Advisory Committee for Aeronautics, *Tech. Rep.* 348, 1930, pp. 323–359.
415. WOOD, W. A.: X-ray Study of Some Tungsten Magnet Steel Residues, *Phil. Mag.*, v. 10, 1930, pp. 659–667.

416. ABORN, R. H., and E. C. BAIN: The Wrought Austenitic Alloys, Am. Soc. Mech. Eng. and Am. Soc. Test. Mat., Symposium on Effect of Temperature on the Properties of Metals, special reprint, 1931, pp. 466–490; discussion, *ibid.*, 1931, pp. 491–494.
417. ALLEN, R. C.: Steam Turbine Materials for High Temperatures, Am. Soc. Mech. Eng. and Am. Soc. Test. Mat., Symposium on Effect of Temperature on the Properties of Metals, special reprint, 1931, pp. 30–46; discussion, *ibid.*, 1931, pp. 47–48.
418. Anon.: Hadfield Patents New Alloy Steel, *Iron Age*, v. 128, 1931, p. 580.
419. Anon.: Molybdenum Production Sustained by New Uses, *Iron Age*, v. 127, 1931, p. 602.
420. Anon.: Rotor d'alternateur en acier nickel-chrome-molybdène (Alternator Rotor of Nickel-chromium-molybdenum Steel), *Aciers Spéciaux*, v. 6, 1931, p. 93.
421. Anon.: Tool Steels, *Vancoram Rev.*, v. 2, no. 1, 1931, pp. 1–3.
422. BAILEY, R. W., J. H. S. DICKENSON, N. P. INGLIS, and J. L. PEARSON: The Trend of Progress in Great Britain on the Engineering Use of Metals at Elevated Temperatures, Am. Soc. Mech. Eng. and Am. Soc. Test. Mat., Symposium on the Effect of Temperature on the Properties of Metals, special reprint, 1931, pp. 218–236; discussion, *ibid.*, 1931, pp. 237–244.
423. BEISSNER, H.: Einfluss der Gasschmelzschweissung auf die Biegungsschwingungsfestigkeit von Chrom-Molybdän-Stahlrohren (Effect of Oxy-acetylene Welding on Torsional Vibration Strength of Chromium-molybdenum Steel Tubing), *Z. Ver. Deutsch. Ing.*, v. 75, 1931, pp. 954–956.
424. BOEGEHOLD, A. L., and J. B. JOHNSON: Engineering Requirements in the Automotive Industry for Metals Operating at High Temperatures, Am. Soc. Mech. Eng. and Am. Soc. Test. Mat., Symposium on Effect of Temperature on the Properties of Metals, special reprint, 1931, pp. 169–193; discussion, *ibid.*, 1931, pp. 194–200.
425. BOLTON, J. W., and H. BORNSTEIN: Effect of Elevated Temperatures on Certain Mechanical Properties of Gray Cast Iron and Malleable Iron, Am. Soc. Mech. Eng. and Am. Soc. Test. Mat., Symposium on Effect of Temperature on the Properties of Metals, special reprint, 1931, pp. 436–458; discussion, *ibid.*, 1931, pp. 459–465.

426. BROMER, H. E.: Electric Process Iron for Cylinder and Cylinder-head Castings, *Trans. and Bull. Am. Foundrymen's Assoc.*, v. 2, 1931, pp. 585–599; discussion, *ibid.*, v. 2, 1931, pp. 599–601.

427. BULL, R. A.: The Performances of Cast-carbon and Low-alloy Steels in High- and Low-temperature Service, Am. Soc. Mech. Eng. and Am. Soc. Test. Mat., Symposium on Effect of Temperature on the Properties of Metals, special reprint, 1931, pp. 394–431; discussion, *ibid.*, 1931, pp. 432–435.

428. BURNS, G.: The Effect of Molybdenum on Medium-carbon Steels Containing 1 to 2.5 per cent of Manganese, *J. Iron Steel Inst.*, v. 124, 1931, pp. 241–256; discussion, *ibid.*, v. 124, 1931, pp. 257–259.

429. BUTLER, B. S., and J. W. VANDERWILT: The Climax Molybdenum Deposit of Colorado, *Proc. Colorado Sci. Soc.*, v. 12, no. 10, 1931, pp. 311–353.

430. CHEVENARD, P.: The Mechanical Properties of Metals at Elevated Temperatures, Am. Soc. Mech. Eng. and Am. Soc. Test. Mat., Symposium on Effect of Temperature on the Properties of Metals, special reprint, 1931, pp. 245–268; discussion, *ibid.*, 1931, pp. 269–270.

431. Climax Molybdenum Co.: "Molybdenum in Cast Iron," New York, 1931. Also: *Automotive Ind.*, v. 65, 1931, pp. 168–171.

432. COFFIN, F. P., and T. H. SWISHER: Flow of Steels at Elevated Temperatures, Am. Soc. Mech. Eng., preprint, 1931, 7 pp.

433. CUNNINGHAM, W. H., and J. S. ASHBURY: The Surface Hardening by Nitrogen of Special Aluminum-chromium-molybdenum Steels on a Production Basis, *J. Iron Steel Inst.*, v. 124, 1931, pp. 215–228; discussion, *ibid.*, v. 124, 1931, pp. 229–239.

434. DAVIS, E. F.: The Heat Treatment and Manufacture of Springs, *Fuels and Furnaces*, v. 9, 1931, pp. 417–428, 571–576, 905–910, 936.

435. DAVIS, E. F.: The Selection and Heat Treatment of Ball and Roller Bearing Steels, *Fuels and Furnaces*, v. 9, 1931, pp. 153–162.

436. DIGGES, T. G.: Influence of Chemical Composition and Heat Treatment of Steel Forgings on Machinability with Shallow Lathe Cuts, Am. Soc. Mech. Eng., advance paper, 1931, 9 pp. Also: *Bur. Stand. J. Res.*, v. 6, 1931, pp. 977–992.

437. EGAN, J. J.: Short-time Nitriding, Am. Soc. Steel Treat., preprint 19, 1931, 16 pp. Also: *Trans. Am. Soc. Steel Treat.*, v. 19, 1932, pp. 481–496; discussion *ibid.*, v. 19, 1932, pp. 496–500.

438. EILENDER, W., and O. MEYER: Ueber die Nitrierung von Eisen und Eisenlegierungen. I. (On the Nitriding of Iron and Iron Alloys. I.), *Arch. f. d. Eisenhüttenwesen*, v. 3, 1931, pp. 343–352.

439. ELMEN, G. W.: New Permalloys, *Bell Laboratories Rec.*, v. 10, no. 1, 1931, pp. 2–5.

439*A*. EMMONS, J. V.: Some Physical Properties of Hardened Tool Steel, *Proc. Am. Soc. Test. Mat.*, v. 31, part 2, 1931, pp. 47–76; discussion, *ibid.*, v. 31, part 2, pp. 77–82.

440. Fansteel Products Co., Inc.: "Rare Metals: the History, Properties, and Uses of the Metals, Tantalum, Tungsten, Molybdenum," North Chicago, Ill., 1931.

441. FEISER, J.: Molybdäntrioxyd (Molybdenum Trioxide), *Metall u. Erz*, v. 28, 1931, pp. 297–302.

442. Firth-Sterling Steel Co.: "Bulletin 1, Sterling Nitard no. 1," Pittsburgh, 1931, 9 pp.

443. FULLER, T. S.: Endurance Properties of Some Well-known Steels in Steam, Am. Soc. Steel Treat., preprint 8, 1931, 16 pp. Also: *Trans. Am. Soc. Steel Treat.*, v. 19, 1931, pp. 97–111; discussion, *ibid.*, v. 19, 1931, pp. 111–114.

444. GEORGE, H. S.: The Cause and Prevention of Heat Cracks in Aircraft Welding, Am. Soc. Mech. Eng., preprint, 1931, 7 pp.

445. GEROLD, E.: Die Abhängigkeit der magnetischen Induktion bei Baustählen von der chemischen Zusammensetzung (The Dependence of Magnetic Induction of Structural Steels on the Chemical Composition), *Stahl u. Eisen*, v. 51, 1931, pp. 613–615.

446. GILL, J. P., and M. R. TREMBOUR: Melting Tool Steel in Basic Electric Furnace, *Metal Progress*, v. 20, no. 4, 1931, pp. 73–76.

447. GOERENS, P.: Neuzeitliche Entwickelung des Edelstahls (Recent Developments in Alloy Steels), *Proc. World Eng. Congress*, Tokyo, 1929, v. 33, part 1, *Mining and Metallurgy* (*Ferrous Metallurgy*), 1931, pp. 285–323; discussion, *ibid.*, v. 33, part 1, 1931, p. 324.

448. GOULD, J. E.: The Ageing of Permanent Magnet Steels, *Proc. World Eng. Congress*, Tokyo, 1929, v. 34, part 2, *Mining and Metallurgy* (*Ferrous Metallurgy*), 1931, pp. 273–292.

449. GRIM: Manufacture of Acid Steel, *Minutes* of Thirteenth Semi-annual Conference of the Open-hearth Committee of the Am. Inst. Min. Met. Eng., 1931, pp. 92–94.

450. GROSSMANN, M. A., and E. C. BAIN: "High-speed Steel," John Wiley & Sons, Inc., New York, 1931.

451. GRUBER, H.: Über hitze- und schwefelbeständige Legierungen (On Heat- and Sulphur-resistant Alloys), *Z. f. Metallkunde*, v. 23, 1931, pp. 151–157.

452. HADFIELD, R.: Recent Progress in the Industrial Application of Alloy Steels, *Proc. World Eng. Congress*, Tokyo, 1929, v. 34, part 2, *Mining and Metallurgy* (*Ferrous Metallurgy*), 1931, pp. 1–24.

453. HARDER, O. E.: Effect of Temperature on the Properties of Nitrided Alloys, Am. Soc. Mech. Eng. and Am. Soc. Test. Mat., Symposium on Effect of Temperature on the Properties of Metals, special reprint, 1931, pp. 631–653; discussion, *ibid.*, 1931, pp. 654–657.

454. HARDER, O. E.: Nitriding for the Engineer, *Metals & Alloys*, v. 2, 1931, pp. 132–142.

455. HARTMANN, E. C.: Comparison of Weights of 17ST and Steel Tubular Structural Members Used in Aircraft Construction, Nat. Advisory Committee for Aeronautics, *Tech. Notes* 378, 1931, 17 pp.

456. HENDERSON, E. L.: The Effects of Molybdenum and Chromium on the Malleablization of White Cast Iron, *Thesis*, Iowa State College, 1931. Also: *Metals & Alloys*, v. 2, 1931, pp. 223–225. (This is by W. H. Jennings and E. L. Henderson.)

457. HENSEL, F. R.: Age-hardening of Austenite, *Trans. Am. Inst. Min. Met. Eng.*, Iron Steel Div., v. 95, 1931, pp. 255–277; discussion, *ibid.*, v. 95, 1931, pp. 278–283.

458. High Speed Steel Alloys, Ltd.: "Molybdenum in Steel and Iron," 1931.
459. Honda, K., and Y. Shimizu: The Effect of Cold-working on the Magnetic Susceptibility of Metals, *Sci. Rep.*, Sendai, Ser. 1, v. 20, 1931, pp. 460–488.
460. Hruska, J. H.: The Composition of Modern Roll Metals, *Rolling Mill J.*, v. 5, 1931, pp. 163–166, 265–267.
461. International Nickel Co.: "Captain Campbell's New Bluebird Hangs Up a Record of 245 m.p.h.," Advertising material of the Company, New York, 1931.
462. Jominy, W. E.: The Surface Decarburization of Steel at Heat-treating Temperatures, Univ. of Michigan, Dept. of Engineering Research, *Engineering Research Bull.* 18, 1931, 51 pp.
463. Jungbluth, H., and H. Müller: Warmfeste und korrosionsbeständige Stahle für den Dampfkesselbau (Heat- and Corrosion-resistant Steels for Steam Boiler Construction), *Kruppsche Monatshefte*, v. 12, 1931, pp. 179–188.
464. Kahlbaum, W., R. L. Dowdell, and W. A. Tucker: The Tensile Properties of Alloy Steels at Elevated Temperatures as Determined by the "Short-time" Method, *Bur. Stand. J. Res.*, v. 6, 1931, pp. 199–218.
465. Kallen, H., and H. Schrader: Die Durchvergütung von Konstruktionsstählen unter Berücksichtigung des Einflusses von Stückquerschnitt und Legierung (The Influence of Cross-section and Alloy on the Depth-hardness of Structural Steels), *Arch. f. d. Eisenhüttenwesen*, v. 4, 1931, pp. 383–392. Abst.: *Stahl u. Eisen*, v. 51, 1931, p. 387.
466. Kinnear, H. B.: One Per Cent Copper Steel Has Desirable Physical Qualities, *Iron Age*, v. 128, 1931, pp. 820–824.
466*A*. Körber, F., and A. Pomp: Mechanische Eigenschaften von niedriglegiertem Stahlguss bei erhöhten Temperaturen (Mechanical Properties of Low-alloy Cast Steel at Elevated Temperatures), *Mitt. K. W. Inst. Eisenforschung*, v. 13, 1931, pp. 223–236.
467. Krivobok, V. N., *et al.*: Further Studies on Chromium-nickel-iron and Related Alloys, Am. Soc. Steel Treat., preprint 33, 1931, 40 pp.
468. Küster, J. H., and C. Pfannenschmidt: Ein Beitrag zur Frage des Einflusses von Molybdän und Titan auf die Eigenschaften von Grauguss (A Note on the Influence of Molybdenum and Titanium on the Properties of Gray Cast Iron), *Giesserei*, v. 18, 1931, pp. 53–58.
469. Lampton, G. T.: Magnesium and Hollow-steel Propellers, Am. Soc. Mech. Eng., preprint, 1931, 6 pp.
470. Luerssen, G. V., and O. V. Greene: The Cold Treatment of Certain Alloy Steels, Am. Soc. Steel Treat, preprint 24, 1931, 45 pp. Also: *Trans. Am. Soc. Steel Treat.*, v. 19, 1932, pp. 501–544; discussion, *ibid.*, v. 19, 1932, pp. 544–552.
471. McAdam, D. J., Jr.: Influence of Stress on Corrosion, Am. Inst. Min. Met. Eng., *Tech. Pub.* 417, 1931, 39 pp.
472. McCloud, J. L.: Steels Used in Ford Industries, *Metal Progress*, v. 19, no. 3, 1931, pp. 32–39.

473. McManus, T. K.: Abstract of Thesis on Arc Welding of Nickel Steel, *J. Am. Weld. Soc.*, v. 10, no. 1, 1931, pp. 16–19. (Thesis submitted in partial fulfilment for the Master of Science degree at the Massachusetts Institute of Technology.)

474. Mahoux, M.: Influence of High-frequency Electrical Oscillations on the Properties of Metals and Alloys, *Met. Ind.*, London, v. 39, 1931, p. 205. (Abst. by J. Grant of paper read before the French Académie des Sciences. See also abstract by D. R. Lewis entitled The Influence of High-frequency Vibrations upon the Heat Treatment of Materials in *Metallurgia*, v. 4, 1931, pp. 126*A*–126*B*.)

475. Mailänder, R.: Einige Beobachtungen bei Dauerstandversuchen (Some Observations on Creep Tests), *Kruppsche Monatshefte*, v. 12, 1931, pp. 242–243.

476. Maita, S.: On Temper-brittleness in Steel, *Proc. World Eng. Congress*, Tokyo, 1929, v. 34, part 2, *Mining and Metallurgy* (*Ferrous Metallurgy*), 1931, pp. 227–235; discussion, *ibid.*, v. 34, part 2, 1931, p. 237.

477. Mathews, J. A.: Discussion of paper by C. E. MacQuigg on High-chromium Steels for Extreme Service Conditions, Am. Soc. Mech. Eng. and Am. Soc. Test. Mat., Symposium on Effect of Temperature on the Properties of Metals, special reprint, 1931, pp. 589–606; discussion, *ibid.*, 1931, pp. 607–609 (607–608).

478. Mathews, J. A.: Discussion of paper by Kinzel and Crafts on Inclusions and Their Effect on Impact Strength of Steel. II., *Trans. Am. Inst. Min. Met. Eng.*, Iron Steel Div., v. 95, 1931, pp. 181–188; discussion, *ibid.*, 1931, v. 95, pp. 188–195 (188–190).

479. Matsushita, T., and K. Nagasawa: On Quench-hardening Properties of Some Iron Alloys, *Proc. World Eng. Congress*, Tokyo, 1929, v. 34, part 2, *Mining and Metallurgy* (*Ferrous Metallurgy*), 1931, pp. 163–178.

480. Merten, W. J.: The Production of a Large Nitrided Locomotive Crankshaft, *Fuels and Furnaces*, v. 9, 1931, pp. 439–442, 470.

481. Merten, W. J.: Special Quality Gray Iron Castings, *Fuels and Furnaces*, v. 9, 1931, pp. 195–198.

482. Molybdenum Corporation of America: "Research on Commercial Molybdenum Iron," Pittsburgh, 1931.

482*A*. Monypenny, J. H. G.: "Stainless Iron and Steel," John Wiley & Sons, Inc., New York, 1931.

483. Murakami, T., and T. Takei: On the Lowering of Critical Points in Molybdenum Steels, *Proc. World Eng. Congress*, Tokyo, 1929, v. 34, part 2, *Mining and Metallurgy* (*Ferrous Metallurgy*), 1931, pp. 39–67. Also: *Sci. Rep.*, Sendai, Ser. 1, v. 19, 1930, pp. 175–208. Abst.: *Foundry Tr. J.*, v. 43, 1930, p. 186.

484. Nelson, H.: Corrosion Resistant Alloys of the Stainless Type in Use and Fabrication, *Year Book Am. Iron Steel Inst.*, v. 21, 1931, pp. 171–205; discussion, *ibid.*, v. 21, 1931, pp. 206–217.

485. Oertel, W., and A. Grützner: "Die Schnelldrehstähle," Verlag Stahleisen, m. b. H., Düsseldorf, 1931.

486. Parmiter, O. K.: Composition, Performance and Heat Treatment of Super-high-speed Steels, *Iron Age*, v. 127, 1931, pp. 943–944.

(Abstract of paper read before the Hartford, Conn., Chapter of the American Society for Steel Treating.)

487. Petar, Alice, V.: Molybdenum, U. S. Bur. Mines, Dept. Commerce, *Economic paper* 15, 1932, 38 pp.

488. Petersen, O.: Die Entwicklung der Baustähle (The Development of Structural Steels), *Proc. World Eng. Congress*, Tokyo, 1929, v. 33, part 1, *Mining and Metallurgy* (*Ferrous Metallurgy*), 1931, pp. 213–229.

489. Phillips, H. D.: Chromium Cast Steels Resist Heat and Corrosion, *Foundry*, v. 59, no. 1, 1931, pp. 65–69.

490. Pohl, E.: German Special Steels, *Eng. Progress*, v. 12, 1931, pp. 1–6.

491. Pohl, E., E. Krieger, and F. Sauerwald: Untersuchung der Ueberhitzungsempfindlichkeit von niedriggekohltem Flusstahl (Investigation on the Sensitiveness to Heat of Low-carbon Ingot Steel), *Stahl u. Eisen*, v. 51, 1931, pp. 324–326.

492. Reed, E. L.: Influence of Special Elements on the Carbon Content of the Iron-carbon Eutectoid, Am. Soc. Steel Treat., preprint 32, 1931, 61 pp. Also: *Trans. Am. Soc. Steel Treat.*, v. 20, 1932, pp. 115–174; discussion, *ibid.*, v. 20, 1932, pp. 174–176.

493. Ritchie, S. B.: Steels Made without Manganese, *Metal Progress*, v. 20, no. 3, 1931, pp. 35–39, 118. (Extracts from a paper for Am. Soc. Steel Treat. convention, 1931.)

494. Rochel, M.: Considérations sur la chaudière Löffler à haute pression au point de vue de la construction (Considerations on the Construction of the Löffler Boiler), *Chaleur Ind.*, v. 12, 1931, pp. 451–458, 537–546.

495. Sawamura, H.: On the Various Methods to Favour the Graphitization in White Cast Iron, *Proc. World Eng. Congress*, Tokyo, 1929, v. 34, part 2, *Mining and Metallurgy* (*Ferrous Metallurgy*), 1931, pp. 307–357.

496. Sergeson, R.: Behavior of Some Irons and Steels under Impact at Low Temperatures, Am. Soc. Steel Treat., preprint 16, 1931, 16 pp. Also: *Trans. Am. Soc. Steel Treat.*, v. 19, 1932, pp. 368–382; discussion, *ibid.*, v. 19, 1932, pp. 382–384.

497. Sharp, W.: Turbo-generator Fans, *Engineering*, v. 131, 1931, pp. 292–293.

498. Sherwin, L. M., and T. F. Kiley: Cupola High-test and Alloy Irons in a Machine Tool and Gray Iron Jobbing Foundry, *Trans. and Bull. Am. Foundrymen's Assoc.*, v. 2, 1931, pp. 115–156; discussion, *ibid.*, v. 2, 1931, pp. 156–160. Abst.: *Foundry*, v. 59, no. 13, 1931, pp. 45–48.

499. Spooner, A. P., and F. B. Foley: High-temperature Creep Properties of Wrought Carbon and Low-alloy Steels, Am. Soc. Mech. Eng. and Am. Soc. Test. Mat., Symposium on Effect of Temperature on the Properties of Metals, special reprint, 1931, pp. 368–372; discussion, *ibid.*, 1931, pp. 373–393.

500. Spring, L. W.: Some Considerations and Tests for Cast Materials for High-temperature, High-pressure Service, *Paper* 478, read before the June 1931 meeting of the Institute of British Foundrymen.

501. Tapsell, H. J.: "Creep of Metals," Oxford University Press, London, 1931.
502. Van Duzer, R. M., Jr.: Detroit Edison Has Completed Its High-temperature Installation, *Power*, v. 74, 1931, pp. 591–595.
503. Waehlert, M.: "Nickel-Handbuch: Nickelstähle," 2. Teil, "Werkzeugstähle," Nickel-Informationsbüro, G. m. b. H., Frankfurt a. M., 1931.
504. Walls, F. J., and A. Hartwell, Jr.: Some Phases of Heat Treatment of Cylinder and Alloy Irons, *Trans. and Bull. Am. Foundrymens' Assoc.*, v. 2, 1931, pp. 865–890; discussion, *ibid.*, v. 2, 1931, pp. 890–896.
505. Watson, J. M.: Steels for American Automobiles, Model 1931, *Metal Progress*, v. 19, no. 2, 1931, pp. 33–37. (Abstract of paper for Western Metal Congress.)
506. Zeyen, K. L.: Untersuchungen über die Gasschmelzschweissbarkeit von chrommolybdänlegierten Stahlen für den Flugzeugbau (Investigation of the Welding of Chromium-molybdenum Steels for Aviation Construction Materials), *Kruppsche Monatshefte*, v. 12, 1931, pp. 214–223.
507. Zieler, W.: Die Verminderung nichtmetallischer Einschlüsse im Stahl durch Zirkonzusatz (The Reduction of Non-metallic Inclusions in Steel by the Addition of Zirconium), *Arch. f. d. Eisenhüttenwesen*, v. 5, 1931, pp. 167–172.

508. Anon.: Mirrors of Motordom, *Steel*, v. 90, no. 12, 1932, pp. 23–24.
509. Bailey, R. W., and A. M. Roberts: Testing of Materials for Service in High-temperature Steam Plant, *Engineering*, v. 133, 1932, pp. 261–265, 295–298. (Condensed from paper read before the Institution of Mechanical Engineers, Feb. 19, 1932.)
509*A*. Emmons, J. V.: Some Physical Properties of High Speed Steel, *Trans. Am. Soc. Steel Treat.*, v. 19, 1932, pp. 289–318; discussion, *ibid.*, v. 19, 1932, pp. 318–332.
510. Furlong, H. P.: "Molybdenum Iron; Some Interesting Characteristics of Molybdenum Grey Iron," Publication of the Molybdenum Corporation of America, Pittsburgh, 1932, 6 pp.
511. Payson, P.: Prevention of Intergranular Corrosion in Corrosion-resistant Chromium-nickel Steels, *Trans. Am. Inst. Min. Met. Eng.*, Iron Steel Div., v. 100, 1932, pp. 306–328; discussion, *ibid.*, v. 100, 1932, pp. 329–333.
511*A*. Pomp, A., and W. Höger: Dauerstandfestigkeitsuntersuchungen an Kohlenstoff- und niedriglegierten Stählen nach dem Abkürzungsverfahren (Short-time Creep Tests on Carbon and Low-alloy Steels), *Mitt. K. W. Inst. Eisenforschung*, v. 14, 1932, pp. 37–57.
512. Redmond, J. C.: Rapid Chemical Test for the Identification of Chromium-molybdenum Steel Aircraft Tubing, National Advisory Committee for Aeronautics, *Tech. Notes* 411, 1932, 4 pp.
513. Schafmeister, P., and A. Gotta: Korrosionsversuche an kaltgewalztem säurebeständigem Chrom-Nickel-Stahl (Corrosion Tests on Cold-

rolled Acid-resistant Chromium-nickel Steel), *Arch. f. d. Eisenhüttenwesen*, v. 5, 1932, pp. 427–430.

514. SCHMIDT, M., and O. JUNGWIRTH: Ein Beitrag zur Kenntnis hochhitzebeständiger Chromstähle (A Note on Heat-resistant Chromium Steels), *Arch. f. d. Eisenhüttenwesen*, v. 5, 1932, pp. 419–426.
515. SHIPLEY, F. W.: Discussion of paper by F. W. Shipley on Characteristics of Alloyed Cast-iron, *S. A. E. Jour.*, v. 30, 1932, pp. 120–126; discussion, *ibid.*, v. 30, 1932, pp. 126–128 (127).

NAME INDEX

(Item numbers of the Bibliography are in **boldface**; numbers of the pages where the reference is quoted follow the boldface numerals.)

A

Aborn, R. H., **416,** 299
Abram, H. H., **263,** 296
Aciers Spéciaux, **314,** 3, 146, 252, 297; **420,** 297
Agte, C., **301,** 58
Aitchison, L., **64,** 145
Alden, C. R., **302,** 384, 386
Allen, H. B., **303,** 273
Allen, R. C., **417,** 297
Allen, R. J., 189
Alterthum, A., **301,** 58
American Machinist, **145,** 254; **309,** 300
American Society for Testing Materials, 69; **191,** 237, 238; **304,** 424; **305,** 434
Anderson, R. J., **84,** 13
Andrew, J. H., **130,** 290; **131,** 199; **186,** 276, 285, 287, 290, 292; **248,** 96; **249,** 296
Angell, W. R., **306,** 93, 231, 232
Ariens, M. S., 194
Armstrong, P. A. E., **132,** 245
Arnfelt, H., **211,** 19, 21, 39, 40
Arnold, J. O., **65,** 61, 62, 79, 110; **76,** 6, 62, 316, 319; **87,** 316, 319, 344
Ashbury, J. S., **433,** 384
Aston, J., **38,** 79; **43,** 101
Atkinson, F., 299
Aubert and Duval, Frères, 360
Aufderhaar, H. C., **294,** 162, 163, 170, 172–174, 192; **406,** 162, 170
Avery, J. W., **244,** 427

B

Bailey, R. W., **422,** 132, 139, 147, 293; **509,** 291
Bain, E. C., **416,** 299; **450,** 8, 315, 335, 345
Ballay, M., **174,** 290
Bannister, L. C., **317,** 299
Bardenheuer, P., **93,** 332
Barton, L. J., **118,** 213, 419
Bashford, D., 2
Baskerville, C., **36,** 344
Battelle Memorial Institute, 188–191, 193, 196, 201, 308–313, 334
Bauerfeld, F., **180,** 433
Baumann, K., **318,** 297, 435
Becker, K., **188,** 59; **212,** 59
Beissner, H., **423,** 235
Benner, R. C., **54,** 245
Binnie, D., **249,** 296
Bird, R. M., 75
Blair, Th., 3, 78
Boegehold, A. L., 164, 165, 197; **319,** 195; **424,** 426
Bolton, J. W., **425,** 189
Bonardi, J. P., **77,** 16
Bonney-Floyd Co., 310, 313, 406, 407
Borchers, W., **55,** 245
Bornstein, H., **425,** 189
Boston, O. W., **319 A,** 248
Boulton, H. W., **165,** 233, 234
Bowman, R. G., **48,** 74
Bratton, W. N., **119,** 154, 202
Bremmer, F. W., **320,** 226, 403, 405
Brick, E. G., 158, 159
British Engineering Standards Association, **88,** 111, 113, 114

British Iron and Steel Institute, **209,** 75, 77
Bromer, H. E., **426,** 188, 189
Brueggeman, W. C., **414,** 213, 233–236
Bull, R. A., **427,** 412
Bullens, D. K., **189,** 138
Burgess, C. F., **38,** 79; **43,** 101
Burgess, G. K., **97,** 261
Burns, G., **428,** 393, 395–402
Butler, B. S., **429,** 12
Buzzard, R. W., **386,** 144

C

Calbiani, G., **385,** 6, 161–163, 173–177, 193, 194, 196, 200
Camp, J. M., **146,** 80, 110, 116, 119–121, 227–229, 262, 265
Campion, A., **73,** 6, 158, 166; **78,** 166
Capp, J. A., 412
Carnot, A., **12,** 18, 60
Carpenter, H. C. H., **29,** 85, 325, 336; **31,** 319, 336; **251,** 296
Cazaud, R., **252,** 202, 321
Challansonnet, J., **322,** 157, 160–162, 164, 174, 175, 178, 198, 199
Chandler, H., **399,** 431
Chartkoff, E. P., **323,** 21, 39
Chase, M. R., 287, 305
Chevenard, P., **430,** 293
Christiansen, S. A., **138,** 425
Christmann, N., **253,** 215; **324,** 130, 139, 147, 422, 435
Clapp, E. C., **147,** 251
Clark, M. M., **402,** 360, 368, 380, 384
Climax Molybdenum Co., 6; **325,** 71, 73, 74; **431,** 70, 156, 158, 162, 181–186, 193, 195, 196, 200, 202
Coffin, F. P., **432,** 294, 413
Cohade, J. J., **79,** 110
Colonial Steel Company, **413,** 367
Colwell, A. T., **326,** 360, 385
Committee, Iron and Steel Institute, **209,** 75, 77
Comstock, G. F., 432
Cone, E. F., **254,** 157, 192, 202; **327,** 253
Coonan, F. L., **255,** 185, 188, 197, 201
Cowan, R. J., **328,** 369, 382
Cowdrey, I. H., **328 A,** 335
Cross, H. C., **193,** 239
Cunningham, W. H., **433,** 384
Curie, M., **14,** 3, 101, 102, 147
Cutter, J. D., 108, 112; **104,** 252
Czepl, Th., 424

D

Dahle, F. B., 161–163, 201
Daily Metal Trade, 72
Dana, E. S., **105,** 9
Daniels, S., **168,** 233, 234, 253
Danse, L. A., 203
d'Arcambal, A. H., **96,** 319, 328, 329
Daubois, **329,** 360, 364
Davis, A. L., 432
Davis, E. F., **434,** 254, 256, 387; **435,** 142, 256
Dawe, C. N., **106,** 140, 225, 226, 242, 252
Deal, H. J., **403,** 382
Debray, H., **3,** 14; **4,** 14
Delaware and Hudson Railroad, 402
Devereaux, F. C., **147,** 251
Dickenson, J. H. S., **422,** 132, 139, 147, 293
Dickie, H. A., **256,** 299
Dickson, T. C., 346; **330,** 155, 413, 414; **331,** 413, 414
Digges, T. G., **149,** 320, 341, 342, 344; **170,** 137; **260,** 321, 342; **436,** 138, 231, 232
Dittus, E. J., **48,** 74
Dowdell, R. L., **133,** 250; **464,** 295
Downes, T. W., **332,** 233, 253
Dreibholz, **134,** 285, 290
Duisberg, C., **58,** 245
Dupuy, E. L., **59,** 100, 101; **66,** 67, 100, 101
Duriron Co., 424

E

Eardley-Wilmot, V. L., **148,** 9, 10, 12–14
Eaton, W. W., **241,** 434
Eckardt, **257,** 419

Egan, J. J., **277,** 361; **361,** 361, 388; **437,** 361
Ehn, E. W., **112,** 392
Eilender, W., **438,** 50, 365, 366
Elmen, G. W., **258,** 272; **439,** 272
Emmons, J. V., 343, 430, 431; **439 A,** 329–332; **509 A,** 329–332
Endo, H., **213,** 146
Engle, E. W., **214,** 14
Escard, J., **74,** 14
Esser, H., **333,** 84, 85
Evans, U. R., **317,** 299

F

Fansteel Products Co., **85,** 14; **440,** 7, 8
Feiser, J., **441,** 9
Field, B. E., **259,** 424
Fink, C. G., **44,** 8
Finkl and Sons Co., 288, 289, 306, 307
Firth Sterling Steel Co., **442,** 360
Fisher, M. S., **186,** 276, 285, 287, 290, 292
Fleck, H., **69,** 1
Foley, F. B., **499,** 237, 241, 294
France, R. D., **335,** 400
Francis, C. B., **146,** 80, 110, 116, 119–121, 227–229, 262, 265
Frank, J. W., **215,** 154
Freeland, H. G., **334,** 364, 384, 385
Freeman, J. R., Jr., **335,** 400; **336,** 237, 402
French, H. J., **107,** 88, 93–95, 112, 113, 116, 221, 222; **108,** 319, 337; **120,** 236, 237; **149,** 320, 341, 342, 344; **169,** 246, 254; **170,** 137; **190,** 137; **192,** 384, 387; **193,** 239; **216,** 253, 426; **260,** 321, 342; **337,** 392, 393; **338,** 238, 241, 419
Friederich, E., **150,** 58
Friend, J. N., **62,** 144
Frost, M. A., **171,** 317
Fry, A., 358; **261,** 360, 366, 369, 370, 383
Fuller, T. S., **339,** 376–378, 381; **443,** 376–378, 381
Furlong, H. P., **510,** 203

G

Gabel, S. B., **340,** 253
Galibourg, J., **262,** 293; **264,** 293
Gas Cylinders Research Committee, **251,** 296
Gebrüder Sulzer Aktiengesellschaft, **341,** 188
George, H. S., **444,** 233
Gerold, E., **445,** 105
Giesen, W., **39,** 316, 327
Gill, J. P., **171,** 317; **342,** 305; **446,** 74
Gillet, H. W., **151,** 4, 80, 89, 92, 94, 95, 108, 112, 113, 117–119, 121–123, 136, 139, 215, 216, 220, 262–264, 275–277, 285, 286, 312, 317, 318, 390, 391, 421, 422
Girod, P., **45,** 316
Gledhill, J. M., **23,** 316
Goerens, P., **447,** 254, 255, 290, 297, 321
Gotta, A., **513,** 299
Gould, J. E., **448,** 433
Goutal, E., **12,** 18, 60
Grard, M., **172,** 426
Greaves, R. H., **152,** 290, 295, 395, 401; **263,** 296
Greene, O. V., **125,** 96, 244; **470,** 272
Grim, H. G., **449,** 420
Grossmann, M. A., **135,** 217, 232; **450,** 8, 315, 335, 345
Grotts, F., **136,** 154
Grube, G., **343,** 21
Gruber, H., **451,** 428
Grützner, A., **155,** 317, 320; **485,** 324
Guertler, W., **98,** 101, 252; **134,** 285, 290; **153,** 422
Guiler, G. M., **181,** 197
Guillet, L., **24,** 4, 63, 79, 95, 96, 108, 110, 116, 316; **25,** 63, 79, 95, 96, 116; **30,** 63, 79; **32,** 260, 261; **49,** 139; **154,** 320; **173,** 365; **174,** 290; **194,** 363; **217,** 273; **262,** 293; **264,** 293
Gurney, D. G., 253

H

Hackett, W., Jr., **265,** 233
Hackett, W. W., **266,** 233, 253
Hadfield, R. A., 429; **67,** 108, 110, 148, 149; **452,** 292
Haenig, A., **37,** 101
Hagon, T., 299
Halcomb, C. H., 6
Hanemann, H., **60,** 94, 109
Hardecker, J. F., **267,** 253
Harder, O. E., **453,** 359; **454,** 359
Hardy, T. W., **218,** 392, 394; **344,** 16, 17, 68, 70, 72, 73, 157
Hartmann, E. C., **455,** 253
Hartwell, A., Jr., **504,** 200
Hatfield, W. H., **219,** 296; **268,** 293; **269,** 293, 428; **270,** 420; **345,** 420
Haynes Stellite Co., 424
Helquist, J. L., **271,** 384, 387
Henderson E. L., **456,** 197, 198
Hengstenberg, O., **346,** 360, 368, 369, 372, 375, 376, 379, 380, 389
Hensel, F. R., **457,** 433, 434
Herb, C. O., **347,** 233
Herbert, E. G., **348,** 360, 368, 371
Herrick, G. S., **272,** 253
Herschman, H. K., **192,** 384, 387; **195,** 251
Herschmann, A. J., 133
Hess, F. L., **56,** 101, 319; **137,** 10, 11, 13; **220,** 11, 12, 13
Hessenbruch, W., **286,** 81, 141
Hibbard, H. D., **70,** 319, 344; **121,** 68
Hiemenz, H., **349,** 272
Higgins, J. H., **350,** 384
High Speed Steel Alloys Ltd., **458,** 6
Hildorf, W. G., **351,** 143
Hobrock, R. H., **221,** 383
Hochstein, H., **286,** 81, 141
Hoffman, M. K., **27,** 57
Höger, W., **511 A,** 135
Hohage, R., **155,** 317, 320; **222,** 321
Hölbling, R., **188,** 59
Homerberg, V. O., **223,** 384; **273,** 360, 364, 372, 373, 383, 384
Honda, K., **196,** 143; **459,** 8
Honegger, E., **274,** 429
Horton, F. W., **71,** 11, 12, 101, 319
Houdremont, E., **352,** 300
Hruska, J. H., **460,** 305, 433
Hultgren, A., **89,** 64
Hunter, A. H., **99,** 217
Hurst, J. E., **80,** 425, 426
Hyman, H., **131,** 199

I

Ibbotson, F., **76,** 6, 62, 316, 319
Inglis, N. P., **422,** 132, 139, 147, 293
International Critical Tables, 8, 9, 52
Iron Age, **94,** 250, 251; **312,** 297; **315,** 210; **419,** 71

J

Janitzky, E. J., **109,** 242
Jenckes, E. K., **224,** 13
Jenge, W., **180,** 433
Jochem, O., **208,** 14
Johnson, C. M., **353,** 427
Johnson, J. B., **138,** 425; **175,** 208, 253; **197,** 233, 253; **225,** 209, 233, 253; **354,** 209–211, 253; **355,** 253; **356,** 207, 209, 253; **424,** 426
Johnson, W. A., **275,** 296
Jominy, W. E., **462,** 244
Jones, J. A., **110,** 142, 274–276, 289–292, 296; **152,** 290, 295, 395, 401; **176,** 5, 75, 80, 89, 91, 116, 117, 120, 121, 137, 142, 215, 218, 262, 266, 276, 278–284, 289, 291, 292, 296, 311
Jungbluth, H., **357,** 131–133, 134, 147; **463,** 240
Jungwirth, O., **514,** 429
Juretzek, H., **393,** 127, 130, 131

K

Kahlbaum, W., **338,** 238, 241, 419; **464,** 295
Kallen, H., **465,** 242, 243
Kanter, J. J., **358,** 238, 241

Kayser, J. F., **226,** 433
Keeney, R. M., **90,** 15; **359,** 256
Kelley, F. C., 53
Kern, S., **18,** 319
Kershaw, H. E., **360,** 433
Ketcham, W. J., **232,** 360, 364, 365, 368–370, 383; **280,** 369
Kiley, T. F., **498,** 159, 179, 180, 193
Kindelberger, J. H., **276,** 253
Kinzel, A. B., **227,** 361; **277,** 361; **361,** 361, 388
Kissock, A., **91,** 70
Kjerrman, B., **198,** 249, 254
Knerr, H. C., **228,** 209, 233, 253; **229,** 209, 253; **278,** 209, 253; **340,** 253; **362,** 209, 253; **363,** 213, 253
Körber, F., **466 A,** 151–154
Kote, 2
Kothny, E., **364,** 201
Kreutzberg, E. C., **365,** 299
Krieger, E., **491,** 81
Krivobok, V. N., **467,** 299
Kříž, A., **366,** 77
Krupp, F., A.-G., **367,** 429
Kühnel, R., **60,** 94, 109
Kurtz, C. M., **156,** 245
Küster, J. H., **468,** 180

L

Laissus, J., **199,** 20
Lake, E. F., **57,** 140; **368,** 210, 253
Lampton, G. T., **469,** 210, 253
Langenberg, F. C., **230,** 142, 262, 265, 267, 270, 273
Langguth, K. H., 254, 307
Lantsberry, F., **63,** 319; **200,** 320
Lauprète, L., **400,** 298
Lautsch, **34,** 2, 19
LeChatelier, H., **16,** 66, 97
Lester, H. H., 59, 64
Lieberwirth, F., **343,** 21
Liebig, J. O., **81,** 228, 231
Liepus, T., **153,** 422
Liestmann, W., **369,** 270, 271
Linke, G. D., **370,** 403, 406, 408
Lipin, W. v., **13,** 3, 78, 110; **15,** 3, 78
Lorenz, A. W., **371,** 307
Lorig, C. H., 157
Losana, L., **372,** 300–305
Lounsberry, F. B., 354
Lowry, E. J., **373,** 188, 200
Lucas, E. A., 17
Luerssen, G. V., **470,** 272

M

Machinery, **187,** 254
Mack, E. L., **151,** 4, 80, 89, 92, 94, 95, 108, 112, 113, 117–119, 121–123, 136, 139, 215, 216, 220, 262–264, 275–277, 285, 286, 312, 317, 318, 390, 391, 421, 422
MacKenzie, J. T., 168, 170, 172–174, 191, 205
MacKenzie, W. J., **231,** 142, 253
MacPherran, R. S., **100,** 235
MacPherson, R. S., 168
Macrae, A. E., **374,** 287
Mahoux, **157,** 425; **474,** 361
Mailänder, R., **346,** 360, 368, 369, 372, 375, 376, 379, 380, 389
Maita, S., **377,** 76; **476,** 290
Majima, M., **75,** 93, 98, 100
Malcolm, V. T., **282,** 370, 381, 382, 384, 386, 387
Malowan, S. L., **378,** 144
Marshall, C. W., **62,** 144
Mathews, J. A., 80, 147, 217; **19,** 4, 79, 85, 97 108, 110; **82,** 319, 323, 324; **99,** 220; **111,** 68, 92, 101, 106, 136, 273; **477,** 240; **478,** 123
Matsushita, T., **479,** 120
Maurer, E., **158,** 98, 320, 326
McAdam, D. J., Jr., **122,** 207, 208, 228; **471,** 380
McCloud, J. L., **472,** 253
McCollam, C. H., **351,** 143
McIntosh, F. F., 71
McKnight, C., 94, 108, 117, 262–264; **101,** 93, 116, 252, 273; **230,** 142, 262, 265, 267, 270, 273; **375,** 273; **376,** 273, 296
McManus, T. K., **473,** 233, 234
McMullan, O. W., **281,** 141, 273
McQuaid, H. W., **112,** 392; **232,** 360, 364, 365, 368, 369, 370, 383;

279, 364, 365; **280,** 369, 370; **281,** 141, 273
Merten, W. J., **233,** 360; **480,** 78, 366; **481,** 163, 193, 203
Messkin, W. S., **283,** 101; **296,** 101, 103–105, 147
Metal Progress, 56; **311,** 253
Metcalf, W., **26,** 319
Meyer, H., **159,** 109, 111
Meyer, O., **438,** 50, 365, 366
Michigan Steel Castings Co., **94,** 254
Miller, H. L., **321,** 270
Mitchell, H. A., **379,** 270, 307
Mochel, N. L., 374; **380,** 379, 385
Mock, R. M., **284,** 233, 253
Moissan, H., 2; **5,** 57; **6,** 57; **7,** 3; **8,** 14, 57; **9,** 3, 57; **27,** 57
Molybdenum Corporation of America, 17, 71, 74, 402; **482,** 181, 187
Monnartz, P., **50,** 245; **55,** 245
Monypenny, J. H. G., **177,** 246, 247, 298; **381,** 298; **382,** 290; **482 A,** 291
Moore, H., **80,** 425, 426
Moore, R. R., **123,** 224, 225; **383,** 253
Morton, H. T., **384,** 274
Müller, A., **201,** 20, 29
Müller, H., **463,** 240
Murakami, T., **297,** 21–42; **483,** 89, 90
Musatti, I., **385,** 6, 161–163, 173–177, 193, 194, 196, 200
Mutchler, W. H., **386,** 144

N

Nagasawa, K., **479,** 120
National Bureau of Standards, 9
National Metals Handbook, 68, 92, 111, 142
Neath, F. K., **387,** 203
Nelson, H., **484,** 299
Nelson, T. H., **113,** 319
Nickel Bulletin, **313,** 297
Niederhoff, O., **285,** 321
Nischk, K., **124,** 58
Norris, G., 262–264; **399,** 431

O

Oberhoffer, P., **160,** 63, 96; **286,** 81, 141
Oertel, W., **114,** 320; **139,** 337–340; **140,** 320, 332, 333; **202,** 248; **485,** 324
Oesterreichische Zeitschrift für Berg- und Hüttenwesen, **11,** 252
Ohio Steel Foundry Co., 308
Ohly, J., **20,** 261, 273; **21,** 261, 273
Okochi, M., **75,** 93, 98, 100; **203,** 321
Okoshi, M., **203,** 321
Ostroga, F. M., **204,** 426

P

Page, A. R., **388,** 427
Parmiter, O. K., **389,** 430; **486,** 321
Parr, S. W., **68,** 424
Partridge, J. H., **388,** 427
Payson, P., **511,** 300
Pearce, J. G., **390,** 169
Pearson, J. L., **422,** 132, 139, 147, 293
Perkins, K., **391,** 233, 253
Persoz, L., **234,** 433
Petar, A. V., **298,** 1; **487,** 11
Petersen, O., **488,** 435
Peterson, A. A., **193,** 239; **338,** 238, 241, 419
Petinot, N., **392,** 413, 431
Pfannenschmidt, C., **468,** 180
Phillips, C. B.; **287,** 305; **288,** 253; **289,** 253
Phillips, H. D.; **489,** 300
Phillips, W. H., 69, 359
Phragmén, G., **185,** 58; **247,** 65
Pierce, E. W., **141,** 136
Piwowarsky, E., **161,** 6, 159, 169–171
Pohl, E., **235,** 5, 111, 112, 126–129, 138, 139, 143, 147, 149, 150, 155; **393,** 127, 130, 131; **490,** 147; **491,** 81
Pokorny, E., **205,** 1, 7–9, 14, 317
Poliakoff, R., **83,** 319
Pölzguter, F., **139,** 337–340; **140,** 320, 332, 333
Pomey, J., **394,** 298
Pomp, A., **466 A,** 151–154, **511 A,** 135

Portevin, A. M., **40,** 66, 97; **51,** 19; **59,** 100, 101; **66,** 67, 100, 101; **72,** 97
Prömper, P., **235,** 5, 111, 112, 126–129, 138, 139, 143, 147, 149, 150, 155
Pugsley, E., 254
Pulsifer, H. B., **125,** 96, 244
Py, G., **236,** 296

Q

Quick, G. W., **336,** 237, 402

R

Rapatz, F., **237,** 321
Read, A. A., **65,** 61, 62, 79, 110
Redmond, J. C., **512,** 144
Reed, E. L., **492,** 63, 64, 78, 90, 120
Rees, S. H., **263,** 296
Richards, J. W., 316
Richardson, E. A., **238,** 210, 253, 296
Ritchie, S. B., **395,** 345, 346
Roberts, A. M., **509,** 291
Robertson, J. M., **186,** 276, 285, 287, 290, 292
Robin, F., **41,** 124; **42,** 124, 125
Robinson, T. L., **206,** 249, 254
Rochel, M., **494,** 148
Rogers, B. A., 46
Rohn, W., **178,** 245, 423; **207,** 427; **239,** 423; **290,** 272
Rolf, R. L., **240,** 137, 253
Rollett, R., **222,** 321
Romer, J. B., **241,** 434
Rosenhain, W., **396,** 427
Roshong, R. G., 384; **291,** 387
Rossi, A. J., **22,** 316
Rowe, F. W., **242,** 80, 290; **397,** 142
Rys, A., **398,** 5, 150, 155

S

Saklatwalla, E. B., **399,** 431
Saladin, E., **28,** 85
Salzmann, C., **369,** 270, 271
Samsoen, M., **262,** 293; **264,** 293
Sargent, G. W., **92,** 2, 68, 75, 76, 168, 192, 201, 252, 285, 296, 390; **102,** 2, 73, 75, 76, 80, 220, 221, 259, 261, 285, 296
Sasagawa, K., **162,** 320
Satô, N., **75,** 93, 98, 100
Satoh, S., **292,** 360, 365
Sauerwald, F., **491,** 81
Sauvageot, M., **400,** 298
Sawamura, H., **179,** 196; **495,** 196
Schaal, E. V., **123,** 224, 225
Schafmeister, P., **513,** 299
Scheele, C. W., **69,** 1; **205,** 1
Schilling, G., **158,** 98, 320, 326
Schmid, M. H., **103,** 68, 72, 73, 80, 93, 136, 252, 285, 296
Schmidt, M., **514,** 429
Scholz, H., **393,** 127, 130, 131
Schrader, H., **465,** 242, 243
Schulz, E. H., **180,** 433
Schwartz, H. A., **181,** 197
Scientific American, **95,** 252
Seljesater, K. S., 46
Sergeson, R., **293,** 364, 369, 370; **401,** 359, 384, 387; **402,** 360, 368, 380, 384; **403,** 382; **496,** 273, 274
Sharp, W., **497,** 297
Shaw, B., **404,** 155, 306
Shepherd, B. F., **163,** 141
Sherwin, L. M., **498,** 159, 179, 180, 193
Shimizu, Y., **459,** 8
Shipley, F. W., **515,** 203
Siedschlag, E., **164,** 423
Sisco, F. T., **165,** 233, 234; **243,** 211–214, 253; **405,** 253
Sittig, L., **150,** 58
Smalley, O., **115,** 158, 159, 168; **126,** 158, 162, 167, 168, 192, 193
Smith, E. K., **294,** 162, 163, 170, 172–174, 192; **406,** 162, 170
Smith, J. K., **407,** 157, 158, 162, 193, 196
Smith, W. G., **46,** 316
Smithells, C. J., **244,** 427
Society of Automotive Engineers, 5, 295; **167,** 253; **295,** 141, 206
Sotter, E., **128,** 146

Spalding, S. C., **116,** 140
Speller, F. N., **142,** 138
Spitzner, W., **182,** 430
Spooner, A. P., **499,** 237, 241, 294
Spring, L. W., **358,** 238, 241; **500,** 239, 240, 294
Stäger, H., **408,** 151, 152, 248
Stahl, E., **245,** 158, 202
Stahl und Eisen, **10,** 3
Steel (Iron Trade Review), **307,** 432; **310,** 254; **508,** 203
Stogoff, A. F., **296,** 101, 103–105, 147
Strauss, J., **108,** 319, 337; **127,** 337; **399,** 431; **409,** 426
Stromeyer, H., **1,** 2; **2,** 2
Studebaker Corporation, 200
Swinden, T., **52,** 4, 60, 61, 63, 64, 66, 78, 79, 95–98, 108, 110–112, 116–118, 121, 122, 144, 316; **61,** 4, 66, 85–87, 98, 99, 108, 112, 117, 215, 220, 223, 261, 413
Swisher, T. H., **432,** 294, 413
Sykes, W. P., **143,** 223; **183,** 2, 20–55; **323,** 21, 39

T

Takahasi, K., **196,** 143
Takei, T., 439, 441; **246,** 59; **297,** 21–42; **483,** 89, 90
Tammann, G., **34,** 2, 19; **117,** 140; **128,** 146
Tapsell, H. J., **501,** 239
Taylor, F. W., **35,** 316, 319, 322, 344
Thallner, O., **17,** 147, 316
Thompson, J. G., **184,** 145
Thorpe, J. B., 12
Thum, E. E., **410,** 253; **411,** 393, 396; **412,** 403
Trembour, M. R., **446,** 74
Tucker, W. A., **120,** 236, 237; **464,** 295
Tupholme, C. H. S., **166,** 253
Tyler, P. M., **298,** 1

U

United Engineering and Foundry Co., 203
Urquart, J. W., **299,** 305

V

Vancoram Review, **308,** 142; **421,** 432
Vanderwilt, J. W., **429,** 12
Van Duzer, R. M., Jr., **502,** 297
Vanick, J. S., **300,** 196, 199, 202
Vigouroux, E., **33,** 19
Voulet, P., **394,** 298

W

Waehlert, M., **503,** 305, 432
Walls, F. J., **504,** 200
Walsted, J. P., **273,** 360, 364, 372, 373, 383, 384
Warner, D. M., **243,** 211–214, 253
Watertown Arsenal, 247, 268, 269, 343, 347–353, 413–419; **395,** 6
Watson, E. A., **144,** 433
Watson, J. M., **505,** 253, 274
Wedekind, E., **208,** 14
Wesseling, W., **159,** 109, 111
Western Crucible Steel Casting Co., 308
Western Electric Co., 47, 51, 53, 54
Westgren, A., **185,** 58; **247,** 65
Whittemore, H. L., **414,** 213, 233–236
Wickenden, T. H., 137
Williams, S. V., **244,** 427
Wills, C. H., 4, 358
Wood, W. A., **415,** 65
Woodward, R. W., **97,** 261
Woodward, W. E., **129,** 320
Worthington Pump and Machinery Co., 188, 196
Würth, K., **202,** 248
Wüst, F., **93,** 332

Z

Zaumeyer, R. J., **156,** 245
Zeitschrift für die gesamte Giessereipraxis, **210,** 250, 406
Zeyen, K. L., **506,** 233
Zieler, W., **507,** 244
Zuege, D., 407, 409–412

SUBJECT INDEX

A

Acid resistance, chromium-nickel-molybdenum austenitic steel, 298–300
molybdenum steel, 145
stainless steel, effect of molybdenum, 246–248
Acid-resistant alloys, molybdenum in, 422–425
Age-hardening iron-nickel-molybdenum alloy, 433, 434
Aging iron-molybdenum alloys, effect on hardness, 47
Aircraft materials, nickel-chromium-molybdenum steel, 296, 297
tubing, chromium-molybdenum steel, welding properties, 233–235
and sheet, properties, 208–214
use of chromium-molybdenum steel for, 253–255
Airplane parts, nitrided steel for, 385
propellers, chromium-molybdenum steel for, 210
Alpha phase in iron-molybdenum alloys, 24
in iron-carbon-molybdenum alloys, 439, 441
Annealing temperatures, nickel-chromium-molybdenum cast iron, 200
Armor, molybdenum in, early use of, 3
plate, chromium-molybdenum steel for, 252
nickel-tungsten-molybdenum steel for, 433
Austenitic alloys, age-hardening, composition of, 433, 434
molybdenum in, corrosion resistance, 298–300
properties, elevated temperature, effect of molybdenum, 299, 300
Automotive cast iron, molybdenum, properties, 182
Automotive materials, nickel-chromium-molybdenum steel, 296, 297
Automotive parts, chromium-molybdenum steel, 252–255
molybdenum cast iron, 202
nickel-molybdenum steel, 273, 274
nitrided steel, 385

B

Ball-bearing steel, properties compared, 249
types of, 249
Bend strength, ball-bearing steels, 249
tests, chromium-molybdenum steel, 213, 229
manganese-molybdenum steel, 404, 408
Bessemer process for molybdenum steel, 73
Blue-brittleness in molybdenum steel, 143
Boiler steels, yield strength, elevated temperatures, 126
Boilers, copper-molybdenum iron for, 434, 435

C

Calcium molybdate, adding to cast iron, 157
  composition of, 17
  manufacture of, 16
  price of, 72
  use in molybdenum steel, 70
Carbide segregation, nickel-chromium-molybdenum steel, 296
Carbides in iron-carbon-molybdenum system, 57–63, 439, 441
Carbon-manganese steel, effect of molybdenum on, 391, 396–401
Carbon steel, cast, properties at elevated temperatures, 150–154
  creep tests, 129, 130
    and yield strength, 133
  heat-treating ranges, effect of molybdenum on, 92–95
  properties, compared to chromium-molybdenum steel, 227, 229
    heat-treated, mass effect, 242, 243
    tensile, effect of molybdenum on, 119
    tensile, at elevated temperatures, 131, 134
  sheet, yield strength, elevated temperatures, 126
Carburized nickel-molybdenum steel, core properties, 265
Carburizing properties, manganese-molybdenum steel, 141, 403
  molybdenum steel, 139
  nickel-molybdenum steel, 141
Cast alloy steels, properties at elevated temperatures, 150–154
Cast iron, adding molybdenum to, 156
  graphite in, effect of molybdenum, 162
  gray, creep tests, 189, 191
    transverse tests vs. alloy iron, 189
  molybdenum (*See* Molybdenum cast iron.)
  structure, effect of molybdenum on, 159
  white, graphitization, effect of molybdenum on, 196
Cast manganese-molybdenum steel, properties, 309–311, 406–412
Cast molybdenum high-speed tools, cutting tests, 340
Cast molybdenum steel, properties and uses, 148–155
Casting molybdenum steel, 74
Casting properties, manganese-nickel-chromium-molybdenum steel, 407, 408
Castings, chromium-molybdenum steel, properties, 250
Chemical properties, molybdenum steel, 144
Chill in molybdenum cast iron, depth, 167
  in molybdenum and nickel cast iron, 160
Chromium, effect on creep, 240
Chromium-aluminum-molybdenum-vanadium steel at elevated temperatures, 422
Chromium ball-bearing steel, 249
Chromium-molybdenum ball-bearing steel, 249
Chromium-molybdenum cast steel, properties at elevated temperatures, 152–154
Chromium-molybdenum castings, properties as heat-treated, 250
Chromium-molybdenum high-speed steel, critical ranges, 325–327

Chromium-molybdenum sheet, properties, effect of gage, 211–214
Chromium-molybdenum steel, acid resistance, 246–248
  bend tests, 213, 229
    compared with other steels, 229
  carburizing properties, 141
  chemical identification, 144
  corrosion resistant, properties, 245–248
  creep, compared with other steels, 237–242
    and yield strength, 133
  inclusions in, effect of silicon-zirconium, 244
  properties, compared with other steels, 221, 224, 227, 229
    effect of molybdenum, 215, 217
    elevated temperatures, 134, 235–242
    heat-treated, effect of mass, 225, 226, 242, 243
    low temperatures, 223
      (*See also* Chromium-molybdenum structural steel.)
  rivets, air-hardening, 251
  S.A.E. numbers, 206, 207, 228
  spark tests, 144
  structure of, 244
  tubing (*See* Chromium-molybdenum structural steel.)
  uses of, 210, 251–256
  welding properties, 233–235
Chromium-molybdenum structural steel, composition, 206
  endurance limit, heat-treated, 207, 216
  hardness, 215, 216, 218–223, 227, 229–232
  impact value, 208, 216–222, 225–229, 232
  sheet, properties, 209–214
  tensile properties, 208, 215, 216, 218–232
  torsion properties, 208
  tubing, welded, endurance properties, 235
  tensile properties and hardness, 234–236
  welding properties, 233–235
Chromium-molybdenum-vanadium steel, accelerated creep tests, 419
  tensile properties, 419
Chromium-nickel austenitic steel, corrosion resistance, effect of molybdenum, 298–300
  embrittlement of, effect of molybdenum, 299
Chromium-nickel-molybdenum austenitic steel, properties, elevated temperatures, 299, 300
  stainless steel, alloys used, 300
  valve steels, oxidation of, 300–305
Chromium-nickel-molybdenum-silicon-aluminum steel, properties, 428
Chromium-nickel-molybdenum-silicon steel, properties of, 428
Chromium-nickel-tungsten valve steels, oxidation of, 300–305
  vanadium in, 300–305
Chromium-nickel valve steels, oxidation of, effect of molybdenum, 300–305
Chromium-nickel-vanadium valve steels, oxidation of, 300–305
Chromium-silicon-cobalt valve steels, molybdenum in, 425, 426

Chromium steel, corrosion resistance, effect of molybdenum, 246–248
  creep and yield strength, 133
  heat resistance, effect of molybdenum, 429
  properties, compared with chromium-molybdenum steel, 227, 229
Chromium-vanadium ball-bearing steel, properties, 249
Chromium-vanadium-molybdenum steel, creep, 241
Chromium-vanadium steel, properties, 221, 224
Cobalt in molybdenum high-speed steel, cutting performance, 341
Cobalt-chromium valve steels, molybdenum in, 425, 426
Cobalt magnet steel, molybdenum in, 433
Coefficient of expansion, effect of molybdenum, 100
  molybdenum and nickel cast iron, 195
Compressive properties, molybdenum steel, 121
Compressive strength, molybdenum cast iron, 167, 171, 176–178
Copper-molybdenum iron for boilers, composition, properties, 434, 435
Corrosion resistance, austenitic alloys, effect of molybdenum, 298–300
  effect of molybdenum on, 245–248
  of molybdenum cast iron, 196
  of nitrided steel, 382
  of stainless steel, effect of molybdenum, 246–248
    (*See also* Acid resistance and Stainless steel.)
Corrosion-resistant alloys, molybdenum in, 422–425
Corrosion-resistant chromium-molybdenum steels, properties, 245–248
Corrosion-resistant open-hearth iron, specification and properties, 434, 435
Creep strength of steel, effect of chromium, 240
    of molybdenum, 239
Creep tests, accelerated, molybdenum steel, value of, 135
  carbon steel, 129, 130
  chromium-molybdenum-vanadium steels, 419
  manganese-molybdenum vs. other steels, 412
  molybdenum cast iron, 189, 191
  molybdenum-containing steels, 133
  molybdenum stainless iron, 248
  molybdenum steels, 129, 130, 135
  nickel-chromium-molybdenum steel, 293
  nickel steel, 130
  nitrided steel, 381
Critical points, carbon steel, effect of cooling rate, 84
      of molybdenum, 83
  manganese-molybdenum steel, 393, 395
  molybdenum and nickel cast iron, 199
  molybdenum steel, 85–92
    effect of cooling rate, 88–91
    lowering temperature, 87, 91
  nickel-chromium steel, 274
    effect of molybdenum, 275
Critical ranges of high-speed steel, effect of molybdenum on, 325–327
Cutting hardness, high-speed steel, described, 335
Cutting performance, molybdenum high-speed steel, 336–344

Cutting tests, of high-speed steel, effect of molybdenum, 341–343
forged tools, 339
molybdenum, cast and hardened, 340
effect of cobalt, 341

D

Delta phase, in iron-carbon-molybdenum alloys, 341
in iron-molybdenum alloys, 29
Die irons, cast, molybdenum, properties, 185
Die steels, molybdenum, 430–432
nickel-chromium-molybdenum, 305, 306
tungsten, compared with molybdenum, 430, 431

E

Electric conductivity, effect of molybdenum, 97
Electric equipment, nickel-chromium-molybdenum steel, 297
Electric process for melting molybdenum steel, 73
Electric resistance, molybdenum steel, 66
Electrochemical potential, iron-molybdenum alloys, 146
Elevated temperatures, alloy steels, creep and yield strength, 133
boiler steels, yield strength, 126
cast alloy steels, properties, 150–154
chromium-molybdenum steel, properties, 235–242
chromium-molybdenum-vanadium steel, properties, 419
chromium-nickel-molybdenum austenitic steel, properties, 299, 300
chromium-nickel valve steels, oxidation, effect of molybdenum, 300–305
heat-resistant alloys, properties, 428, 429
high-speed steel, hardness, 332–334
manganese-molybdenum rail steel, properties, 400–402
molybdenum cast iron, properties, 190, 196
molybdenum-copper-iron for boilers, properties, 435
molybdenum and other steels, properties, 124, 131
nickel-chromium-molybdenum steel, properties, 293–295
nickel-chromium-molybdenum-vanadium steel, time-yield, 420
nickel-molybdenum cast steel, properties, 270
nitrided steel, hot hardness, 371
compared with other steel, 371
properties, 367, 373–375
Endurance limit, ball-bearing steels, 249
chromium-molybdenum, structural steels, 207, 216
welded tubing, 235
manganese-molybdenum steels, 39
cast and heat-treated, 406
molybdenum cast iron, 181
molybdenum steel, 121
nickel-chromium-molybdenum steel, 286
nickel-silicon-molybdenum steel, 421

Endurance limit, nitrided steel, 376–381
    in steam, 378
Epsilon phase, in iron-carbon-molybdenum alloys, 441
  in iron-molybdenum alloys, 30
Equilibrium diagram, of iron-carbon alloys, 57
  of iron-molybdenum alloys, 21
  sections, iron-carbon-molybdenum alloys, 439–444
Erosion, nickel-chromium-molybdenum steel, vs. Armco iron, 296
Eta phase, in iron-carbon-molybdenum system, 439, 441
  in iron-molybdenum alloys, 30
Eutectoid, concentration, in molybdenum steel, 64

F

Ferromolybdenum, adding to cast iron, 156
  grades, and analyses, 69
  manufacture, 15
Forged molybdenum high-speed tools, cutting tests, 340
Forged molybdenum steel, properties, 109
Forged nickel-chromium-molybdenum steel, properties, 268
Forged nickel-molybdenum steel, properties, forged and rolled, 260–265, 268
Forging, iron-molybdenum alloys, 50
  molybdenum high-speed steel, 347, 352
  molybdenum steel, 79
Forgings, large, nickel-chromium-molybdenum steel, 288
Forming properties, molybdenum steel, 139
Free-cutting molybdenum stainless steel, properties, 247

G

Gamma phase, in iron-carbon-molybdenum alloys, 439, 441
  in iron-molybdenum alloys, 28
Grain size, manganese-molybdenum steel, effect on properties, 392
Graphite in molybdenum cast iron, amount of, 159
  form of, 162
Graphitization, temperature, nickel and molybdenum cast iron, 198
  white cast iron, effect of molybdenum, 196
Growth, molybdenum cast iron, 199
  nickel-chromium cast iron, 200
Guns, centrifugally cast, molybdenum-vanadium steel, 413–418
    heat treatment of, 414
  double-barrel, chromium-molybdenum steel for, 254

H

Hardness, ball-bearing steels, 249
  cast iron, molybdenum, 167, 171, 172, 175–178, 180–182, 186, 187, 190
  chromium-molybdenum structural steels, 215–223, 227–232
    welded tubing, 236

Hardness, depth-hardness curves, nitrided steel, 369, 370
heated in hydrogen, 382
high-speed steel, effect of hardening temperature, 339
of tempering, 340
at elevated temperatures, 332–334
iron-molybdenum alloys, 44
effect of quenching and aging, 45–49
manganese-molybdenum steel, 391–405
cast and heat-treated, 407, 409–411
molybdenum alloy cast steel, vs. other steels, 309–311
molybdenum high-speed steel, effect of heat treatment, 330–334
molybdenum steel, 108, 110, 112, 116–119
effect of temperature, 124
of tempering, 95
heat-treated, 120
molybdenum and vanadium steel, at elevated temperatures, 125
molybdenum-vanadium steel, 413, 415
nickel-chromium-molybdenum steel, 278–284, 286
nickel-molybdenum steel, 260–269
nitrided case, depth of, vs. hardness, 369, 370
effect of reheating, 372
effect of molybdenum, 365, 366
nitrided steel, elevated temperatures, vs. other steels, 371
nitriding steel, heat-treated, 368
Hardness tests, mutual indentation, described, 335
Heat-resistant alloys, properties and uses, 427–429
Heat treatment, centrifugally cast guns, 414
mass effect in chromium-molybdenum and other steels, 242, 243, 291
molybdenum high-speed steel, 353
ranges, carbon steel, effect of molybdenum, 92–95
High-carbon molybdenum steel, critical points, 86
High-speed steel, age-hardness, compared with iron-molybdenum alloys, 48
comparison of Taylor speed, 341–343
cutting hardness, described, 335
cutting tests, 333
hardness, effect of hardening temperature, 339
of tempering, 340
elevated temperatures, 332–334
compared with carbon steel, 371
molybdenum, early use of, 322, 325
effect on performance, early work, 322
history of, 6, 316
limitations and advantages, 344, 346
as replacing element, 315–325
typical compositions, 317–325
(*See also* Molybdenum high-speed steel.)
molybdenum-tungsten-chromium-vanadium, torsional properties, 330–332
effect of cobalt, 330–332
raw material cost, 345

High-speed steel, tungsten-replacing elements, 315
High-speed tools, forged, tests of, 339
  requirements for, 335
High temperatures (*See* Elevated temperatures.)
High-test cast iron, creep tests, 189, 191
  molybdenum, properties, 186
Hot-working molybdenum steel, 78
  effect on structure, 96
  temperature for, 80

I

Impact values, chromium-molybdenum structural steel, 208, 216–220, 225–227, 229, 232
  manganese-chromium-molybdenum steel, 221
    cast and heat-treated, 407, 410
  manganese-molybdenum steels, 391–405
    cast and heat-treated, 406, 407, 409
  manganese-nickel-chromium-molybdenum steel, cast and heat-treated, 407, 411, 412
  molybdenum alloy cast steels, compared with others, 312, 313
  molybdenum cast iron, 171, 181
  molybdenum steel, 121
  molybdenum-vanadium steel, 415–417
  nickel-chromium-molybdenum steel, 278–284, 286, 287, 400
    cast and heat-treated, 308, 312
  nickel-molybdenum steel, 260, 265–269
    at low temperatures, 273
  nickel-silicon-molybdenum steel, 421
  nitrided steels, 373
  nitriding steels, 368
  temper-brittle steels, effect of cooling rate, 290
Inclusions in chromium-molybdenum steel, effect of zirconium-silicon alloy, 244
Industrial uses of molybdenum cast iron, 202
Ingots, corner ghosts in, formation, 76
Iron, corrosion-resistant, molybdenum and copper in, 434, 435
    uses of, 434, 435
  lattice, effect of molybdenum, 39
  open-hearth, corrosion-resistant, properties, 434
  pure, properties of, 9
Iron-carbon alloys, critical points, effect of cooling rate, 84
      of molybdenum, 83
  equilibrium diagram, 57
Iron-carbon-molybdenum alloys, microscopic analysis, 63
  properties, effect of molybdenum, 66
  residue analysis, 60
Iron-carbon-molybdenum system, carbides in, 57–63, 439, 441
  constitution, 67, 439

Iron-carbon-molybdenum system, isothermal sections, 440, 441
molybdenum sections, 442, 443
phases present, 439–441
Iron-molybdenum alloys, age-hardness, 47
compared with high-speed steel, 48
alpha phase, 24
delta phase, 29
dilatometric analysis, 36
early studies, 2, 18
effect of heat treatment, 49
of quenching and aging, 45–48
of temperature, 50
electric resistance, 40
electrochemical potential, 146
endurance, 49
epsilon and eta phases, 30
equilibrium diagram, discussed, 21
methods used for, 33
etching reagents, 39
fabricating, 50
gamma phase, 28
hardness, 44–49
impact value, 50
machinability, 49
magnetic analysis, 35
microscopic analysis, 38
peritectic reaction, 31
physical constants, 51
physical properties, 51
preparation of, 20
recent investigations, 19
structure, 23–33
tensile properties, 42
thermal analysis, 33
uses, 51
wear resistance, 49
X-ray analysis, 39
Iron-nickel alloys, effect of molybdenum, on thermal expansion, 272
on properties, 272
(*See also* Permalloy.)
Iron-nickel-chromium-molybdenum alloys for acid resistance, 423
Iron-nickel-molybdenum-manganese alloy, age-hardening, 433, 434

L

Low temperatures, chromium-molybdenum steel, properties, 223
molybdenum steel, properties, 124
Lowering temperature in molybdenum steel, 87, 91

M

Machinability, iron-molybdenum alloys, 49
molybdenum cast iron, 172, 179, 187, 192
molybdenum stainless iron, 248
molybdenum steel, 136
Magnetic analysis, iron-molybdenum alloys, 35
Magnetic properties, iron-nickel alloy (Permalloy), effect of molybdenum, 272
molybdenum steel, early investigations, 101
effect of heat treatment, 102–105
Malleable iron, graphitization, effect of molybdenum, 196
tensile properties, effect of molybdenum, 188
Manganese cast steel, properties, elevated temperatures, 152–154
Manganese-chromium-molybdenum steel, creep, 242
properties, mechanical, 407, 410
Manganese-copper-molybdenum steel for bridges, 435
Manganese electric steel, properties, effect of molybdenum, 396
Manganese-molybdenum cast steel, creep tests, 412
endurance limit, 406
hardness, as cast, and heat-treated, 309–311
heat-treated, 407, 409
impact value, 312, 406, 407, 409
tensile properties, 406–409, 412
Manganese-molybdenum rails, life of, 402
Manganese-molybdenum steel, bend tests, 400, 404, 408
carburizing properties, 141, 403
critical points, 393, 395
endurance limit, 391
hardness, 391–405
heat-treated, mass effect, 402, 404
impact value, 391–405
temper-brittleness, 395, 401
tensile properties, 390–405
effect of grain size, 392
of heat treatment, 404–406
at elevated temperature, 402
torsion tests of, 400, 404, 408
Manganese-nickel-chromium-molybdenum steel, casting difficulties, 407
properties, as cast and heat-treated, 407, 411, 412
Manganese steel, critical points, effect of molybdenum, 393, 395
temper-brittleness, effect of molybdenum, 395, 401
Manganese-vanadium cast steel, creep tests, 412
hardness, cast and heat-treated, 309, 310
impact strength, heat-treated, 312
Mass effect, on properties of chromium-molybdenum steel, 225, 226, 242, 243
on properties of manganese-molybdenum steel, 402
Modulus of rupture, molybdenum cast iron, 174, 175

Molybdenite, described, 9
occurrence of, 11
Molybdenum, in acid-resistant alloys, 422–425
adding to cast iron, 156
amount to replace tungsten in high-speed steel, 316–325
in carbon-manganese alloys, critical points, 393, 395
in chromium-nickel alloy valve steels, oxidation, 300–305
in chromium-nickel austenitic steel, corrosion resistance, 298–300
in chromium steel, heat resistance, 429
in cobalt-magnet steels, composition, 433
discovery of, 1
extraction from ores, 13
and graphitization in white cast iron, 196
in heat- and corrosion-resistant alloys, 422–425
in high-speed steel, amount equivalent to tungsten, 315
in iron-carbon alloys, structure, 66
in iron-nickel alloys, properties, 272
loss of, in adding to cast iron, 157
malleable iron, properties, 188
in manganese electric steel, properties, 396
metal, hardness, 7
properties of, 8
minerals, discussed, 9
in nickel-chromium heat-resistant alloys, 427–429
in nickel-chromium steel, effect on creep strength, 240
on critical points, 276, 277
on tempering temperature, 294
mass effect in heat treatment, 291
in nickel-silicon steel, properties, 421
in nickel steel, effect on properties, 262
in nitrided steel, effect on case-depth and hardness, 364–366
on case toughness, 364
in nitriding steel, effect, summarized, 388
on temper-brittleness, 363
occurrence, in nature, 9
ore, treatment of, 13
ores, deposits in North America, 11
occurrence of, 10
price of, 72
properties of, 7, 8
pure, manufacture of, 14
segregation of, 75
in Harmet process ingots, 76
stainless iron, creep of, 248
effect on machinability, 248
in stainless steel, alloys used, 300
chromium-nickel, corrosion resistance, 298–300
effect on corrosion resistance, 246–248
free-cutting, properties, 247

Molybdenum-carbon alloys, crystal structure, 59
  equilibrium diagram, 59
  possible compounds, 58
  preparation of alloys, 57
Molybdenum-carbon-manganese steel, properties, 391, 396–400
Molybdenum cast iron, adding molybdenum, 156
  amount of graphite, 159
  analysis of, for sulphur, 168
  automotive, properties, 182
  casting properties, 158
  chill in, 160
    depth of, 167
  chromium in, properties, 187
  coefficient of expansion, 195
  compressive strength, 167, 171, 176–178
  corrosion resistance, 196
  creep tests, 189
  die irons, properties, 185
  early reports of, 6
  effect of temperature, 196
  endurance limit, 181
  graphite, form of, 162
  graphitization, temperatures, 198
  growth, 199
  hardness, 167, 171, 172, 175–180, 182, 186, 187, 190
  heat treatment, 200
  high-test, properties, 186
  impact value, 171, 181
  machinability, 172, 179, 187, 192
  manufacture, 156
  melting, 156
  modulus of rupture, 174, 175
  nickel in, properties, 187
  properties, mechanical, 167, 171, 172, 174–178, 180–187
    Challansonnet investigation, 174
    Climax Molybdenum Co. investigation, 181
    early investigations, 166
    effect of nickel, 175
      of section size, 191
    elevated temperatures, 190
    heat-treated, 201
    Küster and Pfannenschmidt investigation, 180
    Molybdenum Corp. of America investigation, 181
    Musatti and Calbiani investigation, 173
    Piwowarsky investigation, 169
    Sherwin and Kiley investigation, 180
    Smith and Aufderhaar investigation, 170
  shrinkage, 158, 179
  sorbite in, 164

Molybdenum cast iron, structure of, 159
    matrix, 163
  tensile strength, 167–188
  transformation temperatures, 199
  transverse tests, 167, 171, 180–187, 189, 190
    on small specimens, 174
  wear resistance of, 193
  wear resistant, properties, 183
  uses of, 201
Molybdenum cast steel, properties, 148–154
    at elevated temperatures, 150–154
  uses of, 154
Molybdenum-chromium cast iron, properties, 187
Molybdenum-chromium-copper steel, properties, 429
Molybdenum-cobalt-chromium-vanadium-tungsten steel, properties, 428
Molybdenum concentrates, use of, in melting, 71
Molybdenum-copper iron, for boilers, properties, elevated temperature, 435
Molybdenum high-speed steel, best composition, 352
  cast and hardened, cutting tests, 340
  cleaning, 353
  compositions, 317–325
  cost, 345
  critical ranges, 325–327
  cutting performance, 336–344
  cutting tests, 333
    compared with other steels, 341–343
  development, Watertown Arsenal, 346–354
  drilling tests, 343
  early use of, 322–325
  effect of cobalt on performance, 341
  forging, 347, 352
    loss of molybdenum in, 347–349
  hardness, effect of hardening temperature, 339
      of heat treatment, 330–332
      of tempering, 340
    elevated temperatures, 332–334
  heat treatment, 329, 349, 353
    effect on structure, 350–352
  history of, 6, 316
  limitations and advantages, 344–346
  manufacture, large-scale, 353
  molybdenum as replacing element, 315–325
  properties, at ordinary temperature, 327
    torsional, 329–332
  protecting, under heat, 353, 354
  rolling, 352, 354
  structure, 328, 329, 350–352
  tungsten-free, critical ranges, 325–327
  white layer in, 348

Molybdenum-manganese cast steel, properties, elevated temperature, 152–154
Molybdenum-nickel cast iron, properties, 187
Molybdenum nitriding steel, composition, 360, 362
(*See also* Nitrided steel or Nitriding steels.)
Molybdenum steel, acid resistance, 145
adding molybdenum to, 68
blue-brittleness in, 143
calcium molybdate, use of, 70
carbides in, composition, 60–62
carburizing properties, 139
effect of nickel on, 141
casting properties, 74
chemical properties, 144
coefficient of expansion, 100
compounds in, X-ray analysis, 65
compressive strength, as heat-treated, 121, 122
creep tests, 129, 130
short-time tests, 135
and yield strength, 133
critical points in, 85–92
early use of, 2, 146
electric conductivity, 97
electric resistance, 66
electromotive force, 101
elevated temperatures, tensile properties, 124–134
endurance properties, heat-treated, 122, 123
eutectoid concentration, 64
forming properties, 139
hardness, annealed, 110
elevated temperatures, 124, 125
forged or rolled, 108
heat-treated, 116, 118
low temperature, 124
vs. vanadium steel, elevated temperatures, 125
hot working, 78
impact value, 108, 112
heat-treated, 116–118, 120, 121
lowering temperature, 87–90
importance of, 91
machinability, 136
magnetic properties, early investigations, 101
effect of heat treatment, 102–105
melting practice, 68
Bessemer process, 73
crucible and electric process, 73
open-hearth process, 72
quenching range of, 92
recent reports on, 4

Molybdenum steel, resistance to acids, 145
to chemical attack, 144
segregation in, 75
sheet, yield strength, elevated temperatures, 126
spark tests of, 143
structural diagram, 63
structure, effect of molybdenum, 64–66
annealed, 97
heat-treated, 97
hot worked, 96
for superheaters, properties, elevated temperatures, 133
temper-brittleness of, 142
tempering, effect on hardness, 94, 95
on tensile properties, 94, 95
range, 94
tensile properties, annealed, 109, 110
elevated temperatures, 124–136
forged or rolled, 108, 109
heat-treated, 113–120
effect of vanadium, 416, 417
normalized, 111–113
vs. quenching temperature, 93
thermal conductivity, 98
thermoelectric properties, 100
uses, 146, 147
welded, properties, 139
welding properties, 138
Wiedemann-Franz ratio, 98
Molybdenum tool and die steel, composition and properties, 430–432
Molybdenum tool steel, compared with tungsten tool steel, 430, 431
Molybdenum-silicon-vanadium tool steel, uses, 432
Molybdenum valve steels, composition, properties, 425–427
Molybdenum-vanadium steel, forged or centrifugally cast, properties, 415–418
for guns, centrifugally cast, 413–418
manganese-free, use of zirconium in, 419
properties, heat-treated, 413–418
Molybdenum wear-resistant cast irons, properties, 183
Molybdenum wire, strength, 8
Molybdite, described, 10
Molyte, composition and use of, 17

N

Nickel cast iron, chill, amount of, 160
cast steel (*See* Nickel steel, cast.)
coefficient of expansion, 195
graphitization temperatures, 199
mechanical properties, effect of molybdenum, 178

Nickel cast iron, transformation temperatures, 199
Nickel-chromium cast iron, growth, 200
  transverse tests, 189
Nickel-chromium-cobalt-molybdenum alloys, for acid resistance, 423
Nickel-chromium-copper-molybdenum-tungsten alloys, composition, 425
Nickel-chromium-iron alloys, molybdenum in, 427–429
Nickel-chromium-iron-molybdenum-manganese alloy, at elevated temperature, 429
Nickel-chromium-molybdenum alloys, for acid resistance, 423
Nickel-chromium-molybdenum cast iron, machinability, 200
Nickel-chromium-molybdenum cast steel, as cast, 308
  impact value, heat-treated, 312
  mechanical properties, heat-treated, 306–313
Nickel-chromium-molybdenum die steels, composition and use, 305, 306
Nickel-chromium-molybdenum-manganese alloy, for acid resistance, 423
Nickel-chromium-molybdenum-silicon steel, creep of, 242
Nickel-chromium-molybdenum steel, carbide segregation, 296
  compared with other steels, 242
  creep of, 293
  critical points, 275–277
  elevated temperature, properties, 293–295
  endurance limit, heat-treated, 286
  erosion, vs. Armco iron, 296
  hardness, heat-treated, 278–284, 286
    effect of mass, 291, 292
  impact value, 268, 278–284, 286, 287
  large forgings, 288
  liquidus and solidus, 296
  temper-brittleness, 288
    effect of cooling rate, 290
  tensile properties, 268, 276–288
    elevated temperatures, 293–295
  uses of, 296
    for automotive and airplane construction, 296, 297
Nickel-chromium-molybdenum-vanadium die steel, uses, 432
Nickel-chromium-molybdenum-vanadium steel, properties, 420
    at elevated temperatures, 420
Nickel-chromium steel, cast, creep, 412
    properties, elevated temperatures, 152–154
  critical points, 274
    effect of molybdenum, 275–277
  hardness, 229, 276–284
    effect of mass, 242, 292
  impact value, 225, 229, 276–283
  structure, compared to chromium-molybdenum steel, 244
  temper-brittleness, effect of cooling rate, 290
      of molybdenum, 288
  tempering temperature, effect of molybdenum, 294
  tensile properties, compared with chromium-molybdenum steel, 224, 229

Nickel-chromium steel, tensile properties, heat-treated, effect of molybdenum, 276–284
Nickel-chromium-tungsten-molybdenum tool steels, uses, 432
Nickel-cobalt-molybdenum alloys, for acid-resistance, 423
Nickel-iron-molybdenum alloys, for acid-resistance, 424
Nickel-iron-molybdenum-manganese alloys, for corrosion resistance, 424
Nickel-manganese cast steel, hardness, 309–311
  impact value, 312
Nickel-manganese-iron-molybdenum alloys, age-hardening, 433–434
Nickel-molybdenum carburizing steel, 141
Nickel-molybdenum, cast iron, graphitization, 198
    properties, 187
    transformation temperatures, 199
  cast steel, elevated temperature properties, 152–154, 270
Nickel-molybdenum-chromium-iron-tungsten alloys, for corrosion resistance, 424
Nickel-molybdenum steel, carburized, core properties, 265
  for carburizing, 141
  creep, compared to other steels, 242
  hardness, heat-treated, 260–268
  impact value, heat-treated, 260, 265–269
    at low temperatures, 273
  tensile properties, 260–269
    elevated temperatures, as cast, 152–154, 270
    elevated temperatures, heat-treated, 267, 269
    forged or rolled, 260–265, 268
    heat-treated, 260–268
  uses of, 273
Nickel-silicon-molybdenum alloys, for acid resistance, 423
Nickel-silicon-molybdenum steel, endurance limit, 421
  tensile properties, 421
Nickel-silicon steel, properties, effect of molybdenum, 421
Nickel steel, cast, impact value, 313
    properties, elevated temperature, effect of molybdenum, 270
  creep tests, 130
    and yield strength, 133
  elevated temperature, properties, 131
  hardness, 229
    effect of mass, 242
  tensile properties, compared with carbon and other steels, 229
    compared with nickel-molybdenum steel, 259, 266
    effect of molybdenum, 259, 262
Nickel-tungsten-molybdenum steel for armor plate, 433
Nitrided steel, case hardness, effect of reheating, 372
  case, toughness, effect of molybdenum, 364
  corrosion resistance, 382
  creep tests, 381
  depth-hardness, 369, 370
    effect of molybdenum, 364–366

Nitrided steel, depth-hardness, heated in hydrogen, 382
  endurance limit, 376–381
    in steam, 378
  hardness, elevated temperature, 371
  impact value, effect of nitriding, 373
  stability of case, 381
  tensile properties, 372–376
    elevated temperatures, 373–375
  uses of, 384
  welding, 383
Nitriding, expansion during, 383
  operation of, described, 359–362
  present status, 388
Nitriding steels, composition, 359
  endurance limit, 376–381
  development of, 358
  molybdenum in, composition, 360–362
    effect of, 388
  properties, elevated temperatures, 367
    heat-treated, 368
  temper-brittleness, 363

O

Omega phase in iron-carbon-molybdenum alloys, 439–441
Open-hearth process for molybdenum steel, 72
Ores, molybdenum, deposits in North America, 11
    occurrence of, 10

P

Permalloy, effect of molybdenum, 272
  (*See also* Iron-nickel alloys.)
Phases in iron-molybdenum system, 24–33
  in iron-carbon-molybdenum system, 439–441
Properties, of iron-molybdenum alloys, 42, 51
  of molybdenum, 7, 8
  pure iron, 9
    (*See also* Hardness; Impact values; Elevated temperatures; Tensile properties, etc.)

Q

Quenching range for molybdenum steel, 92

R

Rail steel, manganese-molybdenum, properties, elevated temperatures, 400–402

Rails, manganese-molybdenum, life of, 402
Railway materials, nickel-chromium-molybdenum steel for, 296
  nickel-molybdenum steel, 273
Rivets, air-hardening, steel for, 251
Rolling, molybdenum steel, 78–81
  molybdenum high-speed steel, 352, 354

S

Segregation, of molybdenum, 75
  in Harmet-process ingots, 76
Sheet, boiler steel, yield strength, elevated temperatures, 126
  chromium-molybdenum, properties, 209–214
  effect of thickness, 211–214
Shrinkage, cast iron, effect of molybdenum, 158
  molybdenum cast iron, 179
Sorbite in cast iron, effect of molybdenum, 164
Spark tests, molybdenum-bearing steel, 144
Springs, nickel-molybdenum steel for, 274
Stainless iron, machinability, effect of molybdenum, 248
Stainless steel, chromium-nickel, effect of molybdenum, 298–300
  corrosion-resistance, effect of molybdenum, 246–248
  molybdenum in, alloys used, 300
  molybdenum, creep of, 248
    effect on heat resistance, 429
    free-cutting, properties, 247
  valves, Losana's investigation, 300
Structural steel, carbon and alloy, elevated temperatures, 134
  chromium-molybdenum, composition and properties, 206–244
  use of chromium-molybdenum steel, 252
Structure, iron-molybdenum alloys, 24–33
  molybdenum cast iron, 159–166
  molybdenum steels, 95–97
    high-speed steel, 349–351
Sulphur in molybdenum cast iron, determination, 168

T

Thermal conductivity, effect of molybdenum, 98
Thermoelectric properties, effect of molybdenum, 100
Theta phase in iron-carbon-molybdenum system, 439, 441
Temper-brittleness, manganese-molybdenum steel, 395, 401
  nickel-chromium steel, effect of cooling rate, 290
  nickel-chromium-molybdenum steel, 143, 288
  nitrided steel, effect of molybdenum, 363
Tempering molybdenum steel, effect on properties, 94, 95
  nickel-chromium steel, effect of molybdenum, 294
  range, molybdenum steel, 94

Tensile properties, cast alloy steels at elevated temperatures, 150–154
chromium-molybdenum steel, 215, 216, 218–232
at elevated temperatures, 235–242
chromium-molybdenum structural steel, 206–244
heat-treated, 207, 208
sheet, 209–214
chromium-molybdenum tubing, welded, 234, 235
chromium-molybdenum-vanadium steel, 419
effect of molybdenum on, 119
iron-molybdenum alloy, 43
manganese-chromium-molybdenum steel, cast and heat-treated, 407, 410
manganese-molybdenum steel, cast and heat-treated, 406, 407, 409
heat-treated, 391, 405
manganese-nickel-chromium-molybdenum steel, 407, 411, 412
molybdenum cast iron, 167–188, 190
effect of section size, 191
elevated temperatures, 189, 191, 192
heat-treated, 201
molybdenum cast steel, 148–150
elevated temperatures, 150–154
molybdenum steel, 107–120
annealed, 109
effect of quenching temperature, 93
of tempering, 94
elevated temperatures, 126–128, 131
forged or rolled, 109
heat-treated, 113
normalized, 111
molybdenum-vanadium steel, 413, 415–417
nickel-chromium-molybdenum steel, 278–289
as cast and heat-treated, 308, 313
elevated temperatures, 295
nickel-chromium-molybdenum-vanadium steel, 420
nickel-molybdenum steel, 260–269
nickel-silicon-molybdenum steel, 421
nitrided steel, 372–376
elevated temperatures, 367
heat-treated, 368
special heat-resistant alloys, 428, 429
structural steels, elevated temperature, 134
Tool steels, molybdenum in, composition, properties, 430–432
nickel-chromium-tungsten-molybdenum, 432
tungsten, compared with molybdenum tool steel, 430, 431
Torsion properties, chromium-molybdenum structural steels, 208
manganese-molybdenum steel, 400, 404, 408
molybdenum high-speed steel, 330–332
Transverse properties, molybdenum cast iron, 167, 170–190
compared with other irons, 171–180, 187–190
on small specimens, 174

Tungsten, in high-speed steel, other elements equivalent to, 315
  in valve steels, effect on oxidation resistance, 302–305
Tungsten cast steel, properties, elevated temperatures, 152–154
Tungsten-chromium-vanadium-molybdenum valve steel, 426
Tungsten tool and die steels, 430, 431

V

Valve steels, composition, properties, 425–427
  Losana's investigation, 300
  oxidation resistance, effect of molybdenum, 300–305
Valves, nitrided steel for, use of, 385–387
Vanadium, cast steel, properties, elevated temperature, 150–154
  in high-speed steel, equivalent to tungsten, 315
  in molybdenum steel, effect on properties, 416, 417
Vanadium steel, creep tests, 129
  hardness, elevated temperature, 125
  sheet, yield strength, elevated temperatures, 126

W

Wear resistance, iron-molybdenum alloys, 49
  molybdenum cast iron, 193
Wear-resistant molybdenum cast iron, 183
Welded chromium-molybdenum tubing, endurance, 235
  tensile properties and hardness, 234–236
Welded molybdenum steel, properties, 139
Welding, nitriding steel, 383
Welding properties, chromium-molybdenum steel, 233–235
  molybdenum steel, 138
Wiedemann-Franz ratio, effect of molybdenum, 98
Wulfenite, described, 10

Z

Zirconium, in chromium-molybdenum steel, 244
  in manganese-vanadium steel, 419